D1196208

ELECTRICAL CIRCUITS

DIRECT AND ALTERNATING CURRENT

Other Titles
by
CHARLES S. SISKIND

Alternating-current Armature Windings: Theory, Practice, and Design
Direct-current Armature Windings: Theory and Practice
Electrical Machines: Direct and Alternating Current
Electricity: Direct and Alternating Current
Direct-current Machinery

ELECTRICAL CIRCUITS

DIRECT AND ALTERNATING CURRENT

CHARLES S. SISKIND, M.S.E.E.
Associate Professor of Electrical Engineering
Purdue University

NEW YORK TORONTO LONDON
McGRAW-HILL BOOK COMPANY, Inc.
1956

ELECTRICAL CIRCUITS

DIRECT AND ALTERNATING CURRENT

Library of Congress Catalog Card Number: 55-8910

III

THE MAPLE PRESS COMPANY, YORK, PA.

PREFACE

The *circuit* is the basis of all energy conversions and transformations associated with electrical equipment; it is logical, therefore, to precede the study of electrical machines and systems by a first course that thoroughly prepares the student to deal effectively with electric, magnetic, and dielectric circuits.

In organizing and developing the subject matter in this book the author has endeavored to build a foundation of circuit principles that is both rigorous and consistent with good engineering practice. The wide range of topics is divided into two major sections: Part I deals with circuits in direct-current systems, while Part II builds upon the former and is concerned with alternating-current systems. Much emphasis is placed on similarities and differences between circuits that are energized by direct current and by alternating current and on relationships that involve combinations of electric, magnetic, and dielectric circuits.

An important aspect of the arrangement is an Appendix of mathematical derivations in which basic equations are developed by the use of differential and integral calculus. This practice was followed to give the text its broad base for use (1) in colleges and universities where such material may be studied and (2) in technical institutes where such derivation procedures are ordinarily omitted and basic equations are applied to typical circuit analyses and the solution of problems.

Special attention was given to the preparation of clear, carefully labeled, easy-to-trace illustrations that are, for the most part, counterparts of practical systems, devices, and machines. Moreover, numerous illustrative examples and problems are presented that correspond to existing electrical systems; such treatment of circuit theory is not only interesting but serves to develop reasonably good judgment with regard to dimensions and magnitudes. Another advantage is that this treatment provides a realistic approach to courses in circuits and machines that are more advanced in character.

Since the text is completely basic in nature, special phases of circuit theory have been omitted; it does, however, provide the necessary background material for the study of most branches of electrical engineering.

Furthermore, important concepts are crystallized by frequent reemphasis, often in a new dress and from a different point of view. Particularly useful are the sets of questions and problems that follow each chapter. Since their sequence was carefully planned to parallel the discussions and illustrative examples, it is suggested that the material be studied in assignments that combine theory, questions, and problems.

The author's efforts will be amply rewarded if the use of this book establishes a pleasant and profitable teacher-student relationship.

CHARLES S. SISKIND

CONTENTS

Part I

ELECTRICAL CIRCUITS
DIRECT CURRENT

CHAPTER 1

BASIC ELECTRICAL IDEAS AND UNITS

Electron Theory and Electric Current. It is now generally recognized that all matter is composed of atoms each of which is made up of a positively charged nucleus surrounded by one or more indivisible, negatively charged particles. The latter, revolving in orbits around the positive nucleus, are called *electrons,* after the Greek word *elektron,* which means amber. In one class of substances, called *insulators,* the electrons are normally restricted to single atoms or several atoms in a molecule and are dislodged with considerable difficulty. The converse is true of a second class of substances, called *conductors,* where the orbital electrons in the outermost shell move freely from atom to atom; in these materials, usually metals, there are also enormous numbers of *free* electrons that move about at random so that their average velocity in any direction is zero.

The unattached negatively charged particles can be made to drift slowly in a given direction if an electrical pressure is applied to the ends of a conductor, i.e., a substance containing a large number of free electrons; under this condition the movement of the electrons is toward the positive terminal of the applied electrical pressure (unlike charges attract). Now then, since a movement of electrons constitutes a continuous displacement of electrical particles, it is proper to regard the phenomenon as a *current of electricity,* or briefly an electric current; the latter is sometimes referred to as *dynamic* electricity as differentiated from *static* electricity.

The real secret of electrical conductivity, i.e., the degree to which an electric current can be established, is the number of free electrons in a substance. If a material is prolific in this respect the electric current will be comparatively large for a certain applied electrical pressure; if, on the other hand, the number of free electrons is strictly limited the electric current will be correspondingly low. The metals are, in general, excellent current carriers because they *naturally* contain great numbers of free electrons per unit of volume; the nonmetals suffer in this regard because the electrons are very securely bound to their atoms and are not easily pulled free of their positive nuclei. Copper, for example, an excellent conductor, is the most common of all electrical conductors because it has the enormous number of 1,640,000 million million million (1.64×10^{24}) free electrons per cubic inch; in contrast, hard rubber, an extremely poor conductor of electric current, has about 3 free electrons per cubic inch under normal conditions. Silver, slightly better than copper, has about 1.68×10^{24}, while aluminum and Nichrome, other widely used electrical conductors, have 10^{24} and 2.56×10^{22}, respectively.

All electrons are unimaginably small and physically alike; each one has a diameter of 2×10^{-13} cm, and a mass that is 1/1,845 that of a hydrogen atom, or 8.999×10^{-28} gm. It is for this reason, obviously, that great numbers of electrons may be confined in exceedingly small volumes.

Electric Charge and Electric Current. As was previously pointed out, the application of an electrical pressure to a conductor imparts lateral motion to its free electrons because the latter are charged. The magnitude of the charge is commonly given in *coulombs*, and for each negatively charged electron it is 1.59×10^{-19} coulomb. Or, putting it another way, it would be necessary to have a concentration of 6.28×10^{18} electrons before a charge of one coulomb is accumulated. Furthermore, when one coulomb of electric charge continuously passes a given point every second the electric current is said to be one *ampere*. Stating the foregoing in equation form it should, therefore, be clear that the average electric current is

$$I = \frac{Q}{t} \tag{1}$$

where I = current, amp
Q = charge, coulombs
t = time, sec, during which electrons move

If the current in amperes is constant, charge in coulombs is transferred at a constant rate; under this condition the total transferred charge is merely equal to the product of amperes and seconds, whence $Q = It$. For a nonuniform current, on the other hand, the transferred charge will vary with current changes; in such cases the electron motion will be constant only during such short intervals as the current is steady. The latter condition is generally represented in equation form by writing lower-case symbols for coulombs and amperes, thus:

$$q = it \tag{2}$$

The quantity q in Eq. (2) is, geometrically, an area, if i is plotted along one axis, the ordinate, for example, and t is plotted along a perpendicular axis, the abscissa. This is shown in Fig. 1 for a current that varies with time and in which the shaded area represents the number of coulombs q_x transferred in t_x sec.

EXAMPLE 1. The current in a conductor changes uniformly from zero to 2 amp in 3 sec, remains steady at 2 amp for 6 sec, and then drops

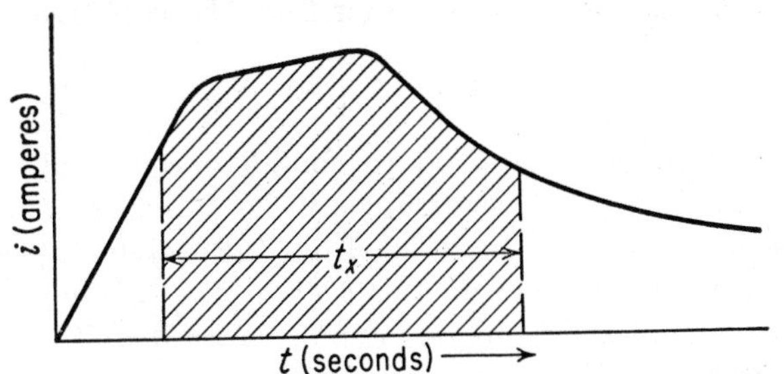

FIG. 1. Graph illustrating variations of current with time. The shaded area is the electric charge for time t_x.

uniformly to 1.5 amp in 8 sec. Calculate the total amount of charge transferred in the elapsed time of 17 sec.

Solution

$$q = \frac{3 \times 2}{2} + (6 \times 2) + (8 \times 1.75) = 29 \text{ coulombs}$$

Electron Velocity in Conductors. Although *all* the free electrons in a conductor begin moving almost instantaneously upon the application of an electrical pressure, their actual velocity, or drift, is exceedingly slow; this, as will presently be shown, depends only upon the *current density* in the conductor, i.e., the number of amperes per unit of cross-sectional area.

Consider a *copper* conductor having a cross-sectional area of A sq in. and carrying a constant current of I amp. Since there are 6.28×10^{18} electrons per coulomb, and 1 amp of current involves a motion of 1 coulomb per sec, it follows that $6.28 \times 10^{18} \times I$ electrons are moved per second. Furthermore, 1 in. of conductor length contains A cu in., and each cubic inch of copper has 1.64×10^{24} free electrons; this means, therefore, that there are $1.64 \times 10^{24} \times A$ electrons in each inch of conductor length. Now then, using simple dimensional analysis, it should be clear that velocity of electrons in *inches per second* is equal to the ratio of *electrons per second* to *electrons per inch:*

$$v = \frac{\text{electrons per sec}}{\text{electrons per in.}} = \text{in. per sec}$$

Using the foregoing values in the given general expression,

$$v = \frac{6.28 \times 10^{18} \times I}{1.64 \times 10^{24} \times A} = 3.83 \times 10^{-6} \left[\frac{I}{A}\right]$$

The quantity I/A in the bracket is the current density in the conductor, and this is conveniently replaced by Δ, which is specified in amperes per square inch of cross-sectional area; therefore, the equation for electron velocity becomes

$$v = 3.83 \times 10^{-6}\Delta \qquad (3)$$

Equation (3) cannot be applied to conductor materials other than copper, since a copper wire was assumed in its derivation. This is true because a poorer (or better) material, from the standpoint of free electrons, involves no reduction (or increase) in the numerator (*electrons per sec*) of the general expression for v, but a very definite reduction (or increase) in the denominator (*electrons per in.*); it follows, therefore, that the constant 3.83×10^{-6} will not be the same for all substances. Looking at the matter in a different way, it can be argued that two dissimilar conductors joined end to end (in series) carry the same value of current and must therefore transfer electrons at exactly the same rate; if the latter condition did not obtain there would be a "piling up" of electrons, an impossible situation. The constant is, therefore, proportional to resistivity.

EXAMPLE 2. A No. 12 copper wire, common to house-wiring installations, has a cross-sectional area of 0.00513 sq in. Calculate the electron velocity when the conductor current is 15 amp.

Solution

$$\Delta = \frac{15}{0.00513} = 2{,}920 \text{ amp per sq in.}$$

$$v = 3.83 \times 10^{-6} \times 2{,}920 = 0.0112 \text{ in. per sec}$$

It is important to recognize from the foregoing analysis that any change in the current in a given conductor comes about only by an increase or decrease in velocity of *all* the electrons; it does *not* imply that a change has taken place in the number of moving electrons.

Electromotive Force (EMF). Mention was made several times of the term electrical pressure; this is more accurately called *electromotive force*, or briefly *emf*, and is the characteristic of a device or machine that tends to create electron flow. When an emf is applied to the ends of a conductor it is proper to refer to the existence of a *potential difference* between such ends; also, since increments of emf are required for successive increments of conductor, it is customary to regard a potential difference as a *drop in potential* along the length of the conductor. Still another term, more commonly used than those already given, is *voltage;* it too suggests the existence of force that tends to create a current.

Several methods are employed to develop an emf. One scheme is to combine certain kinds of metals and chemicals into a device called a battery; these are constructed in a number of ways and, in some types, may be used over and over again by a process of chemical rejuvenation called charging. A more common and powerful method is to build a machine, called a generator, which functions to generate voltages when conductors are rotated near magnets.

The unit of emf is the *volt* and, as defined by Act of Congress (agreeing with definitions adopted by other countries) is 1/1.083 part of the potential difference developed by a special type of electrochemical cell—a so-called *Weston* cell—consisting of plates of cadmium and mercury in a solution—an electrolyte—of mercurous sulphate and cadmium sulphate, the cell being made in accordance with standard prescribed specifications.

Electrical Resistance and Resistivity. The magnitude of the current passing through a conducting material depends not only upon the impressed emf but on the properties of the conductor as well; this may be inferred from previous electron-theory discussions. Since electrical conductivity varies with different materials it is therefore proper and convenient to assume that all substances possess a reciprocal property, i.e., a tendency to *oppose* a current. This property (to be distinguished from the object possessing it) is called *electrical resistance,* or briefly *resistance.* The object possessing this property is designated a *resistor.* Understand that resistance is as much the property of a copper wire, for example, as is its hardness or its malleability, or as is the wetness of water or the stiffness of a spring.

The unit of resistance is the *international ohm* and is defined as *the resistance at zero degrees centigrade of a column of mercury of uniform cross section, having a length of* 106.3 *centimeters and a mass of* 14.4521 *grams.* From the careful wording of the definition of an ohm it should be clear that the resistance of a conductor of electricity of homogeneous and symmetrical construction depends upon four factors: (1) kind of material, (2) length, (3) cross-sectional area, and (4) temperature. The *reproducible standard* (1) makes use of mercury as the *material,* (2) has a *length* of 106.3 cm, (3) has a definite and uniform *cross section* because the mass is fixed at 14.4521 gm, and (4) is at a *temperature* of 0°C.

Resistance, symbolized by R, may be likened to the friction that exists between two surfaces that are in contact when one body moves with respect to another; this implies that, because of the resistance property of the material, heat will be developed in the conductor just as it is when one body is rubbed against another.

It is frequently desirable, for purposes of comparison and calculation, to know the resistances of electrical materials in terms of unit dimensions of length and cross-sectional area. Such resistances are generally given in tables (to be discussed subsequently) and are based on any arbitrary and convenient system of units such as inch and square inch, centimeter and square centimeter, foot and circular mil, etc. When specified in this way the opposition to current is called *resistivity* and is symbolized by the Greek letter ρ; it merely indicates that it is the resistance of the given conductor material having unit length and unit cross section. In one system of units, for example, the resistivities of copper, aluminum, nickel, brass, and Manganin (an alloy) are respectively given as 10.37, 17, 47, 42, and 265. This would, of course, indicate that the materials having the higher resistivity values are the poorer conductors; it would also mean that, for a certain value of current, and equal dimensions of length and area, the higher-resistivity materials would develop correspondingly more heat.

EXAMPLE 3. A coil of copper wire ($\rho = 10.37$) has a resistance of 46 ohms. What would be the resistance of a coil of aluminum wire ($\rho = 17$) having similar dimensions of length and area?

Solution

$$R = \frac{17}{10.37} \times 46 = 75.4 \text{ ohms}$$

Kinds of Current. There are two general types of electric current, distinguished from each other by the manner in which they vary in magnitude and direction; these are classified as (1) direct current and (2) alternating current.

A *direct current*, sometimes called a *continuous* current, is one in which an energy transfer takes place unidirectionally, with changes in value from instant to instant that are either zero or so small that they may be neglected. When the current does vary somewhat in magnitude but does not reverse in direction it is referred to as a *unidirectional* direct current. Still another form of direct current is one in which the magnitude varies considerably and pulsates regularly, there being no reversal in direction; it is called a *pulsating* direct current. As indicated, all three forms of direct current, i.e., continuous, unidirectional, and pulsating, involve a motion of electrons in one direction only; they are illustrated graphically in Fig. 2. Since the current in most d-c systems is continuous, i.e., unvarying, it is this particular form that is usually implied, unless otherwise specified, when mention is made of direct current.

An *alternating current* is one in which the direction alternates regularly and, unless otherwise definitely stated, changes *periodically* in magnitude as well as direction. The fact that it is a periodic current means, of course, that the average lateral motion of electrons in a conductor is zero; the electrons merely oscillate back and forth past a fixed point. In most of the electrical systems in this country the current reversals take place at the rate of 120 per second so that each cycle of two reversals is repeated 60 times a second; such an alternating current is said to have a frequency of 60 cycles. Other frequencies are 50 cycles (in countries abroad) and 25 cycles (in some sections of this country).

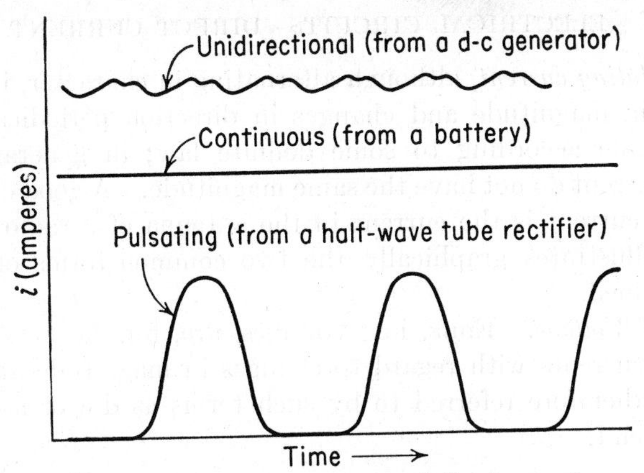

FIG. 2. Graphs illustrating forms of direct current.

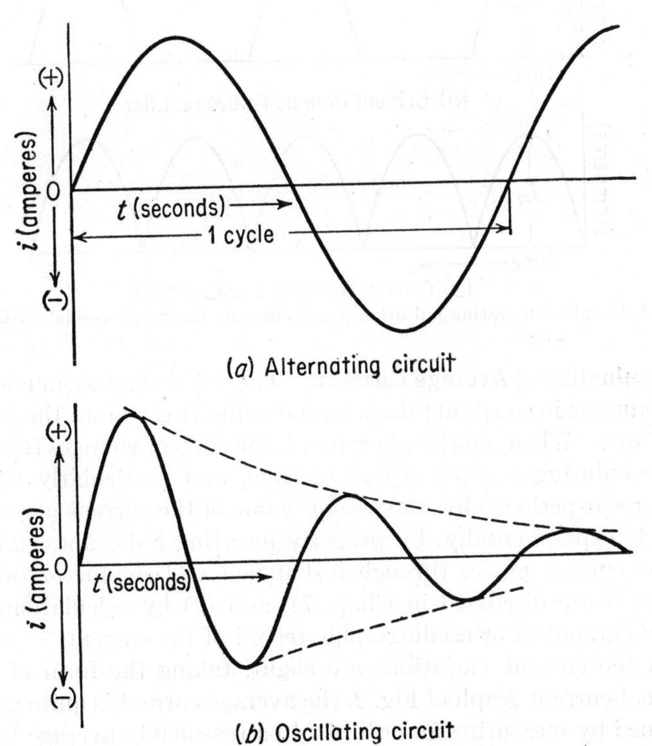

FIG. 3. Graphs illustrating forms of alternating current.

An *oscillating current*, although alternating in character, increases and decreases in magnitude and changes in direction periodically with respect to time according to some definite law; in general, successive waves of current do not have the same magnitude. A good example of an oscillating current is the current in the antenna of a radio transmitter. Figure 3 illustrates graphically the two common forms of alternating current defined.

Kinds of Voltage. Emfs, i.e., voltages, are, for the most part, quite similar to currents with regard to changes in magnitude and direction. These are therefore referred to by such terms as d-c or a-c voltage or oscillating emf.

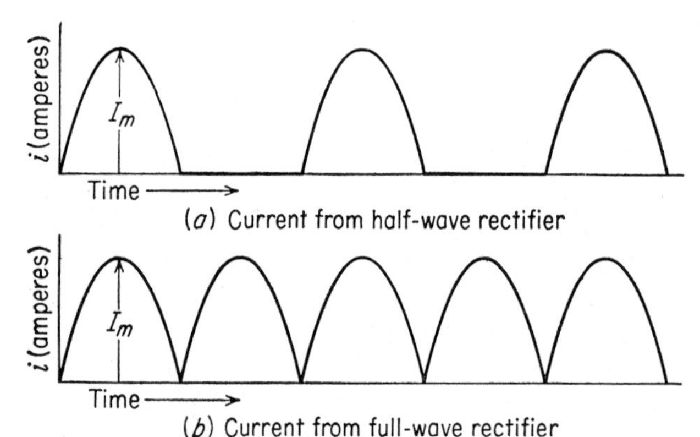

FIG. 4. Graphs illustrating pulsating direct currents having sinusoidal variations.

Determination of Average Current. The value of a continuous current in a conductor is constant; the average value is therefore the current at any instant. When, on the other hand, the current changes from instant to instant during a given period of time, and particularly when such changes recur periodically, the *average* value of the current may be determined (1) experimentally, by properly inserting a d-c ammeter so that the same current passes through instrument and conductor (measuring instruments are discussed in Chap. 7), and (2) by calculation, making use of the graphical or oscillographic record of the current.

When the current variations are slight, taking the form of the unidirectional-current graph of Fig. 2, the average current is quite accurately determined by measuring an ordinate to a reasonably average horizontal line through the irregularly shaped wave. Pulsating direct currents, quite common in some types of electrical systems, have certain degrees of mathematical regularity and periodicity, so that simple calculations may be performed to yield average values. This is especially true when some kinds of rectifiers are used to change alternating current to direct current, in which cases the wave shapes of the current may take the forms illustrated by Fig. 4; these wave shapes are, in fact, *sinusoidal;* i.e., they follow variations in accordance with a sine function and are furnished by what are known as *half-wave* and *full-wave* rectifiers. If the maximum value I_m of the sinusoidal wave is known, the average values of the current are

$$I_{av} = \frac{I_m}{\pi} \quad \text{for a half-wave rectifier} \tag{4}$$ [1]

and

$$I_{av} = \frac{2I_m}{\pi} \quad \text{for a full-wave rectifier} \tag{5}$$ [2]

EXAMPLE 4. Referring to Fig. 4 the maximum value of the pulsating rectified current is 6 amp. Calculate the average value of the current (that which a d-c ammeter would register) if the supply comes from (*a*) a half-wave rectifier, (*b*) a full-wave rectifier.

Solution

(*a*) $$I_{av} = \frac{6}{\pi} = 1.91 \text{ amp}$$

(*b*) $$I_{av} = \frac{2 \times 6}{\pi} = 3.82 \text{ amp}$$

The average value of a current that is neither regular nor periodic may be determined, as before, by using a d-c ammeter, or by performing certain mathematical operations upon the graphical wave form. Remembering that the area under the *current* vs. *time* curve is the total charge for a given time t_x (see Fig. 1), it should be clear that an *average* value of current, represented by a properly located horizontal line, can be determined by dividing the total area under the curve by the time t_x; i.e., I_{av} = total charge/t_x = area/t_x. A convenient way to measure the area is to employ a planimeter if one is available. Another scheme is to subdivide the area into a number of horizontally thin sections so that each average height (in amperes) multiplied by the increment of time represents a fairly good measure of each slice of area; the total area is then equal to the sum of the individual thin areas, whence the average current I_{av} may be readily calculated. Example 5 illustrates this procedure.

EXAMPLE 5. Referring to Fig. 5, determine the average current for a period of time t, using the method of area subdivision.

[1] See Appendix 1A for derivation.
[2] See Appendix 1B for derivation.

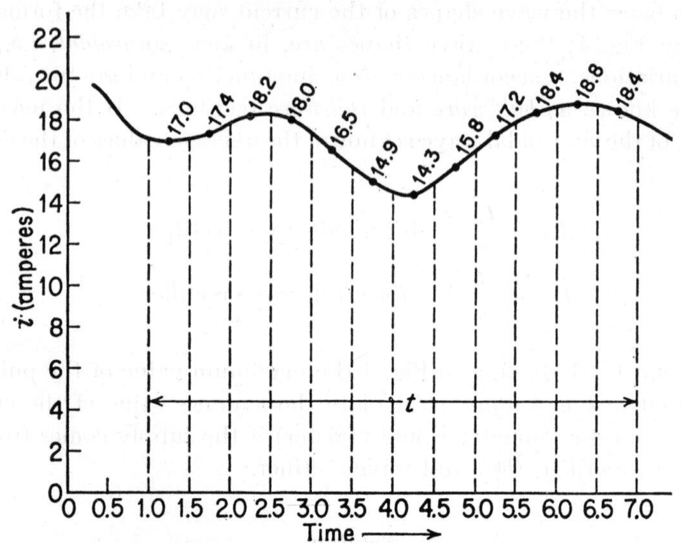

FIG. 5. Current vs. time graph for Example 5.

Solution

The total area was arbitrarily divided into 12 sections, each represented by a 0.5-sec time increment. The average current for each section was then assumed to be the point on the curve halfway between the vertical sides of each time increment; these are indicated on the graph. The total area is therefore

$$A = 0.5(17.0 + 17.4 + 18.2 + 18.0 + 16.5 + 14.9 + 14.3 + 15.8 + 17.2 + 18.4 + 18.8 + 18.4) = 102.45$$

Hence the average current for a period of 6 sec is

$$I_{av} = \frac{102.45}{6} = 17.075 \text{ amp}$$

Questions

1. Distinguish between conductors and insulators on the basis of the electron theory.
2. What is meant by an *electric current* when defined in terms of the electron theory?
3. Distinguish between *dynamic* and *static electricity*.
4. How does the electron theory explain the *degree* of conductivity?
5. Why are metals better electrical conductors than the nonmetals?
6. List several metals in the order of their electrical conduction abilities.
7. When does electric charge become electric current?
8. Define an *ampere* in terms of the electron theory.
9. How is it possible to determine graphically the quantity of charge that is moved through a conductor in a given time?
10. Upon what factors does the electron velocity depend?
11. Clearly explain why the electron velocity in a conductor is independent of the material, assuming all other conditions to be similar.

12. In accordance with the electron theory, state definitely what happens when there is current increase or decrease in a conductor.
13. Define *electromotive force (emf)*. Give three other commonly used names for the term.
14. How is an electromotive force developed?
15. What is the *unit* of emf? Define it accurately.
16. Distinguish between the terms *resistance* and *resistivity*.
17. Distinguish between the terms *resistance* and *resistor*.
18. To what may resistance be likened? Explain.
19. What important effect is produced when current passes through a resistor? To what physical phenomenon can this be compared?
20. List several metals in the order of their resistivities.
21. Distinguish between *continuous*, *unidirectional*, and *pulsating* direct currents.
22. What form of direct current is generally implied when d-c systems are discussed?
23. Define an *alternating current* accurately.
24. What is meant by the term *frequency?*
25. Define an *oscillating current* accurately. Where is this kind of current encountered?
26. What is meant by the *average* current in a conductor?
27. What is the average value of a continuous direct current? of a sinusoidal direct current?
28. What is the average value of one-half of a cycle of sinusoidal alternating current, in terms of the maximum value?
29. When a d-c ammeter is inserted in a current-carrying conductor, what does it register?
30. Explain carefully how the average current can be determined graphically when (*a*) the current varies slightly from instant to instant, (*b*) the current varies considerably from instant to instant.

Problems

1. The electric charge that moves through a conductor varies in accordance with the equation $q = 800t$, where q and t are given in μcoulombs and milliseconds, respectively. Calculate the current in amperes, and draw graphs of q vs. t and i vs. t.
2. The current in a conductor varies as follows: during the first 8 sec there is a linear change from zero to 4 amp; during the next 15 sec the current is constant at 4 amp; during a third period of 20 sec the current decreases linearly to 3 amp. Determine (*a*) the total charge transferred in the elapsed time of 43 sec, (*b*) the average current.
3. A conductor having a cross-sectional area of 0.00161 sq in. carries a current of 4.5 amp. Calculate the electron velocity, assuming the wire to be copper.
4. Calculate the number of free electrons in a 100-ft length of copper wire if its diameter is 0.46 in.
5. The current density in the wires of an electrical machine is not to exceed 4,500 amp per sq in. What is the maximum permissible current in each conductor if its diameter is 0.032 in.?
6. The average velocity in a conductor carrying a current of 65.5 amp is 0.0153 in. per sec. What is the cross-sectional area of the conductor?
7. A 500-ft length of conductor is connected to a source of emf and carries a steady current of 30 amp. If the cross-sectional area of the wire is 0.0082 sq in., calculate the number of trips the electrons make during a 24-hr period.

8. A coil of copper wire ($\rho = 10.37$) has a length of 600 ft. What is the length of an aluminum conductor ($\rho = 17$), if its cross-sectional area and resistance are the same as those of the copper coil?

9. The Nichrome unit ($\rho = 660$) in a toaster has a resistance of 24 ohms. What is the resistance of a copper conductor of equal cross-sectional area, but 10 times as long as the Nichrome wire?

10. An alternating current having a sinusoidal wave shape has a maximum value of 28.2 amp. What is the average value (*a*) for a complete cycle, (*b*) for each alternation or half cycle?

11. The current supplied by a rectifier has a sinusoidal wave shape (see Fig. 4) with a maximum value of 7.85 amp. What is the average current if the rectifier is (*a*) of the full-wave type, (*b*) of the single-wave type?

12. A conductor carries a current that may be regarded as *equivalent* to the sum of two components, one of them being a continuous direct current of 6.2 amp and the other a superimposed full-wave rectifier current (see Fig. 4*b*). If the latter has a maximum value of 4.4 amp, calculate the average current in the wire (*a*) if both components have the same direction, (*b*) if the two components are oppositely directed.

13. Solve Prob. 12 assuming that the superimposed rectified component is half-wave with a maximum value of 4.4 amp.

14. A conductor carries a current that is equivalent to a 5-amp continuous current in one direction and a superimposed full-wave rectifier current in the opposite direction. What is the maximum value of the latter if the average conductor current is zero?

15. Solve Prob. 14 assuming that the superimposed rectified component is half-wave.

CHAPTER 2

WIRES, CABLES, AND INSULATION

Resistivity in Circular-mil–foot Units. It was previously stated that the term *resistivity* is applied to the resistance of a substance having unit dimensions of length and cross-sectional area. Since electrical conductors are generally round and have rather small diameters that are conveniently expressed in mils (0.001 in. = 1 mil), it is desirable to use *circular units* rather than square units to denote the cross-sectional area; moreover, a satisfactory measure of length is the foot unit, commonly employed in this country. Arbitrarily calling the area of a circle one *circular mil* if its diameter is one mil, the standard dimension for the resistivity unit becomes the *circular mil–foot;* the term, therefore, indicates that it represents the dimensions of a round wire whose length and diameter are, respectively, 1 foot and 1 mil. The standard of reference for the resistivity is accordingly defined as the resistance of one circular mil–foot of conductor.

The fact that the circular mil is a circular unit means, of course, that it is no longer necessary to use the irrational number π to determine the area of a round wire. Remembering that area varies directly with the diameter squared, i.e., d^2, it should be clear that the area in circular mils is determined by merely squaring the diameter d, where the latter is expressed in mils; this is illustrated for a few diameters in the accompanying table.

Diameter, mils	*Area, circular mils*
1	1
2	4
3	9
5	25
32	1,024
72	5,184
162	26,244
460	211,600

Considered from the standpoint of the electron theory it should be obvious that the resistivity ρ of a conductor is inversely proportional to the number of free electrons in unit volume (circular mil–foot), and this in turn depends upon the nature of the substance. Accurate resistivity measurements have been made upon a great many elements and alloys, and these, in terms of the standard ohm (see definition on page 7), are given in Table 1.

TABLE 1. RESISTIVITIES OF COMMON ELEMENTS AND ALLOYS AT 20°C

Elements		*Alloys*	
Silver	9.9	Brass	42
Copper, annealed	10.37	German silver	199
Copper, hard-drawn	10.65	Manganin	265
Gold, pure	14	Lucero	280
Aluminum	17	Advance	294
Magnesium	28	Constantan	302
Tungsten	33	Excello	550
Zinc	36	Nichrome	600
Nickel	47	Nichrome II	660
Iron, cast	54	Chromel	625–655
Platinum	60		
Iron, commercial	75		
Lead	132		
Mercury	577		

Note particularly that the elements are, for the most part, better conductors than are the alloys; the resistivities are lower. It should also be noted that the listed alloys—german silver to Chromel—were developed to have special properties in addition to comparatively high values of resistivity. The elements copper and aluminum are generally used for electrical-transmission purposes in most indoor and outdoor installations. Copper is nearly always employed in electromagnets, and it is for this reason that it is generally referred to in the trade as *magnet* wire. The other elements are used only occasionally, with the exceptions of iron for rheostats and tungsten for filaments in incandescent lamps. Observe that silver has a slightly lower resistivity, about 4.5 per cent less, which implies that it would replace copper for most requirements if it were as plentiful and cheap. The alloys Lucero, Advance, Excello, Nichrome, and Chromel find wide application in heating units because they resist oxidation at high temperatures, are mechanically strong and hard, are easy to work, and, because of their relatively high resistivities, occupy less space per unit resistance than do the elements. The alloy Manganin has the unusual and desirable characteristic that its resistivity is unaffected by wide temperature variations.

Resistance Calculations. In defining resistivity it was necessary to adopt certain units for length and cross-sectional area, the reason being that resistance is affected by the *magnitudes* of both dimensions, although in different ways. Considering the length of a conductor, it should be clear that, for a given applied emf, the volts per foot will diminish as the wire is lengthened; as a consequence the electron velocity will diminish, and this in turn results in a reduction in current. It is obvious, therefore, that an increase in length is accompanied by an equivalent increase in the opposition to current, which is to say that *resistance is directly proportional to conductor length*. Enlarging the cross section of a wire, on the other hand, has an inverse effect upon the resistance because the number of free electrons per unit length increases with the area; under this condition the current will increase since more electrons will be moved in unit time. Thus a change in area is accompanied by an equivalent *inverse* change in the opposition to current, which is to say that *resistance is inversely proportional to cross-sectional area*.

The foregoing analysis, together with the fact that resistivity is a function of the material (see Table 1), leads to a resistance formula in terms of resistivity ρ, length l in feet, and area CM in circular mils; that is,

$$R = \rho \frac{l}{CM} \tag{6}$$

EXAMPLE 1. Using the given particulars calculate the resistances of the following conductors at 20°C: (*a*) material = copper, l = 1,000 ft, CM = 3,220 cir mils; (*b*) material = aluminum, length = 4 miles, diameter = 162 mils; (*c*) material = Advance, length = 486 in., diameter = 0.0159 in.

Solution

(*a*) $$R = 10.37 \times \frac{1{,}000}{3{,}220} = 3.22 \text{ ohms}$$

(*b*) $$R = 17 \times \frac{4 \times 5{,}280}{(162)^2} = 13.7 \text{ ohms}$$

(*c*) $$R = 294 \times \frac{40.5}{(15.9)^2} = 47.1 \text{ ohms}$$

EXAMPLE 2. A copper wire has a diameter of 0.325 in. and a resistance of 0.6 ohm at 20°C. Calculate its length.

Solution

$$l = \frac{R \times CM}{\rho} = \frac{0.6 \times (325)^2}{10.37} = 6{,}120 \text{ ft}$$

EXAMPLE 3. What kind of material is used in the construction of a 39-ohm rheostat (a variable resistance) if the wire has a length of 266 ft and a diameter of 22.6 mils?

Solution

$$\rho = \frac{R \times CM}{l} = \frac{39 \times (22.6)^2}{266} = 75$$

Referring to Table 1, it will be seen that *commercial iron* has a resistivity of 75.

Resistivity and Per Cent Conductivity. It should be noted, in connection with the solution of Example 3, that the term resistivity has the dimensional units *ohm–circular mils per foot;* this results from the fact that $\rho = R \times CM/l$. Expressed in general units, the resistivity therefore becomes *ohm-area per unit length;* recognizing this, it is thus possible to determine the resistivity in any system of units.

A useful value, especially for basic calculations and comparative purposes, is the resistivity in centimeter units, i.e., in *ohm–square centimeters per centimeter;* this merely implies the resistance between the opposite faces of a cube 1 cm on a side. For standard annealed copper at 20°C this would be

$$\rho = 10.37 \times \frac{1 \text{ cir mil}}{\text{cir mils per sq cm}} \times \frac{\text{ft per cm}}{1 \text{ ft}} = 10.37 \times \frac{\text{ft per cm}}{\text{cir mils per sq cm}}$$

which will be recognized as ohm–square centimeters per centimeter. Converting centimeters to feet it is found that 1 cm $= 1/(12 \times 2.54) =$ 0.0328 ft. Furthermore, 1 in. = 1,000 mils and, for a circle 1 in. in diameter, 1,000,000 cir mils $= \pi/4$ sq in.; it follows, therefore, that 1 sq in. contains $(4/\pi) \times 10^6$ cir mils. Since 1 sq in. also contains $(2.54)^2 =$ 6.45 sq cm, the number of circular mils per square centimeter becomes $(4/\pi)10^6/6.45 = 0.1978 \times 10^6$. Substituting these values in the foregoing equation,

$$\rho = 10.37 \times \frac{0.0328}{0.1978 \times 10^6} = 1.724 \times 10^{-6} \text{ ohm–sq cm per cm}$$

This unit of resistivity is more conveniently called the resistance per cubic centimeter, and its value is often given as 1.724 microhms per cubic centimeter, or briefly 1.724 microhm-cm.

It is sometimes desirable to compare electrical materials on the basis of their conducting abilities. This is appropriately done by using the resistivity of 1 cu cm of annealed copper at 20°C as a standard, i.e., 1.724 microhm-cm, arbitrarily calling this 100 *per cent conductivity.* Thus, for example, if a material such as hard-drawn copper has a conductivity of 97.3 per cent, its resistivity is 1.77 microhm-cm. Aluminum, a widely used substance, has a resistivity of $(17/10.37)1.724 = 2.83$ microhm-cm; its conductivity is therefore $(1.724/2.83)100 = 61$ per cent.

Electrolytic copper, i.e., copper that is refined by an electrochemical process, may contain varying traces of impurities, and since the latter have an important effect upon the per cent conductivity, the purity of the copper will determine its per cent conductivity. This generally means that ordinary annealed copper will have conductivities that range between 98 and 100 per cent and, when extreme care is taken in its manufacture, may overshoot the standard to have a value greater than 100 per cent.

EXAMPLE 4. Using Table 1, applying the method of proportionality, calculate the resistivities in microhm-centimeters and the per cent conductivities of silver, tungsten, cast iron, Manganin, Nichrome II.

Solution

Material	Microhm-centimeters	Per cent conductivity
Silver	$\frac{1.724}{10.37} \times 9.9 = 1.65$	$\frac{1.724}{1.65} \times 100 = 104.5$
Tungsten	$\frac{1.724}{10.37} \times 33 = 5.50$	$\frac{1.724}{5.50} \times 100 = 31.4$
Cast iron	$\frac{1.724}{10.37} \times 54 = 8.98$	$\frac{1.724}{8.98} \times 100 = 19.2$
Manganin	$\frac{1.724}{10.37} \times 265 = 44.1$	$\frac{1.724}{44.1} \times 100 = 3.92$
Nichrome II	$\frac{1.724}{10.37} \times 660 = 110$	$\frac{1.724}{110} \times 100 = 1.57$

EXAMPLE 5. Calculate the resistivity of a manufactured "run" of annealed copper wire at 20°C, in ohm–circular mils per foot, if its conductivity is (*a*) 96.5 per cent, (*b*) 100.8 per cent.

Solution

(*a*) $$10.37 \times \frac{100}{96.5} = 10.746 \text{ ohm–cir mils per ft}$$

(*b*) $$10.37 \times \frac{100}{100.8} = 10.288 \text{ ohm–cir mils per ft}$$

Temperature-Resistance Effects. It was previously stated that the resistance of an electrical conductor depends, among other things, upon the temperature; this characteristic is the reason, therefore, for the 20°C notation in the foregoing discussions of resistance. Experiment has, in fact, demonstrated that the resistance of all wires generally used in practice in electrical systems increases as the temperature is raised; moreover, within the usual operating temperatures the resistance changes *uniformly*. In the case of copper wire, for example, the resistance changes by 42.7 per cent for *any* 100°C temperature change; i.e., the indicated per cent change takes place whether the temperature rises from 0 to 100°C or from −20 to 80°C, or drops from 120 to 20°C. This implies, therefore, that a graph of *resistance* vs. *temperature* will be a straight line

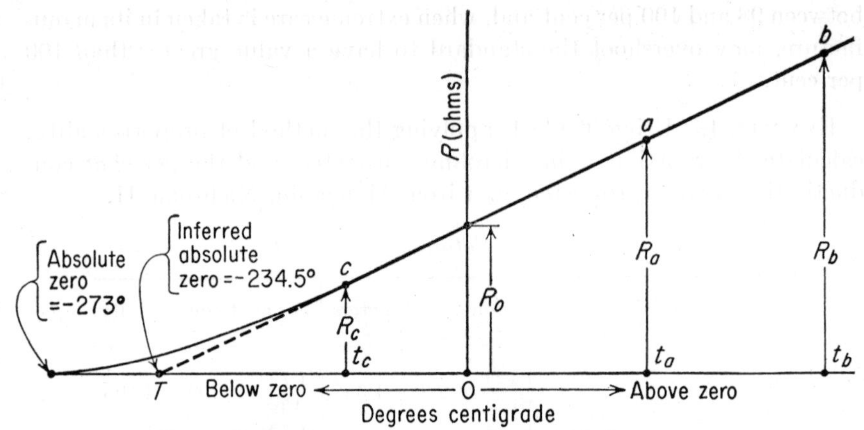

FIG. 6. Resistance vs. temperature relationship for copper.

with a positive slope, as represented by Fig. 6. Making use of the straight-line relationship it is thus possible to derive a simple formula for use in making certain calculations and predictions. Referring to the graph, note that the results of a resistance-temperature test are shown by a heavy oblique line, and that the extrapolated broken portion of the line is merely *inferred* for convenience to be a continuation of the actual experimental data. Understand that the region indicated by the broken line is generally below ordinary operating temperatures and is drawn only because it serves to locate an arbitrary but convenient *inferred absolute zero* for the metal concerned. The intersection of the extended experimental line with the X axis is usually above the *true absolute zero* of $-273°C$. For copper the inferred absolute zero, hereafter represented by T, is $-234.5°C$ (an easy number to remember because it is a succession of numbers from 2 to 5). Other values of T are given in Table 2.

TABLE 2. INFERRED ABSOLUTE TEMPERATURES FOR SEVERAL METALS

Material	*Inferred absolute zero (T), degrees centigrade*
Aluminum	−236
Copper, annealed	−234.5
Copper, hard-drawn	−242
Iron	−180
Nickel	−147
Steel, soft	−218
Tin	−218
Tungsten	−202
Zinc	−250

Also of interest is the fact that the resistance of metals will become zero at $-273°C$, the true absolute zero; and, from values of resistance somewhat above this basic temperature, the experimental graph curves gradually to the $-273°C$ point on the X axis.

Referring to Fig. 6 it is obvious, by similar right triangles, that

$$\frac{at_a}{bt_b} = \frac{OT + Ot_a}{OT + Ot_b} \quad \text{or} \quad \frac{R_a}{R_b} = \frac{T + t_a}{T + t_b}$$

also

$$\frac{R_a}{R_c} = \frac{T + t_a}{T - t_c} \quad \text{and} \quad \frac{R_b}{R_c} = \frac{T + t_b}{T - t_c}$$

where t_a and t_b are plus temperatures and t_c is a minus temperature. Written in general form, the above equations become

$$\frac{R_2}{R_1} = \frac{T + t_2}{T + t_1} \tag{7}$$

where R_1 and R_2 are the resistances at the respective temperatures t_1 and t_2. To use the equation it is, of course, merely necessary to substitute the proper value of T as given in Table 2 and apply the proper plus and minus signs for t_1 and t_2.

EXAMPLE 6. A coil of copper wire has a resistance of 62 ohms at a room temperature of 24°C. (*a*) What will be its resistance at 80°C, (*b*) at $-20°C$?

Solution

(*a*)
$$R_{80} = 62 \times \frac{234.5 + 80}{234.5 + 24} = 75.5 \text{ ohms}$$

(*b*)
$$R_{-20} = 62 \times \frac{234.5 - 20}{234.5 + 24} = 51.5 \text{ ohms}$$

EXAMPLE 7. The moving part of an electrical machine was allowed to remain at rest sufficiently long to acquire the same temperature as that of the room, i.e., 23°C; the resistance of the copper winding was then measured and found to be 0.18 ohm. A second measurement was taken of the same resistor after the machine had been operated for a period of time and, because of normal heating, the resistance rose to 0.206 ohm. Calculate the temperature and temperature rise of the winding.

Solution

Rewriting Eq. (7) in terms of the final temperature,

$$t_2 = \frac{R_2}{R_1}(234.5 + t_1) - 234.5$$

Therefore
$$t_2 = \frac{0.206}{0.18}(234.5 + 23) - 234.5 = 60°C$$

Hence the temperature rise is $(t_2 - t_1) = 60 - 23 = 37°C$.

Temperature Coefficient of Resistance. Since the *ohmic change* in resistance per degree is constant (that is obvious from the straight-line *resistance* vs. *temperature* characteristic, Fig. 6), the fractional change in resistance *per ohm* will vary on the basis of the reference value. To clarify this statement, assume a copper resistance of 100 ohms at 20°C. At 100°C the resistance will be 100 × (334.5/254.5) = 131.4 ohms, and the *constant* resistance change *per degree* will be (131.4 – 100)/80 = 0.393 ohm. However, the *fractional change per ohm* at 20°C will be (0.393/100) = 0.00393 ohm, while at 100°C it will drop to (0.393/131.4) = 0.00299 ohm. To put it in general terms, therefore, it may be said that the per cent change in resistance per ohm decreases with increasing reference values. An expression frequently used to indicate the extent to which the resistance of a given material will change per ohm is *temperature coefficient of resistance;* it is defined as the *ohmic change per degree per ohm at some specified temperature;* in practice the specified temperature is most commonly 20°C. A useful formula for temperature coefficient of resistance will now be derived.

Writing Eq. (7) in terms of the final resistance,

$$R_2 = R_1\left(\frac{T + t_2}{T + t_1}\right) = R_1\left(\frac{T}{T + t_1} + \frac{t_2}{T + t_1}\right)$$

When $[t_1/(T + t_1)]$ is added to and subtracted from the bracketed term this becomes

$$R_2 = R_1\left[\left(\frac{T}{T + t_1} + \frac{t_1}{T + t_1}\right) + \left(\frac{t_2}{T + t_1} - \frac{t_1}{T + t_1}\right)\right]$$

$$= R_1\left[1 + \left(\frac{1}{T + t_1}\right)(t_2 - t_1)\right]$$

Substituting α_1 for the term $[1/(T + t_1)]$, the final equation is

$$R_2 = R_1[1 + \alpha_1(t_2 - t_1)] \tag{8}$$

The value α_1 is the temperature coefficient of resistance at a temperature t_1. Note that the values for copper, previously calculated at reference temperatures of 20 and 100°C, are more easily evaluated as follows:

$$\alpha_{20^\circ} = \left(\frac{1}{234.5 + 20}\right) = 0.00393$$

and

$$\alpha_{100^\circ} = \left(\frac{1}{234.5 + 100}\right) = 0.00299$$

Table 3 lists values of α at 20°C for some of the more commonly used electrical materials; their magnitudes indicate the extent to which the resistances may be expected to change with temperature.

TABLE 3. TEMPERATURE-RESISTANCE COEFFICIENTS AT 20°C

Material	$\alpha_{20°}$
Nickel	0.006
Iron, commercial	0.0055
Tungsten	0.0045
Copper, annealed	0.00393
Aluminum	0.0039
Lead	0.0039
Copper, hard-drawn	0.00382
Silver	0.0038
Zinc	0.0037
Gold, pure	0.0034
Platinum	0.003
Brass	0.002
Nichrome	0.00044
German silver	0.0004
Nichrome II	0.00016
Manganin	0.00003
Advance	0.000018
Constantan	0.000008

Note particularly that the last three alloys, Manganin, Advance, and constantan, have, for practical purposes, negligible temperature coefficients of resistance.

EXAMPLE 8. The tungsten filament in an incandescent lamp has a resistance of 9.8 ohms at a room temperature of 20°C and a resistance of 132 ohms at normal operating temperature. Using Eq. (8) and Table 3 calculate the temperature of the heated filament.

Solution

Rewriting Eq. (8) in terms of t_2 and substituting $\alpha_{20°} = 0.0045$ for α_1,

$$t_2 = \frac{(R_2/R_1) - 1}{\alpha_1} + 20 = \frac{(132/9.8) - 1}{0.0045} + 20 = 2800°\text{C}$$

Wire Tables. Wires used as electrical conductors are manufactured in accordance with standard specifications prepared by the Bureau of Standards and adopted by the American Institute of Electrical Engineers (AIEE). The various sizes were selected so that successively larger cross-sectional areas differ by a factor of 1.26; the latter number represents the ratio of the square mil to the circular mil. For convenience it is customary to designate wires by numbers, the largest commercial size being No. 0000. Then come No. 000, No. 00, and No. 0, and series of numbers beginning with No. 1 and continuing to No. 46 and higher. Note particularly that the larger the number the smaller the area. In this country gage numbers follow the original Brown and Sharpe (B&S) plan, now commonly referred to as the American Wire Gage (AWG); in

TABLE 4. ROUND WIRES, STANDARD ANNEALED COPPER (AMERICAN WIRE GAGE)

AWG No.	Diam, mils	Area, cir mils	Ohms per 1,000 ft at 20°C	Lb per 1,000 ft	Ft per lb
0000	460	211,600	0.0490	640.5	1.561
000	410	167,770	0.0618	507.9	1.968
00	365	133,080	0.0779	402.8	2.482
0	325	105,560	0.0983	319.5	3.130
1	289	83,690	0.1239	253.3	3.947
2	257	66,360	0.1563	200.9	4.977
3	229	52,620	0.1970	159.3	6.276
4	204	41,740	0.2485	126.4	7.914
5	182	33,090	0.3133	100.2	9.980
6	162	26,240	0.3951	79.46	12.58
7	144	20,820	0.4982	63.02	15.87
8	128	16,510	0.6282	49.98	20.01
9	114	13,090	0.7921	39.63	25.23
10	102	10,380	0.9989	31.43	31.82
11	90.7	8,226	1.260	24.92	40.12
12	80.8	6,529	1.588	19.77	50.59
13	72.0	5,184	2.003	15.68	63.80
14	64.1	4,109	2.525	12.43	80.44
15	57.1	3,260	3.184	9.858	101.4
16	50.8	2,580	4.016	7.818	127.9
17	45.3	2,052	5.064	6.200	161.3
18	40.3	1,624	6.385	4.917	203.4
19	35.9	1,289	8.051	3.899	256.5
20	32.0	1,024	10.15	3.092	323.4
21	28.5	812	12.80	2.452	407.8
22	25.3	640	16.14	1.945	514.2
23	22.6	511	20.36	1.542	648.2
24	20.1	404	25.67	1.223	817.7
25	17.9	320	32.37	0.9699	1,031
26	15.9	253	40.81	0.7692	1,300
27	14.2	202	51.47	0.6100	1,639
28	12.6	159	64.90	0.4837	2,067
29	11.3	128	81.83	0.3836	2,607
30	10.0	100	103.2	0.3042	3,287
31	8.9	79.2	130.1	0.2413	4,145
32	8.0	64.0	164.1	0.1913	5,227
33	7.1	50.4	206.9	0.1517	6,591
34	6.3	39.7	260.9	0.1203	8,310
35	5.6	31.4	329.0	0.0954	10,480
36	5.0	25.0	414.8	0.0757	13,210
37	4.5	20.3	523.1	0.0600	16,660
38	4.0	16.0	659.6	0.0476	21,010
39	3.5	12.3	831.8	0.0377	26,500
40	3.1	9.6	1,049	0.0299	33,410

Great Britain the Birmingham Wire Gage (BWG) is in general use. Tables of various kinds are available and are consulted frequently by electrical workers; they contain much useful information that is helpful not only in the solution of many kinds of electrical problems but also in the design of electrical equipment.

Table 4 lists wire sizes from No. 0000 to No. 40, with such important data as diameter in mils, area in circular mils, resistance in ohms per 1,000 ft at 20°C, pounds per 1,000 ft, and number of feet per pound. Standard wires smaller than No. 40 are manufactured and are listed in the usual way by number. Conductors having areas larger than 211,600 cir mils are generally made in the form of cables for flexibility; such stranded conductors are always specified in terms of their circular-mil areas.

A careful study of a wire table such as Table 4 yields some rather interesting and useful facts. They may be summarized as follows:

1. Every change of three gage numbers changes the circular-mil area and resistance in the ratio of 2 to 1 or 1 to 2, depending upon the direction of the change.

2. Every change of 10 gage numbers changes the circular-mil area and resistance in the ratio of 10 to 1 or 1 to 10, depending upon the direction of the change.

3. Every change of one gage number changes the circular-mil area and resistance in the ratio of 1¼ to 1 or 1 to 1¼, depending upon the direction of the change.

4. A No. 10 wire may be assumed, for practical purposes, to have a diameter of 100 mils, an area of 10,000 cir mils, and a resistance of 1 ohm per 1,000 ft.

5. A No. 5 wire has a weight of 100 lb per 1,000 ft; moreover, for every change of three gage numbers the weight is halved or doubled, depending upon the direction of the change.

6. A No. 15 wire has 100 ft per lb (very nearly); moreover, for every change of three gage numbers the number of feet per pound is doubled or halved, depending upon the direction of the change.

7. Every change of 10 gage numbers changes the pounds per 1,000 ft and the feet per pound in the ratio of 10 to 1, depending upon the direction of the change.

If wire tables are used frequently it will be very helpful to memorize the foregoing rules: rapid and fairly accurate wire calculations are then possible without tables, should they not be available. An example will now be given with this in mind.

EXAMPLE 9. Without consulting the wire table, determine the following data for a No. 17 copper wire: (*a*) circular mils; (*b*) resistance per 1,000 ft; (*c*) pounds per 1,000 ft; (*d*) feet per pound.

Solution

(*a*) A No. 10 wire has 10,000 cir mils (rule 4). A No. 20 wire has 1,000 cir mils (rule 2). Therefore a No. 17 wire has 2,000 cir mils (rule 1). The table gives 2,052 cir mils.

(*b*) A No. 10 wire has a resistance of 1 ohm per 1,000 ft (rule 4). A No. 20 wire has a resistance of 10 ohms per 1,000 ft (rule 2). Therefore a No. 17 wire has a resistance of 5 ohms per 1,000 ft (rule 1). The table gives 5.064 ohms per 1,000 ft.

(*c*) A No. 5 wire has a weight of 100 lb per 1,000 ft (rule 5). Progressing three numbers at a time, Nos. 8, 11, 14, and 17 have weights that are, respectively, 50, 25, 12.5, and 6.25 lb per 1,000 ft (rule 5). The table gives 6.2 lb per 1,000 ft.

(*d*) A No. 15 wire has 100 ft per lb (rule 6). Progressing three numbers at a time, Nos. 18 and 21 have 200 and 400 ft per lb, respectively (rule 6). A No. 11 wire has 40 ft per lb (rule 7). Progressing three numbers at a time once again, Nos. 14 and 17 have 80 and 160 ft per lb (rule 6). The table gives 161.3 ft per lb.

Cables. As the area of a conductor increases it becomes more difficult to handle because it loses flexibility. This is particularly true in outdoor transmission systems or factory wiring where conductors must be sufficiently large in cross section to carry high values of current. For such purposes it is customary to employ *stranded cables,* which are bundles of small wires arranged in concentric layers and twisted lengthwise. The numbers of strands in the various sizes of cables have been carefully worked out to provide maximum copper area in the minimum space. The simplest combination contains seven similar strands, arranged with

TABLE 5. NUMBER OF STRANDS IN CONCENTRIC-LAY CABLES

Layer number	Number of strands in layer	Total number of strands in cable	Outside diameter of cable, mils
Core	1	1	d*
1	6	7	$3d$
2	12	19	$5d$
3	18	37	$7d$
4	24	61	$9d$
5	30	91	$11d$
6	36	127	$13d$
7	42	169	$15d$
8	48	217	$17d$
9	54	271	$19d$

* d = diameter of each strand in mils.

a central core conductor surrounded by six conductors. If more strands are needed in the cable, 12 additional wires surround the first layer of 6. Thereafter, each successive layer has six more conductors than the previous concentric layer so that standard cables are built up as indicated in Table 5.

As indicated in the table, standard cables are manufactured in accordance with definite numbers of strands, the size of each of the latter being determined on the basis of the desired flexibility as well as the total area in circular mils. A partial list of some of the more commonly used stranded cables is given in Table 6.

TABLE 6. BARE CONCENTRIC-LAY CABLES, ANNEALED COPPER WIRE

AWG No.	Area, cir mils	Number of strands	Diam of each strand	Outside diam, mils	Resistance, ohms per 1,000 ft	
					At 20°C	At 75°C
	500,000	61	90.5	815	0.0212	0.0257
	450,000	61	85.9	773	0.0236	0.0286
	400,000	61	81.0	729	0.0265	0.0321
	350,000	37	97.3	681	0.0302	0.0368
	300,000	37	90.0	630	0.0353	0.0428
	250,000	37	82.2	575	0.0422	0.0515
0000	212,000	19	105.5	528	0.0500	0.0607
000	168,000	19	94.0	470	0.0630	0.0765
00	133,000	19	83.7	418	0.0796	0.0966
0	106,000	19	74.5	373	0.100	0.121
1	83,700	19	66.4	332	0.126	0.154
2	66,400	7	97.4	292	0.159	0.193
3	52,600	7	86.7	260	0.201	0.245
4	41,700	7	77.2	232	0.254	0.309
5	23,100	7	68.8	206	0.320	0.388
6	26,300	7	61.2	184	0.402	0.488
7	20,800	7	54.5	164	0.509	0.618
8	16,500	7	48.6	146	0.642	0.780

The resistance per 1,000 ft of a stranded cable is slightly more than that of an equivalent single conductor—equivalent, that is, in material and cross-sectional area; this results from the fact that the spiraled conductors are slightly longer than the central core wire. Moreover, the cable resistance increases with the number of layers, although it seldom exceeds the ohmic value of the equivalent single wire by 5 per cent.[1]

[1] *National Bureau of Standards (U.S.) Circular* 31.

Uninsulated cables used for overhead transmission lines are sometimes constructed with 3 or 12 twisted strands; there is no central core. This is done because experiment seems to indicate that wind causes less vibration on such cables than on those with smooth surfaces.

Another departure from the standard cable previously discussed is the steel-core aluminum-strand construction. This type of cable is often used when the span between transmission towers is sufficiently long to require a conductor that not only has good conductivity but is, in addition, mechanically strong and light in weight. Referring to Table 1, note that the resistivity ratio of aluminum to copper is $17/10.37 = 1.64$; for the same conductivity, therefore, an aluminum conductor must have a cross-sectional area that is 64 per cent more than one made of copper. However, aluminum weighs only 30 per cent as much as copper. This means, then, that an aluminum conductor will weigh $30 \times 1.64 = 49.2$ per cent as much as a copper conductor, although to have the same conductivity as the latter, it must be 64 per cent larger in area. When aluminum cables, because of their weight advantage, replace copper cables, they nevertheless expose considerably more surface to ice loads and, having less tensile strength than copper, are subject to breaking during severe weather conditions. To augment the mechanical strength of the aluminum cable, a steel-core reinforcing wire is used.

Copper-clad Steel Wire. Whenever it is necessary to use a wire having a combination of fairly good current-carrying ability and extremely high mechanical strength, the *copper-clad steel wire* serves very well. In one manufacturing process a steel wire is first coated by an electrochemical process with a thin layer of copper and is then inserted in a copper tube. Both ends are next closed, whereupon the rod is heated and rolled; the final step is to draw the rod through successively smaller dies until the wire reaches the desired diameter.

There are two commercial grades of copper-clad wires, and these are designated as 30 per cent conductivity and 40 per cent conductivity (see page 18); the terms indicate the merits of the wires with respect to copper of the same cross section. In the accompanying table are shown the relative diameters and areas of steel and copper for the two grades, based on commercial resistivities of the two metals.

Per cent conductivity	Per cent diam of steel	Per cent areas	
		Steel	Copper
30	89.2	79.5	20.5
40	82.7	68.2	31.8

TABLE 7. COPPER-CLAD HIGH-STRENGTH WIRE*

AWG No.	Actual diam mils	Area, cir mils	Resistance, ohms per 1,000 ft	
			30 per cent conductivity	40 per cent conductivity
0000	460	211,600	0.165	0.124
000	410	168,100	0.208	0.156
00	365	133,225	0.262	0.197
0	325	105,625	0.330	0.248
1	289	83,520	0.422	0.317
2	258	66,565	0.530	0.397
3	229	52,440	0.673	0.504
4	204	41,615	0.848	0.636
5	182	33,125	1.065	0.798
6	162	26,245	1.344	1.008
7	144	20,735	1.701	1.276
8	128	16,385	2.153	1.615
9	114	12,995	2.714	2.036
10	102	10,404	3.390	2.543
11	91	8,281	.....	3.195
12	81	6,561	.....	4.032

* Copperweld Steel Co.

Table 7 lists some of the more commonly used copper-clad wires with their respective resistances. It will be noted that the resistances of the 30 per cent conductivity material, when checked against the values given in Table 4 are 3⅓ times as much (1/0.30) as the corresponding copper wires; for the 40 per cent conductivity copper-clads the resistances are 2½ times as much (1/0.40) as the corresponding copper wires.

Insulation. Wires used in the construction of coils of various kinds must be covered with a thin layer of insulating material to prevent a current *across* the conductor from wire to wire or from wire to the metallic frame (the ground). Such insulations add as little as 2½ mils to the copper-wire diameters in the case of high-grade enamel coatings, or as much as 15 mils when two layers of cotton are wrapped over previously enameled conductors. In electrical wiring and transmission systems, heavy wrappings of impregnated cotton, paper, varnished cambric, rubber, and other materials must be applied to the bare conductor, the quality and amount depending upon the system voltage and the kind of service.

All materials that are generally called insulators conduct electricity in some degree, and especially so if the voltage and/or the temperature is raised sufficiently. Under normal conditions, however, the resistivity of most insulating substances is so high that, for practical purposes, they may be considered to be complete "current stoppers." In fact, compared with copper, which has a resistivity of 1.724×10^{-6} ohm-cm (0.000001724 ohm-cm), good insulations may have values higher than 10^{16} ohm-cm (10,000,000,000,000,000 ohm-cm). Average volume resistivities of some common insulating materials are: hard rubber, 10^{18}; mica, 2×10^{17}; shellac, 10^{16}; paraffin, 10^{16}; unglazed porcelain, 3×10^{14}; plate glass, 2×10^{13}; red fiber, 5×19^{9}; slate, 10^{8}.

Unlike conductors, insulating materials have *negative* temperature-resistance coefficients, i.e., the resistance drops rapidly with increasing temperatures. This property must therefore be taken into account in connection with their employment in electrical machines that are subject to high-temperature operation. It is, in fact, generally known that some insulators become fairly good conductors at high temperatures; the resistivity of glass, for example, drops as much as 10 per cent for each degree centigrade change in temperature.

Common magnet-wire coverings include such insulations as plain and heavy-plain enamel, single and heavy Formvar, single and double cotton, single and double silk, single-cotton enamel, single-silk enamel, double-cotton enamel, double-silk enamel, spun glass, asbestos, and silicone. Each has special properties that give it preference in the design of many types of electrical equipment that must operate under varying conditions of temperature, humidity, and safety. For example, *Formvar*, a trade name for an enamel that is specially applied to the bare copper, is very tough and can stand tremendous mechanical beating. It also has a high space factor, i.e., the insulation takes up very little space; this factor is particularly important in the construction of electrical machines where the ability to perform is a direct function of the total volume of *copper* that can be put into the windings. The widespread use of spun-glass fiber is also significant because it has extended the high-temperature operating ranges of electrical equipment; in fact, it can withstand temperatures so high that it is frequently possible to increase the current ratings of machines by as much as 30 per cent without subjecting them to the normal hazards due to burnout failures. The material is, furthermore, nonhygroscopic as well as mechanically and electrically strong.

Asbestos insulation for magnet wire has only one important application, and that is where the temperatures are very high. The electric cords for toasters, flatirons, waffle irons, and the like, and the wires used in electric motors located where the temperature is abnormally high, are always covered with asbestos. However, it is thicker than cotton, has poor mechanical strength, and is comparatively expensive. For house-wiring purposes rubber-covered wire with a layer of braided cotton is standard practice. There are several grades of these insulated wires, though they are all usually dipped in tarlike compounds to give the surface material better mechanical and weatherproof qualities.

Coils of wire used in electrical machines are usually dipped in special insulating varnishes after which they are baked to add stiffness, mechanical strength, and high insulation value to the finished products. Dipping in varnish and baking generally serve to preserve the insulation covering, act as a partial heat conductor, add mechanical strength, and resist water, oil, and sometimes destructive fumes. Two general kinds of varnish are employed by electrical-machine manufacturers, namely, air-drying and baking varnishes. Since air-drying varnish dries rapidly, it becomes brittle in time and loses its mechanical strength; it is used only on coils previously treated to a dipping and baking service. Baking varnishes dry very slowly and will remain sticky and wet for several days unless properly baked. The varnishes are usually applied to the whole preheated units in a tank containing the hot liquid until all the pores and air spaces have been penetrated. After the baking process at temperatures up to about 260°F for several hours in gas-heated or electrically heated ovens or by directly applied infrared rays, the assembly becomes a strong, stiff mass capable of withstanding considerable mechanical abuse.

Insulation in High-voltage Cables. When cables are used in underground high-voltage systems, each of the current-carrying conductors is often surrounded by a considerable thickness of high-grade insulation and encased in a lead sheath. Although normal current is along the length of the conductor, there exist nevertheless certain small crosswise currents—leakage currents—from one conductor in one cable to a similar conductor in an adjacent cable; this undesirable condition results because the insulating material is not perfect and is, moreover, subject to a rather high voltage gradient (volts per mil across the insulation). Figure 7 roughly illustrates such an electrical system where the cables are assumed to be buried in the earth; because of the large cross section of the latter its leakage resistance, generally very small compared with the insulation resistance of the cables, may be neglected in leakage-current computations.

Remembering that resistance is directly proportional to the length of the path measured along the direction in which the current passes, and *inversely* proportional to the area of the same current path, it should be clear that the insulation resistance between conductor and sheath cannot be determined by as simple an equation as that given for conductors, i.e., Eq. (6). This results from the fact that the area of the leakage-current path per unit of cable length is smallest at the conductor surface and greatest at the inside surface of the lead sheath. Referring to Fig. 7, the leakage-current paths are seen to be radial; this means that $2\pi r_c$ is the area of the insulation per unit of cable length at the surface of the conductor, and $2\pi r_s$ is the area of the same material per unit of cable length at the inside surface of the lead sheath. It follows, therefore, that an equation giving the insulation resistance of the cable must not only include a resistivity factor and an insulation thickness represented by $(r_s - r_c)$, but must also involve an area per unit length of cable that increases differentially from $2\pi r_c$ to $2\pi r_s$. Such an equation, derived by

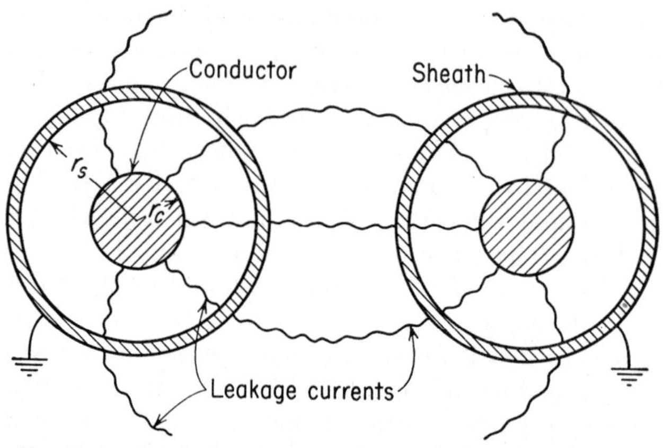

FIG. 7. An electrical system consisting of lead-sheathed cables.

setting up a so-called differential equation and integrating by the method of calculus (given in Appendix 1), is

$$R = \frac{2.3\rho}{10^6} \log_{10}\left(\frac{r_s}{r_c}\right) \qquad \text{ohms per mile} \qquad (9)^1$$

where ρ is the resistivity of the insulation in ohm-centimeters, and r_s and r_c are, respectively, the radii of the inside of the sheath and the conductor, in *any similar units*.

EXAMPLE 10. A lead-sheath cable has an internal sheath diameter of 3 in. and a conductor whose diameter is 0.8 in. If the insulating material has an average resistivity of about 1.6×10^{14} ohm-cm, calculate the insulation resistance per mile of cable.

Solution

$$R = \frac{2.3 \times 1.6 \times 10^{14}}{10^6} \log_{10}\left(\frac{1.5}{0.4}\right) = 3.68 \times 10^8 \times 0.574$$
$$= 2.11 \times 10^8 \text{ ohms per mile}$$
$$= 200 \text{ megohms per mile approx}$$

[1] See Appendix 1C for derivation.

Questions

1. Define a *circular mil–foot.*
2. How is the circular-mil area of a round wire determined?
3. How are the resistivity magnitudes of various conductors explained in terms of the electron theory?
4. Under what conditions is it desirable to use low-resistivity conductors? high-resistivity conductors? Name several of each.
5. Explain why the resistance of a given conductor material is (*a*) directly proportional to its length, and (*b*) inversely proportional to its cross-sectional area.
6. Distinguish between resistivity in terms of *ohm–circular mils per foot* and *ohm–square centimeters per centimeter.*
7. How does the term *microhm-centimeters* arise?
8. Define *per cent conductivity.* What is the standard of reference for per cent conductivity?
9. How is it possible to have a per cent conductivity greater than 100 per cent? Explain carefully.
10. In general, how does temperature affect the resistance of conducting materials?
11. What is meant by *inferred absolute* resistance when referring to resistance-temperature effects? What is the *true* absolute zero?
12. Define *temperature coefficient of resistance.*
13. Why does the temperature coefficient of resistance change when referred to resistances at different temperature? When is it higher? When is it lower?
14. What materials have temperature coefficients of resistance that may be considered negligible? Name several uses of such materials.
15. What is the largest wire size in the standard AWG table? How are the numbers related to their circular-mil areas?
16. How do the resistance and circular-mil area change for every change of 3 gage numbers? 10 gage numbers? successive gage numbers?
17. How do the pounds per 1,000 ft and the feet per pound change for every change of 3 gage numbers? 10 gage numbers?
18. What is a *stranded cable?* When and why is it used in preference to a single-wire conductor?
19. How are standard stranded cables constructed?
20. Why is the resistance of a stranded cable more than that of an equivalent single-wire conductor?
21. What is a *steel-core aluminum-strand cable?* What advantage does it possess over the standard copper cable?
22. Explain why an aluminum cable weighs less than an equivalent copper cable.
23. Describe a *copper-clad steel wire.* How is it manufactured?
24. Distinguish between 30 per cent and 40 per cent conductivity copper-clad steel wires.
25. What is the term applied to the current that passes through insulation? Under what conditions will this current be comparatively large? small?
26. What are approximate magnitudes of insulation resistivities?
27. How does temperature affect insulation resistance?
28. List several kinds of wire coverings, and indicate what approximate thicknesses they add to the bare copper diameters.
29. What is a *lead-sheath cable?*
30. Why is the insulation-resistance calculation of a lead-sheath cable different from that for a conductor? Explain carefully.

31. What is the general order of magnitude of the insulation resistance per mile of a lead-sheath cable?

Problems

1. A coil of annealed copper wire has 820 turns, the average length of which is 9 in. If the diameter of the wire is 32 mils, calculate the total resistance of the coil at 20°C.

2. A single layer of No. 24 AWG ($d = 0.0201$ in.) commercial iron wire is wound over a ceramic tube whose diameter is 3.25 in. If the total wire resistance is 41 ohms, determine the number of turns.

3. How many turns would be necessary if the same size of Manganin wire replaced the iron wire of Prob. 2?

4. The heating unit for an electric ironer has a resistance of 12 ohms. If the cross section of the material is rectangular, 0.0045×0.125 in., and its total length is 13 ft, determine (*a*) the resistivity of the material used, and (*b*) the kind of wire [1 sq in. $= (4/\pi)\ 10^6$ cir mils].

5. A copper wire of unknown length has a diameter of 0.25 in. and a resistance of 0.28 ohm. By several successive passes through drawing dies the diameter of the wire is reduced to 0.05 in. Assuming that the resistivity of the copper remains unchanged in the drawing process, calculate the resistance of the reduced-size wire.

6. The steel of the third rail of railway system has a resistivity of 21.4 microhm-cm. If its cross-sectional area is 8.2 sq in., calculate the resistance per mile of rail, neglecting the effect of joints between sections.

7. A certain batch of copper wire was found to have a conductivity of 95.5 per cent at 20°C. What is its resistivity (*a*) in ohm–circular mils per foot, (*b*) in microhm-centimeters?

8. A 1,000-ft length of aluminum wire, whose diameter is 0.365 in., has a resistance of 0.13 ohm at 20°C. What is its per cent conductivity?

9. The copper field winding of an electrical machine has a resistance of 46 ohms at a temperature of 22°C. What will be its resistance at a temperature of 75°C?

10. An incandescent lamp has a tungsten filament whose resistance is 96 ohms at its operating temperature of 2900°C. Calculate the filament resistance when the lamp is disconnected from the electrical source, under which condition its temperature is 24°C.

11. Calculate the temperature coefficient of resistance of aluminum at 2°C. Using the value thus obtained, determine the resistance of an aluminum conductor at 62°C if its resistance at 2°C is 7.5 ohms.

12. The resistance of a given electrical device is 46 ohms at 25°C. If the temperature coefficient of resistance of the material is 0.00454 at 20°C, determine the temperature of the device when its resistance is 92 ohms.

13. A certain copper winding has a resistance of 0.25 ohm at a temperature of 18°C. Calculate the temperature rise in the winding, when, after a period of operation, the resistance increases to 0.31 ohm.

14. The resistivity of a copper rod 50 ft long and 0.25 in. in diameter is 1.76 microhm-cm at 20°C. What is its resistance at −20°C?

15. A 400,000-cir-mil cable is composed of 37 strands. What is the diameter, in mils, of each strand?

16. Each of the 19 strands of a copper cable has a diameter of 59 mils. Calculate the resistance of a mile of such cable at a temperature of 20°C.

17. How many strands are there in a 1,500,000-cir-mil cable, if each strand has a diameter of 0.094 in.?

18. The copper in a 40 per cent conductivity copper-clad steel wire has a resistivity of 10.37 ohm–cir-mils per ft. What is the resistivity of the steel?

19. The following particulars are given in connection with a copper-clad steel wire: steel-core diameter = 0.25 in.; over-all diameter = 0.289 in.; resistivity of copper = 10.37; resistivity of steel = 86.3. Calculate the per cent conductivity of the conductor.

20. The internal diameter of the sheath in a lead-sheath cable is 2.75 in. and the diameter of the copper conductor is 0.65 in. Assuming an average resistivity of 2.2×10^{14} for the insulating material, calculate the insulation resistance per mile of the cable.

21. Using the data in Prob. 20, calculate the insulation resistance per 1,000 ft of cable.

CHAPTER 3

DIRECT-CURRENT CIRCUITS I
OHM'S LAW—POWER—ENERGY

Electrical Effects and Energy Transformations. Dynamic electricity, i.e., motion of electrons, produces several important *effects;* these, in turn, give rise to transformations involving conversion from electrical energy to some other form of energy. To be sure, the great science of electricity is useful only through these effects, because electrical energy must be converted to some other form of energy if devices and machines of many types are to function and serve.

The electrical effects are few in number, follow well-known basic laws, and, taken singly or in various combinations, are responsible for the proper functioning of all electrical apparatus. Fortunately, each one is rather simple to understand, although such simplicity may often be obscured by what appears to be, and frequently really is, complicated equipment. It will therefore be desirable to comment briefly on some of the more important electrical effects since, as indicated, these are basic to all electrical phenomena.

The Heating Effect. It was observed early that heat is always developed in a conductor when a current of electricity passes through it. Several factors are responsible for the *amount* of heat; these are the magnitude of the current (squared), the resistance of the conductor, and the time during which the current is present. However, the *temperature rise* of the current-carrying assembly will be determined by the kind and physical size of the heat-absorbing device and the temperature, density, and motion (or lack of motion) of the surrounding air, as well as by the amount of heat. If the rate at which heat is developed exceeds the dissipation rate, i.e., the rate at which heat is carried off by the air or surrounding objects, then the temperature continues to rise. If, on the other hand, heat is dissipated as rapidly as it is produced, the temperature levels off and becomes constant.

In many common electric-heating units found in the home, such as toasters, percolators, flatirons, waffle irons, curling irons, stoves, heating pads, and incandescent lamps, the heating is not only desirable but under perfect control. In other applications, however, excessive heating may result in severe damage to electrical equipment unless protective measures are taken to disconnect the current before this happens. In electric-motor wiring systems, for example, it is customary to employ low-melting-point metal links called *fuses*, or *circuit breakers*, which function to break the current if, for some reason, the temperature should rise above safe limits. This is also true of house-wiring systems, where over-heated wires are likely to cause serious fire hazards. The laws governing this *natural* heating effect of a current are well known and will be considered in detail subsequently.

The Magnetic Effect. The great scientist Hans Christian Oersted observed, in 1820, that a compass was deflected when placed near a current-carrying wire. This simple but far-reaching discovery definitely demonstrated the direct connection between electricity and magnetism; it was indeed the beginning of what ultimately developed into the new science of electromagnetism. Further investigation showed that the magnetic effect can be strengthened by the use of coils of wire instead of straight wires, by employing cores of iron or good-quality magnetic alloys, and by properly proportioning and arranging (i.e., designing) the current-carrying coil and magnetic core. The principle of operation of such electromagnetic devices and machines as bells, telephone and telegraph equipment, lifting magnets, track and elevator brakes, electrical measuring instruments, dynamos, and transformers, and many others quite as well known, depends upon the *natural* magnetic effect of a current. The subjects of magnetism and electromagnetism are treated in a later chapter.

The Chemical Effect. Another early experimenter and scientist, Michael Faraday, first showed the close connection between electricity and chemical action. His pioneer investigations, as well as those of many others, are responsible for such modern processes as electroplating, electrorefining, electrotyping, the production of oxygen, hydrogen, and chlorine gas, and the manufacture of metallic sodium, potassium, and caustic soda. In this connection it is significant that electrochemical reactions are absolutely exact in the sense that they are governed by rigid laws. This point is particularly important because, among other things, it is the basis for the accepted unit of current, the *international ampere;* this is defined as *the unvarying current which, when passed through a solution of nitrate of silver in accordance with standard specifications, deposits silver at the rate of* 0.001118 *gram per second.*

The Electromagnetic-induction Effect. Even more important than Faraday's original work in the field of electrochemistry was his fundamental research in the new branch of science, electromagnetism. His brilliant discoveries, resulting from persistent and painstaking effort, are basic to present-day electric-power generation and distribution systems. When, in 1831, he discovered that changes in electromagnetism give rise to induced voltages and currents in neighboring, i.e., coupled, wires and coils, he laid the foundation for what are now known as transformer action, generator action, and motor action, and the development of present-day transformers, generators, and motors.

Other Electrical Effects. In addition to the four important electrical effects briefly described in the foregoing sections, four others should be mentioned. There is, for example, the well-known *physiological effect* wherein the living body experiences strange and sometimes fatal reactions when a current of electricity is passed through it.

Another interesting phenomenon is the heating that takes place at the junction between two dissimilar metals when current passes across the junction from one metal to the other. Called the *thermoelectric effect,* it is applied practically *in reverse* in connection with the measurement of high temperatures or high-frequency electric currents. Here a thermocouple, which is a junction of two dissimilar metals such as iron and copper, is placed where the temperature is to be measured or in contact with an electrically heated conductor; as a result of the temperature rise in the *couple,* due to heat conduction, a current is produced in an electrical instrument that is connected across the ends of the wires forming the couple. Since the magnitude of the current is a function of the temperature rise, the instrument indirectly measures the primary temperature or current as the case may be.

An extremely important modern electrical device is the so-called *photoelectric cell.* Depending upon the *photoelectric effect* for its functioning, it contains a substance that is photosensitive, i.e., a chemical compound that emits electrons when exposed to light. When properly connected in many kinds of control systems the current resulting from the emitted electrons may be amplified to perform numerous useful services. Practical examples of the photoelectric effect are talking moving pictures, automatic sorting and counting devices, burglar-alarm systems, animated advertising signs, and automatic door openers and drinking fountains.

Mention should also be made of the *piezoelectric effect,* useful, for example, in connection with the measurement of high pressures in large guns, and accurate frequency control in radio oscillators. This effect is characterized by the presence of current in certain crystals when they are subjected to changes in pressure.

Electron Theory and Current. In accordance with the electron theory (Chap. 1) it is generally accepted that a current of electricity is a flow of electrons; moreover, since *the electrons* are negatively charged they *move toward the positive pole* of the source of potential. However, previous to the proposal of the electron theory, at the end of the nineteenth century, and before the performance of a great variety of experiments that have since proved it to be completely valid, it was *arbitrarily assumed* that the direction of current was *from* (*not to*) the positive terminal of the source of emf. Understand that this is the direct opposite of the actual direction of electron motion. Now then, on the basis of that assumption several important rules were formulated so that certain electromagnetic actions could be predicted from other known conditions. These involve such phenomena as magnetic polarities of coils and the resulting directions of the exerted forces, the polarities of electric generators, the direction of rotation of motors, induced voltages resulting from transformer action, and others. As will be pointed out later, these rules, based on an arbitrary assumption of current direction, are purposely worded in such a way that they merely state the results of actual experimental evidence. And since it makes little difference whether the rules are based upon a current direction that is represented by electron motion or its opposite,

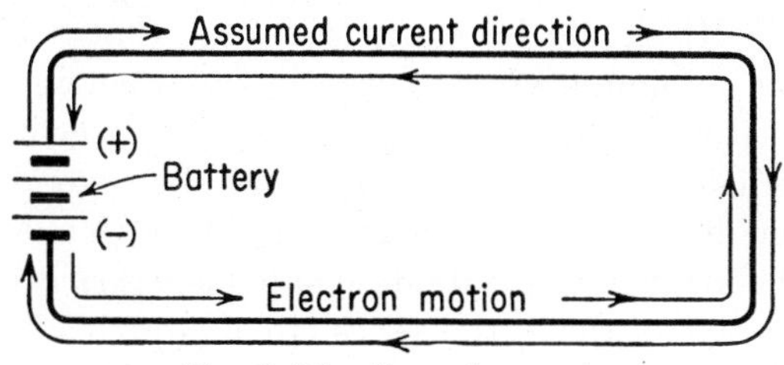

FIG. 8. Directions of current.

it was decided to retain the original statements that postulate a current *from the positive terminal* of the source of supply; both directions are indicated in Fig. 8. It was thought, and properly so, that less confusion would result. All references to current, therefore, will hereafter imply the generally adopted direction, i.e., that opposite to the electron motion.

Electric Circuits. Electrical energy is commonly transmitted through wires from a *source* of emf to a consuming device or machine; it is in the latter, usually referred to as the *load*, that the electrical energy is converted into other forms such as heat, magnetic, or chemical energy. With the aid of supplementary equipment such transmission can not only be provided to any convenient location, but can be made to traverse great distances efficiently and cheaply. It is, in this respect, far superior to steam, which is usually sent short distances through rather large pipes.

The transfer of electrical energy always takes place through an *electric circuit*. In its simplest form this consists of a voltage source, a load, and a pair of connecting wires. Other elements may, and frequently are, included, among them devices that control the current, protective devices or mechanisms, and measuring instruments. Figure 9 illustrates an electric circuit complete with generator, switch, fuses, measuring instruments, and connecting wires. Considered primarily from the standpoint of energy conversion, the resistance of the load generally accounts for a major part of the total resistance of the electric circuit; this means, of course, that, when a current exists in a circuit that is intact, most of the available emf of the source is effective to service the load, while a fractional part is lost in whatever wires and equipment are used between

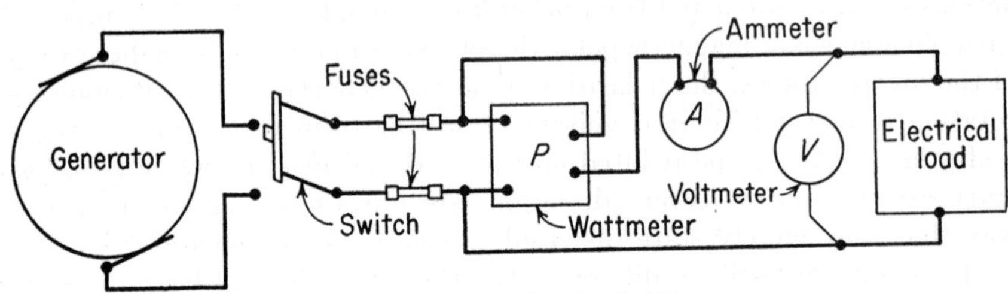

FIG. 9. A simple electric circuit.

source and load. It should be clear, therefore, that a highly efficient circuit involves a minimum voltage drop in those portions that are not directly concerned with the load, i.e., the energy conversion.

Assuming a single source of emf (there may be several in a complex electrical system) load resistances may be interconnected in two fundamental ways; the arrangements are designated *series circuits* and *parallel circuits*. In the first of these, the series circuit, the load resistances are

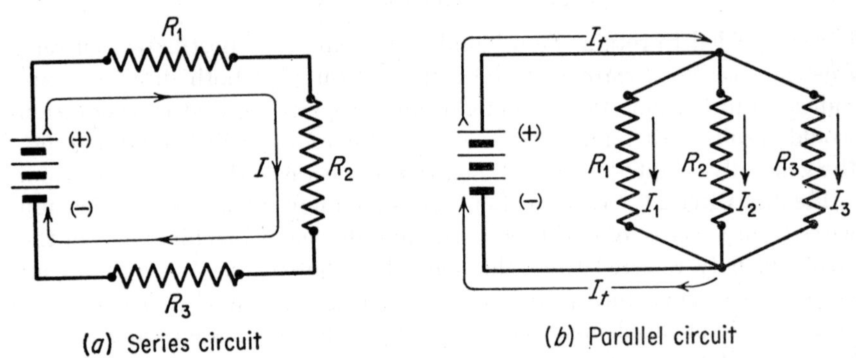

FIG. 10. Two fundamental types of circuit.

joined together end to end so that the *same current* passes from one to the other around one complete path; in the second, the parallel circuit, the load resistances are connected across one another so that the total current, entering one junction, divides to pass through the individual parts in definite ratios and combines at the other junction to leave the latter. Figure 10 illustrates the two types of circuit; note in the series circuit that only *one current* I passes through resistors R_1, R_2, and R_3, while in the parallel circuit the total current I_t divides into three parts I_1, I_2, and I_3 to pass through the respective resistors R_1, R_2, and R_3.

Complex circuits are frequently found in practice to consist of two or more interconnected sections, each of which may be a single resistor or two or more resistors in series or parallel; the interconnection of the several sections may likewise be arranged in series or parallel. Figure 11 illustrates two possible combinations designated *series-parallel* and *parallel-series* circuits. In the series-parallel circuit (Fig. 11*a*) the major (series) circuit is made up of three minor sections, two of which combine resistors in parallel. (Note that the hyphenated term "series-parallel" uses the word *series* first to emphasize the major circuit, and the word

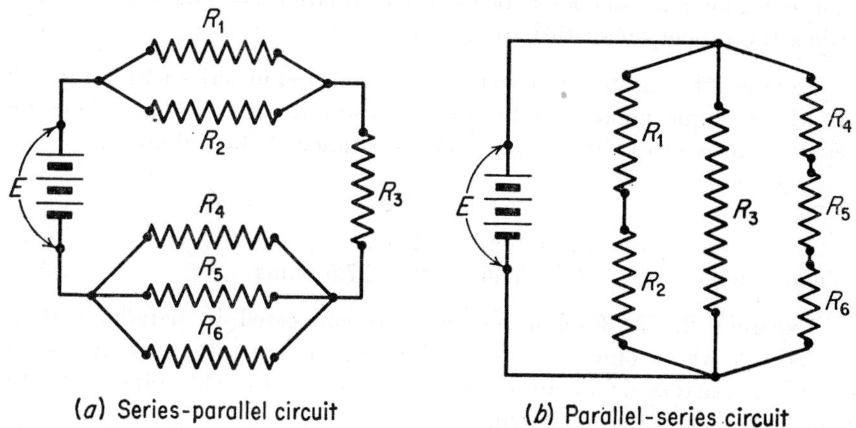

Fig. 11. Two fundamental types of combination circuit.

parallel second to indicate the minor connections.) In the parallel-series circuit (Fig. 11*b*) the major (parallel) circuit is made up of three minor sections, two of which combine resistors in series. (Again note that the hyphenated word "parallel-series" uses the word *parallel* first to emphasize the major circuit, and the word *series* second to indicate the minor connections.) Circuits such as these, as well as others that are more complex, will be analyzed mathematically in subsequent articles and will, moreover, be shown to break down into the elemental circuit forms.

Ohm's Law and the Electric Circuit. The value of the current in any electric circuit depends upon two factors, namely, the impressed emf and the total resistance; the latter represents the equivalent opposition to current in the entire circuit, although, as was previously pointed out, this often omits the resistances of wires, instruments, and other necessary elements when these are negligibly small. The law that relates the three factors, i.e., current, emf, and resistance, is practically obvious now but was not particularly so in 1826 when George Simon Ohm proved experimentally that:

The current is {*directly proportional to the impressed emf.*
inversely proportional to the resistance.

This statement, known as *Ohm's law*, embodies one of the most important fundamental laws in the realm of electrical science and, written in equation form, becomes

$$I = \frac{E}{R} \tag{10}$$

where I = circuit current
E = impressed emf
R = circuit resistance

The equation may, of course, be used to evaluate $E\ (= IR)$ or $R\ (= E/I)$ when the proper quantities are known.

EXAMPLE 1. A 30-ohm resistance is connected in series with a resistor R whose ohmic value is unknown. If the current is 2 amp when the circuit emf is 115 volts, calculate the resistance of the unknown.

Solution

$$R_t = 115/2 = 57.5$$

Therefore $$R = 57.5 - 30 = 27.5 \text{ ohms}$$

EXAMPLE 2. A 30-ohm resistance is connected in parallel with a resistor R whose ohmic value is unknown. If the total current (taken by both resistors) is 5.7 amp when the circuit emf is 114 volts, calculate the resistance of the unknown.

Solution

$$I_{30} = 114/30 = 3.8 \text{ amp}$$
$$I_R = 5.7 - 3.8 = 1.9 \text{ amp}$$

Therefore $$R = 114/1.9 = 60 \text{ ohms}$$

EXAMPLE 3. A series circuit like that shown in Fig. 10a has a 24-volt battery that delivers a current of 1.5 amp. If $R_1 = 3.4$ ohms and $R_3 = 6.2$ ohms, calculate the ohmic value of R_2.

Solution

R_1 requires $1.5 \times 3.4 = 5.1$ volts. R_3 requires $1.5 \times 6.2 = 9.3$ volts. The available voltage for R_2 is therefore $24 - 5.1 - 9.3 = 9.6$ volts. Hence $R_2 = 9.6/1.5 = 6.4$ ohms.

Measurement of Amperes and Volts. The two instruments most commonly employed in d-c circuits are ammeters and voltmeters. These are both *indicating* instruments since their pointers deflect to their instantaneous values and move up and down scale as their magnitudes change.

If no change occurs the pointers will, of course, remain stationary; however, if the changes are very rapid and the moving element of the instrument cannot follow the fluctuations, an *average* current or voltage is indicated (see Examples 4 and 5, Chap. 1). The *internal resistance of a good ammeter is extremely low* so that the insertion of such an instrument *in a circuit* does not alter the total resistance appreciably. The *internal resistance of a good voltmeter*, on the other hand, is very large, so that its insertion *across a circuit* does not alter the total circuit current appreciably. Referring to Fig. 9, note particularly that the ammeter is connected in series in the upper line wire; its resistance, which is a very small fraction of an ohm, acts in much the same way as do the low line-wire resistances. Also observe that the voltmeter is connected across the electrical load and, having a very high resistance, takes very little current; the ammeter deflection is therefore unaffected by the insertion of the voltmeter in the circuit and indicates the electrical-load current quite accurately. The presence of the wattmeter in the circuit to measure power (discussed in the next article) is, strictly speaking, similar to the insertion of a combination ammeter-voltmeter.

Electrical Power. Power is the *rate* at which work is done, and in the mechanical system is generally expressed in horsepower, abbreviated hp; it is equivalent to the rate of 33,000 ft-lb of work per minute. This unit was originated by James Watt in 1782 because he found it necessary to specify how much power his new steam engines would develop in terms of the horses they were intended to replace. The practice then was to have the horses push a crank as they walked in a 24-ft-diameter circle; this action resulted in the operation of pumps that raised water to elevated tanks. Since the average horse was *assumed* to exert a force of about 175 lb and made $2\frac{1}{2}$ complete revolutions per minute, it followed that 1 hp was equivalent to $175 \times (24\pi) \times 2\frac{1}{2}$, or 33,000 ft-lb per min. Later, when the unit of electrical power was adopted, it was designated the *watt* in honor of the mechanical inventor James Watt.

Following the fundamental definition of power, i.e., *the time rate of doing work*, the *unit of electrical* power is defined in terms of the *joule per second*, the latter being *the work done when one coulomb of electricity is moved through a potential difference of one volt in one second.* Remembering that 1 coulomb per second is 1 amp [see Eq. (1)], it follows that 1 joule per sec = 1 watt, and this is any product of E (volts) and I (amperes) that is unity. In general, therefore, the *power in watts* is

$$P = EI \tag{11}$$

Since $E = IR$, P may be written in terms of I and R; thus

$$P = (IR)I = I^2R \tag{12}$$

Also, E/R may be substituted for I in Eq. (11), in which case

$$P = E\frac{E}{R} = \frac{E^2}{R} \tag{13}$$

Any one of the above equations may be used to determine the circuit power if two proper values of E, I, and R are known; they may also be employed to evaluate E, I, or R if two of the latter three terms and P are known.

Electrical power is frequently converted to mechanical power as, for example, in the case of the electric motor; a precise relationship is therefore required between the mechanical and electrical equivalents of power. Accurate measurements indicate that

$$1 \text{ hp} = 746 \text{ watts}$$

and, since 1,000 watts = 1 kilowatt (1 kw), 1 hp is sometimes taken to be approximately ¾ kw.

EXAMPLE 4. A building load consists of thirty 100-watt, fifty 75-watt, and forty 60-watt incandescent lamps, all connected in parallel to a 116-volt source. Calculate (*a*) the total power, (*b*) the total current, (*c*) the current through each size of lamp.

Solution

(*a*)
$$P_{100} = 30 \times 100 = 3{,}000 \text{ watts}$$
$$P_{75} = 50 \times 75 = 3{,}750 \text{ watts}$$
$$P_{60} = 40 \times 60 = 2{,}400 \text{ watts}$$
$$P_t = 3{,}000 + 3{,}750 + 2{,}400 = 9{,}150 \text{ watts}$$

(*b*)
$$I_t = \frac{9{,}150}{116} = 78.9 \text{ amp}$$

(*c*)
$$I_{100} = \frac{3{,}000}{30 \times 116} = 0.863 \text{ amp}$$
$$I_{75} = \frac{3{,}750}{50 \times 116} = 0.646 \text{ amp}$$
$$I_{60} = \frac{2{,}400}{40 \times 116} = 0.518 \text{ amp}$$

EXAMPLE 5. Using the data from Example 4, calculate (*a*) the equivalent resistance of the entire load; (*b*) the resistance of each size of lamp.

Solution

(*a*) $R_{eq} = \frac{E}{I_t} = \frac{116}{78.9} = 1.47 \text{ ohms}$ or $R_{eq} = \frac{P}{I^2} = \frac{9{,}150}{(78.9)^2} = 1.47 \text{ ohms}$

(b)
$$R_{100} = \frac{116}{0.863} = 135 \text{ ohms}$$
$$R_{75} = \frac{116}{0.646} = 180 \text{ ohms}$$
$$R_{60} = \frac{116}{0.518} = 224 \text{ ohms}$$

EXAMPLE 6. An electric motor drives a mechanical load, taking 18.8 amp from a 230-volt source. Calculate (*a*) the power input to the motor, (*b*) the horsepower output of the motor if it operates at an efficiency of 86.4 per cent.

Solution

(a)
$$P_{in} = 230 \times 18.8 = 4{,}320 \text{ watts}$$

(b)
$$P_{out} = \frac{4{,}320 \times 0.864}{746} = 5 \text{ hp}$$

EXAMPLE 7. What is the resistance of a load that takes 2,500 watts from a 115-volt source?

Solution

$$R = \frac{E^2}{P} = \frac{(115)^2}{2{,}500} = 5.29 \text{ ohms}$$

Electrical and Heat Energy. Since power is the time rate of doing work, sometimes stated as the rate of expenditure of energy, it should be clear that *electrical energy* is the product of power (watts) and time. If the power remains constant during the period of time t, energy is equal to Pt where t can be in any convenient units; however, where power changes do occur during an extended period of time, it is necessary to sum up the energies of a number of constant power-time intervals, or employ some sort of integration (summation) process that takes account of the power variations. Assuming constant electrical quantities during a period of t sec,

$$W = Pt = EIt = I^2Rt = \frac{E^2}{R}t \quad \text{joules} \tag{14}$$

Note that a *joule* is equal to a *watt-second* where P is given in watts and t is in seconds.

Since the watt-second is ordinarily too small for practical computations a larger unit, the *kilowatthour*, abbreviated *kwhr*, is generally used. Thus

$$\text{kwhr} = \frac{P \times \text{hr}}{1{,}000} \tag{14a}$$

EXAMPLE 8. How much electrical energy, in kilowatthours, is delivered to an electric motor during an 8-hr period when operating from a constant 230-volt source, if the average currents are 34 amp for 2 hr, 38 amp for 1½ hr, 26 amp for 4 hr, and 12 amp for ½ hr?

Solution

$$\text{Energy} = [(230 \times 34 \times 2) + (230 \times 38 \times 1.5) + (230 \times 26 \times 4) + (230 \times 12 \times 0.5)] \times 1/1{,}000 = 54.05 \text{ kwhr}$$

EXAMPLE 9. A water heater has a resistance of 5.3 ohms and takes 43.5 amp when in operation. If it is in service on the average of 2 hr per day, how many kilowatthours of energy will be expended during a 30-day month?

Solution

$$\text{Energy} = \frac{(43.5)^2 \times 5.3 \times 2 \times 30}{1{,}000} = 600 \text{ kwhr}$$

A current through a resistor always involves a conversion of electrical energy into heat energy. If the heat energy raises the temperature of transmission-line conductors, or windings in motors, electromagnets, or other electrical devices whose function it is to do work *not* related to heating, it is proper to regard it as an energy loss. On the other hand, if the heat energy is made useful in such utilities as water heaters (Example 9), toasters, percolators, flatirons, and electric furnaces, only the portion that *escapes* is considered as heat loss; the latter is generally referred to as a *power loss* if, during the period of operation, the power is constant. Moreover, since the power loss is assumed to take place at a current I through a resistance R it is designated as an *I square R loss*, or briefly I^2R. Thus, in a transmission line having a resistance of 0.03 ohm and carrying a current of 150 amp, the power loss will be $(150)^2 \times 0.03 = 675$ watts.

When electrical energy is applied to useful heating such as a water heater, it is desirable to know how many gram-calories[1] or British thermal units[2] (Btu) of heat energy are represented by 1 unit of electrical energy. Precisely performed experiments have shown that 1 watt-sec of electrical energy, i.e., 1 joule, is equivalent to 0.24 gm-cal. Applying this conversion unit to Eq. (14), it follows that

$$H = 0.24Pt = 0.24EIt = 0.24I^2Rt = 0.24\left(\frac{E^2}{R}\right)t \quad \text{calories} \quad (15)$$

Since there are 453.6 gm in 1 lb, the heat energy imparted to water (specific heat = 1) may be written in terms of its electrical-energy equivalent as follows:

[1] One gram-calorie is the heat required to raise the temperature of 1 gm of water 1°C.
[2] One Btu is the heat required to raise the temperature of 1 lb of water 1°F.

$$(\text{lb } H_2O) \times 453.6 \times (^\circ\text{C temperature rise}) = \begin{cases} 0.24Pt \\ 0.24EIt \\ 0.24I^2Rt \\ 0.24(E^2/R)t \end{cases} \quad (16)$$

EXAMPLE 10. How long will it take to raise the temperature of 1 qt of water in a percolator from 18 to 100°C if the supply voltage is 120 and the heater resistance is 24 ohms? Assume a heat loss by radiation of 25 per cent.

Solution

The heat energy required by 1 qt (= 2.08 lb) of water is

$$2.08 \times 453.6 \times (100 - 18) = 77{,}400 \text{ gm-cal}$$

Since the heat loss by radiation is 25 per cent, the heater unit must supply (77,400/0.75) = 103,200 gm-cal to the water. Therefore

$$103{,}200 = 0.24[(120)^2/24]t$$

from which

$$t = \frac{103{,}200 \times 24}{0.24 \times (120)^2} = 717 \text{ sec or 12 min (approx)}$$

Cost of Electrical Service. Monthly charges to residential consumers of electrical energy are generally made on the basis of a sliding-rate scale, the rate per kilowatthour decreasing in steps with increasing amounts of used energy. In most cases where the energy consumption is very low, or where special electrical installations are necessary for the convenience of those who are not in the direct load center, fixed minimum charges are made. For large consumers, especially in connection with industrial loads, it is customary, on the other hand, to have a sliding scale of rates lower than residential rates for *energy* and, in addition, several extra charges that take into account such factors as maximum demand, low power factor, variable costs of generation fuel, etc. In shops and factories where power demands generally swing between rather wide limits, public-service companies must install sufficient equipment and wiring to take care of the maximum requirements even though the average demand is considerably less than this. And since this adds to fixed charges for electrical service without increasing the energy income in proportion to the cost of added equipment, it is generally agreed that a *demand charge* should be made in such cases on the basis of maximum *power demand* when it exists for specified periods of time.

It must be understood, of course, that the primary basis for the cost of all electrical service is *energy*, measured in kilowatthours. For the measurement of such energy all installations are provided with watthour meters—integrating meters—usually at a point in the circuit where the wires enter the building to be served. Watthour meters are, in reality, small electric motors in which the speed of rotation of a flat aluminum disk is directly proportional to the power taken by its connected circuit. As the disk revolves, it actuates a register, through a system of gears, on the dials of which the energy consumption is indicated. The energy cost is calculated from meter readings, usually taken at monthly intervals.

A typical residential rate schedule might be the following: 5 cents per kilowatthour for the first 35 kwhr, 4 cents per kilowatthour for the second 35 kwhr, 2½ cents per kilowatthour for the next 130 kwhr, 2 cents per kilowatthour for all energy over 200 kwhr. Where an electric water heater is installed all energy over 200 kwhr shall be billed at 1.3 cents per kilowatthour.

EXAMPLE 11. Using the foregoing rate schedule, calculate the cost of service for electrical energy if the difference between two successive monthly meter readings is 224 kwhr.

Solution

Step 1: $35 \times 0.05 = \$1.75$
Step 2: $35 \times 0.04 = 1.40$
Step 3: $130 \times 0.025 = 3.25$
Step 4: $24 \times 0.02 = 0.48$
Total cost $= \$6.88$

Rate schedules for industrial power and light service, generally three-phase alternating current, vary somewhat on the basis of connected load, maximum demand, and energy consumption. In addition to the basic charge for energy (kilowatthours) there are at least three other items of cost, representing property investment and operating expense, that must be included in the bill for service. The latter come under the headings of (1) maximum load and load factor,[1] (2) adjustment for power factor,[2] and (3) adjustment for the cost of powerhouse fuel.

One such schedule for power and light service, available to customers having a billing maximum load of 25 kw or more, is the following:

Maximum-load Charge

$1.50 per month per kilowatt of billing maximum load in the month, where the maximum load is adjusted, for billing purposes, to a basic power factor of 0.80 lagging. For power factors *less* than 0.80 lagging,

[1] The maximum load shall be measured by suitable indicating or recording instruments, and in any month the maximum load shall be the average number of kilowatts in the 30-min interval during which the energy metered is greater than in any other 30-min interval in such month.

[2] See p. 392.

as determined from installed reactive kilovolt-ampere-hour meters, the maximum load is *increased proportionately,* whereas for power factors *greater* than 0.80 lagging the maximum load is *decreased proportionately.*

Energy Charge

2.25 cents per kilowatthour for the first 3,000 kwhr used in any month
1.8 cents per kilowatthour for the next 7,000 kwhr used in the same month
1.2 cents per kilowatthour for the next 10,000 kwhr used in the same month
1.0 cents per kilowatthour for the next 80,000 kwhr used in the same month
0.8 cent per kilowatthour for the next 100,000 kwhr used in the same month
0.7 cent per kilowatthour for all over 200,000 kwhr used in the same month

An actual bill taken from the files of the Public Service Company of Indiana, Inc., for electric service rendered a Lafayette, Ind., manufacturer, is given on p. 392, Chap. 17 to illustrate how the monthly bill is calculated on the above schedule.

Equal Resistors in Series or Parallel. When *n equal resistors* are connected in *series* (Fig. 12*a*) to a source of emf of E volts, each one having a resistance of R ohms, the following conditions prevail:

1. The current I through all resistors is the same.
2. The total equivalent resistance of the circuit $R_t = nR$.
3. The voltage drops across the individual resistors are equal.
4. The voltage drop across each resistor $E_R = E/n = IR$.
5. The power taken by each resistor $P_R = EI/n = E_RI$.

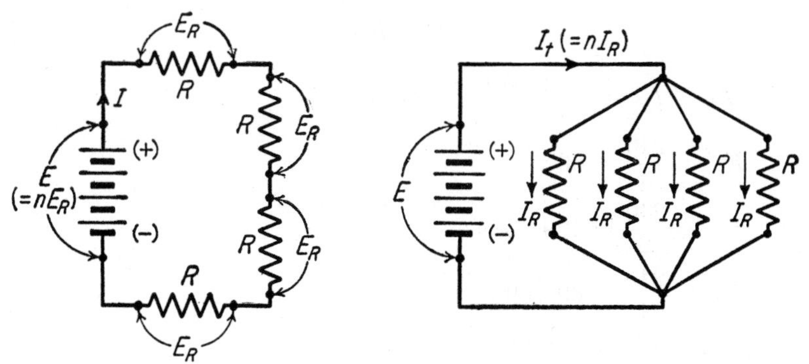

FIG. 12. Simple series and parallel circuits.

A good practical example of such a circuit is one group of five 120-volt incandescent lamps connected in series in a streetcar where the trolley-to-track voltage is 600. Here, each lamp "receives" one-fifth of 600 volts, or 120 volts, so that it operates at rated voltage and power. True, if one lamp should burn out, all five series-connected lamps will be extinguished, as they would be in a "string" of Christmas-tree lights.

When n *equal resistors* are connected in *parallel* (Fig. 12*b*) to a source of E volts, each one having a resistance of R ohms, the following conditions prevail:

1. The same voltage E is impressed across all resistors.
2. The individual-resistor currents are equal, and each current $I_R = E/R$.
3. The total current $I_t = nE/R = nI_R$.
4. The total equivalent resistance of the circuit $R_t = E/I_t = E/(nE/R) = R/n$.
5. The power taken by each resistor $P_R = EI_R = EI_t/n = I_R^2R = (I_t/n)^2R$.

An example, combining both types of circuit, i.e., equal resistors in series and equal resistors in parallel, will now be given to illustrate the foregoing rules.

EXAMPLE 12. A parallel-series circuit (see Fig. 11*b*) consists of three equal-resistance branches. Branch A has three 40-ohm resistors in series, branch B has two 60-ohm resistors in series, and branch C has four 30-ohm resistors in series. If the total impressed emf is 240 volts, calculate (*a*) the current through each resistor; (*b*) the voltage drop across each resistor in branches A, B, and C; (*c*) the total current; (*d*) the total equivalent resistance of the circuit; (*e*) the power taken by each resistor in branches A, B, and C; (*f*) the total power.

Solution

(*a*) $$I_A = I_B = I_C = \frac{240}{120} = 2 \text{ amp}$$

(*b*) $$E_{40} = \frac{240}{3} = 80 \text{ volts}$$

$$E_{60} = \frac{240}{2} = 120 \text{ volts}$$

$$E_{30} = \frac{240}{4} = 60 \text{ volts}$$

(*c*) $$I_t = 3 \times 2 = 6 \text{ amp}$$

(*d*) $$R_t = \frac{E}{I_t} = \frac{240}{6} = 40 \text{ ohms}$$

also

$$R_t = \frac{\text{resistance per branch}}{\text{number of branches}} = \frac{120}{3} = 40 \text{ ohms}$$

(e) $P_{40} = 80 \times 2 = 160$ watts
$P_{60} = 120 \times 2 = 240$ watts
$P_{30} = 60 \times 2 = 120$ watts

(f) $P_t = EI_t = 240 \times 6 = 1{,}440$ watts

also

$$P_t = (3 \times 160) + (2 \times 240) + (4 \times 120) = 1{,}440 \text{ watts}$$

Unequal Resistors in Series. Circuits are, for the most part, made up of resistors whose ohmic values are *not* the same. When a number of

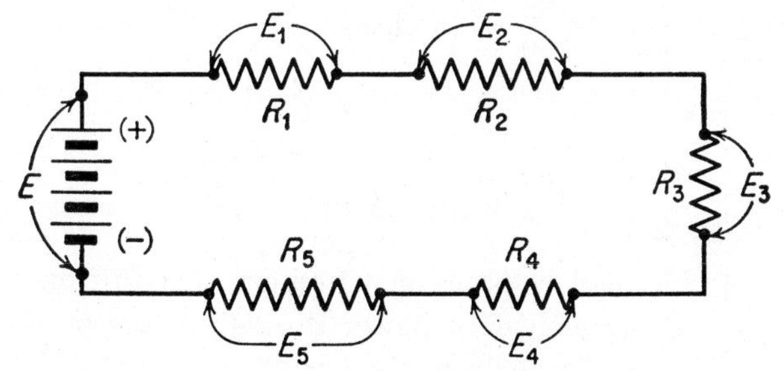

FIG. 13. A series circuit with unequal resistors.

unequal resistors are connected in *series* (Fig. 13) to a source of emf of E volts, the following conditions prevail:

1. The current through all resistors is the same.
2. The total resistance of the circuit is equal to the sum of the individual resistances, i.e.,

$$R_t = R_1 + R_2 + R_3 + R_4 + \cdots \tag{17}$$

3. The circuit current $I = E/R_t$.
4. The voltage drops across the individual resistors are directly proportional to the magnitudes of the respective resistances; i.e.,

$$\frac{E_x}{E_y} = \frac{R_x}{R_y} \tag{18}$$

This important general relationship follows from the fact that

$$E_1 = IR_1 \qquad E_2 = IR_2 \qquad E_3 = IR_3 \qquad \text{etc.}$$

Therefore, setting up ratios for any pair of voltage drops,

$$\frac{E_1}{E_2} = \frac{R_1}{R_2} \qquad \frac{E_2}{E_3} = \frac{R_2}{R_3} \qquad \frac{E_1}{E_3} = \frac{R_1}{R_3} \qquad \text{etc.}$$

5. The total circuit power is

$$P_t = EI \qquad \text{or} \qquad P_t = I(E_1 + E_2 + E_3 + E_4 + \cdots)$$

Examples illustrating the foregoing principles are given herewith.

EXAMPLE 13. A series circuit consists of three resistors A, B, and C, connected to a 120-volt source. If the voltage drop across resistor A is 30 volts when the circuit current is 2 amp, and $R_B = 1.5R_C$, calculate the values of R_A, R_B, and R_C.

Solution

$$R_A = \frac{30}{2} = 15 \text{ ohms}$$

Since $E_{(B+C)} = 120 - 30 = 90$ volts

$$R_{(B+C)} = 15 \times \frac{90}{30} = 45 \text{ ohms}$$

But $R_{(B-C)} = 45 = R_B + R_C = 1.5R_C + R_C = 2.5R_C$

Therefore

$$R_C = \frac{45}{2.5} = 18 \text{ ohms} \qquad \text{and} \qquad R_B = 27 \text{ ohms}$$

EXAMPLE 14. A load resistor of 4.1 ohms, 425 ft from a 240-volt generator, is to be supplied with power through a pair of standard-size copper wires. If the voltage drop in the wires is not to exceed 5 per cent of the generator emf, calculate (*a*) the proper AWG wire that must be used, (*b*) the power loss in the transmission line, (*c*) transmission efficiency.

Solution

(*a*) This simple transmission system may be considered to be a circuit consisting of a 4.1-ohm resistor in series with an 850-ft length of copper wire connected to a 240-volt generator.

$$\text{Line voltage drop} = 240 \times 0.05 = 12 \text{ volts}$$
$$\text{Load voltage} = 240 - 12 = 228 \text{ volts}$$
$$\text{Line current} = 228/4.1 = 55.6 \text{ amp}$$
$$\text{Line resistance } R_l = \frac{12}{55.6} = 0.216 \text{ ohm}$$

Resistance per 1,000 ft must not exceed $(1{,}000/850) \times 0.216 = 0.254$ ohm. Consulting Table 4, Chap. 2, it is found that the nearest standard wire size is No. 4; this wire has a resistance of 0.2485 ohm per 1,000 ft.

(*b*)

$$\text{Actual line resistance } R_l = 0.85 \times 0.2485 = 0.211 \text{ ohm}$$
$$\text{Total series-circuit resistance } R_t = 4.1 + 0.211 = 4.311 \text{ ohms}$$
$$\text{Total current } I = 240/4.311 = 55.7 \text{ amp}$$
$$\text{Per cent line drop} = (55.7 \times 0.211)/240 = 4.9$$
$$\text{Line power loss} = (55.7)^2 \times 0.211 = 655 \text{ watts}$$

(c)
$$\text{Eff} = \frac{\text{load power}}{\text{total power}} \times 100$$
$$= \frac{(55.7 \times 4.1) \times 55.7}{240 \times 55.7} \times 100 = 95.2 \text{ per cent}$$

Unequal Resistors in Parallel. When a number of *unequal resistors* are connected in *parallel* (Fig. 14) to a source of emf of E volts, the following conditions prevail:

1. The same voltage E is impressed across all resistors.
2. The individual-resistor currents are inversely proportional to their respective magnitudes, i.e.,

$$\frac{I_x}{I_y} = \frac{R_y}{R_x} \tag{19}$$

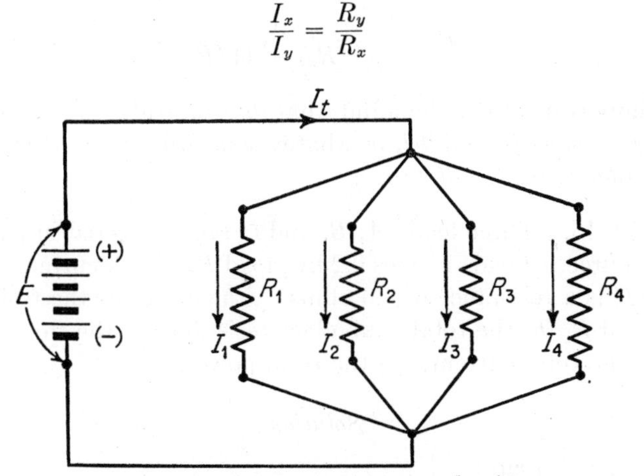

FIG. 14. A parallel circuit with unequal resistors.

This important general relationship follows from the fact that

$$I_1 = \frac{E}{R_1} \qquad I_2 = \frac{E}{R_2} \qquad I_3 = \frac{E}{R_3} \qquad \text{etc.}$$

Therefore, setting up ratios for any pair of currents,

$$\frac{I_1}{I_2} = \frac{R_2}{R_1} \qquad \frac{I_2}{I_3} = \frac{R_3}{R_2} \qquad \frac{I_1}{I_3} = \frac{R_3}{R_1} \qquad \text{etc.}$$

3. The total current for the complete circuit is

$$I_t = I_1 + I_2 + I_3 + I_4 + \cdots \tag{20}$$

4. The total equivalent resistance of the circuit is

$$R_{eq} = \frac{1}{(1/R_1) + (1/R_2) + (1/R_3) + (1/R_4) + \cdots} \tag{21}$$

This follows from the fact that

$$R_{eq} = \frac{E}{I_t} = \frac{E}{(E/R_1) + (E/R_2) + (E/R_3) + (E/R_4) + \cdots}$$

4*a*. When *two* unequal resistors are connected in parallel their *equivalent resistance is equal to their product divided by their sum,* i.e.,

$$R_{xy} = \frac{R_x \times R_y}{R_x + R_y} \tag{22}$$

This follows from the fact that

$$R_{xy} = \frac{1}{(1/R_x) + (1/R_y)}$$

It is important to understand that *the equivalent resistance of any number of resistors in parallel,* of whatever magnitude, *is always less than the magnitude of the smallest unit.*

EXAMPLE 15. Three loads A, B, and C are connected in parallel to a 230-volt source. Load A takes 9.2 kw, load B takes a current of 60 amp, and load C is a resistance of 4.6 ohms. Calculate (*a*) the resistances of loads A and B, (*b*) the total equivalent resistance of the three paralleled loads, (*c*) the total current, (*d*) the total power.

Solution

(*a*) $$R_A = \frac{E^2}{P_A} = \frac{(230)^2}{9{,}200} = 5.75 \text{ ohms}$$

$$R_B = \frac{230}{60} = 3.83 \text{ ohms}$$

(*b*) $$R_{eq} = \frac{1}{\frac{1}{5.75} + \frac{1}{3.83} + \frac{1}{4.6}} = \frac{1}{0.174 + 0.261 + 0.217} = 1.53 \text{ ohms}$$

(*c*) $$I_t = \frac{230}{1.53} = 150 \text{ amp}$$

Also

$$I_A = \frac{9{,}200}{230} = 40 \text{ amp}$$

and

$$I_C = \frac{230}{4.6} = 50 \text{ amp}$$

Therefore

$$I_t = 40 + 60 + 50 = 150 \text{ amp}$$

(*d*) $P_t = 9{,}200 + (230 \times 60) + \frac{(230)^2}{4.6} = 34{,}500$ watts, or 34.5 kw

Also

$$P_t = 230 \times 150 = 34{,}500 \text{ watts, or } 34.5 \text{ kw}$$

EXAMPLE 16. A coil of wire having a resistance of 3.84 ohms and carrying a current of 0.15 amp is in parallel with an unknown resistance through which there is a current of 1.44 amp. Calculate (*a*) the unknown resistance, (*b*) the total equivalent resistance.

Solution

(*a*) Using Eq. (19):

$$R = 3.84 \times \frac{0.15}{1.44} = 0.4 \text{ ohm}$$

(*b*) Using Eq. (22):

$$R_{eq} = \frac{3.84 \times 0.4}{3.84 + 0.4} = 0.362 \text{ ohm}$$

Series-Parallel and Parallel-Series Circuits. Circuits combining series and parallel sections, with *one* source of supply, are treated in much the same way as simple circuit arrangements. In most series-parallel or parallel-series circuits it is generally convenient to consider each series or parallel section as an independent unit, using the rules given in the foregoing articles for each one. An example will now be given to illustrate such a procedure.

EXAMPLE 17. The following information is given in connection with the series-parallel circuit of Fig. 11*a*: $E = 48$, $R_1 = 6$, $R_2 = 12$, $R_3 = 3$, $R_4 = 15$, $R_5 = 90$, $R_6 = 30$. Calculate (*a*) the total equivalent resistance of the entire circuit, (*b*) the total current, (*c*) the voltage drop across each section, (*d*) the current through each resistor, (*e*) the total power taken by the entire circuit.

Solution

(*a*)
$$R_{eq} = \left(\frac{6 \times 12}{18}\right) + 3 + \frac{1}{(1/15) + (1/90) + (1/30)} = 4 + 3 + 9 = 16 \text{ ohms}$$

(*b*)
$$I_t = \frac{48}{16} = 3 \text{ amp}$$

(*c*)
$$E_{(6+12)} = 4 \times 3 = 12 \text{ volts}$$
$$E_3 = 3 \times 3 = 9 \text{ volts}$$
$$E_{(15+90+30)} = 3 \times 9 = 27 \text{ volts}$$

(*d*)

$$I_6 = \frac{12}{6} = 2 \text{ amp}$$

$$I_{12} = \frac{12}{12} = 1 \text{ amp}$$

$$I_3 = \frac{9}{3} = 3 \text{ amp}$$

$$I_{15} = \frac{27}{15} = 1.8 \text{ amp}$$

$$I_{90} = \frac{27}{90} = 0.3 \text{ amp}$$

$$I_{30} = \frac{27}{30} = 0.9 \text{ amp}$$

(*e*)

$$P_t = 48 \times 3 = 144 \text{ watts}$$

The student is urged to substitute the given data of Example 17 in the parallel-series circuit of Fig. 11*b* and solve for the various quantities indicated above.

Sources of Supply in Series or Parallel. It is sometimes necessary to connect two or more sources of supply in series or parallel to deliver power to one or more loads. When this is done it is desirable, and often imperative, that the individual sources, such as batteries, generators, or both, be exactly similar. This implies that the terminal voltages of the individual sources are equal to one another and, in the case of batteries, that the resistances inside the several units, i.e., the resistances of the internal chemical substances, are equal; the latter, designated *internal resistance,* is usually quite small in comparison with the main circuit and, although often neglected in computations involving single batteries, must generally be taken into account when several such sources are used.

Assuming for the present that all n sources are exactly alike (the more general case, where this does not obtain, is considered in detail in Chap. 4), the following conditions prevail:

1. For series-connected sources:
   a. The total voltage is equal to the algebraic sum of the individual voltages, i.e., $E_t = nE$, where the cells are connected additive.
   b. The currents and powers delivered by the individual units are equal.
2. For parallel-connected sources:
   a. The terminal voltage of the combination is the same as that of a single unit, i.e., $E_t = E$.
   b. The currents delivered by the individual units are equal, i.e., $I = I_t/n$.
   c. The powers delivered by the individual units are equal, i.e., $P = P_t/n$.

EXAMPLE 18. A group of 12 similar dry cells, each one having an emf of 1.5 volts, are connected in parallel-series as shown in Fig. 15. If a load resistance of 0.4 ohm is connected across the combination, determine the following, neglecting the internal resistances of the cells: (*a*) the total

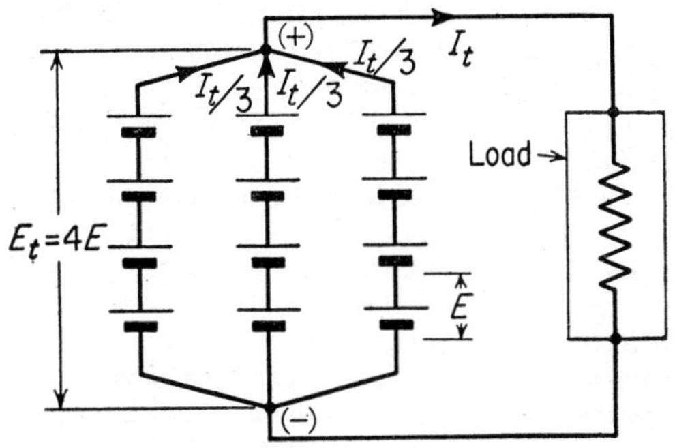

FIG. 15. A parallel-series group of dry cells delivering power to a load resistor.

load voltage, current, and power; (*b*) the current and power delivered by each cell.

Solution

(*a*)
$$E_t = 4 \times 1.5 = 6 \text{ volts}$$
$$I_t = \frac{6}{0.4} = 15 \text{ amp}$$
$$P_t = 6 \times 15 = 90 \text{ watts}$$

(*b*)
$$I_{\text{cell}} = \frac{15}{3} = 5 \text{ amp}$$
$$P_{\text{cell}} = 1.5 \times 5 = 7.5 \text{ watts}$$

or
$$P_{\text{cell}} = \frac{90}{12} = 7.5 \text{ watts}$$

Questions

1. What important process must take place before electricity becomes useful?
2. List the various electrical effects.
3. Under what conditions is the heating effect desirable? undesirable? Give several practical illustrations of each.
4. Name several devices and machines that function because of the magnetic effect of electricity.
5. Under what conditions is the magnetic effect strong? weak?
6. What useful processes depend upon the chemical effect of electricity?
7. Define the *ampere* in terms of the chemical effect of electricity.
8. Why is the electromagnetic-induction effect fundamental to the operation of equipment in power and distribution systems?
9. What is a *thermocouple?* How is it applied practically?
10. What is a *photoelectric cell* ("electric eye")? Give several practical uses of this device.
11. Explain the *piezoelectric effect* in connection with several useful applications.

12. What is implied when the current *direction* is based on the electron theory? when it is based on the generally adopted practice?
13. List the important elements of an electric circuit.
14. What is meant by a *load?* What forms can it take?
15. Distinguish between *series* and *parallel* circuits.
16. Distinguish between *series-parallel* and *parallel-series* circuits. Indicate how the two terms are derived on the basis of the interconnection of the circuit elements.
17. State *Ohm's law* in words; in equation form.
18. What types of instruments are used in the measurement of amperes and volts? Why are they *indicating* instruments?
19. What "ampere value" is measured by a d-c ammeter when the current fluctuates rapidly?
20. Distinguish between the general terms *power* and *energy*.
21. Define the *horsepower* in mechanical terms. How was this originally determined?
22. Define the *joule* in electrical terms.
23. Write three forms of the power equation, in terms of volts, amperes, and ohms.
24. What is the numerical relation between the *watt* and the *horsepower?*
25. What is the numerical relation between the *joule* (watt-second) and the *gram-calorie?*
26. Define a *gram-calorie;* a Btu.
27. How are residential consumers charged for electrical service?
28. How are large industrial consumers charged for electrical service?
29. Briefly describe the watthour meter and its function in measuring energy consumption.
30. Why is it proper to make a *maximum-load charge* when billing industrial consumers of energy?
31. State the general rules that apply to equal resistors in series; to equal resistors in parallel.
32. How is the total resistance determined when a number of resistors are connected in series? when a number of unequal resistors are connected in parallel?
33. When unequal resistors are connected in series, how are the respective voltage drops related to each other?
34. When unequal resistors are connected in parallel, how are the respective currents related to each other?
35. What simple rule can be used to determine the equivalent resistance of two resistors in parallel?
36. Explain why the equivalent resistance of a number of resistors in parallel is always *less* than the ohmic value of the smallest unit.
37. In solving series-parallel and parallel-series circuits what procedure is it desirable to follow?
38. How is the total voltage determined when several sources of supply are connected in series? What procedure must be followed in connection with polarities if the maximum voltage is to result?
39. What important conditions must be fulfilled by the several batteries if they are to operate satisfactorily in parallel?
40. When similar batteries are interconnected in parallel what relationships exist with regard to current and power?

Problems

1. Three resistors A, B, and C are connected in series to a 117-volt source. If $R_A = 64$ ohms, and $E_B = 40$ volts when the current is 0.5 amp, calculate the resistances R_B and R_C.

2. A 6-ohm load is connected to a 119.6-volt source through a pair of 0.25-ohm conductors. Calculate (*a*) the load current and voltage, (*b*) the voltage drop in the line wires.

3. Three resistors *A*, *B*, and *C* are connected in parallel and take a total of 7.9 amp. Resistor *A* takes 2.5 amp and has a resistance of 48 ohms; also, the current through *B* is twice as much as that through *C*. Calculate (*a*) I_B and I_C, (*b*) the line voltage, (*c*) R_B and R_C.

4. Calculate the resistances of (*a*) a 100-watt 120-volt incandescent lamp, (*b*) a 750-watt 115-volt toaster, (*c*) a 1,300-watt 110-volt portable ironer.

5. A 12-ohm resistor is connected in parallel with a series combination of resistors of 8 and 16 ohms. If the drop across the 8-ohm resistor is 48 volts, determine the total impressed emf and the total current.

6. A 72-ohm coil of wire is connected in series with an adjustable resistor (rheostat) whose resistance can be varied from 0 to 88 ohms. If the line potential is 115 volts, calculate (*a*) the range through which the coil current can be varied, (*b*) the rheostat resistance when the power taken by the coil is 90 watts.

7. Using the given data of Prob. 6, calculate the power taken by the coil when the voltage drops across rheostat and coil are equal.

8. A telegraph circuit consists of a 250-ohm relay in series with line wires having a resistance of 150 ohms. If it takes 72 milliamperes (1 ma = 0.001 amp) to operate the relay what voltage must be impressed at the sending end of the circuit?

9. To determine the resistances of three resistors *A*, *B*, and *C* the following procedure is followed: R_A and R_B are connected in series and an emf of 21 volts is impressed for a current of 1 amp; R_B and R_C are next connected in series and an emf of 27 volts is impressed for the *same* adjusted current; finally R_C and R_A are connected in series and an emf of 24 volts is impressed for the *same* adjusted current. What are the ohmic values of *A*, *B*, and *C*?

10. Two resistors $R_A = 1.95$ ohms and $R_B = 0.05$ ohm are connected in parallel and take a total of 50 amp. What is the current through each resistor?

11. A generator delivers a load through a pair of wires, each of which has a resistance of 0.06 ohm. If the load voltage and power are, respectively, 120 volts and 4.8 kw, calculate (*a*) the generator voltage, (*b*) the power loss in the line wires.

12. The following data are given in connection with the series-parallel circuit of Fig. 11*a*; $E = 97.5$ volts, $R_1 = 18$ ohms, $R_2 = 9$ ohms, $R_3 = 16$ ohms, $R_4 = 14$ ohms, $R_5 = 7$ ohms, $I_2 = 2.5$ amp. Calculate (*a*) the resistance of R_6, (*b*) the total equivalent resistance of the circuit, (*c*) the total power.

13. Two resistors, $R_A = 7{,}500$ ohms and $R_B = 15{,}000$ ohms, are connected in series. If a 120-volt source is applied to the combination, (*a*) determine E_A and E_B when a 15,000-ohm resistance (in the form of a voltmeter) is first connected across resistor *A* and then across resistor *B*; (*b*) determine E_A and E_B if one 15,000-ohm resistance (in the form of a voltmeter) is connected across *A* at the same time that another 15,000-ohm resistance is connected across *B*.

14. The following data are given in connection with the parallel-series circuit of Fig. 11*b*; $R_1 = 6$ ohms, $R_2 = 14$ ohms, $E_2 = 86.8$ volts, $R_3 = 16$ ohms, $R_4 = 20$ ohms, $R_6 = 25$ ohms, total power $P_t = 1{,}922$ watts. Calculate (*a*) the impressed voltage *E*, (*b*) the total current I_t, (*c*) the resistance R_5.

15. A 50-hp 230-volt motor operates at full load at an efficiency of 90 per cent. It is 560 ft from a generator, the wires connecting the motor and generator being No. 0000 (see Table 4). (*a*) What current does the motor take? (*b*) What is the voltage drop in the line wires? (*c*) What is the generator voltage?

16. How long will it take a 480-watt 120-volt percolator to raise the temperature of 1 qt of water from 15 to 100°C? Assume a heat loss of 22 per cent. (Water weighs 8.33 lb per gal.) What is the resistance of the heating element?

17. What is the distance in feet between a 240-volt source and a 228-volt load if No. 7 B&S gage copper wires carry 50 amp?

18. A 16-ohm resistor is connected in series with a parallel combination of two resistors, one of which has an ohmic value of 48 ohms, the other one R being unknown. What is the resistance of R if the power taken by the 16-ohm unit is equal to the power in the parallel-connected pair of resistors?

19. Using the residential rate schedule for energy given on page 48, determine the monthly bill for a consumption of 268 kwhr.

20. Three 120-ohm resistors are to be connected in four possible ways. Calculate the equivalent resistance for each connection.

21. When two resistors are connected in series the total resistance is 108 ohms; when connected in parallel the equivalent resistance is 24 ohms. What is the value of each unit?

22. Make sketches showing how eighteen 1.5-volt dry cells may be interconnected, using symmetrical arrangements only. For each connection determine the terminal voltage.

23. Referring to the circuit shown in Fig. 16, calculate (*a*) the total equivalent resistance, (*b*) the total current I_t, (*c*) the power delivered to the 16-ohm load resistor.

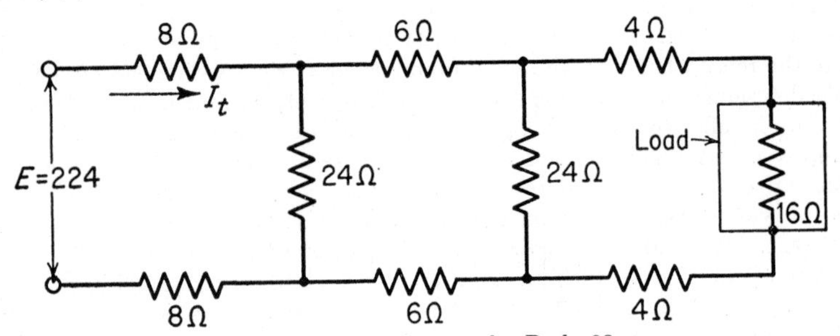

FIG. 16. Circuit diagram for Prob. 23.

CHAPTER 4

DIRECT-CURRENT CIRCUITS II
KIRCHHOFF'S LAWS—BASIC THEOREMS

Kirchhoff's Laws. Electric circuits that are more complex than those considered in Chap. 3, and particularly those which contain more than one source of emf, are solved readily by the application of laws and theorems that relate the several currents, emfs, and resistance voltages in such circuits. Two simple but important laws that were first expressed by Gustav Kirchhoff, one for currents and the other for voltages, are known as *Kirchhoff's laws.* For d-c circuits they may be stated as follows:

1. *The current law: the algebraic sum of the currents at any junction of an electric circuit is zero.*

2. *The voltage law: the algebraic sum of the emfs and the resistance voltages in any continuous path of an electric circuit is zero.*

To properly understand the meaning and use of these laws it is important to recognize that the term *algebraic* refers to arbitrarily assumed *signs* (+ or −) given to indicate current directions, emfs, and resistance voltages. Note particularly that there are three kinds of quantities, namely, currents represented by $+I$ or $-I$, voltages of sources of emf such as batteries or generators and represented by $+E$ or $-E$, and resistance voltages involving products of currents and resistances and represented by $+(IR)$ or $-(IR)$; a current or voltage is, therefore, correctly represented only when it is preceded by a plus (+) or minus (−) sign. Moreover, to be meaningful *all current directions and emf polarities must be properly identified on a circuit diagram* before current and voltage equations are written in accordance with the basic current and voltage laws. Assuming (1) that an *algebraic plus* is denoted by a current *to* a junction or a *potential rise in passing through a source of emf or a resistor,* and (2) that an *algebraic minus* is denoted by a current *away from* a junction or a *potential drop in passing through a source of emf or a resistor,* current and voltage equations may be correctly written; these may then be used simultaneously to determine unknown quantities.

To illustrate the application of the Kirchhoff-law method in solving a complex circuit, Fig. 17 has been drawn. Carefully observe that the plus and minus polarities of the two batteries are properly shown, and that arrows indicate arbitrary current directions through the six resistors. It should be pointed out, in this connection, that the choice of the current directions is immaterial, and may or may not be correct; an incorrectly assumed current direction will merely yield a negative answer for that

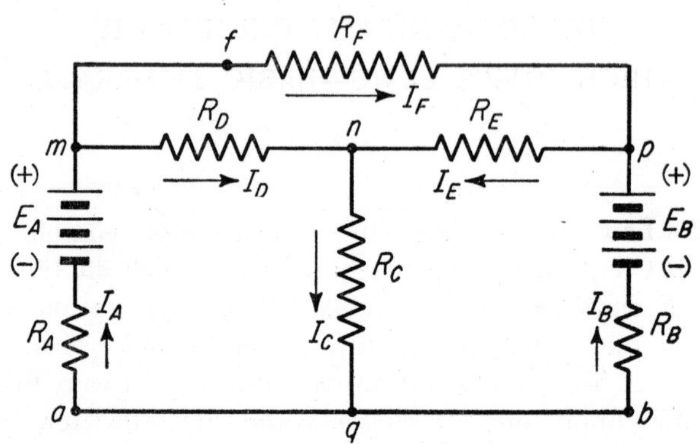

FIG. 17. Circuit diagram to illustrate Kirchhoff's laws.

quantity although the numerical result will be correct. Referring to Fig. 17, *current equations* may be written as follows:

At junction m: $+I_A - I_D - I_F = 0$
At junction n: $+I_D + I_E - I_C = 0$
At junction p: $+I_B + I_F - I_E = 0$
At junction q: $+I_C - I_A - I_B = 0$

Also, *voltage* equations may be written for the following loops:

For loop *amnqa*:

$$-I_AR_A - I_DR_D - I_CR_C + E_A = 0$$

For loop *bpnqb*:

$$-I_BR_B - I_ER_E - I_CR_C + E_B = 0$$

For loop *amfpbqa*:

$$-I_AR_A - I_FR_F + I_BR_B - E_B + E_A = 0$$

Several numerical examples will now be given to illustrate the principles discussed.

EXAMPLE 1. Figure 18 shows a circuit in which two batteries A and B deliver current to a load resistor R_L through line resistors R_A and R_B. For the values given (the internal resistances of the batteries are included in R_A and R_B), calculate (*a*) the currents I_A, I_B, and I_L; (*b*) the load voltage V_L; (*c*) the power P_L delivered to the load.

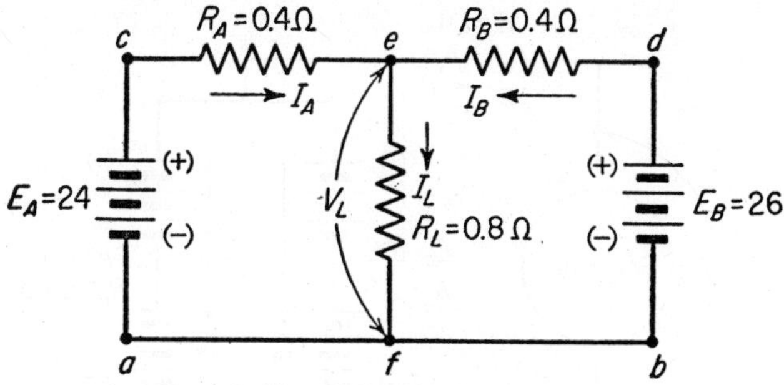

FIG. 18. Circuit diagram for Example 1.

Solution

(*a*) At junction *e*:

$$+I_A + I_B - I_L = 0 \qquad \text{or} \qquad I_L = I_A + I_B$$

For loop *acedba*: $+24 - 0.4I_A + 0.4I_B - 26 = 0$

from which (1) $I_B = \dfrac{0.4I_A + 2}{0.4} = I_A + 5$

For loop *acefa*: $+24 - 0.4I_A - 0.8\,I_L = 0$

$$+24 - 0.4I_A - 0.8(I_A + I_B) = 0$$

from which (2) $+24 - 1.2I_A - 0.8I_B = 0$

Substituting (1) in (2),

$$+24 - 1.2I_A - 0.8I_A - 4 = 0$$

so that $I_A = \dfrac{20}{2} = 10$ amp

also $I_B = 10 + 5 = 15$ amp

and $I_L = 10 + 15 = 25$ amp

(*b*) For loop *acefa*: $24 - 0.4I_A - V_L = 0$

from which $V_L = 24 - (0.4 \times 10) = 20$ volts

also $V_L = 26 - (0.4 \times 15) = 20$ volts

(*c*) Finally $P_L = 20 \times 25 = 500$ watts

EXAMPLE 2. Figure 19 represents a circuit in which a d-c generator is connected to two storage batteries in parallel so that the latter may be charged. If the open-circuit battery voltages are $E_A = 108$ volts and $E_B = 110$ volts, and the several resistances are as indicated on the diagram, calculate (*a*) I_A, I_B, and I; (*b*) the total power delivered by the generator; (*c*) the total power (I^2R) loss in the resistors; (*d*) the efficiency of the system.

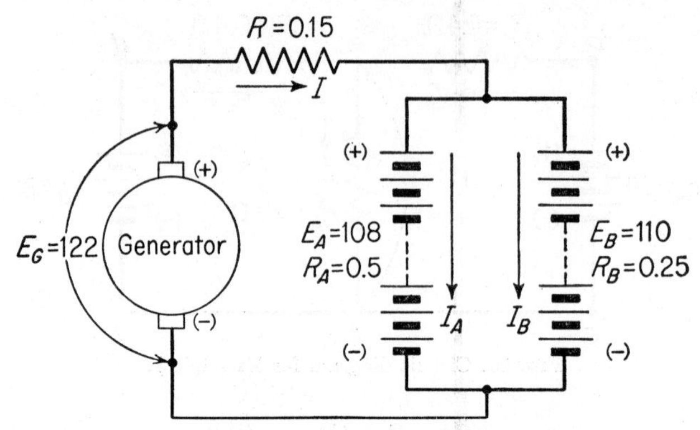

FIG. 19. Circuit diagram for Example 2.

Solution

(*a*) Writing two loop equations of voltage,

$$+122 - 0.15(I_A + I_B) - 0.5I_A - 108 = 0$$
$$+122 - 0.15(I_A + I_B) - 0.25I_B - 110 = 0$$

By inspection, these equations indicate that

$$0.5I_A + 108 = 0.25I_B + 110$$

from which
$$I_A = \frac{2 + 0.25I_B}{0.5} = 4 + 0.5I_B$$

Substituting this value of current in the second voltage equation,

$$122 - 0.15(4 + 0.5I_B) - 0.15I_B - 0.25I_B - 110 = 0$$
$$122 - 0.6 - 0.075I_B - 0.15I_B - 0.25I_B - 110 = 0$$

from which
$$I_B = \frac{11.4}{0.475} = 24 \text{ amp}$$
$$I_A = 4 + (0.5 \times 24) = 16 \text{ amp}$$
$$I = 24 + 16 = 40 \text{ amp}$$

(*b*) Generator power $= P_G = 122 \times 40 = 4{,}880$ watts

(*c*) Total I^2R loss $= [(40)^2 \times 0.15] + [(16)^2 \times 0.5] + [(24)^2 \times 0.25]$
$= 512$ watts

(*d*)
$$\text{Eff} = \left(1 - \frac{512}{4{,}880}\right) \times 100 = 89.5 \text{ per cent}$$

In some complex circuits it is frequently possible to write, by inspection, the values of several unknown currents in terms of a single unknown current; moreover, this may be done by indicating directly such quantities on the circuit diagram. Such a procedure, involving as it does fewer voltage equations, generally leads to a simpler, more straightforward solution. An example will now be given to illustrate such a problem.

EXAMPLE 3. A 250-volt generator supplies power to loads A and B, I_A being 160 amp and I_B being 140 amp. A pair of wires, each 0.1 ohm, connects the generator terminals to those of load A; another pair of similar conductors, each 0.1 ohm, connects the A and B loads; finally, a third pair of wires, called feeders, each 0.05 ohm, joins the generator and load B terminals. Determine the voltages at loads A and B.

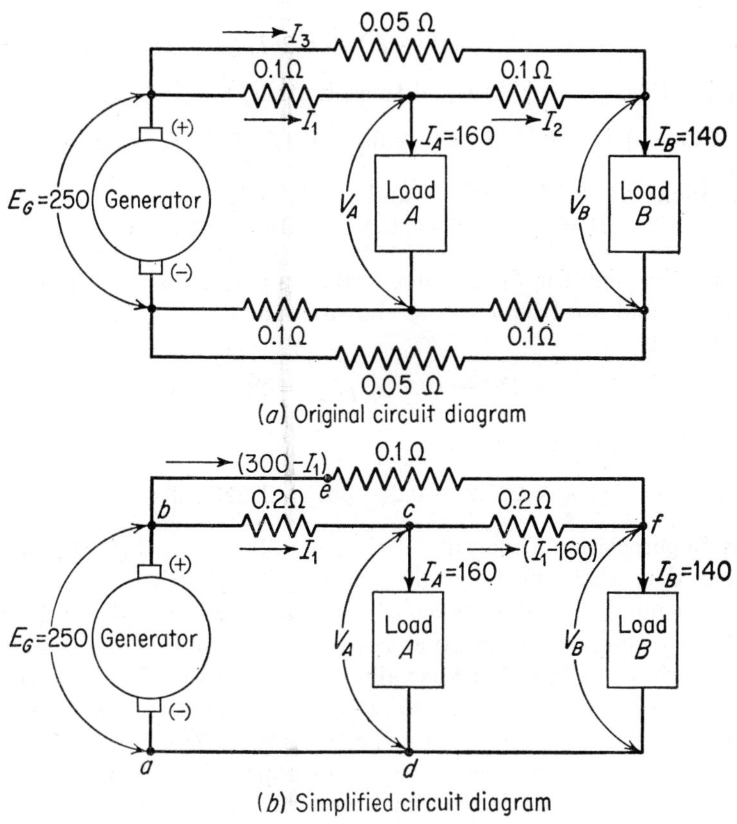

FIG. 20. Circuit diagrams for Example 3.

Solution

A wiring diagram representing the distribution system, and showing all resistance values and voltages, is given in Fig. 20a; note particularly that there are *three* unknown currents, namely, I_1, I_2, and I_3. Since the system is completely symmetrical, top and bottom, it is quite proper to combine each pair of resistors that carry equal currents to yield a greatly simplified circuit diagram. Furthermore, since the generator must deliver a total of $(160 + 140) = 300$ amp, it should be clear that I_3 may be replaced by $(300 - I_1)$ amp; also I_2 may be replaced by $(I_1 - 160)$ amp because, by Kirchhoff's first law, $(I_1 - 160 - I_2) = 0$. With these simplifications Fig. 20*b* may be made to represent the problem.

For loop *abcda*:

$$(1) \qquad +250 - 0.2I_1 - V_A = 0$$

For loop *abefcda*:

$$(2) \qquad +250 - 0.1(300 - I_1) + 0.2(I_1 - 160) - V_A = 0$$

Setting Eqs. (1) and (2) equal to each other,

$$250 - 0.2I_1 - V_A = 250 - 30 + 0.1I_1 + 0.2I_1 - 32 - V_A$$

from which $\quad 0.5I_1 = 62 \quad$ and $\quad I_1 = 124$ amp

Also $\quad I_2 = I_1 - 160 = 124 - 160 = -36$ amp

The negative sign for I_2 indicates that this current is actually directed from *f* to *c* and not from *c* to *f* as shown in the figure.

By Eq. (1),

$$V_A = 250 - (0.2 \times 124) = 225.2 \text{ volts}$$

Also, since $V_B = V_A - 0.2I_2$,

$$V_B = 225.2 - 0.2(-36) = 232.4 \text{ volts}$$

The Superposition Theorem. It is generally accepted, for mechanical systems, that when effects are directly proportional to causes, the total effect of a number of simultaneously applied causes is exactly the same as that of a composite cause that is equal to the sum of the component causes. This principle is just as valid when applied to electrical systems, where the individual components of currents, caused by the individual components of several emfs, are directly proportional to one another. Since electric circuits frequently have several properly distributed sources of voltage, the principle is sometimes found to be very helpful in the solution of special types of problems. It has, in this regard, become an extremely worthwhile "electrical tool," and as such has been given the status of a *theorem*. Called the *superposition theorem*, it may be stated as follows:

In a network of resistors that is energized by two or more sources of emf, (a) the current in any resistor or (b) the voltage across any resistor is equal to (a) the algebraic sum of the separate currents in the resistor or (b) the voltages across the resistor, assuming that each source of emf, acting inde-

pendently of the others, is applied separately in turn while the others are replaced by their respective internal values of resistance.

This theorem is illustrated in the following numerical example.

EXAMPLE 4. A generator and a battery whose voltages are, respectively, $E_G = 129.6$ and $E_B = 126$, are connected in parallel, through line resistances R_1 and R_2, to deliver power to a common load R_L of 6 ohms. Using the method of superposition, calculate (*a*) the currents supplied by the generator and the battery, and the current "taken" by the load; (*b*) the load voltage V_L; (*c*) the load power P_L. Figure 21*a* represents a wiring diagram of the circuit and shows the internal resistances of the generator and battery as well as those of the line wires.

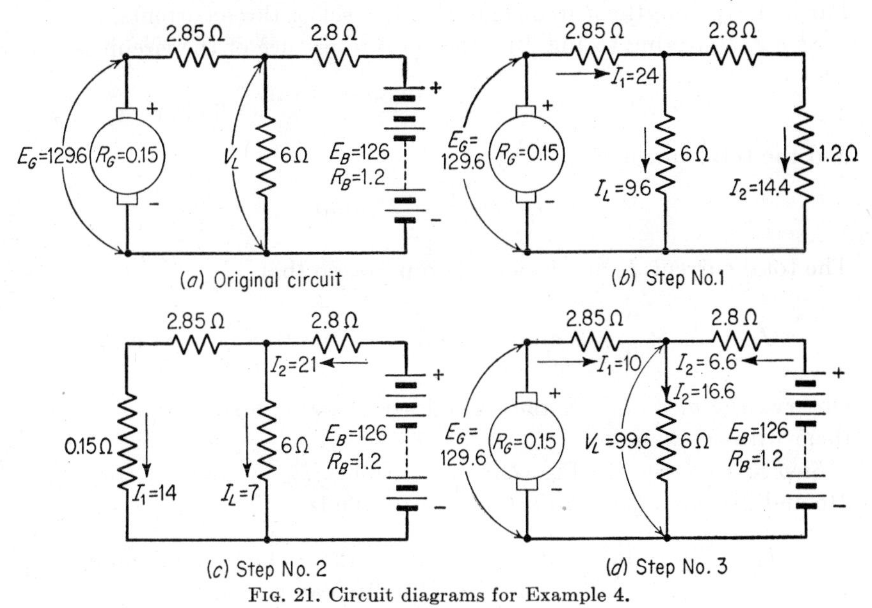

FIG. 21. Circuit diagrams for Example 4.

Solution

The problem will be solved in three steps. In step 1 the battery will be replaced by its internal resistance of 1.2 ohms, and the circuit will be assumed to be energized by the 129.6-volt generator alone; this is shown in Fig. 21*b*. In step 2 the generator will be replaced by its internal resistance of 0.15 ohm, and the circuit will be assumed to be energized by the 126-volt battery alone; this is shown in Fig. 21*c*. In step 3 the separate currents in the various parts of the circuit will be combined algebraically to give the actual values in the composite circuit; this is done in Fig. 21*d*. The load voltage and power may then be readily determined.

(*a*) *Step 1:* Referring to Fig. 21*b*, the total resistance of the circuit is

$$R_t = (0.15 + 2.85) + \frac{6 \times (2.8 + 1.2)}{(6 + 4)} = 5.4 \text{ ohms}$$

and the total current is

$$I_1 = \frac{129.6}{5.4} = 24 \text{ amp}$$

The total current I_1 divides into two parts, so that

$$I_L = 24 \times \frac{4}{10} = 9.6 \text{ amp} \qquad \text{and} \qquad I_2 = 24 \times \frac{6}{10} = 14.4 \text{ amp}$$

Particularly note the *directions* of the first set of three currents.

Step 2: Referring to Fig. 21*c*, the total resistance of the circuit is

$$R_t = (1.2 + 2.8) + \frac{6 \times (2.85 + 0.15)}{(6 + 3)} = 6 \text{ ohms}$$

and the total current is

$$I_2 = \frac{126}{6} = 21 \text{ amp}$$

The total current I_2 divides into two parts, so that

$$I_L = 21 \times \frac{3}{9} = 7 \text{ amp} \qquad \text{and} \qquad I_1 = 21 \times \frac{6}{9} = 14 \text{ amp}$$

Observe the *directions* of the second set of three currents and compare them with the first set.

Step 3: Referring to Fig. 21*d*, the currents I_1, I_2, and I_L, from Figs. 21*b* and 21*c*, are *algebraically* combined. Thus

$$I_1 = (24 - 14) = 10 \text{ amp} \qquad I_2 = (21 - 14.4) = 6.6 \text{ amp}$$
$$I_L = (9.6 + 7) = 16.6 \text{ amp}$$

(*b*) The load voltage is

$$V_L = 129.6 - 10(0.15 + 2.85) = 99.6 \text{ volts}$$

or

$$V_L = 126 - 6.6(1.2 + 2.8) = 99.6 \text{ volts}$$

(*c*) The load power is

$$P_L = 99.6 \times 16.6 = 1{,}653.4 \text{ watts}$$

Thévenin's Theorem. When a network of fixed resistances and constant sources of emf, of any degree of complexity, is so disposed that only two terminals are accessible, the current through a load resistor that is connected to the two terminals may be readily determined if two simple tests are performed. These are (1) the open-circuit test and (2) the short-circuit test.

Consider Fig. 22*a*, which schematically represents a two-terminal network of constant emf's and resistances; a high-resistance voltmeter, connected to the accessible terminals, will indicate the so-called *open-circuit voltage* V_o. If an extremely low-resistance ammeter is next connected to the same terminals, as in Fig. 22*b*, the so-called *short-circuit current* I_{sc} will be measured. The two quantities thus determined may now be used to represent *an equivalent simple network* consisting of a single emf V_o in series with a single resistance R_o, in which the latter is

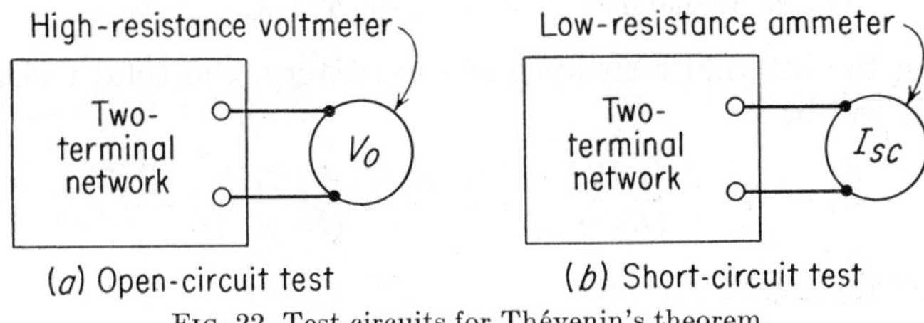

FIG. 22. Test circuits for Thévenin's theorem.

equal to V_o/I_{sc}. Now then, if a resistor R_L is connected to the two terminals, the load current will be

$$I_L = \frac{V_o}{R_o + R_L} \tag{23}$$

EXAMPLE 5. The open-circuit voltage at the two terminals of a two-terminal network was measured and found to be 96 volts. A short-circuit test was next performed and an ammeter reading of 6 amp was indicated. Determine (*a*) the equivalent resistance R_o (looking back from the two terminals into the network), (*b*) the current and power "taken" by a load resistance of 176 ohms.

Solution

(*a*) $$R_o = \frac{96}{6} = 16 \text{ ohms}$$

(*b*) $$I_L = \frac{96}{(16 + 176)} = 0.5 \text{ amp}$$

$$P_L = (0.5)^2 \times 176 = 44 \text{ watts}$$

The accuracy of the foregoing will now be demonstrated by considering the circuit illustrated in Fig. 23*a*. The network consists of a battery whose voltage is E, and three resistances R_1, R_2, and R_3 connected to form a so-called T. Since R_3 and R_L are in series it will be convenient, before proceeding, to replace $(R_3 - R_L)$ by R; this is shown in Fig. 23*b*.

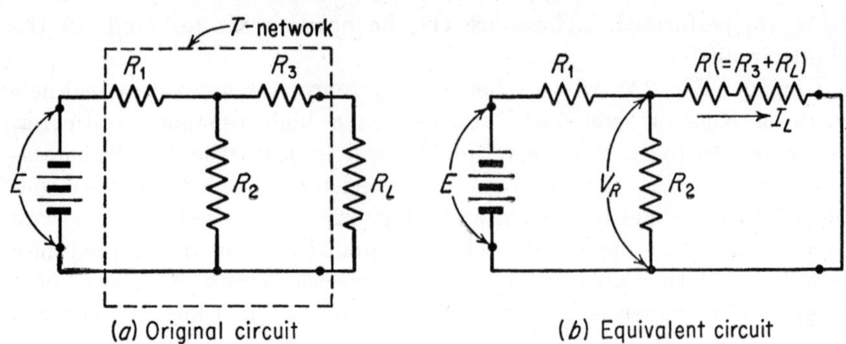

FIG. 23. Circuit diagrams to illustrate Thévenin's theorem.

Neglecting the internal resistance of the battery, the total resistance of the circuit will be

$$R_t = R_1 + \frac{R_2R}{(R_2 + R)} = \frac{(R_1R_2 + R_1R + R_2R)}{(R_2 + R)}$$

and the total current will be

$$I = \frac{E(R_2 + R)}{(R_1R_2 + R_1R + R_2R)}$$

But

$$V_R = E - IR_1$$

Therefore

$$I_L = \frac{E - ER_1[(R_2 + R)/(R_1R_2 + R_1R + R_2R)]}{R}$$

which, when simplified, becomes

$$I_L = \frac{ER_2}{R_1R_2 + R(R_1 + R_2)} \tag{24}$$

It will now be shown that the same value of I_L [Eq. (24)] may be obtained by applying the analysis that resulted in Eq. (23).

Looking back from the two load terminals into the network, the total resistance is

$$R_o = R + \frac{R_1R_2}{(R_1 + R_2)} = \frac{(R_1R + R_2R + R_1R_2)}{(R_1 + R_2)}$$

Also, with the output terminals *opened*, there will be no current through R; this means that the same voltage will be measured across R_2 as across the *open-circuited* network terminals (the resistance R would merely become an extension of the voltmeter leads when V_o is measured). It follows, therefore, that

$$V_o = E\frac{R_2}{(R_1 + R_2)}$$

By Eq. (23), the load current becomes

$$I_L = \frac{ER_2}{(R_1 + R_2)} \times \frac{(R_1 + R_2)}{(R_1R + R_2R + R_1R_2)}$$

which reduces to

$$I_L = \frac{ER_2}{R_1R_2 + R(R_1 + R_2)} \tag{24}$$

Note that this equation for the load current I_L is exactly the same as that previously determined by a straightforward solution of Fig. 23.

The analysis leading to Eq. (23) was first proposed by M. L. Thévenin in the latter part of the nineteenth century, and has since been recognized as an important principle in electric-circuit theory. Properly called *Thévenin's theorem*, it may be stated as follows:

In any two-terminal network of fixed resistances and constant sources of emf, the current in a load resistor connected to the output terminals is equal to the current that would exist in the same resistor if it were connected in series with (a) *a simple emf whose voltage is measured at the open-circuited network terminals and* (b) *a simple resistance whose magnitude is that of the network looking back from the two terminals into the network with all the sources of emf replaced by their internal resistances.*

In addition to its great usefulness in experimental laboratory procedures, Thévenin's theorem has been applied to the solution of many networks in which the values of V_o and R_o are readily computed. In such cases it is often possible to simplify the calculation considerably, as well as reduce the number of computations. The following example is given to illustrate the application of the theorem to a practical problem.

EXAMPLE 6. The two-terminal battery-resistor network shown in Fig. 24 is to be connected to a load resistance of 150 ohms. What load current and power will be delivered?

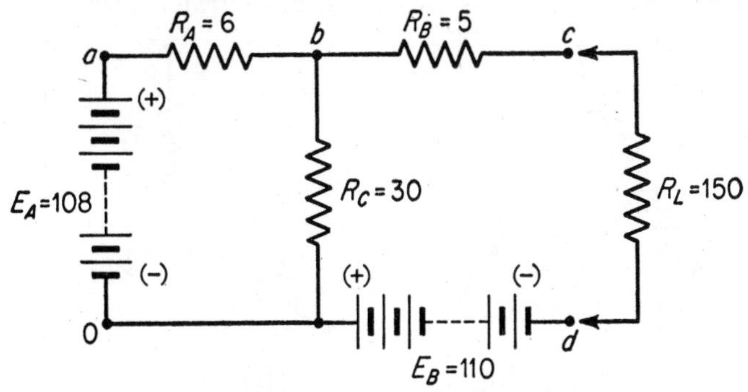

FIG. 24. Circuit diagram for Example 6.

Solution

With load terminals *cd* open, the current in loop *OabO* will be

$$I = \frac{108}{(6 + 30)} = 3 \text{ amp}$$

Under this condition, the voltage drop across resistor R_c will be

$$V_c = 30 \times 3 = 90 \text{ volts}$$

If point O is assumed to be at *zero* potential, point b will be at a $+90$-volt potential; furthermore, point c will have the same potential as point b, i.e., $+90$ volts, because there is no current in R_B. But point d is at a potential that is 110 volts *below* point O, i.e., at -110 volts. It follows, therefore, that the *potential difference* between points c and d is

$$V_o = +90 - (-110) = +200 \text{ volts}$$

Next, looking back into the network from points c and d, and neglecting the internal resistances of the batteries, the equivalent resistance is

$$R_o = 5 + \frac{30 \times 6}{(30 + 6)} = 10 \text{ ohms}$$

Hence, by Eq. (23),

$$I_L = \frac{200}{150 + 10} = 1.25 \text{ amp}$$

and

$$P_L = (1.25)^2 \times 150 = 234.4 \text{ watts}$$

Δ-Y and Y-Δ Transformations. Resistors are sometimes interconnected to form rather complex networks; they may, in fact, be so complex that the common rules applicable to simple series and parallel circuits cannot be used for the calculation of equivalent resistances, branch currents, and voltage drops. Under such conditions it is generally necessary to transform all or parts of the complex circuits into *electrically equivalent* circuits that lend themselves to simple and straightforward solutions.

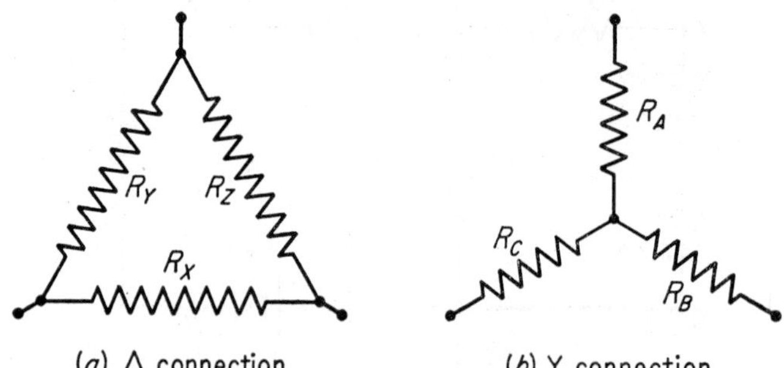

FIG. 25. Resistors connected in delta and star.

Two elemental arrangements of resistors, within and parts of larger networks, that are frequently responsible for the difficulties indicated are Δ-*connected* resistors and *Y-connected* resistors; they are shown in Fig. 25. Significantly, the transformation of a delta (Δ) into an equivalent star (Y) or of a star (Y) into an equivalent delta (Δ) may often convert a circuit that is difficult to handle into one that is comparatively simple. The following analysis will show how this may be done.

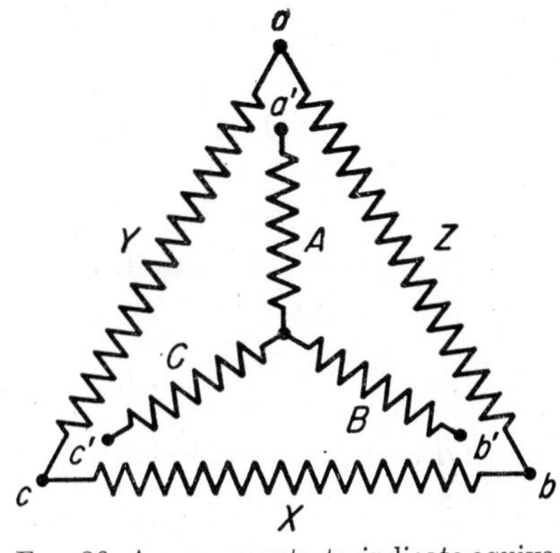

Fig. 26. Arrangements to indicate equivalence of delta and star connections of resistors.

Consider Fig. 26 which, for convenience, shows a star inside a delta. The star-connected resistors are labeled A, B, and C, and the delta-connected resistors are labeled X, Y, and Z. Note particularly the symmetrical placement of X opposite A, Y opposite B, and Z opposite C; this has been done for a special reason that will become clear later. Now then, if the delta is to be electrically equivalent to the star the resistance between any pair of terminals on the delta must be equal to *corresponding* terminals on the star. That is, R_{ab} must equal $R_{a'b'}$; R_{bc} must equal $R_{b'c'}$; R_{ca} must equal $R_{c'a'}$. Mathematically, therefore,

$$(1) \qquad A + B = \frac{Z(X + Y)}{X + Y + Z} = \frac{XZ + YZ}{X + Y + Z}$$

$$(2) \qquad B + C = \frac{X(Y + Z)}{X + Y + Z} = \frac{XY + XZ}{X + Y + Z}$$

$$(3) \qquad C + A = \frac{Y(X + Z)}{X + Y + Z} = \frac{XY + YZ}{X + Y + Z}$$

Subtracting (1) from (2),

$$(4) \qquad C - A = \frac{XY - YZ}{X + Y + Z}$$

Adding (3) to (4),

$$(5) \qquad 2C = \frac{2(XY)}{X + Y + Z}$$

from which

$$C = \frac{XY}{X + Y + Z} \tag{25}$$

By a similar procedure it will be found that

$$B = \frac{XZ}{X + Y + Z} \tag{26}$$

and

$$A = \frac{YZ}{X + Y + Z} \tag{27}$$

Equations (25), (26), and (27) represent transformations from delta to star. Observe that *each of the resistances in the star is equal to the product of the resistances of the adjacent arms of the delta divided by the sum of the three delta resistances.*

The following analysis will yield the three equations that transform a star into an equivalent delta. Dividing Eq. (25) by Eq. (26),

$$(6) \qquad \frac{C}{B} = \frac{Y}{Z} \qquad \text{or} \qquad Z = \frac{B}{C} Y$$

and dividing Eq. (26) by Eq. (27),

$$(7) \qquad \frac{B}{A} = \frac{X}{Y} \qquad \text{or} \qquad X = \frac{B}{A} Y$$

Substituting (6) and (7) in Eq. (27),

$$\begin{aligned} A &= \frac{Y[(B/C)Y]}{[(B/A)Y] + Y + [(B/C)Y]} = \frac{(B/C)Y}{(B/A) + 1 + (B/C)} \\ &= \frac{(B/C)Y}{[(AB + BC + CA)/AC]} = \frac{(AB)Y}{AB + BC + CA} \end{aligned}$$

from which

$$Y = \frac{AB + BC + CA}{B} \tag{28}$$

By a similar procedure it will be found that

$$Z = \frac{AB + BC + CA}{C} \tag{29}$$

and

$$X = \frac{AB + BC + CA}{A} \tag{30}$$

Equations (28), (29), and (30) represent transformations from star to delta. Observe that *each of the resistances in the delta is equal to the sum of the products of the resistances in the star, taken two at a time, divided by the resistance in the opposite leg.*

Several examples will now be given to illustrate the practical application of the two sets of equations.

EXAMPLE 7. Referring to Fig. 26, the three resistances in a delta-connected group of resistors are $X = 35$ ohms, $Y = 25$ ohms, and $Z = 40$ ohms. (*a*) Calculate the three resistances A, B, and C of an equivalent star. (*b*) Using the three star resistances computed in (*a*) show that, when reconverted to a delta, they will yield the values originally given.

Solution

(*a*) Since a transformation from a delta to a star involves a denominator $(X + Y + Z)$ that is common to the three equations (25), (26), and (27), this sum will first be determined; it is equal to $(35 + 25 + 40)$, or 100 ohms. Therefore

$$A = \frac{YZ}{100} = \frac{25 \times 40}{100} = 10 \text{ ohms}$$

$$B = \frac{XZ}{100} = \frac{35 \times 40}{100} = 14 \text{ ohms}$$

$$C = \frac{XY}{100} = \frac{35 \times 25}{100} = 8.75 \text{ ohms}$$

(*b*) Since the transformation from star to delta involves a numerator $(AB + BC + CA)$ that is common to the three equations (28), (29), and (30), this quantity will first be determined; it is equal to $(10 \times 14) + (14 \times 8.75) + (8.75 \times 10)$, or 350 ohms. Therefore

$$X = \frac{350}{A} = \frac{350}{10} = 35 \text{ ohms}$$

$$Y = \frac{350}{B} = \frac{350}{14} = 25 \text{ ohms}$$

$$Z = \frac{350}{C} = \frac{350}{8.75} = 40 \text{ ohms}$$

EXAMPLE 8. The wiring diagram shown in Fig. 27*a* is known as a Wheatstone-bridge circuit; when the potential difference between points a and b is zero the bridge is said to be balanced. For the resistance values given the bridge is *unbalanced*, and it is desired to find (*a*) the equivalent resistance of the circuit, (*b*) the total current I, (*c*) the current in the 110-ohm resistor between points a and b.

Solution

(*a*) The equivalent resistance of Fig. 27*a* will be found by first transforming the delta-connected resistances X, Y, and Z into an equivalent star; the latter is shown represented by A, B, and C, inside the delta.

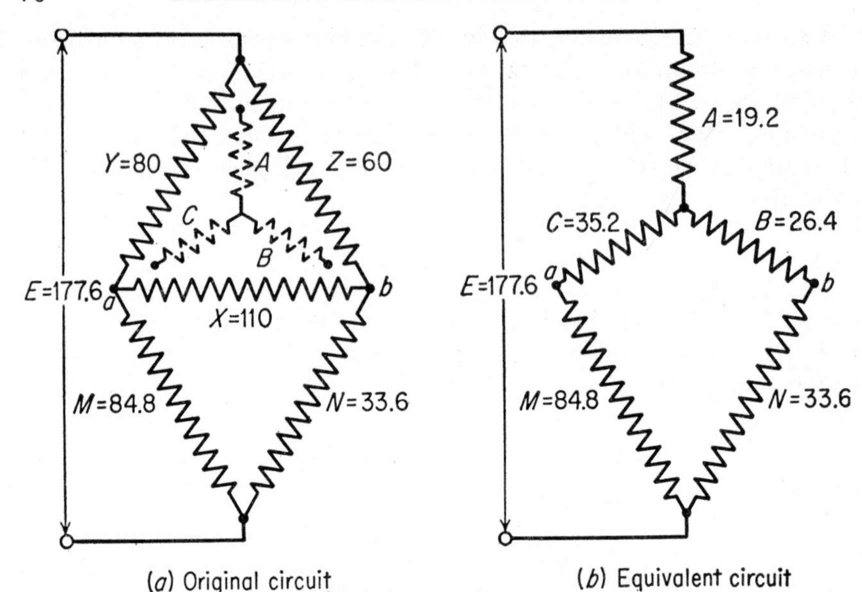

FIG. 27. Circuit diagrams for Example 8.

The individual values of resistance may be readily computed by Eqs. (25), (26), and (27):

$$A = \frac{60 \times 80}{250} = 19.2 \text{ ohms}$$

$$B = \frac{60 \times 110}{250} = 26.4 \text{ ohms}$$

$$C = \frac{80 \times 110}{250} = 35.2 \text{ ohms}$$

Joining the equivalent star to the remaining two arms M and N, the simplified circuit appears like Fig. 27*b*. Solving the latter,

$$R_{eq} = 19.2 + \frac{(35.2 + 84.8) \times (26.4 + 33.6)}{(120 + 60)} = 59.2 \text{ ohms}$$

(*b*) The total current is

$$I = \frac{177.6}{59.2} = 3 \text{ amp}$$

(*c*) To compute the current through the 110-ohm resistor it will first be necessary to find the potential difference between points a and b. To do this, the currents through the two branches of the parallel circuit of Fig. 27*b* must be found. These are:

$$I_{120} \text{ (left branch)} = \frac{60}{120 + 60} \times 3 = 1 \text{ amp}$$

$$I_{60} \text{ (right branch)} = \frac{120}{120 + 60} \times 3 = 2 \text{ amp}$$

The voltage drop across M is $84.8 \times 1 = 84.8$ volts, and the voltage drop across N is $33.6 \times 2 = 67.2$ volts. Therefore the potential difference between a and b will be

$$E_{a-b} = 84.8 - 67.2 = 17.6 \text{ volts}$$

Hence the current through the 110-ohm resistor is

$$I_{110} = \frac{17.6}{110} = 0.16 \text{ amp}$$

EXAMPLE 9. Figure 28a illustrates a rather complex network of six resistors, in which four units are interconnected to form a four-sided geometrical pattern, while the other two units join diametrically opposite points. For the values given on the diagram it is desired to determine the equivalent resistance of the network between points a and b.

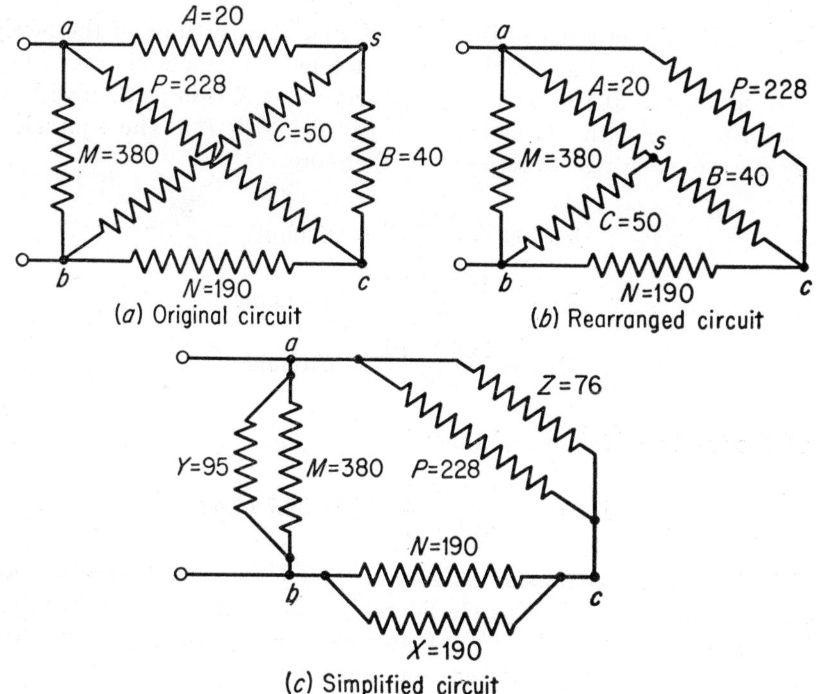

FIG. 28. Circuit diagrams for Example 9.

Solution

Before attempting to solve the circuit it will first be desirable to rearrange the resistors to show clearly that the three star-connected units, labeled A, B, and C, may be transformed into a delta to yield a comparatively simple network. Figure 28b indicates the rearrangement suggested. To recognize the electrical similarity of the two sketches, note particularly in Fig. 28*b* that: point *s* has been moved to the center of the diagram; M, N, and P are still connected, respectively, to points *ab*, *bc*, and *ca*; A, B, and C are still connected, respectively, to points *as*, *cs*, and *bs*. If the star-connected resistors A, B, and C are next transformed into an equivalent delta, the individual values of X, Y, and Z may be readily found by Eqs. (28), (29), and (30). These are:

$$X = \frac{(20 \times 40) + (40 \times 50) + (50 \times 20)}{20} = 190 \text{ ohms}$$

$$Y = \frac{3{,}800}{40} = 96 \text{ ohms}$$

$$Z = \frac{3{,}800}{50} = 76 \text{ ohm}$$

Rearranging the original resistors M, N, and P with those of the newly computed resistors X, Y, and Z, the simplified equivalent circuit of Fig. 28*c* is obtained. It is interesting to observe that X is in parallel with N, Y is in parallel with M, and Z is in parallel with P. The equivalent resistance of each pair of resistors is, therefore,

$$R_{MY} = \frac{380 \times 95}{475} = 76 \text{ ohms}$$

$$R_{NX} = \frac{190 \times 190}{380} = 95 \text{ ohms}$$

$$R_{PZ} = \frac{228 \times 76}{304} = 57 \text{ ohms}$$

and the total equivalent resistance is

$$R_{\text{eq}} = \frac{76 \times (95 + 57)}{76 + (95 + 57)} = 50.7 \text{ ohms}$$

Maximum-power-transfer Theorem. Direct-current generators are usually capable of delivering considerably more current and power than they are designed to deliver. Being electromagnetic machines their maximum outputs are, however, somewhat limited by internal magnetic reactions which, in part, are responsible for changes in terminal voltage; under conditions of excessive load, often as much as two or three times normal, such machines are incapable of maintaining voltages that are considered satisfactory from an operating point of view. Moreover, as currents exceed name-plate ratings, heat losses—I^2R losses—may be developed at rates that are greater than the heat-dissipating abilities of such machines; in such cases temperatures may reach values that are considered unsafe. Finally, since the power transferred from generator to load is usually large it is imperative that over-all efficiencies be kept as high as possible; this latter point is particularly important because efficiencies of electrical generators drop off very rapidly as load currents approach maximum values.

What has been said about power-distribution systems involving generators does not usually apply to small battery circuits and communication networks. The latter generally involve comparatively small amounts of power so that *maximum power transfer* is often more important than other considerations. What follows will therefore be concerned with small battery-powered networks in which it is desired to determine the conditions that prevail when the *load power* is a maximum.

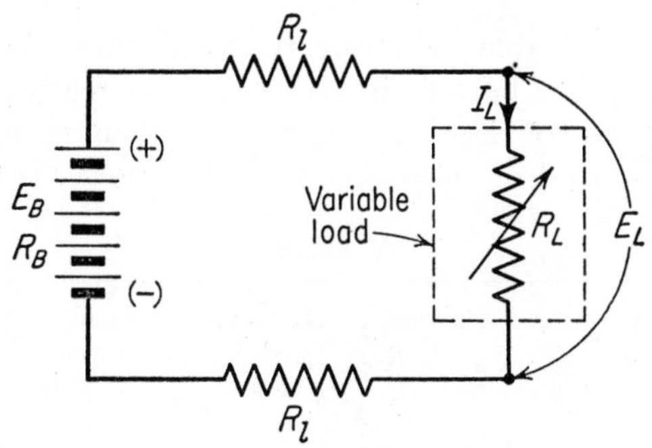

FIG. 29. Circuit diagram involving a variable load resistor.

Consider Fig. 29, which illustrates a simple series circuit and consists of a battery, a pair of line wires, and a variable load resistor. When the load resistance R_L is very large the current will be small and the load power P_L will be low. Moreover, as the load resistance is reduced to a very low value the current approaches a maximum, the voltage drop in $R_B + 2R_l$ will be large, the load voltage E_L will be small, and the power P_L will again be low. For limiting values, if $R_L = \infty$ (an open circuit), $I_L = 0$ and $P_L = 0$; also, if $R_L = 0$ (a short circuit), $E_L = 0$ and $P_L = 0$. It should be clear, therefore, that for some value of R_L, not ∞ or 0, the power P_L will be a maximum; in fact, as the following illustrative example will show, the maximum power transferred to the load will occur when $R_L = R_B + 2R_l$.

Figure 30 duplicates Fig. 29 but shows numerical values for the various elements of the circuit; note particularly that the load resistance R_L is variable. Assuming arbitrary values between 7.2 ohms and 0.2 ohm for R_L, Table 8 has been prepared to indicate that (*a*) the maximum power transfer occurs when $R_L = R_B + 2R_l$; (*b*) the efficiency at maximum load power is 50 per cent.

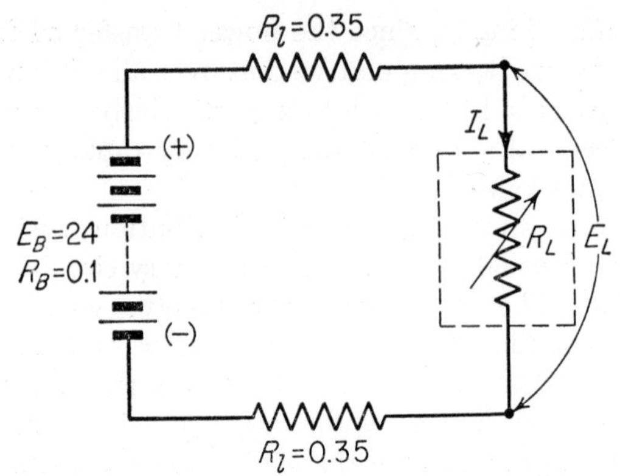

Fig. 30. Circuit diagram to illustrate numerically the maximum-power-transfer theorem.

A careful study of Table 8 shows very clearly that, although the total power delivered by the battery increases with increasing values of load current, the *load power* rises to a maximum when $I_L = 15$ amp, after which it continues to drop; also, when the load power is a maximum, at

Table 8

Load resistance R_L	Total resistance $R_t = R_L + 0.8$	Current $I_L = \frac{E}{R_t}$	Battery power $P_B = E_B I_L$	Load power $P_L = I_L^2 R_L$	Efficiency Eff $= \frac{P_L}{P_B} \times 100$
7.2	8.0	3.0	72	64.8	90.0
3.2	4.0	6.0	144	115.2	80.0
2.2	3.0	8.0	192	140.8	73.3
1.6	2.4	10.0	240	160.0	66.7
1.2	2.0	12.0	288	172.8	60.0
1.0	1.8	13.33	320	177.8	55.5
0.8	1.6	15.0	360	180.0	50.0
0.6	1.4	17.14	412	176.3	42.8
0.4	1.2	20.0	480	160.0	33.3
0.2	1.0	24.0	576	115.2	20.0

15 amp, the circuit efficiency is 50 per cent. This can only mean that above the 15 amp load current the power losses increase at a faster rate than does the total battery power. It is also interesting to observe that the point of maximum load transfer occurs when the load resistance R_L is equal to the resistance looking back into the circuit from the load terminals; i.e., $R_L = R_B + 2R_l = 0.8$ ohm.

Although the foregoing numerical example is not a rigid mathematical proof that all d-c circuits will behave similarly, this is nevertheless a fact, and it can be shown that *the maximum power transferred to a load resistor occurs when it has a value equal to the resistance of the network looking back from the load terminals with all the sources of voltage replaced by their internal resistances.* This is the *maximum-power-transfer theorem.*

EXAMPLE 10. A 120-volt battery, having an internal resistance of 0.5 ohm, is connected through line resistances of 9.5 ohms to a variable load resistor. For what load resistance will the latter consume maximum power, and what will be the maximum power?

Solution

$$R_L = 0.5 + 9.5 = 10$$

$$P_L = \left(\frac{120}{10 + 10}\right)^2 \times 10 = 360 \text{ watts}$$

EXAMPLE 11. Figure 31 represents a circuit in which two batteries supply power through line resistors to a variable load resistor. For the values given on the diagram calculate (*a*) the ohmic value of R_L when its power is a maximum, (*b*) the maximum load power P_L, (*c*) the total power delivered by both batteries, (*d*) the over-all efficiency under the above condition.

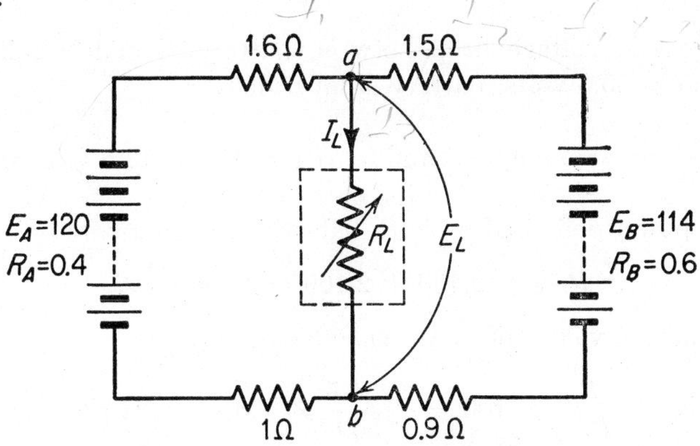

FIG. 31. Circuit diagram for Example 11.

Solution

(*a*) Looking back from the load terminals, with the two sources of emf replaced by their internal resistances, the circuit consists of two 3-ohm resistances in parallel; thus

$$R_L = \frac{3}{2} = 1.5 \text{ ohms}$$

(*b*) With the load resistor disconnected, the circulating current is

$$I = \frac{E_A - E_B}{R_{\text{circuit}}} = \frac{120 - 114}{(0.4 + 1.6 + 1.5 + 0.6 + 0.9 + 1.0)} = \frac{6}{6} = 1 \text{ amp}$$

and the open-circuit voltage at terminals *ab* is

$$E'_{ab} = 120 - 1 \times 3 = 114 + 1 \times 3 = 117 \text{ volts}$$

For maximum load power, the load voltage must be

$$E_L = \frac{E'_{ab}}{2} = \frac{117}{2} = 58.5 \text{ volts}$$

Therefore for maximum power the load current is

$$I_L = \frac{E_L}{R_L} = \frac{58.5}{1.5} = 39 \text{ amp}$$

and the maximum load power is

$$P_L = 58.5 \times 39 = 2{,}281.5 \text{ watts}$$

(*c*) Since the voltage drop between battery *A* and terminals *ab* is $120 - 58.5 = 61.5$ volts, battery *A* must deliver

$$I_A = \frac{61.5}{3} = 20.5 \text{ amp} \qquad \text{and} \qquad P_A = 120 \times 20.5 = 2{,}460 \text{ watts}$$

Also, since the voltage drop between battery *B* and terminals *ab* is $114 - 58.5 = 55.5$ volts, battery *B* must deliver

$$I_B = \frac{55.5}{3} = 18.5 \text{ amp} \qquad \text{and} \qquad P_B = 114 \times 18.5 = 2{,}109 \text{ watts}$$

The total power delivered by both batteries will therefore be

$$P_{\text{total}} = 2{,}460 + 2{,}109 = 4{,}569 \text{ watts}$$

(*d*) Using the values of power calculated above,

$$\text{Eff} = \frac{P_L}{P_{\text{total}}} \times 100 = \frac{2{,}281.5}{4{,}569} \times 100 = 49.93 \text{ per cent}$$

or slightly less than 50 per cent.

Questions

1. State *Kirchhoff's law* that applies to the *current* at any junction in an electric circuit.
2. State *Kirchhoff's law* that applies to the *emf's* and the *resistance voltages* in any continuous path of an electric circuit.
3. How are the plus and minus current signs determined?
4. How are the plus and minus voltage signs determined for batteries and generators?
5. How are the plus and minus voltage signs determined for resistors?
6. What will be the effect upon the solution of a problem if a current direction is arbitrarily assumed incorrectly?
7. In a complex circuit containing several unknown currents and voltages how is it possible to reduce the number of simultaneous equations to effect a solution?

8. State the *superposition theorem.*
9. Under what circuit conditions may the superposition theorem be used to advantage?
10. State *Thévenin's theorem.*
11. Under what circuit conditions may Thévenin's theorem be used to advantage?
12. What is meant by the *open-circuit voltage,* in Thévenin's theorem?
13. What is meant by the resistance of the network "looking back into the network," in Thévenin's theorem?
14. State the rule that will make it possible to find the equivalent star for a given delta.
15. State the rule that will make it possible to find the equivalent delta for a given star.
16. Make a sketch of a simple Wheatstone bridge. (*a*) Show how an equivalent star can be made of one of the deltas to simplify the circuit. (*b*) Show how an equivalent delta can be made of one of the stars to simplify the circuit.
17. State the *maximum-power-transfer theorem.*
18. What is meant by the resistance of the network looking back from the load terminals with all sources of voltage replaced by their internal resistances?
19. Why is it not desirable to overload d-c generators?
20. In a simple series circuit having a battery source of power what is the efficiency when maximum power is transferred to a load?
21. Why is the power transferred to a load very low when the load resistance is extremely high or extremely low?
22. Why is the efficiency of a system very low when the transferred power is high?
23. Assume two batteries having equal open-circuit voltages and delivering currents through equal line resistances. If the internal resistance of one battery is larger than the other, which will be capable of transferring more maximum power? Why?

Problems

1. Referring to Fig. 17, reverse the polarity of battery E_B and the current direction through resistor R_B. (*a*) Write Kirchhoff's current equation at junction *p*. (*b*) Write Kirchhoff's voltage equation for circuit *bqnmfpb*.
2. Referring to Fig. 18, change R_A to 0.2 ohm, R_B to 0.3 ohm, and R_L to 0.5 ohm. With the same battery polarities, and with $E_A = 24$ volts and $E_B = 26$ volts as shown, calculate (*a*) the currents I_L, I_A, and I_B; (*b*) the load voltage V_L; (*c*) the load and battery powers P_L, P_A, and P_B.
3. Referring to Fig. 16, what will be the current in the load resistor R_L if (*a*) battery *B* is replaced by a wire of negligible resistance? (*b*) battery *A* is replaced by a wire of negligible resistance?
4. What will be the current in the circuit of Fig. 18 if the load resistor R_L is removed?
5. How much power would be delivered to a load resistance R_L of 0.2 in the circuit of Fig. 18?
6. Referring to Fig. 19, assume a 6-volt battery, having negligible resistance, to be connected in series between the positive terminal of the generator and the 0.15-ohm resistor. Calculate the battery currents I_A and I_B if the added line battery is connected (*a*) additive, (*b*) subtractive.
7. Figure 32 represents a circuit in which a load resistance is connected to a slide-wire rheostat. Calculate the power delivered to R_L when the slider (*a*) is at point *a*, (*b*) is moved down to a point one-third from *a*, (*c*) is moved down to a point two-thirds from *a*.

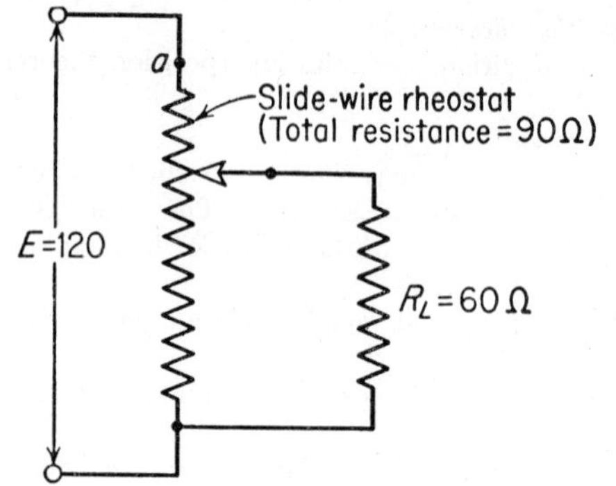

FIG. 32. Circuit diagram for Prob. 7.

8. Referring to Fig. 32, determine the value of R_L for a load voltage of 48 volts, when the slider is halfway between the ends of the slide-wire rheostat. For this condition calculate the power taken by the load resistance.

9. Referring to Fig. 20, assume that the current in load A is 140 amp and that the current in load B is 160 amp. With all other data similar to the values given in the diagram, calculate the load voltages V_A and V_B.

10. Referring to Fig. 33 determine (a) the currents I_A and I_B, (b) the load voltage V_L.

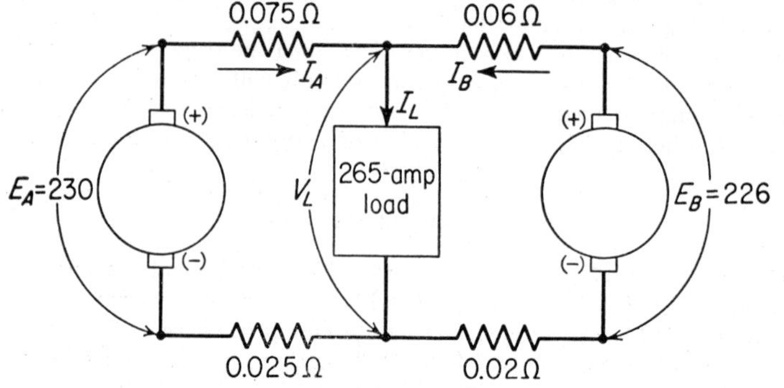

FIG. 33. Circuit diagram for Prob. 10.

11. Referring to Fig. 34, calculate (a) the generator currents I_1 and I_2, (b) the total battery-charging current I_B, (c) the total power delivered to the battery.

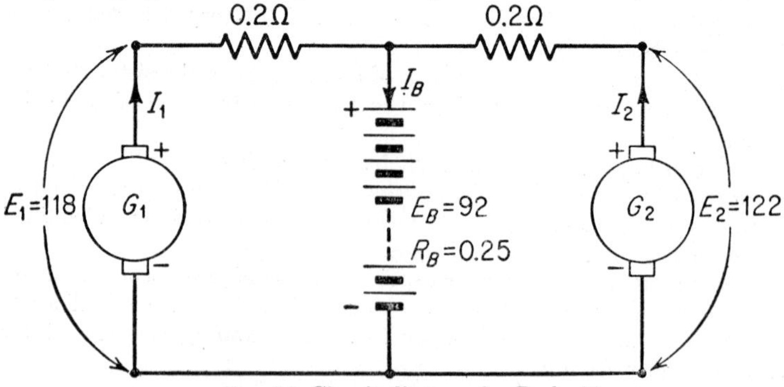

FIG. 34. Circuit diagram for Prob. 11.

12. For the circuit of Fig. 35 calculate (*a*) the currents delivered by generators 1 and 2, (*b*) the load voltages E_A and E_B.

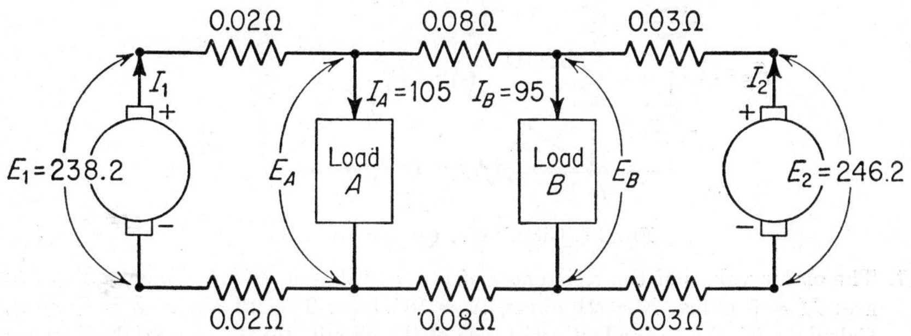

FIG. 35. Circuit diagram for Prob. 12.

13. The wiring arrangement shown in Fig. 36 is known as an *Edison three-wire* system. For the values indicated, calculate (*a*) E_A, E_B, and E_C; (*b*) the powers delivered to loads *A*, *B*, and *C*.

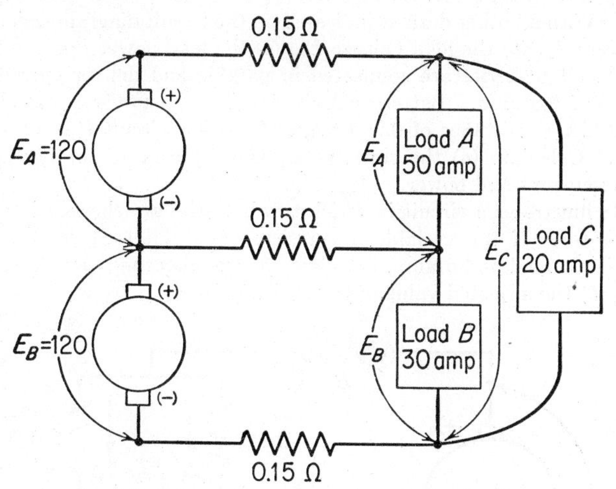

FIG. 36. Edison three-wire system for Prob. 13.

14. Referring to Fig. 24, what would be the current in a conductor of negligible resistance (a short circuit) that connects points *c* and *d*?

15. Referring to Fig. 36, calculate the load currents I_A and I_B for the condition that $I_C = 20$ amp, and $E_A = E_B = 111$ volts.

16. For the circuit of Fig. 37, calculate (*a*) the total equivalent resistance of the network to which power is delivered by the battery, (*b*) the battery current. (*Hint:* Transform the star-connected resistors, *A*, *B*, and *C* into an equivalent delta in which *X* is connected to points *c* and *b*, *Y* is connected to points *a* and *b*, and *Z* is connected to points *a* and *c*.)

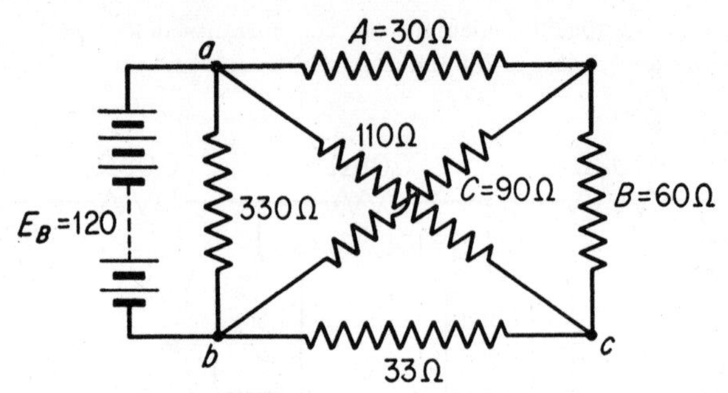

FIG. 37. Circuit diagram for Prob. 16.

17. The ohmic values of the resistances of the Wheatstone-bridge circuit of Fig. 27*a* are: $M = 6$ ohms, $N = 21$ ohms, $X = 18$ ohms, $Y = 12$ ohms, $Z = 6$ ohms. Calculate (*a*) the equivalent resistance of the circuit, (*b*) the potential difference between points *a* and *b* if the applied voltage is 120, (*c*) the current through resistor X.

18. A 24-volt battery having an internal resistance of 0.2 ohm is connected by two 0.3-ohm conductors to a variable resistor (see Fig. 30). (*a*) For what value of load resistance R_L will the load power be a maximum? (*b*) What will be the maximum load power and the corresponding efficiency?

19. Referring to Fig. 31, assume that a resistance of 1.2 ohms is connected to points *a* and *b*. With all other data as indicated on the circuit diagram, calculate (*a*) the load current I_L, (*b*) the load voltage E_L, (*c*) the load power P_L.

20. Three 24-volt batteries are connected in parallel and deliver current to a load resistance of 0.8 ohm. Battery circuit A has a resistance of 0.2 ohm, battery circuit B has a resistance of 0.25 ohm, and battery circuit C has a resistance of 0.3 ohm. Calculate (*a*) the currents supplied by each of the batteries, (*b*) the total load current and power.

21. Figure 38 illustrates a circuit in which two batteries are charged in parallel by a d-c generator. If the variable line resistor R is adjusted so that the second battery is charged at 35 amp, calculate (*a*) the charging current I_1 in the first battery, (*b*) the adjusted value of line resistor R.

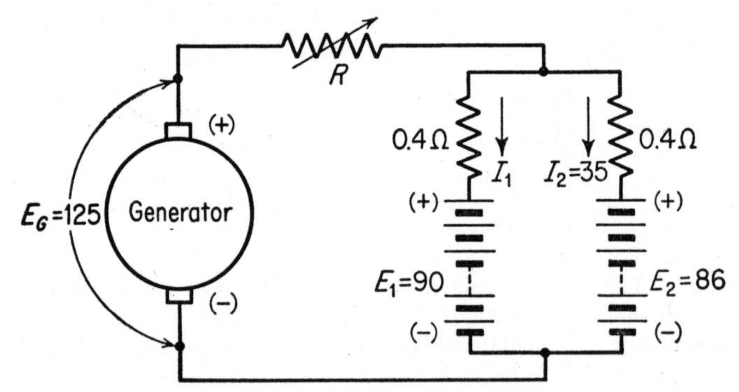

FIG. 38. Circuit diagram for Prob. 21.

CHAPTER 5

MAGNETISM AND MAGNETIC FIELDS

Natural and Artificial Magnets. Magnetism, one of the most remarkable of all natural phenomena, was first discovered by the ancients. They found an oxide of iron, Fe_3O_4, that not only had the property of attracting other ferrous substances but, when properly fashioned and suspended, always oriented itself in a *north-south* direction. This strange and wonderful material was named "magnet" after the town of Magnesia in Lydia, Asia Minor, where it was first discovered; when used practically in navigation as a compass it was called *lodestone*, i.e., *leading stone*. The *natural magnet*, the lodestone, has little value today except as a museum or laboratory curiosity, because its attractive force is feeble compared with the modern, more powerful, *artificial magnet*.

There are only three known *elements* that can be magnetized artificially, namely, iron, nickel, and cobalt. The latter two are, individually, rather weak magnetic materials in comparison with iron; however, when iron is alloyed with one or both of the other elements, or even with substances that are themselves not magnetic, extremely powerful magnets may be produced. Thus, for example, such alloys of iron and nickel as *Permalloy* (22 per cent iron and 78 per cent nickel) and *Hipernik* (40 per cent iron and 60 per cent nickel), and alloys of iron, nickel, and cobalt such as *Perminvar* and *Alnico*, have astonishing magnetic properties. Also, the addition of nonmagnetic elements like silicon, tungsten, titanium, and certain precious metals to the iron-nickel-cobalt group has resulted in many useful types of special magnetic alloys.

Artificial magnets may be created in several ways, their attractive power and permanency depending, among other things, upon the kinds and proportions of the elements used and their method of manufacture. Generally, it is best to magnetize a substance by wrapping a coil of wire around it, after which a direct current is passed through the coil for a short time. Less effective methods involve stroking the substance with a strong magnet or placing the material to be magnetized in contact with a powerful magnet.

The lodestone is, of course, a permanent magnet, retaining its original magnetic quality indefinitely. Artificial magnets, on the other hand, may be made to have almost any desired degree of permanency. The hard steels—tungsten steel and cobalt steel—and special alloys such as Alnico make excellent permanent magnets; when they are properly manufactured and aged, their retentive property is unaffected by extended use. Soft iron or soft steel will, however, lose much of its magnetic strength soon after it is strongly magnetized; it is, in this respect, regarded as a temporary magnet.

Magnet Poles and Magnetic Fields. Magnets, of whatever shape, always exhibit their strongest force actions in regions that seem to center about the projections or ends of the materials; the latter are called *magnet poles*, and it is here that magnetism is assumed to be concentrated in the substance. In the case of a simple bar magnet, or U-shaped and E-shaped magnets (Fig. 39), the strong magnetic forces exist at the ends because a

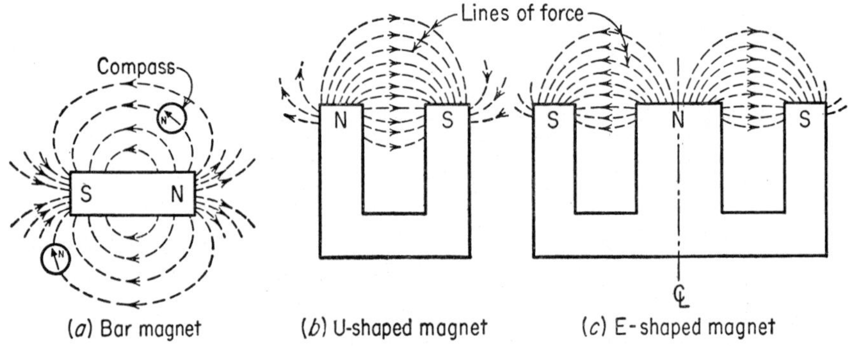

Fig. 39. Flux distributions for three types of magnet.

major portion of the magnetism appears to emerge at one pole and enter at the other; the magnetic effect is, in fact, so pronounced at the ends that the latter have been given names that indicate direction, the *north pole* being the end from which the magnetism is supposed to emerge and the *south pole* representing the end into which the magnetism enters.

The familiar compass needle is, of course, a freely suspended magnet and points directly north and south (or very nearly so) because the earth is itself a sort of magnet. This property of the earth was discovered about the tenth century when, as previously pointed out, the natural magnet, in the form of a lodestone, was first employed in navigation. *Arbitrarily* designating the end of the compass needle that points *north* as the *north pole* it thus becomes the *north-seeking* pole. Now then, if the north poles of two compasses are brought close together they are found to repel; moreover, if a north pole of one compass is brought near the south end of another compass, they will attract. This extremely important observation leads to the first law of magnetism:

Like poles repel and unlike poles attract.

Since all magnetic effects occur in the space surrounding magnets or, in fact, wherever magnetism is present, the space is given the distinguishing name of *magnetic field;* for convenience it is also assumed that the magnetic field is a region of stress. In order to visualize this *fictitious* stressed magnetic field Faraday invented the term "lines of force" and pictured the latter as uniformly distributed around symmetrically shaped sources of magnetism. Considerable study has since demonstrated the great usefulness of the *lines-of-force* conception, because it has become the basis for most mathematical relationships that involve magnetic actions and forces.

The magnetic fields surrounding a bar magnet, a U-shaped magnet, and an E-shaped magnet are illustrated in Fig. 39. The following points should be noted particularly: (1) the magnetic fields surrounding *uniformly* constructed magnets are always *symmetrical* unless they are disturbed by the presence of other magnetic substances somewhere in the field; (2) the lines of force have direction and are always represented as *leaving* the north pole and *entering* the south pole; (3) a compass needle placed anywhere in the magnetic field will always orient itself along the direction of the lines of force, with its north pole pointing to the magnet's south pole; (4) the greatest field density—lines of force per unit area—always occurs near the magnet-pole surfaces and diminishes with increasing distances from the poles; (5) a symmetrically shaped E-shaped magnet may conveniently be considered as two U-shaped magnets with the side faces of identical poles brought in contact (Fig. 39*c*).

Whenever an unmagnetized piece of iron is placed in an otherwise symmetrical magnetic field that is created by a magnet, the lines of force—often called *magnetic flux*—are urged away from their normal uniform distribution and are drawn to the magnetic substance. This action may be attributed to the fact that iron is a better conductor of magnetic flux than air; it is actually very much better, as will be pointed out subsequently in connection with the discussion of the term *permeability*. As a result of such flux concentration the iron becomes a magnet *by induction*, with its north pole nearest the south pole of the inducing magnet (or vice versa); following this process of induction a force of attraction is developed between the two magnets. This leads to a second important law of magnetism:

A magnetic field always tends to arrange itself so that the greatest number of lines of force are created.

Figure 40 illustrates the actions described, showing how the normal flux pattern is altered by the presence of the soft iron and that the latter becomes a magnet by induction.

Electromagnetism. Magnetism that is created by the passage of currents of electricity through wires, or coils of wire, is generally referred to

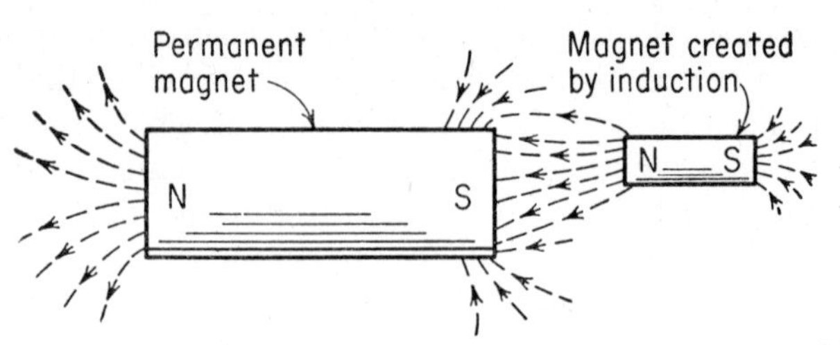

FIG. 40. Unsymmetrical flux pattern surrounding a permanent magnet resulting from an adjacent soft-iron bar.

as *electromagnetism*. Oersted's original discovery in 1820 that a magnetic field encircles a straight current-carrying conductor soon led to observations indicating that magnetic fields could be strengthened by employing coils of wire, or better yet, by wrapping many turns of wire around magnetic substances. Further studies made possible the development of important rules and laws concerned with current direction, field direction, and magnet polarity, as well as the precise mathematical relations between such factors as amperes, turns of wire, and physical arrangements of materials on the one hand, and the resulting field intensity and magnetic forces on the other.

Field around a Current-carrying Conductor. When a straight conductor carries a current, a magnetic field is created in such a way that *the flux surrounds the wire in concentric circles.* The flux density—lines of force per unit area—is densest at the surface of the conductor and diminishes with increasing distances from the latter. In fact, it may be shown mathematically and verified experimentally that *in free space the flux density is inversely proportional to the distance from the center of the wire.* Also, following the accepted rule that the flux direction is always the same as that indicated by the north pole of a compass, the direction of the encircling lines of force may be determined by the following rule:

Grasp the wire with the right hand so that the thumb points in the direction of the current; the encircling fingers will then indicate the direction of the lines of force around the wire (see Fig. 41).

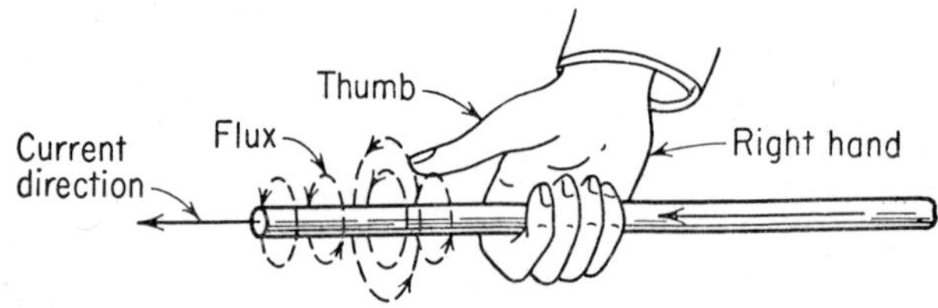

FIG. 41. Sketch illustrating the method of determining the flux direction around a current-carrying conductor.

Thus, in Fig. 41, a compass needle placed horizontally above the wire will be deflected so that its north pole will point away from the observer;

when placed horizontally below the conductor the north pole will point toward the observer.

Field through a Current-carrying Solenoid. Unless straight wires carry extremely high values of current the magnetic effects are comparatively weak. However, if a conductor is coiled to form a solenoid as in Fig. 42, the magnetic flux is confined to the inside of the coil before it has an opportunity to spread out in free space; such flux concentration greatly increases the flux density at both ends of the coil as well as within. It is therefore possible to magnify the magnetic effect of a given current by using coils instead of straight wires, and, as will presently be shown, such

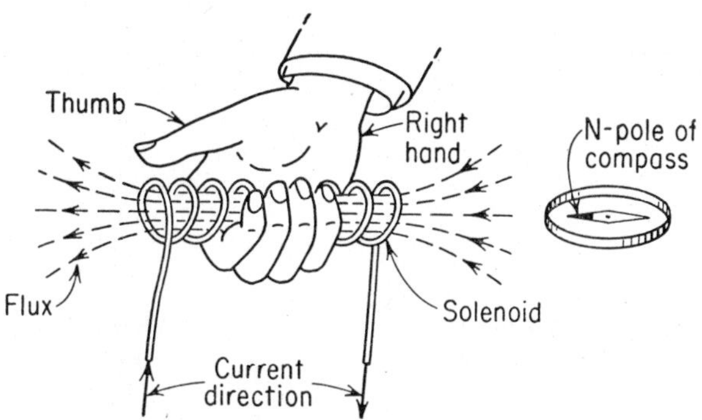

FIG. 42. Sketch illustrating the method of determining the flux direction in a solenoid.

flux-density amplification is practically proportional to the number of turns of wire. Concerning the direction of the field through the solenoid, the following rule may be applied:

Grasp the solenoid with the right hand so that the fingers point in the direction in which the current passes through the coiled wires; the thumb will then point in the direction of the magnetic field (see Fig. 42).

Thus, in Fig. 42, looking into the solenoid from the right, the current will pass through the wires in a clockwise direction; the field (and the north end of the compass needle) will therefore be directed to the left.

Polarity of an Electromagnet. Still further flux-density increases may be produced by inserting an iron core, or other good magnetic substance, within the solenoid. The iron core then becomes a magnet; moreover, since the *magnet* is created by the passage of a current of *electricity* through the coil, it is called an *electromagnet.* Applying a rule similar to the one given for the solenoid, the polarity of an electromagnet may be determined as follows:

Grasp the coil of wire with the right hand so that the fingers point in the direction in which the current passes through the coiled wires; the thumb will then point to the north pole of the electromagnet (see Fig. 43).

Thus, in Fig. 43, looking into the electromagnet from the left, the current will pass through the wires in a counterclockwise direction; the left end of the core will therefore become a north pole.

Strength of an Electromagnet. Although the principles and practical aspects of electromagnets will be considered in some detail in Chap. 6 under the heading, Magnetic Circuits, it will be desirable at this point to make some general statements concerning the factors that determine their strength. From what has previously been said it should be clear that the force exerted by an electromagnet will depend, among other things, upon *current, turns of wire,* and *kind and size of magnetic core;* these are mainly responsible for the creation of flux, which in turn is a measure of magnetic force. Equally important, however, is the way in which the electromagnet is constructed, and this, of course, involves the matter of design.

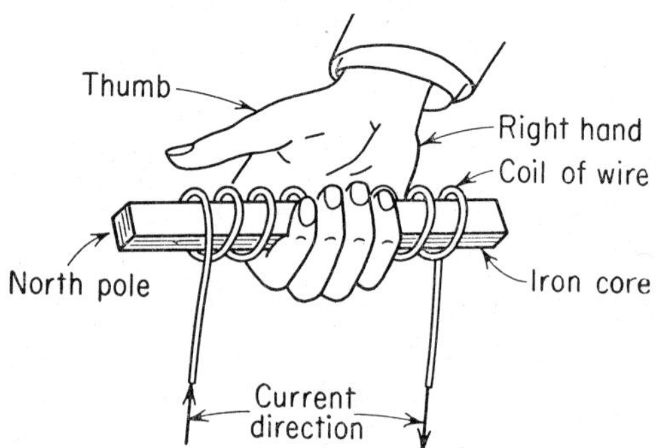

Fig. 43. Sketch illustrating the method of determining the polarity of an electromagnet.

Recognizing the fact that an electromagnet is strong only in proportion to the total number of lines of force it can produce, and that the flux is greatly affected by the amount of iron in the magnetic path, two general constructions will be compared. If a straight bar is magnetized as in Fig. 44*a*, it will not be especially strong, because the coil must act upon and magnetize a long path of air besides the good magnetic core and the block of iron which is to be lifted; note particularly that the lines of force must pass through a considerable distance in air from the north pole of the magnet to the block of iron. Since air is the poorest of all magnetic conductors, the effectiveness of the excitation—the magnetizing coil—is greatly reduced. A U-shaped electromagnet like that of Fig. 44*b* is very much better than a bar electromagnet because the flux is confined very largely to a good magnetic path consisting almost entirely of iron; the only air spaces are at the contact surfaces between electromagnet and block of iron, and it is here, of course, that the magnetic force is exerted. The quality of the magnetic core also has much to do with the lifting ability of the magnet since this material, like the kind of wire in an electric circuit, determines the conductivity of the magnetic circuit, i.e., the path taken by the magnetic flux.

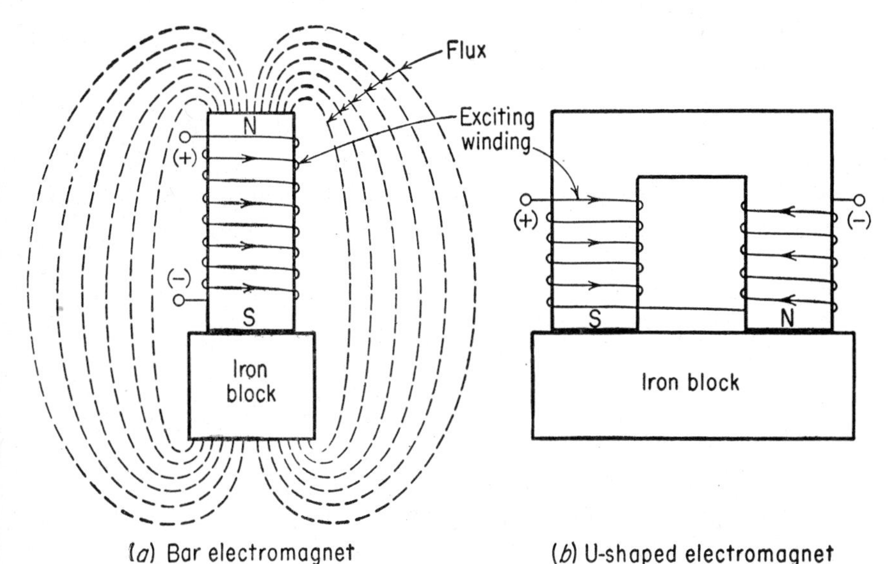

FIG. 44. Two general types of electromagnet.

Magnetic Field Surrounding a Straight Conductor. The magnetic field associated with a straight current-carrying conductor is completely symmetrical, and theoretically extends out into free space indefinitely; moreover, each increment of wire adds its share of flux that magnetizes the air. However, all increments of wire are not equally effective in creating flux at a given point in space because (1) the distances from successive increments of wire, on either side of an element of wire that is directly opposite, i.e., normal to, the point in question, increase, and (2) increments of wire that are successively farther from the point in question act at continually smaller angles. These conditions should be borne in mind in connection with the following discussions and formulas.

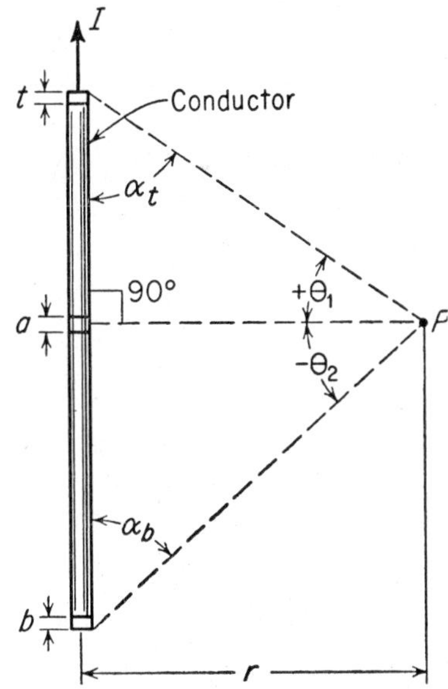

FIG. 45. Sketch illustrating current-carrying conductor of finite length.

Flux Density Due to a Wire of Finite Length. Referring to Fig. 45, which represents a current-carrying conductor of finite length, note that increment of wire a is most effective in creating flux at point P because it not only is closest to the point but acts at right angles with respect to it; using the right-hand rule, page 90, the field is directed away from the observer at point P. Increments of wire t (at the top) and b (at the bottom) are less effective than increment a because not only are their distances greater but they act at angles α_t and α_b, respectively, both less than 90°. The foregoing statements, therefore, lead to the conclusion that the composite effect of a straight conductor in creating flux must sum up, i.e., integrate, the actions of an infinite number of increments of wire; such a process of integration yields a formula which conveniently expresses the flux density in *gauss* (1 *gauss* = 1 *line per square centimeter*) in terms of known quantities.

$$B_P = \frac{I}{10r} (\sin \Theta_1 - \sin \Theta_2) \qquad (31)^1$$

where B_P = flux density, gauss
I = current, amp
r = perpendicular distance between point P and the center of the conductor, cm

and Θ_1 and Θ_2 are angles, measured as indicated. Note particularly that Θ_1 and Θ_2 are given opposite signs (+ and −) when the angles are on opposite sides of a normal line from point P to the conductor; they should both be given positive signs if both angles are measured on the same side of a horizontal line P drawn through point P.

Example 1. A conductor 36 in. long carries a current of 1,500 amp. What is the flux density at a point 12 in. from the wire, and (*a*) 12 in. from one end toward the other end? (*b*) directly opposite the center of the conductor? (*c*) directly opposite one end of the conductor?

Solution

(*a*)

$$\Theta_1 = \tan^{-1} \frac{12}{12} = 45°$$

$$\sin \Theta_1 = 0.707$$

$$-\Theta_2 = \tan^{-1} \frac{24}{12} = -63.5°$$

$$\sin \Theta_2 = -0.895$$

$$B = \frac{1{,}500}{10 \times 12 \times 2.54} (0.707 + 0.895) = 7.88 \text{ gauss}$$

(*b*)

$$\Theta_1 = \tan^{-1} \frac{18}{12} = 56.3°$$

$$\Theta_2 = -56.3°$$

$$\sin \Theta_1 = 0.832$$

$$\sin \Theta_2 = -0.832$$

$$B = \frac{1{,}500}{10 \times 12 \times 2.54} (0.832 + 0.832) = 8.19 \text{ gauss}$$

[1] See Appendix 1D for derivation.

(c)
$$\Theta_1 = \tan^{-1}\frac{36}{12} = 71.6°$$
$$\Theta_2 = 0$$
$$\sin\Theta_1 = 0.949$$
$$\sin\Theta_2 = 0$$
$$B = \frac{1{,}500}{10 \times 12 \times 2.54}(0.949) = 4.67 \text{ gauss}$$

EXAMPLE 2. For the 36-in. 1,500-amp conductor of Example 1, calculate the flux density at a point 12 in. beyond one end of the conductor and at a 12 in. radius therefrom.

Solution

$$\Theta_1 = \tan^{-1}\frac{48}{12} = 76°$$
$$\sin\Theta_1 = 0.970$$
$$\sin\Theta_2 = 0.707$$
$$B = \frac{1{,}500}{10 \times 12 \times 2.54}(0.970 - 0.707) = 1.3 \text{ gauss}$$

Flux Density Due to an Extremely Long Wire. When it is desired to determine the flux density at a radius r from a current-carrying conductor that is small with respect to the length of the wire, the latter may be regarded as infinitely long. This implies that Θ_1 and Θ_2 are both nearly 90°, one plus (+) and the other minus (−), under which condition $\sin\Theta_1 = +1$ and $\sin\Theta_2 = -1$. Equation (31) therefore reduces to

$$B_P = \frac{2I}{10r} \qquad (32)[1]$$

EXAMPLE 3. Calculate the flux density at the surface of a very long No. 0000 conductor that carries a current of 2,500 amp.

Solution

The diameter of a No. 0000 conductor (Table 4) = 0.460 in.

$$B = \frac{2 \times 2{,}500}{10 \times 0.23 \times 2.54} = 855 \text{ gauss}$$

EXAMPLE 4. How far from the surface of the conductor of Example 3 will the flux density be one-third of its value at the surface?

Solution

$$\frac{855}{3} = \frac{2 \times 2{,}500}{10 \times r}$$
$$r = \frac{1{,}500}{855} = 1.75 \text{ cm, or } 0.69 \text{ in.}$$

Therefore, distance from wire surface = 0.69 − 0.23 = 0.46 in.

[1] See Appendix 1D for derivation.

Flux Density along the Axis of a Flat Coil. If a flat coil of wire is energized it will create a magnetic field which, in general, will be directed through the coil as shown in Fig. 46; the lines of force will, of course, be completely symmetrical and extend through and around the coil on all sides as closed loops, but for this discussion only a few lines are shown on one side of the coil. Since all of the flux must pass *through* the coil and flare out into free space beyond the coil ends, it should be clear that the

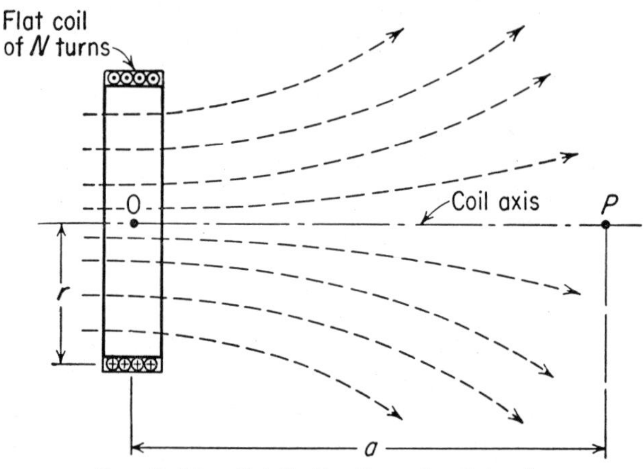

FIG. 46. Flux distribution through a flat coil.

flux density is greatest along the plane of the coil. Of particular importance is the field intensity at the very *center* of the coil O, and this value is given by the equation

$$B_O = \frac{2\pi NI}{10r} \qquad (33)[1]$$

where N = number of turns in the coil
r = radius of the coil, cm

It is interesting to note that this equation is, in general, similar to Eq. (32); it does, however, give values of flux density that account for the total length of N turns of wire all elements of which are exactly the same distance from the center of the coil.

For any point P on the coil axis, a cm from the center of the coil O, the flux density will be

$$B_P = \frac{0.2\pi r^2 NI}{\sqrt{(r^2 + a^2)^3}} \qquad (34)[1]$$

where all dimensions are in centimeter units. Note particularly that this formula reduces to Eq. (33) when a is zero, and that the flux density diminishes with increasing values of a.

[1] See Appendix 1E for derivation.

EXAMPLE 5. A 1,200-turn flat coil, having an average diameter of 3.0 in., carries a current of 40 ma. Calculate the flux density (*a*) at the center of the coil, and (*b*) at a point on the axis 2 in. from the center of the coil.

Solution

(*a*) $$B_O = \frac{2\pi \times 1{,}200 \times 0.04}{10 \times 1.5 \times 2.54} = 7.9 \text{ gauss}$$

(*b*) $$B_P = \frac{0.2\pi \times (1.5)^2 \times 1{,}200 \times 0.04}{2.54\sqrt{(2.25 + 4)^3}} = 1.71 \text{ gauss}$$

Flux Density along the Axis of a Long Solenoid. It was previously pointed out that a *solenoid* is a coil of wire wound on a circular form whose axial length is large in comparison with its diameter. Such coils are commonly used in many types of electromagnets to operate valves, relays, circuit breakers, ratcheting devices, and other mechanisms; in these devices iron cores are usually employed to amplify the magnetic effect of the current as it passes through the winding. This discussion will, however, be limited to air-core or, in general, nonmagnetic-core solenoids.

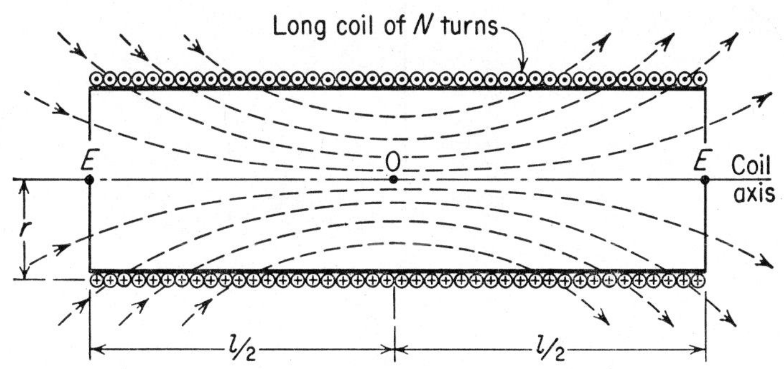

FIG. 47. Flux distribution through an air-core solenoid.

When an energized coil is flat, as in Fig. 46, all elements of *all* turns act similarly on a given point because they are all exactly the same distance away from that point. However, in a solenoid where the turns are spread out on a long form as in Fig. 47, the elements of successive turns, next to one another, are different distances from a given point. This implies, of course, that the magnetic effect at the center of the solenoid will, for example, be less than that of an equivalent flat coil; the same reasoning applies equally well to all other points along the axis of the coil. It should be obvious, therefore, that a flux-density equation for a solenoid must take the coil's length into account by having an l term in the denominator. This is exactly what happens when the derivation is performed, the flux density at the exact center O of a solenoid being

$$B_O = \frac{2\pi NI}{10\sqrt{r^2 + (l/2)^2}} \qquad (35)^1$$

where l is the axial length of the coil in centimeters, and the other terms are as previously defined.

Further analysis of flux-density relationships along the coil axis indicates that the value obtained by Eq. (35) remains substantially constant to distances that are about $l/4$ unit to either side of point O. Also, at point E, along either edge of the coil on the axis, the flux density is practically equal to about one-half its value at the center; it is, in fact, given by the equation

$$B_E = \frac{2\pi NI}{10\sqrt{r^2 + l^2}} \qquad (36)^1$$

Comparing Eqs. (35) and (36), it should be noted that $B_O = 2B_E$ when l is large compared with r, in which case r may be omitted in solving for

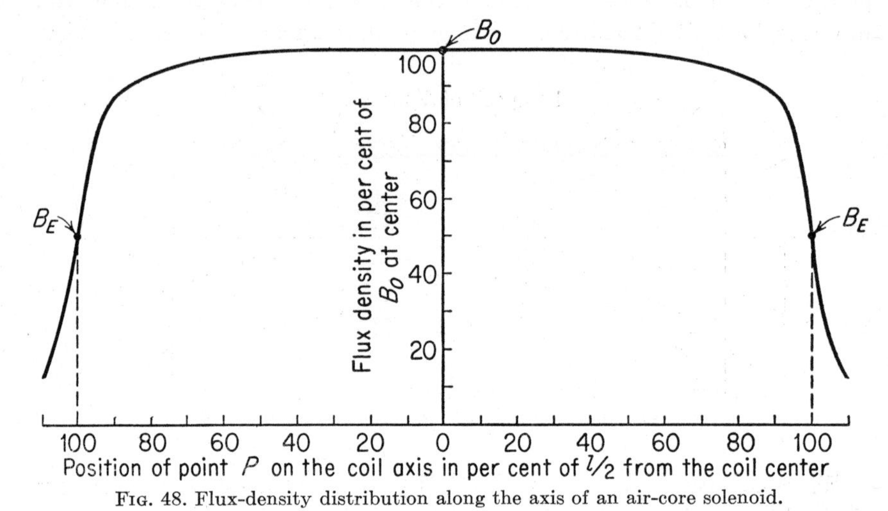

FIG. 48. Flux-density distribution along the axis of an air-core solenoid.

the flux density. Figure 48 is a graphical representation of the flux density along the axis of a solenoid, where the maximum density is given as 100 per cent at the coil center and all other values are indicated as percentages of this maximum value. Note particularly the values of B_O and B_E and the fact that density drops off very rapidly beyond the coil ends.

EXAMPLE 6. A 1,200-turn solenoid, having an average diameter of 3.0 in. and a length of 12 in., carries a current of 40 ma. Calculate the

[1] See Appendix 1F for derivation.

flux density (*a*) at the center of the solenoid, (*b*) at a point on the axis that lines up with one edge of the solenoid.

Solution

(*a*) $$B_O = \frac{2\pi \times 1{,}200 \times 0.04}{10 \times 2.54 \sqrt{(1.5)^2 + (6)^2}} = 1.92 \text{ gauss}$$

(*b*) $$B_E = \frac{2\pi \times 1{,}200 \times 0.04}{10 \times 2.54 \sqrt{(1.5)^2 + (12)^2}} = 0.982 \text{ gauss}$$

Vector Properties of Magnetic Fields. The magnetic flux that is set up at any point in space by a current-carrying-conductor, whether the latter is straight or formed into a coil, has *direction* as well as magnitude; it possesses, in this respect, the properties of a *vector*, i.e., a quantity that is properly defined by both magnitude and direction. The general rules for determining the direction of the field around wires and through coils are given on pages 90–92, and Figs. 46 and 47 illustrate the directional aspect of magnetic fields. This important directional property of a magnetic field means, therefore, that two or more current-carrying conductors or coils will set up independent fields that will combine *vectorially* to create a composite field; moreover, the magnitude and direction of the flux at any point in space are properly determined only if the quantities are treated as vectors. For example, if two straight parallel conductors carry equal currents in opposite directions (Fig. 49*a*), the flux densities

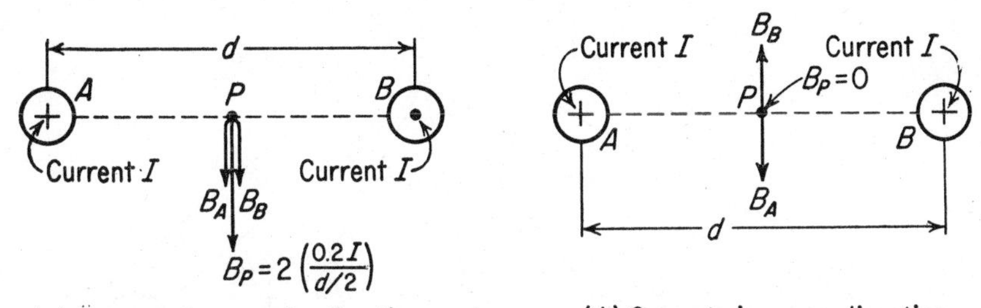

(*a*) Currents in opposite directions (*b*) Currents in same direction

FIG. 49. Flux densities due to parallel current-carrying conductors.

will add directly for points midway between the conductors on the plane that bisects both conductors; in this case the field will be perpendicular to the indicated plane and will have a magnitude equal to $2 \times 0.2I/(d/2)$, where d is the distance between conductors; the left and right current-carrying conductors will produce respectively a clockwise and a counter-clockwise field. However, if the currents are in the same direction the clockwise field of one conductor and the clockwise field of the other conductor will cancel on all mid-points between conductors, and the flux density will be zero there; this is illustrated in Fig. 49*b*.

Consider next two flat coils which carry equal currents and with axes that are collinear. Under this condition (Fig. 50*a*) both fields have the *same* direction—to the right—and the flux density at point P, on the common axis and midway between the coils, will be twice the value given

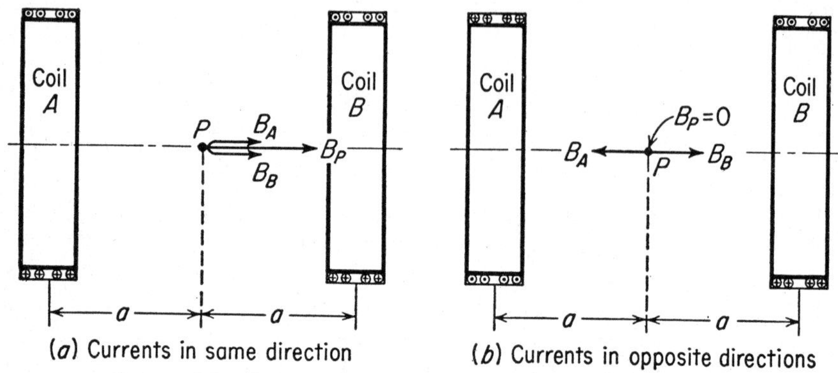

FIG. 50. Flux densities due to collinear flat current-carrying coils.

in Eq. (34). If, on the other hand, the coil currents are oppositely directed, the flux density at point P (Fig. 50*b*) will be zero.

A more general situation involves the determination of the flux density at any point in space due to two unequal currents in a pair of parallel conductors. Referring to Fig. 51, note that B_A, the flux density at point

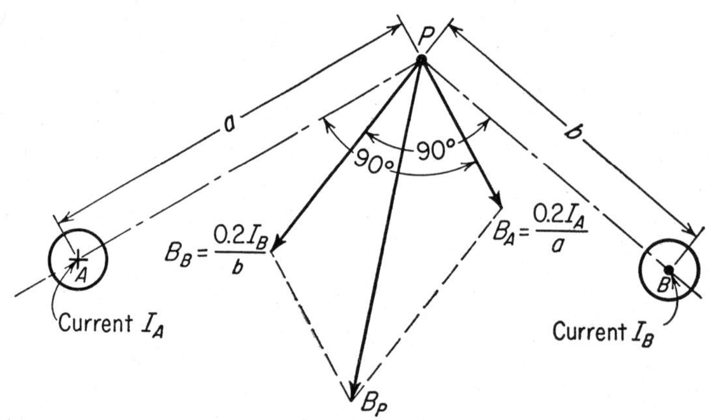

FIG. 51. Sketch illustrating how the flux density at any point P may be determined when two parallel conductors carry different values of current.

P due to conductor A, is $0.2I_A/a$ and has a clockwise direction that is at right angles to the line joining point P and the center of wire A; also, B_B, the flux density at point P due to conductor B, is $0.2I_B/b$ and has a counterclockwise direction that is perpendicular to the line joining point P and the center of wire B. Finally, the resultant flux density at point

P due to both current-carrying conductors is the *vector sum* (the diagonal of the parallelogram) of B_A and B_B.

EXAMPLE 7. Two very long parallel conductors A and B are 12 in. apart and carry currents in opposite directions. If I_A (on the left) = 800 amp away from the observer and I_B (on the right) = 1,200 amp toward the observer, calculate the magnitude and direction of the flux density (*a*) at a point 4 in. from the left conductor on a line joining their centers, (*b*) at a point that is 8 in. above the center of a line joining the centers of the conductors.

Solution

(*a*)

$$B_A = \frac{0.2 \times 800}{4 \times 2.54} = 15.8 \text{ gauss, vertically down}$$

$$B_B = \frac{0.2 \times 1{,}200}{8 \times 2.54} = 11.8 \text{ gauss, vertically down}$$

$$B_P = 15.8 + 11.8 = 27.6 \text{ gauss, vertically down}$$

(*b*) $a = b = \sqrt{(6)^2 + (8)^2} = 10$ in. (see Fig. 51)

$$B_A = \frac{0.2 \times 800}{10 \times 2.54} = 6.3 \text{ gauss, } 36.9° \text{ below horizontal to the right}$$

$$B_B = \frac{0.2 \times 1{,}200}{10 \times 2.54} = 9.45 \text{ gauss, } 36.9° \text{ below horizontal to the left}$$

The resultant horizontal component = $(9.45 \times 0.8) - (6.3 \times 0.8) =$ 2.52 gauss to the left. The resultant vertical component = $(9.45 \times 0.6) + (6.3 \times 0.6) = 9.45$ gauss down.

$$B_P = \sqrt{(2.52)^2 + (9.45)^2} = 9.8 \text{ gauss}$$

The total resultant field at point P is directed at an angle with the horizontal, the sine of which is $9.45/9.8 = 0.965$; the angle with the horizontal is therefore 75°.

EXAMPLE 8. Using the given data of Example 7, calculate the point, on a line joining the centers of conductors A and B, where the flux density is zero.

Solution

Since conductor B carries 1,200 amp and creates a counterclockwise field, and conductor A carries 800 amp and creates a clockwise field, the only place the fields tend to cancel each other completely is to the left of conductor A. Denoting the distance to the left of the center of conductor A by a, it follows that

$$\frac{0.2 \times 800}{2.54a} = \frac{0.2 \times 1{,}200}{2.54(12 + a)}$$

$$(12 + a)800 = 1{,}200a$$

from which

$$a = 24 \text{ in.}$$

Flux Distribution around Parallel Conductors. Conductors that carry currents in *opposite* directions create magnetic fields that are directed oppositely with respect to each other; i.e., one is clockwise (for a current away from the observer), and the other is counterclockwise (for a current toward the observer). When a pair of such conductors are parallel, their independent fields, therefore, tend to react to produce a strengthening effect in the space between wires and a weakening effect in the outside space; this is illustrated in the flux map of Fig. 52 in which the resultant field is represented. Note particularly that the flux density is greatest where the lines of force are shown close together and tends to grow weaker where the flux lines are shown farther apart. This latter point is extremely important because flux maps between magnetic structures that are irregularly shaped are frequently studied to determine regions of high

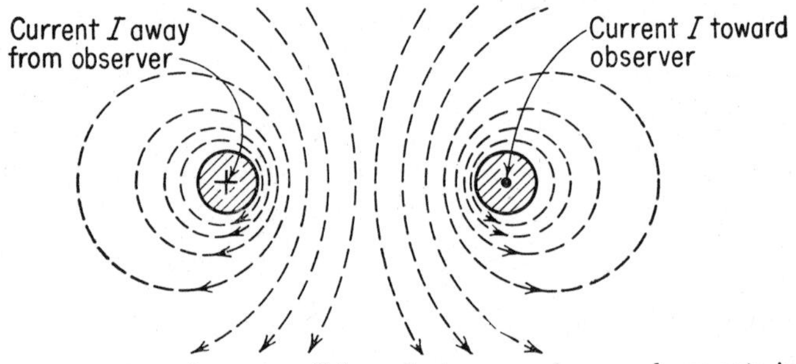

Fig. 52. Flux map around two parallel conductors carrying equal currents in opposite directions.

flux density; intense fields are, in general, to be avoided in the design of electrical apparatus.

When a pair of parallel conductors carry currents in the *same* direction their fields are, of course, similarly directed; i.e., both are either clockwise or counterclockwise; under this condition the independent fields tend to react to produce a weakening effect in the space between the wires, and a strengthening effect in the outside space. In fact, if the two currents are equal, the resultant field is zero at points midway between the conductors on a plane through their centers. The flux map of Fig. 53 illustrates the lines-of-force distribution for a pair of conductors that carry currents away from the observer. Here again, the field is strongest where the lines of force are shown bunched together and tends to become weaker in the spaces where the flux lines are more widely separated.

Force Action between Parallel Conductors. One of the important laws of the magnetic field relates to the interaction of two or more sets of lines of force; it may be stated as follows:

When two or more magnetic fields react with respect to each other they produce a resultant field, which in turn tends to adjust itself so that the maximum number of lines of force are created.

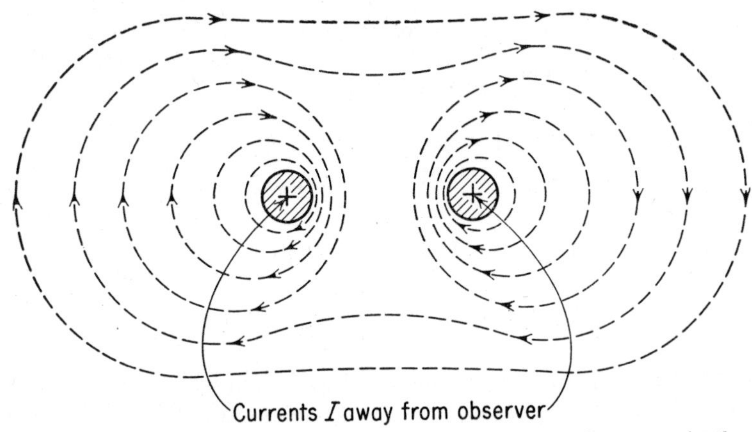

FIG. 53. Flux map around two parallel conductors carrying equal currents in the same direction.

Applying the law to Fig. 52, where two independent fields are produced by oppositely directed currents in a pair of parallel conductors, *the wires attempt to separate* to provide a greater area between them where the resultant flux tends to become a maximum. On the other hand, if the conductors carry currents in the same direction, as in Fig. 53, *the wires will tend to come together* for the reason that the nullifying effect of two oppositely directed fields *between the wires* is diminished as the latter approach one another; the resultant field thereby conforms itself to create the maximum number of lines of force.

The force action between current-carrying conductors was first studied quantitatively by Ampère, and his important *BIl rule* is basic to all electromagnetic relationships that involve current-carrying conductors placed in magnetic fields. Known as *Ampère's rule*, it states that

The force exerted upon a current-carrying conductor that is placed perpendicular to a uniform magnetic field is directly proportional to the flux density (B), *the conductor current* (I), *and the conductor length* (l).

Written in equation form, it becomes

$$F = \frac{BIl}{10} \tag{37}$$

where F = force exerted on the conductor, dynes
B = flux density, gauss
I = current, amp
l = conductor length, cm

EXAMPLE 9. Calculate the force exerted upon a conductor 6 in. long if it carries a current of 180 amp and is placed at right angles to a field whose flux density is 48,000 lines per square inch.

Solution

$$B = \frac{48{,}000}{6.45} = 7{,}450 \text{ gauss}$$

$$l = 6 \times 2.54 = 15.25 \text{ cm}$$

$$F = \frac{7{,}450 \times 180 \times 15.25}{10} = 20.4 \times 10^5 \text{ dynes}$$

Since 980 dynes = 1 gm and 453.6 gm = 1 lb

$$F \text{ (lb)} = \frac{20.4 \times 10^5}{980 \times 453.6} = 4.6$$

Considering two parallel conductors A and B, in which the currents are I_A and I_B, respectively, the flux density at conductor B due to the current I_A in conductor A is $B_A = 0.2I_A/d$, by Eq. (32). The force exerted upon conductor B will therefore be

$$F_B = \frac{B_A \times I_B \times l}{10} = \frac{0.02 I_A I_B l}{d} \quad \text{dynes}$$

Similarly, the flux density at conductor A due to the current I_B in conductor B is $B_B = 0.2I_B/d$. The force exerted upon conductor A will (as it should) also be

$$F_A = \frac{B_B \times I_A \times l}{10} = \frac{0.02 I_A I_B l}{d} \quad \text{dynes}$$

It follows, therefore, that the force exerted upon either conductor is

$$F = \frac{0.02 I_A I_B l}{d} \quad \text{dynes}$$

Using practical units, where l is expressed in feet, d in inches, and F is calculated in pounds,

$$F = \frac{0.02 I_A I_B (l \times 12 \times 2.54)}{(d \times 2.54) \times 980 \times 453.6}$$

whence

$$F = \frac{5.4}{10^7} \times \frac{I_A I_B}{d} \times l \qquad (38)$$

EXAMPLE 10. Two parallel conductors hang in space 4 in. apart, and carry equal currents of 150 amp in opposite directions. Calculate the force on each conductor for an exposure of 40 ft.

Solution

$$F = \frac{5.4}{10^7} \times \frac{150 \times 150}{4} \times 40 = 0.121 \text{ lb} \qquad \text{(force of repulsion)}$$

Force Action in Parallel Multiconductor Systems. Forces, like fluxes, are vector quantities since they possess the properties of magnitude and direction. This was noted in connection with two parallel current-carrying conductors, where it was shown that a force of repulsion exists when the currents are in opposite directions (Fig. 52) and a force of attraction is developed when the currents are in the same direction (Fig. 53). Extending the discussion to three (or more) parallel current-carrying wires, it should first be clear that each one is acted upon by all the others, and that the resultant force on any one conductor is the *vector sum* of the component forces. Thus, for example, if three parallel conductors are placed *in the same plane* and carry currents I_A, I_B, and I_C *in the same direction*, all six individual forces between pairs of conductors will be those of attraction; these are $\overrightarrow{F_{AB}}$, $\overrightarrow{F_{AC}}$, $\overleftarrow{F_{BA}}$, $\overrightarrow{F_{BC}}$, $\overleftarrow{F_{CB}}$, and $\overleftarrow{F_{CA}}$. In this method of notation, observe that the first subscript letter refers to the conductor upon which the force is exerted, and the second subscript letter indicates that it is the current-carrying conductor that creates the flux density at the first wire; also, the arrows above the various terms stand for the directions of the forces. Since two forces act upon each conductor it is a simple matter to determine, by addition or subtraction (in this case), the resultant forces that act upon wires A, B, and C; these are $\overrightarrow{F_A} = \overrightarrow{F_{AB}} + \overrightarrow{F_{AC}}$; $\overrightarrow{F_B} = \overrightarrow{F_{BC}} - \overleftarrow{F_{BA}}$; $\overleftarrow{F_C} = \overleftarrow{F_{CB}} + \overleftarrow{F_{CA}}$. The six component forces and the three resultant forces are represented in Fig. 54. The algebraic sum is zero.

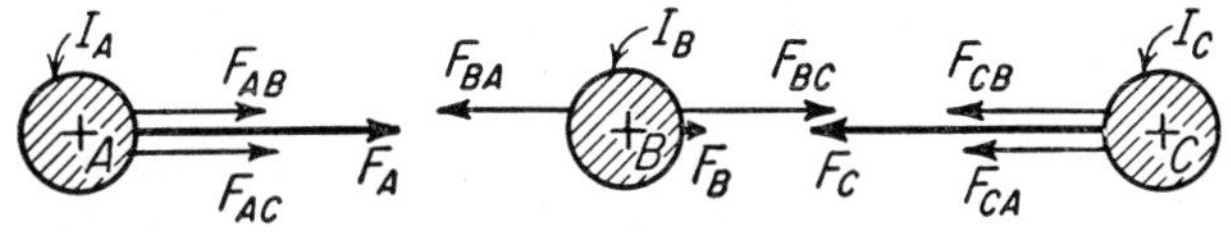

FIG. 54. Sketch illustrating the forces acting on three parallel conductors carrying currents in the same direction.

Consider next three parallel conductors in the same plane, two of which carry currents in the same direction, while the third current is oppositely directed. Referring to Fig. 55, note that currents I_A and I_B are away from the observer, while I_C is indicated toward the observer. Using the same procedure as that given for Fig. 54, the resultant forces are $\overleftarrow{F_A} = \overleftarrow{F_{AC}} - \overrightarrow{F_{AB}}$; $\overleftarrow{F_B} = \overleftarrow{F_{BC}} + \overleftarrow{F_{BA}}$; $\overrightarrow{F_C} = \overrightarrow{F_{CB}} + \overrightarrow{F_{CA}}$.

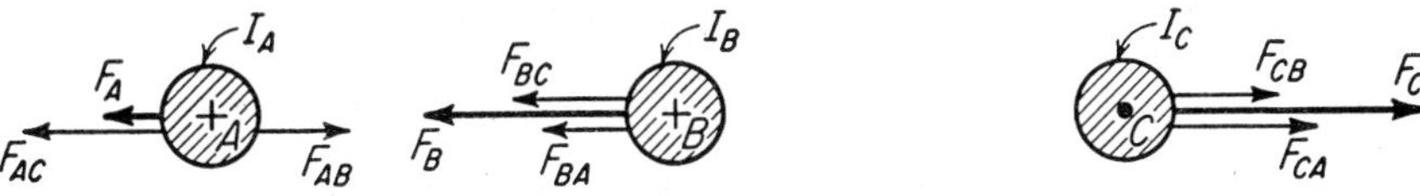

FIG. 55. Sketch illustrating the forces exerted on three parallel conductors, two currents being away from the observer and the other being directed toward the observer.

A more general configuration involves three parallel conductors arranged in the form of a triangle as illustrated by Fig. 56. The individual forces between pairs of wires are, of course, calculated as before, but their directions are always along lines joining the conductor centers. Then, to determine the resultant force at each wire, it is necessary to combine each pair of forces *vectorially*, as was done in Fig. 51 for flux-density magnitudes and directions. Referring to the diagram, note that $F_A = \dot{F}_{AB} + \dot{F}_{AC}$; $\dot{F}_B = \dot{F}_{BA} + \dot{F}_{BC}$; $\dot{F}_C = \dot{F}_{CA} + \dot{F}_{CB}$. (The dots above

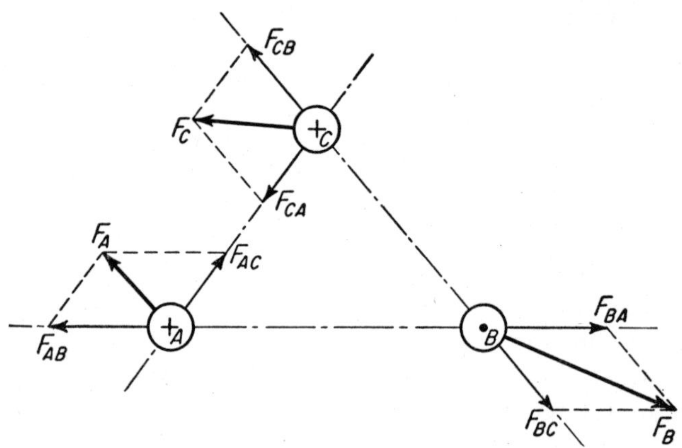

FIG. 56. Sketch illustrating the forces exerted on three parallel conductors arranged in the form of a triangle.

the various values of F indicate that the forces are vectors and are treated as such for calculation purposes.)

EXAMPLE 11. Referring to Fig. 55, assume that $I_A = 800$ amp $I_B = 400$ amp, and $I_C = 1{,}200$ amp. Calculate the values of F_A, F_B, and F_C in pounds per 100 ft, if the distance between adjacent conductors is 6 in.

Solution

$$\overrightarrow{F}_{AB} = \overleftarrow{F}_{BA} = \frac{5.4}{10^7} \times \frac{800 \times 400}{6} \times 100 = 2.88 \text{ lb}$$

$$\overleftarrow{F}_{BC} = \overrightarrow{F}_{CB} = \frac{5.4}{10^7} \times \frac{400 \times 1{,}200}{6} \times 100 = 4.32 \text{ lb}$$

$$\overrightarrow{F}_{CA} = \overleftarrow{F}_{AC} = \frac{5.4}{10^7} \times \frac{800 \times 1{,}200}{6} \times 100 = 8.64 \text{ lb}$$

$$\overleftarrow{F}_A = \overleftarrow{F}_{AC} - \overrightarrow{F}_{AB} = 8.64 - 2.88 = 5.76 \text{ lb}$$

$$\overleftarrow{F}_B = \overleftarrow{F}_{BC} + \overleftarrow{F}_{BA} = 4.32 + 2.88 = 7.20 \text{ lb}$$

$$\overrightarrow{F}_C = \overrightarrow{F}_{CB} + \overrightarrow{F}_{CA} = 4.32 + 8.64 = 12.96$$

Note that the vector sum of F_A, F_B, and F_C is zero.

EXAMPLE 12. Referring to Fig. 56, assume that $I_A = 800$ amp, $I_B = 1{,}200$ amp, and $I_C = 400$ amp. If the conductors are arranged in the form of an equilateral triangle 8 in. between centers, calculate the magnitudes and directions of the forces exerted on conductors A, B, and C per 100 ft.

Solution

$$\dot{F}_{AB} = \dot{F}_{BA} = \frac{5.4}{10^7} \times \frac{800 \times 1{,}200}{8} \times 100 = 6.48 \text{ lb}$$

$$\dot{F}_{BC} = \dot{F}_{CB} = \frac{5.4}{10^7} \times \frac{1{,}200 \times 400}{8} \times 100 = 3.24 \text{ lb}$$

$$\dot{F}_{CA} = \dot{F}_{AC} = \frac{5.4}{10^7} \times \frac{400 \times 800}{8} \times 100 = 2.16 \text{ lb}$$

The three vector diagrams shown in Fig. 57 combine the proper forces in the proper directions (see Fig. 56) to yield the resultant forces acting

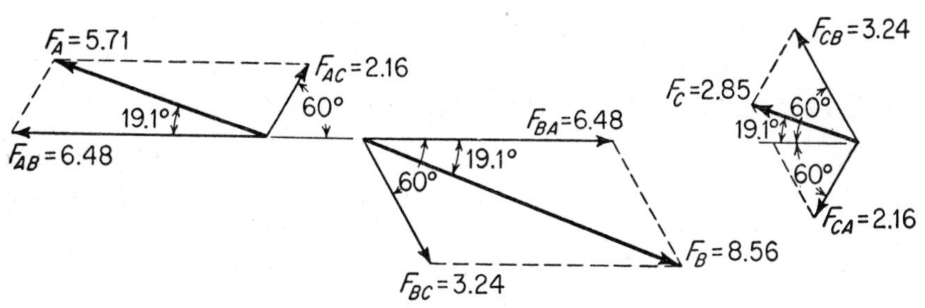

FIG. 57. Vector diagrams showing the solution to Example 12.

on conductors A, B, and C. These were calculated to be $F_A = 5.71$ lb, $F_B = 8.56$ lb, and $F_C = 2.85$, at the angles of 19.1° with the horizontal as indicated. In the method used for these calculations each pair of forces was resolved into horizontal (H) and vertical (V) components, after which the resultant was determined by $\sqrt{H^2 + V^2}$.

Magnitude of the Flux Surrounding a Straight Conductor. The terms *lines of force* (originated by Faraday), *magnetic flux*, or briefly *flux*, are aptly used to indicate the *apparent stress* in the space surrounding a magnet or energized wire or coil; such an *imaginary* field in a state of tension has proved extremely useful in the study of magnetism and associated phenomena. The idea has, in fact, become so powerful a tool in magnetics that the *unit of magnetic flux—one line of force*—has been named the *maxwell*, honoring James Clerk Maxwell who did much fundamental research in the important science of magnetism and electromagnetism.

As previously pointed out, a straight current-carrying conductor in free space creates a magnetic flux that, for its full length, surrounds the wire with a continuous succession of concentric lines of force (see Fig. 41). The number of maxwells that are produced will, obviously, depend upon the magnitude of the current and the length of the wire. Moreover, the field extends into space indefinitely and becomes weaker with increasing distances from the conductor ($B = 0.2I/r$); this means that some limiting radius from the wire must be specified when calculations are made for the flux around a wire. Since the flux at successively increasing radii diminishes differentially, a formula including the factors mentioned must be derived on the basis of a summation—an integration—of an infinite number of varying cylinders of flux, and this leads to the following equation:

$$\Phi = 14Il \log_{10} \frac{R}{r} \qquad (39)[1]$$

where Φ = flux, maxwells
I = current, amp
l = conductor length, ft
R = radius to the desired limiting cylinder
r = radius of the conductor
(R and r are given in the *same* units.)

EXAMPLE 13. A conductor having a diameter of 365 mils carries a current of 180 amp. Calculate the total flux in maxwells, created out in space to a radius of 3 in., for a conductor length of 1 mile.

Solution

$$\Phi = 14 \times 180 \times 5{,}280 \times \log_{10}\left(\frac{3}{0.1825}\right) = 16{,}150{,}000 \text{ maxwells}$$

Magnitude of Flux between Two Parallel Conductors. When two parallel conductors carry currents in opposite directions the flux that is established between them results from the *aiding* action of the individual-conductor fluxes; this is clearly indicated in Fig. 52. Since the resultant flux is a combination of two sets of lines of force, each of which is given by Eq. (39), it must therefore be determined on a basis similar to that given for a single conductor. Considering the special, and most common, case, where the two wires are similar in size and carry equal currents (see Fig. 58), conductor A and conductor B will each create flux equal to

$$\Phi_A = \Phi_B = 14Il \log_{10}\left(\frac{d - r}{r}\right)$$

[1] See Appendix 1G for derivation.

Thus, the resultant total flux between conductors will be twice the value given above, or

$$\Phi = 28Il \log_{10}\left(\frac{d-r}{r}\right) \tag{40}$$

where all terms are as previously defined.

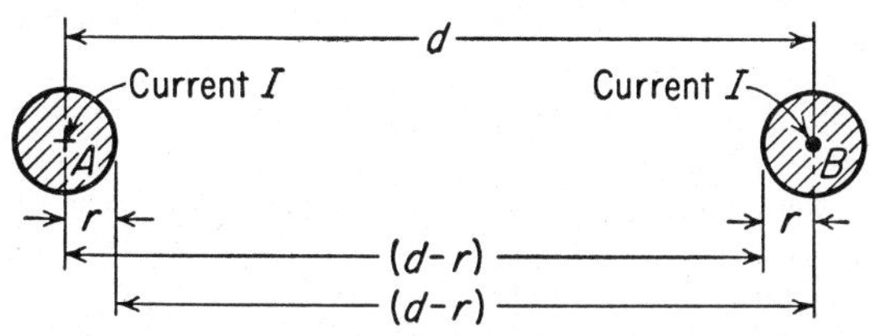

Fig. 58. Sketch used in derivation of Eq. (40).

Example 14. Two parallel conductors carry equal currents of 250 amp in opposite directions. If the wires are 12 in. apart and each one has a diameter of 410 mils, calculate the flux between the wires per 1,000 ft of exposure.

Solution

$$\Phi = 28 \times 250 \times 1{,}000 \times \log_{10}\left(\frac{12 - 0.205}{0.205}\right) = 12.3 \times 10^6 \text{ maxwells}$$

Questions

1. Differentiate between *natural* and *artificial magnets.*
2. Why is a natural magnet called a *lodestone?*
3. Distinguish between *temporary* and *permanent magnets.*
4. Name several types of high-grade permanent-magnet materials.
5. Explain how artificial magnets may be created.
6. What is meant by *magnet pole?* Where are these poles formed?
7. Explain how the polarity (north or south) of a magnet may be determined.
8. State the *first law of magnetism.*
9. What is meant by a *magnetic field? lines of force?*
10. How are lines of force distributed around uniformly shaped magnets?
11. Make sketches showing flux distributions around bar-, U-, and E-shaped magnets.
12. What happens when a magnetic substance is placed in an otherwise symmetrical magnetic field?
13. Where does the greatest flux density exist in the space surrounding a magnet?
14. How is it possible to make a magnet by induction? Where are the north and south poles formed in such a magnet?
15. State the *second law of magnetism* relating to the arrangement of lines of force.
16. What is meant by *electromagnetism?*
17. State the rule to determine the direction of the magnetic field around a straight current-carrying conductor.
18. Where is the magnetic field densest around a current-carrying wire?
19. How is the flux density related to the current and distance from a current-carrying wire?
20. State the rule to determine the direction of the magnetic field through a solenoid.

21. State the rule to determine the polarity of an electromagnet.
22. Upon what factors does the strength of an electromagnet depend?
23. Why is a U-shaped electromagnet much stronger than an equivalent bar electromagnet?
24. What two factors determine the flux density at a given point from a current-carrying wire with respect to an incremental length of the wire?
25. Assuming no change in current, how will the flux density at a given point from a straight wire be affected if the latter is lengthened? shortened?
26. Assuming no change in current, how will the flux density at a given point from a straight wire be affected if the wire is bent into a circle having a radius equal to the original distance from the wire?
27. In a flat coil that is energized, where, along the coil axis, is the flux density a maximum?
28. In a long solenoid that is energized, where, along the axis, is the flux density a maximum?
29. On the axis of a long solenoid, how does the flux density at the end compare with the value at the center?
30. Why does a magnetic field possess the properties of a vector?
31. What happens when two freely suspended parallel conductors carry currents in opposite directions? in the same direction? Explain carefully.
32. Where is the flux density zero when two parallel conductors carry currents in opposite directions? in the same direction? Explain carefully.
33. When two flat coils are collinear and separated by a distance d, where is the flux density zero, when the windings carry currents in opposite directions?
34. State the rule that relates to the field that results when two magnetic fields react with each other.
35. Applying the rule of Question 34, explain why two parallel conductors attempt to separate when they carry currents in opposite directions.
36. Applying the rule of Question 34, explain why two parallel conductors attempt to come together when they carry currents in the same direction.
37. State *Ampère's rule* relating to the force action exerted upon a current-carrying conductor.
38. When three or more parallel conductors carry currents, how do the exerted forces act upon the individual wires? Illustrate the answer, using examples such as three conductors in one plane, and three conductors arranged to form a triangle.
39. What is the unit of magnetic flux?
40. Upon what factors does the flux surrounding a current-carrying conductor depend?
41. Upon what factors does the flux between two parallel conductors depend when the currents are in opposite directions?

Problems

1. Calculate the flux density at a point 3 in. from a very long straight conductor that carries a current of 600 amp.
2. A conductor 24 in. long is placed in a vertical position and carries a current of 2,000 amp upward. What is the magnitude and direction of the flux density to the right of the wire directly opposite its center?
3. For the conductor of Prob. 2, calculate the flux density (*a*) 12 in. to the right of one end, (*b*) 12 in. to the right of a point that is 12 in. below the wire.
4. A flat coil containing 800 turns of wire is wound in the form of a square, 4 in. on a side. If the current is 0.62 amp, calculate the flux density at the center of the coil.

5. A conductor 8 in. long produces a certain flux density B at a point 3 in. opposite its center when it carries a given current. At what distance from the center of the conductor will the flux density have the same value B if the wire is very long and carries the same current?
6. What is the flux density at any point from the end of a finite length of a current-carrying conductor, along its axis?
7. A flat coil containing 450 turns of wire is wound on a rectangular form 6 by 8 in. Calculate the flux density at the center of the coil for a current of 0.37 amp.
8. How far from the surface of a long current-carrying conductor, whose diameter is 0.46 in., will the flux density be one-half of the density at the surface?
9. A flat coil having 2,020 turns has an average diameter of 2.5 in. If the current is 150 ma, calculate (*a*) the flux density at the center of the coil, (*b*) the flux density at a point on the axis 1.25 in. from the center.
10. A 900-turn solenoid, having an average diameter of 2.0 in. and a length of 6 in., carries a current of 0.35 amp. Calculate the flux density (*a*) at the center of the solenoid, (*b*) at a point on the axis in line with an end turn.
11. Using the graph of Fig. 48, calculate the flux density on the axis of the solenoid of Prob. 10, at a point that is (*a*) 2.4 in. from the center, (*b*) 3.3 in. from the center.
12. A pair of long parallel conductors are 12 cm apart and carry equal currents of 3,000 amp in opposite directions. Calculate the flux density (*a*) at a point midway between the wires on a line joining their centers, (*b*) at a point that is located 6 cm above the one indicated for (*a*).
13. In Prob. 12, will the flux density be zero at any point on a line joining the wire centers? Explain.
14. Two long parallel conductors, A on the left and B on the right, are 6 in. apart. If $I_A = 900$ amp toward the observer, and $I_B = 600$ amp away from the observer, calculate the magnitude and the direction of the flux density (*a*) at a point midway between wires on a line joining their centers, (*b*) at a point 3.6 in. from conductor A toward B on a line joining the wire centers.
15. Using the given data of Prob. 14, calculate the flux density on the line joining the wire centers (*a*) at the inside surface of wire A, (*b*) on the inside surface of wire B. (The wire diameters are 0.46 in. each.)
16. Solve Prob. 15 for (*a*) the outside surface of wire A, (*b*) the outside surface of wire B.
17. Using the given data of Prob. 14, calculate the point, on a line joining the centers of conductors A and B, where the flux density is zero.
18. Using the given data of Prob. 14, calculate the magnitude and direction of the flux density at a point that is 8 in. directly above conductor A.
19. Each of the conductors in the armature of a motor is 8 in. long and is at right angles to a magnetic field whose density is 58,000 lines per square inch. When the current is 230 amp, calculate the force exerted on the wire.
20. A bus bar is supported by insulators that are 36 in. apart. What force is exerted on each section of the bus bar under short-circuit conditions when the current is 25,000 amp, and the perpendicularly directed flux density is 500 gauss?
21. Calculate the magnitude and direction of the force per 100 ft exerted between two parallel conductors, if they have a separation of 6 in. and carry equal currents of 225 amp in opposite directions.
22. Three parallel conductors A (on the left), B, and C (on the right) lie in the same plane and are 4 in. apart. If $I_A = 500$ amp toward the observer, $I_B = 750$ amp away from the observer, and $I_C = 250$ amp toward the observer, calculate the magnitude and direction of the force exerted on wire C.

23. Three parallel conductors are arranged to form a right triangle. *A* on the left, and *B* on the right are in a horizontal plane, and *C* is directly above *A*; also, *A* is 6 in. from *B* and 8 in. from *C*. If $I_A = 300$ amp toward the observer, $I_B = 500$ amp toward the observer, and $I_C = 800$ amp away from the observer, calculate the force exerted on wire *B* per 100 ft of exposure.

24. Three parallel conductors 50 ft long are arranged to form an equilateral triangle 12 in. apart. *A* (on the left) and *B* are in a horizontal plane. If $I_A = I_B = 450$ amp toward the observer, and $I_C = 900$ amp away from the observer, calculate the magnitude and the direction of the force exerted on wire *B*.

25. A No. 4 conductor (diameter = 0.204 in.) carries a current of 80 amp. How much flux is created per 1,000 ft in the space surrounding the wire to a radius of 6 in.?

26. Calculate the flux created between two such conductors as in Prob. 25 when they are parallel and 6 in. apart, and carry equal currents of 80 amp in opposite directions.

CHAPTER 6

MAGNETIC CIRCUITS

Electric- and Magnetic-circuit Comparisons. From previous discussions it should be clear that an electric circuit is a system of electrical conductors through which a current (or currents) of electricity may be transmitted upon the application of an electromotive force (or electromotive forces). Similarly, a *magnetic circuit* is a system of magnetic conductors in which magnetism, i.e., flux, may be established upon the application of a *magnetomotive force* (or magnetomotive forces), abbreviated *mmf*. Moreover, just as a generator or battery functions as a *source of emf* to cause a current in an electric circuit, so does a current-carrying wire or coil act as a *source of mmf* to create the magnetism in a magnetic circuit; from these generalizations it is therefore proper to liken mmf to emf, and flux (maxwells) to current (amperes). A third analogy may be made between the opposition to current in the electric circuit and the opposition to the establishment of flux in the magnetic circuit; in the former it is resistance, and in the latter it is termed *reluctance*. Now then, since the flux that is produced is directly proportional to the mmf and inversely proportional to the reluctance, in the same way that the current is directly proportional to the emf and inversely proportional to the resistance, the relations in the two kinds of circuit may be compared on the basis of an electrical Ohm's law and a so-called magnetic Ohm's law, thus:

$$\text{Current} = \frac{\text{emf}}{\text{resistance}} \qquad \text{Flux} = \frac{\text{mmf}}{\text{reluctance}}$$

In addition to the similarities indicated, there are several important differences between electric and magnetic circuits. For example, in an electric circuit the current may be reduced to zero by merely opening the main switch; under this condition *there is an emf but no current.* In a magnetic circuit, however, there is no such thing as a magnetic switch that may be opened or closed; *if an mmf exists, there will be flux,* because the difference between the reluctance of air and that of solid magnetic substances is not so great as the difference in resistance between electrical conductors and insulators. Another significant difference concerns the resistance and reluctance properties of electrical and magnetic substances. Except for the comparatively minor changes resulting from temperature variations, the resistance of an electrical conductor is substantially constant; i.e., resistance is not affected by the magnitude of the current. On the other hand, reluctance of a magnetic substance (other than air) is very definitely a function of the flux that is created; to put it another way, flux and reluctance are so interrelated that for a given mmf, the reluctance depends on the flux density, and vice versa. This sometimes means that the solutions of some kinds of magnetic-circuit problems are often difficult and indefinite, for the reason that the desired value of flux depends upon a property of the material, which, in turn, is related to the very result (the flux) being sought.

General Magnetic-circuit Law. In a simple magnetic circuit consisting of a single ferromagnetic substance that is magnetized by a current-carrying coil of wire, the magnitude of the flux in maxwells will be determined by, among other things, the magnetomotive force, which, in turn, depends upon the number of turns N in the coil and the coil current I; as usually stated, Φ *is proportional to ampere-turns* NI. Since the flux is also inversely proportional to the reluctance $\mathcal{R}$ of the magnetic circuit, the general Ohm's law equation for the magnetic circuit may be written as follows:

$$\Phi = \frac{\mathcal{F}}{\mathcal{R}} \tag{41}$$

where Φ = flux, maxwells
$\mathcal{F}$ = magnetomotive force, gilberts
$\mathcal{R}$ = reluctance (unit unnamed)

Like resistance, for electrical conductors, the reluctance $\mathcal{R}$ is directly proportional to the length and inversely proportional to the area of the magnetic circuit. Moreover, since it is desirable to use air as a *basis of comparison* when rating ferromagnetic substances, the permeability of air has arbitrarily been assigned a value of unity; this implies that the permeabilities of all ferromagnetic substances are greater than unity, where the permeability μ represents the ratio of the flux that is created in the material to the flux that will exist in the same space when the substance is replaced by air, the number of ampere-turns remaining unchanged. In equation form reluctance then becomes

$$\mathcal{R} = \frac{l}{\mu A} \tag{42}$$

where l = length of magnetic circuit, cm
A = cross-sectional area of magnetic circuit, sq cm
μ = permeability

The use of cgs units and the arbitrary choice of unity for the permeability of air in the equation for reluctance $\mathcal{R}$ make it necessary to employ a proportionality factor of 0.4π to convert ampere-turns NI to mmf in gilberts $\mathcal{F}$, if the flux equation (41) is to be valid in terms of maxwells, thus:

$$\mathcal{F} = 0.4\pi NI \tag{43}$$

Combining Eqs. (41), (42), and (43), the general expression for the flux that is set up in a simple magnetic circuit becomes

$$\Phi = \frac{0.4\pi NI}{l/\mu A} = \frac{0.4\pi NI\mu A}{l} \tag{44}$$

A much more desirable form of Eq. (44) involves a rearrangement of terms, the use of the more common *inch* units, and a flux-density quantity B to replace Φ/A. Rearranging Eq. (44),

$$NI = \left(\frac{\Phi}{A}\right)\left(\frac{l}{0.4\pi\mu}\right) = B\frac{l}{0.4\pi\mu}$$

Converting centimeter units to inch units, this becomes

$$NI = \left(\frac{B_{\text{in.}}}{6.45}\right)\left(\frac{l_{\text{in.}} \times 2.54}{0.4\pi\mu}\right) = 0.313\left(\frac{B_{\text{in.}}}{\mu}\right)l_{\text{in.}} \tag{45}$$

where $B_{\text{in.}}$ = flux density, lines per *square inch*
$l_{\text{in.}}$ = length of magnetic circuit, *inches*

Example 1. A toroid (see Fig. 59) of cast steel has an average diameter of 5 in. and a cross-sectional area of 0.72 sq in. If it is desired to establish a flux density of 70,000 lines per square inch in the core, under which condition the permeability of the iron is 1,200, calculate the current that must be sent through a properly wound 900-turn winding.

Solution

$$NI = 0.313\left(\frac{70{,}000}{1{,}200}\right)(\pi \times 5) = 287 \text{ amp-turns}$$

$$I = \frac{\text{amp-turns}}{\text{turns}} = \frac{287}{900} = 0.319 \text{ amp}$$

Although Eq. (45) is quite general, since it applies to all magnetic circuits in which flux is established, it will be desirable to write a similar formula for nonmagnetic substances, and particularly air. Since the permeability of the latter is unity,

$$NI_{\text{air}} = 0.313B_{\text{in.}}\delta \tag{46}$$

where δ = air-gap length, in.

EXAMPLE 2. Calculate the number of ampere-turns that will be required to establish a flux density of 48,000 lines of force in the ⅛-in. air gap of a relay.

Solution

$$NI_{\text{air}} = 0.313 \times 48{,}000 \times 0.125 = 1{,}878 \text{ amp-turns}$$

Magnetization of Ferromagnetic Substances. It was pointed out in Chap. 5 (p. 92) that the strength of an electromagnet, in terms of the number of lines of force it creates, will depend, among other things, upon the number of ampere-turns developed by the exciting winding. In a given electromagnet having a fixed number of turns of wire the flux will therefore depend upon the value of the current. If an electric circuit is provided with a potential divider (Fig. 59), it is possible to vary the flux (or flux density) within certain limits. Starting with a completely

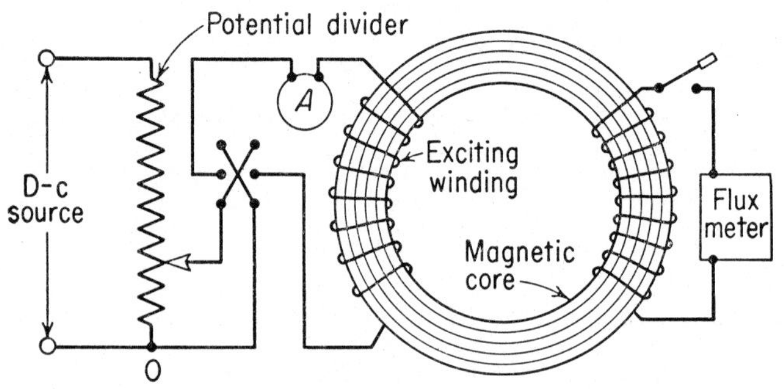

FIG. 59. Circuit for magnetization-curve measurements in a toroid.

demagnetized core, with the slider at point O, it is found experimentally that the flux density will increase in direct proportion with an increase in ampere-turns for a rather narrow range; beyond the range where B is proportional to NI, the flux density increases less rapidly with further increases in magnetizing force. Curves plotted from experimental data will generally appear like those of Fig. 60; note particularly the limited straight-line ranges for the three kinds of material, in each case up to the so-called *knee*, and the tendency of the curves to flatten out at comparatively high values of magnetizing force.

Such curves—called *magnetization curves*—in which the flux density is plotted with respect to the *magnetizing force*, i.e., the required ampere-turns per unit length of magnetic substance, are extremely important to the designer of all types of electromagnetic devices; with their aid it is possible to determine in advance the core dimensions, shape, and number of turns and wire size of the exciting winding. In that portion of magnetization curve that lies above the knee the core material is said to be in a state of *saturation*, although, of course, only slightly so at first and

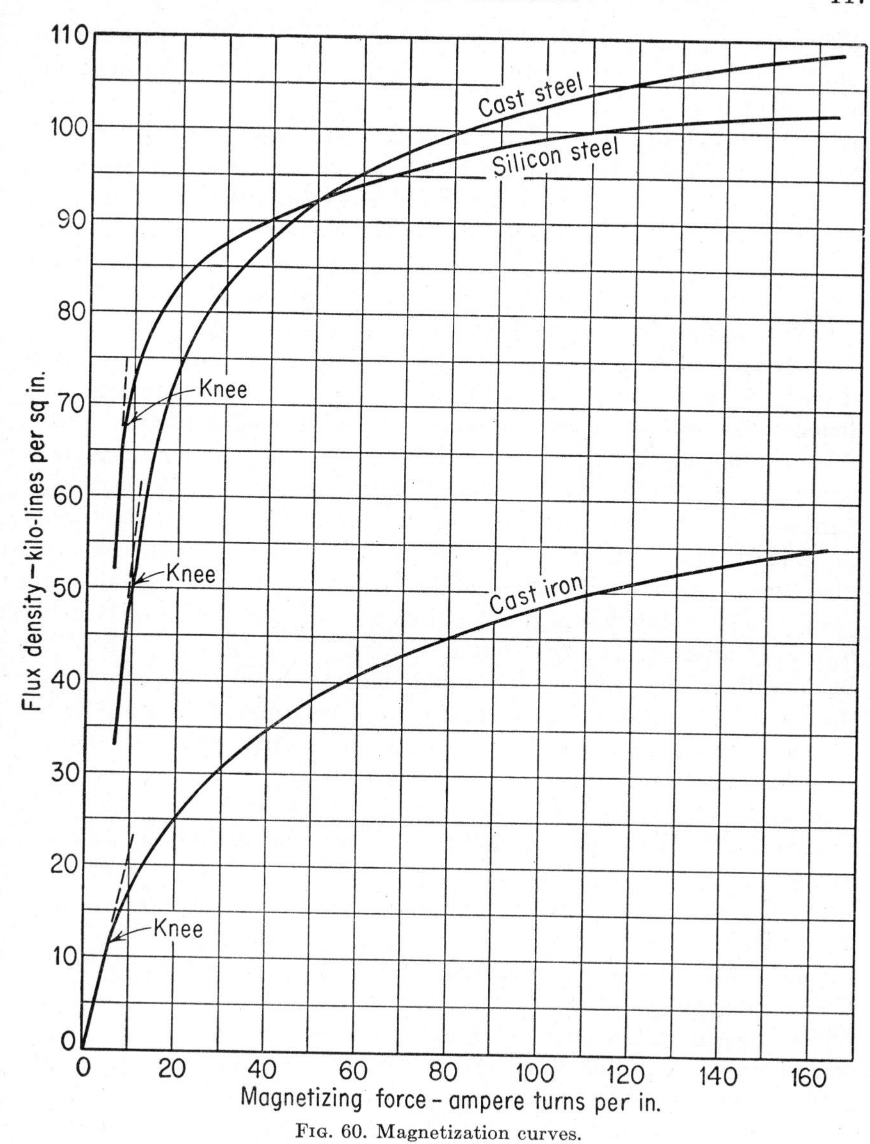

FIG. 60. Magnetization curves.

more completely at high values of ampere-turns. It must be understood that saturation is a condition of the magnetic core that indicates that the flux increases less rapidly than does the magnetizing force. It is aptly explained by the Weber-Ewing theory of magnetic phenomena, which assumes that each of the substance's molecules is an elemental magnet with its own north and south pole. When the magnetizing force is zero and the substance is completely demagnetized, the tiny magnets are arranged at random so that north and south poles tend to neutralize one another; under this condition the material presents no distinguishing magnetic poles. As the magnetizing force is applied, however, the pole-formed molecules tend to orient themselves with north and south poles lining up in similar directions; moreover, as increasing numbers of molecules are lined up the magnetizing force becomes less effective in its ability to strengthen the magnet, under which condition the latter is said to attain the condition of saturation. Complete saturation is obviously not possible, although this tendency is closely approached at extremely high values of magnetization. The theory, incidentally, also explains the *retentive property* of ferromagnetic substances, which accounts for *residual magnetism,* as well as the need for a demagnetizing force to completely demagnetize iron; these are considered in a subsequent section.

In practice, electromagnets are rarely operated at very high degrees of saturation, since this would mean inefficient use of electric power. Furthermore, they are nearly always made to operate at densities above the knee because, under this condition, the commonly used irons and steels tend to remain more or less stable; this means that the flux does not change appreciably when the exciting current varies slightly for one reason or another. In the electric generator, for example, where the generated emf depends directly upon the flux density, the iron in the electromagnets must be worked in regions well above the knee of the magnetization curve, for otherwise the voltage that is responsible for magnetizing current would fluctuate annoyingly.

All irons and steels behave in essentially the same way when magnetized, since they follow the same curve pattern as those indicated in Fig. 60. But different *grades* of material differ widely when comparison is made between specimens on the basis of the *extent* to which they become magnetized for the same value of magnetizing force. This is well illustrated by Fig. 60 where, for example, the curves for cast steel and silicon steel are well above the graph for cast iron; also, comparing cast steel with silicon steel, note that the latter develops more flux than the former at densities up to about 93,000 lines per square inch and reverses this trend at the higher flux densities. Concerning ferromagnetic substances in general, it can be stated that the behavior in creating flux under the influence of magnetizing force, i.e., the *quality* of the substance, depends, among other things, upon (1) its metallurgical composition, (2) the heat-treatment to which it is subjected, (3) the thickness of the material, and (4) the value of the magnetizing force.

Permeability. As represented in Eq. (42), permeability μ is a *measure* of the reluctance of magnetic substance; in this respect it therefore determines how much flux will be created by a given number of ampere-turns [see Eq. (44)]. Customary practical values of permeability, based upon a rating scale of unity for air, vary between several hundred and perhaps 2,500 or more; special substances, which, for various reasons, are not generally employed, have been developed to have permeabilities well over 100,000. Considered in another way, permeability may be regarded as a sort of "goodness index," since it indicates how much more effective a given magnetizing force will be when a magnetic substance replaces air (or its equivalent). Furthermore, two magnetic substances may be compared on the basis of their permeabilities; thus, for example, if cast iron and cast steel have permeabilities of 150 and 1,500, respectively, *at a given flux density*, cast steel would be said to be 10 times "as good" as cast iron. Or, to illustrate the example in more practical terms, an electromagnet constructed with a cast-iron core will require 10 times as many ampere-turns to produce the same flux as one similar in every respect but with a cast-steel core.

The frequent mention of *permeability at a given density* was intentional, and was meant to leave the impression that *the permeability depends not only upon the material but also upon the flux density* at which it operates. The reason for this is that permeability is a function of both flux density and magnetizing force, and, as the curves of Fig. 60 clearly show, $B_{\text{in.}}$ is *not* directly proportional to $NI/l_{\text{in.}}$ Rewriting Eq. (45),

$$\mu = 0.313 \frac{B_{\text{in.}}}{NI/l_{\text{in.}}} \tag{47}$$

This equation indicates that the permeability is a measure of the *slope* of the magnetization curve because it is determined by the ratio of the flux density $B_{\text{in.}}$ to the magnetizing force $NI/l_{\text{in.}}$; since the magnetization curve for ferromagnetic materials does not have a constant slope, i.e., a constant ratio of $B_{\text{in.}}/NI$ per inch, it follows that μ must vary for different values of flux density.

EXAMPLE 3. Referring to Fig. 60, determine the permeabilities of cast iron, cast steel, and silicon steel for flux densities of 45,000, 75,000, and 80,000 lines per square inch, respectively.

Solution

For cast iron: $$\mu = 0.313 \frac{45{,}000}{80} = 176$$

For cast steel: $$\mu = 0.313 \frac{75{,}000}{21} = 1{,}120$$

For silicon steel: $$\mu = 0.313 \frac{80{,}000}{15} = 1{,}670$$

Typical permeability vs. flux-density curves for three kinds of material are given in Fig. 61; data for these graphs were taken from magnetization curves similar to those of Fig. 60, and calculations were made as in Example 3. It is important to observe the wide variation of values of μ, and to understand that electromagnets perform most satisfactorily when the cores operate at flux densities that yield high permeabilities.

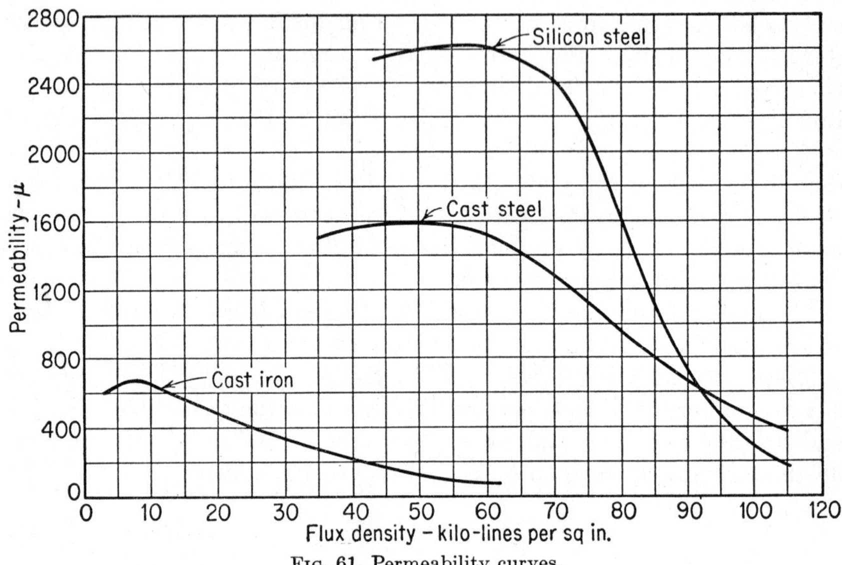

FIG. 61. Permeability curves.

Tractive Force of an Electromagnet. When a block of iron is placed near the ends, i.e., poles, of an electromagnet a tractive effort will be exerted *along* the magnetic lines of force. This force of attraction between magnet and iron is explained by assigning an important property to the imaginary flux, namely, *that property which tends to make the flux contract and become as short as possible.* The fact that there is always an air space, usually called an *air gap*, between surfaces, means, of course, that the lines of force must cross it in passing from one iron section to the other. And since the air gap is obviously the only place where the flux can be shortened when the surfaces move closer together, a force of attraction exists there.

The tractive effort is clearly a function of the air-gap flux density and the area of the air gap. Maxwell's formula, resulting from his fundamental investigations of electromagnetic theory, is

$$\text{Force (dynes)} = \frac{B^2 A}{8\pi}$$

Since it is desirable to modify the terms in the formula to make use of more practical units, it becomes

$$\text{Force (lb)} = \frac{(B_{\text{in.}}/6.45)^2(A \times 6.45)}{8\pi \times 980 \times 453.6}$$

from which

$$F = \frac{B_{\text{in.}}^2 A_{\text{in.}}}{72 \times 10^6} \quad \text{lb} \tag{48}$$

EXAMPLE 4. Each of the pole faces of an electromagnet has an area of 6 sq in. If the exciting winding creates a flux density of 50,000 lines per square inch in the air gap between magnet poles and a smooth block of iron, calculate the tractive effort exerted upon the latter. (Assume a U-type electromagnet like Fig. 62.)

Solution

$$F = \frac{(50{,}000)^2 \times (2 \times 6)}{72 \times 10^6} = 417 \text{ lb}$$

The U-type Electromagnet. An electromagnet that is extremely common to many devices and machines is the symmetrical U-type. It consists of a pair of similar pole cores, which may be circular, square, or rectangular in section, a yoke that fastens the poles together, and an armature upon which the electromagnet operates. The exciting winding is sometimes placed around the yoke section but is more often wound in two sections with each coil placed over one of the poles; in the latter case the coils may be connected in series or parallel. Figure 62 illustrates

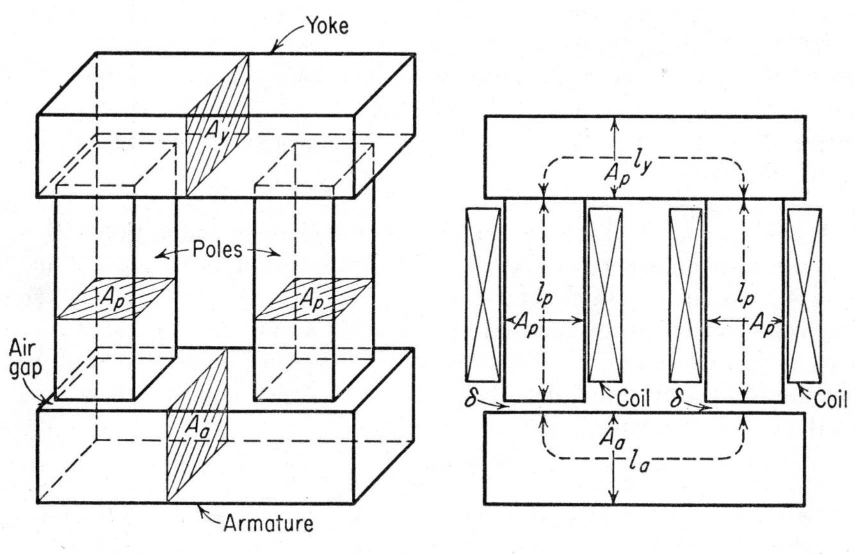

FIG. 62. Drawings illustrating a symmetrical U-type electromagnet, with all identifying dimensions.

an electromagnet of this type, with all identifying dimensions indicated thereon. The complete magnetic circuit consists of four distinct parts *in series;* these are:

1. The yoke section, whose length and area are, respectively, l_y and A_y.
2. The pole cores, whose length and area are, respectively, $2l_p$ and A_p.
3. The armature core, whose length and area are, respectively, l_a and A_a.
4. The air gaps, whose length and area are, respectively, 2δ and A_p.

Since the flux in every part of the series magnetic circuit is the same, the lines of force are set up as continuous closed paths, passing freely from section to section. Where the flux must bend around as it passes from one part to another, the length of that portion of the magnetic circuit must be averaged; this will be noted for lengths l_y and l_a. Another important point that should be recognized is that the flux densities in the various parts will be related to each other as the *inverse ratio* of their areas; this is obviously true because the flux is constant throughout (neglecting some flux that may pass across the air space between the vertical sides of the pole cores, i.e., leakage flux), and $B = \Phi/A$. The air-gap lengths are sometimes difficult to determine accurately but, since these consume a considerable per cent of the total ampere-turns, should nevertheless be measured or estimated as carefully as possible.

Bearing the foregoing statements in mind, it will now be desirable to consider a particular U-type electromagnet for which it will be required to determine the number of ampere-turns to set up a given air-gap flux density. A straightforward problem such as this can best be solved by tabulating such items as lengths, areas, flux densities, ampere-turns per inch for the various magnetic substances (referring to appropriate curves), ampere-turns per magnetic section, air-gap ampere-turns, and total ampere-turns.

EXAMPLE 5. The following particulars are given in connection with a U-type electromagnet such as that illustrated by Fig. 62: $l_p = 4$ in., $l_y = 4.75$ in., $l_a = 5.75$ in., $A_p = 4.25$ sq in., $A_y = 5$ sq in., $A_a = 6.5$ sq in., yoke and pole core material = cast steel, armature-core material = cast iron. Calculate the total number of ampere-turns that will be required to set up a flux density of 70,000 lines per square inch in each of the 0.06-in. air gaps.

Solution

As previously indicated, it will be helpful to prepare a table to systematically show all necessary data and calculations. For $NI/l_{\text{in.}}$ values for iron and steel, reference is made to the magnetization curves of Fig. 60.

Part of circuit	Material	$l_{in.}$	$A_{in.}$	$B_{in.}$	$NI/l_{in.}$	NI
Poles.......	Cast steel	8.0	4.25	70,000	17	136
Yoke.......	Cast steel	4.75	5.0	$70{,}000 \times \frac{4.25}{5.0} = 59{,}500$	13	62
Armature...	Cast iron	5.75	6.5	$70{,}000 \times \frac{4.25}{6.5} = 45{,}700$	84	483
Gaps........	Air	0.12	4.25	(Neglect fringing) 70,000	$0.313 \times 70{,}000 = 21{,}910$	2,629
Total						3,310

It is interesting to note that the two short air gaps ($\delta = 0.12$ in.) require nearly 80 per cent of the total number of ampere-turns.

A more difficult kind of problem, one that is not so straightforward as illustrative Example 5, and which must generally be solved by a trial-and-error method, involves the calculation of the air-gap flux density when the total exciting ampere-turns are known. The difficulty arises from the fact that it is necessary to match the *given total* NI with the sum of the individual values of ampere-turns for several portions of the series magnetic circuit and, at the same time, have the *desired flux density* yield values of $NI/l_{in.}$ from the various magnetization curves that will properly conform to the afore-mentioned total NI. The difficulty is, moreover, multiplied when the magnetic circuit consists of several kinds of magnetic substance where the flux densities all differ from one another. The following example, greatly simplified, illustrates the calculation procedure when the magnetic circuit is made up of one kind of iron and the air gaps.

EXAMPLE 6. Assume that the U-type electromagnet of Fig. 62 and the armature are cast iron and that the total length of the iron in the magnetic circuit is 15 in. If the cross-sectional area of the flux path throughout the circuit is constant, and each air gap has a length of 0.064 in., calculate the flux density when the exciting winding develops 3,000 amp-turns.

Solution

Trial 1: Assume $B_{in.} = 42{,}000$ lines / square inch. $NI/l_{in.}$ (for iron) $= 64$.

$$NI \text{ for air} = 0.313 \times 42{,}000 \times 0.128 = 1{,}685$$
$$NI \text{ for iron} = 64 \times 15 = 960$$
$$\text{Total} = 2{,}645 \quad (\textit{too low})$$

Trial 2: Assume $B_{in.} = 47{,}000$ lines / square inch. $NI/l_{in.}$ (for iron) $= 89$.

$$NI \text{ for air} = 0.313 \times 47{,}000 \times 0.128 = 1{,}880$$
$$NI \text{ for iron} = 89 \times 15 = 1{,}335$$
$$\text{Total} = 3{,}215 \quad (\textit{too high})$$

Trial 3: Assume $B_{\text{in.}} = 45{,}000$ lines / square inch. $NI/l_{\text{in.}}$ (for iron) $= 80$.

$$NI \text{ for air} = 0.313 \times 45{,}000 \times 0.128 = 1{,}800$$
$$NI \text{ for iron} = 80 \times 15 = 1{,}200$$
$$\text{Total} = 3{,}000 \qquad (\textit{correct})$$

The E-type Electromagnet. Another widely used electromagnet construction employs a symmetrical E-shaped core with a single coil of wire placed around the center leg. As illustrated in Fig. 63, the exciting winding acts on *two magnetic circuits in parallel,* in much the same way as a single source of emf energizes two equal resistors in parallel. As a

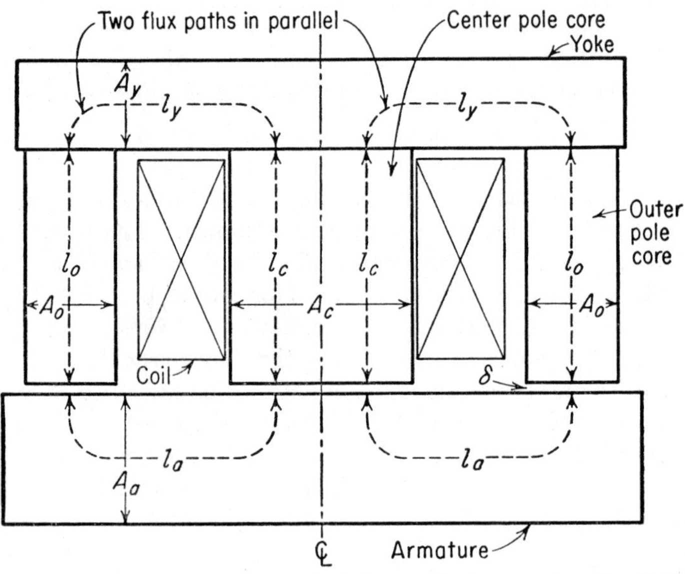

FIG. 63. Drawing illustrating a symmetrical E-type electromagnet, with all identifying dimensions.

result of the two similar parallel flux paths, the end of the center pole core, having a given polarity, serves with a pair of *similarly polarized outer pole cores.* Neglecting leakage flux through the air space between poles, this means that the center-core flux—the total flux—will be twice the outer-core flux; moreover, if all pole-core flux densities are to be equal, and this is frequently so, the cross section of the center core must be twice as much as each of the outer pole cores. All this therefore leads to the observation that a symmetrical E-type electromagnet may be regarded as made up of two identical U-type electromagnets with pole-core sides butted against each other; also, an exciting winding that is designed to create a certain set of flux densities in the various sections of one of U magnetic circuits will automatically develop like flux densities in similar sections of the other U magnetic circuit.

The foregoing discussion should make it clear that E-type electromagnet problems may be given the same treatment as those considered in the previous section on U-type electromagnets.

EXAMPLE 7. The following information is given for an E-type electromagnet similar to that illustrated by Fig. 63: $l_c = l_o = 5$ in., $l_y = 4.5$ in., $l_a = 5.5$ in., $A_c = 4.75$ sq in., $A_y = 2.0$ sq in., $A_o = 2.25$ sq in., $A_a = 3.25$ sq in., δ (uniform throughout) $= 0.04$ in., yoke and pole-core material = cast steel, armature-core material = cast iron. If the center-core flux is 3.08×10^5 maxwells, calculate (*a*) the exciting-coil ampere-turns, (*b*) the force exerted by the electromagnet.

Solution

(*a*) A table, listing all given data and calculated results, is given herewith.

Part of circuit	Material	$l_{in.}$	$A_{in.}$	Φ	$B_{in.}$	$NI/l_{in.}$	NI
Center pole....	Cast steel	5.0	4.75	3.08×10^5	65,000	15	75
Yoke..........	Cast steel	4.5	2.0	1.54×10^5	77,000	23	104
Outer pole.....	Cast steel	5.0	2.25	1.54×10^5	68,500	16	80
Armature......	Cast iron	5.5	3.25	1.54×10^5	47,300	92	506
Center gap.....	Air	0.04	4.75	3.08×10^5	65,000	..	814
Outer gap......	Air	0.04	2.25	1.54×10^5	68,500	..	858
Total........							2,437

$$(b) \quad F = \left[\frac{(65{,}000)^2 \times 4.75}{72 \times 10^6}\right] + 2\left[\frac{(68{,}500)^2 \times 2.25}{72 \times 10^6}\right]$$
$$= 279 + 293 = 572 \text{ lb}$$

The Unsymmetrical-type Electromagnet. To fulfill special operating functions it is sometimes necessary to construct electromagnets that are not completely symmetrical. In such cases the flux and flux-density distributions are frequently complex since they result from a variety of combinations of series and parallel magnetic circuits. However, considered from the standpoint of elemental sections, in much the same way as it is customary to treat their electric-circuit counterparts, these magnetic circuits may be analyzed without too much difficulty. Examples will now be given to illustrate several unusual electromagnetic arrangements, and procedures in the solution of typical problems.

Parallel Magnetic Circuits. Some special relays have two or more air gaps where different values of flux density and/or flux must be created by a single exciting winding. These gaps are usually arranged in parallel; since the reluctance of each one is very much greater than that of the iron portions of the magnetic circuits, it is practically proper to neglect the mmf drop in the iron; this means that the total ampere-turns act across each of the air gaps. An electromagnet of this type is shown in Fig. 64. Note that there are two magnetic circuits A and B in parallel, and that the mmf between x and y, created by the exciting winding, is the same for both air gaps *if the reluctance of the iron is neglected;* the latter is quite feasible if high-grade steel, operating at low flux density, is used.

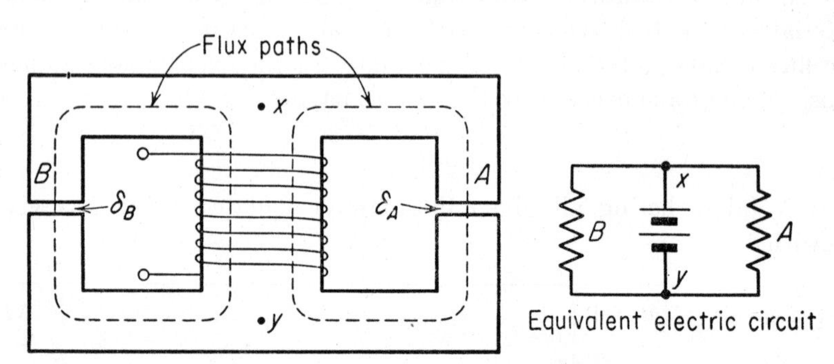

FIG. 64. Sketch illustrating two magnetic circuits in parallel.

EXAMPLE 8. The following data are given for the parallel circuit of Fig. 64: $\delta_A = 0.25$ in., $\delta_B = 0.2$ in., area of air gap $A = 0.75$ sq in., flux density in air gap $A = 20{,}000$ lines per square inch. Neglecting the reluctance of the iron portions of the magnetic circuit, calculate (*a*) the ampere-turns required for the exciting coil, (*b*) the flux density in air gap B, (*c*) the area of air gap B if $\Phi_B = \Phi_A$, (*d*) the total flux in the iron section under the exciting winding.

Solution

(*a*) $$NI_A = NI_B = 0.313 \times 20{,}000 \times 0.25 = 1{,}565$$

(*b*) $$B_B = \frac{1{,}565}{0.313 \times 0.2} = 25{,}000 \text{ lines per square inch}$$

(*c*) $$\Phi_A = \Phi_B = 20{,}000 \times 0.75 = 15{,}000 \text{ maxwells}$$

$$A_B = \frac{\Phi_B}{B_B} = \frac{15{,}000}{25{,}000} = 0.6 \text{ sq in.}$$

(*d*) $$\Phi_t = 2 \times 15{,}000 = 30{,}000 \text{ maxwells}$$

Parallel-Series Magnetic Circuits. Figure 65 illustrates an arrangement that may be termed a parallel-series magnetic circuit. If it is assumed that the cross-sectional area of the iron under the exciting winding xy is large and, working at low flux density, the iron requires a negligible number of ampere-turns, the *total mmf* is effective in producing flux in circuits A and B between points x and y. Differing from Fig. 64, however, this electromagnet has two magnetic paths A and B in parallel, each of which is composed of an iron portion and an air gap in series; its electric-circuit counterpart is shown in the sketch to the right of the magnetic circuit.

EXAMPLE 9. Referring to Fig. 65, assume that the reluctance between x and y, under the exciting winding, is negligible, and that in the magnetic paths A and B the ampere-turns required for the air gap is 75 per cent of the total ampere-turns. If $\delta_A = \frac{1}{8}$ in., $\delta_B = \frac{3}{16}$ in., and the winding

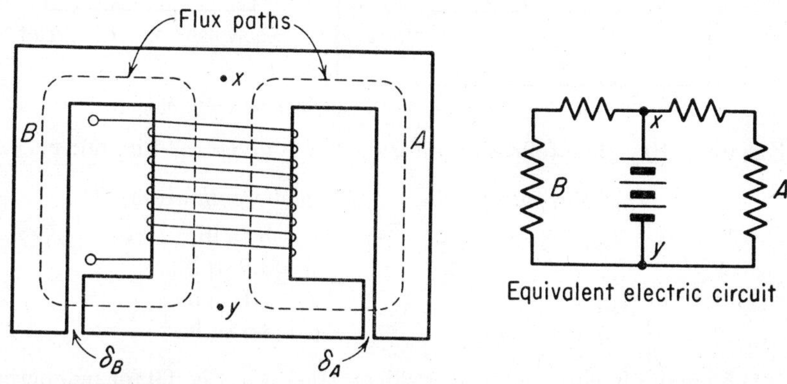

FIG. 65. Sketch illustrating a parallel-series magnetic circuit.

contains 2,300 turns, what will be the flux density in each air gap when the coil current is 1.5 amp?

Solution

$$NI_A = NI_B = 2{,}300 \times 1.5 = 3{,}450 \text{ amp-turns}$$

$$NI \text{ per gap} = 0.75 \times 3{,}450 = 2{,}590 \text{ amp-turns}$$

$$B_A = \frac{2{,}590}{0.313 \times 0.125} = 66{,}200 \text{ lines per square inch}$$

$$B_B = \frac{2{,}590}{0.313 \times 0.1875} = 44{,}200 \text{ lines per square inch}$$

Series-Parallel Magnetic Circuits. A more general type of electromagnet involves a combination of two parallel magnetic paths in series with a third; this arrangement has its counterpart in the familiar series-parallel electric circuit, and is represented in Fig. 66. Analyzing the mmf and flux paths, note that (1) the exciting winding must magnetize two magnetic paths in parallel, namely, xby and xay *through the series path* xcy; (2) the same mmf between x and y magnetically energizes parallel paths xby and xay; (3) the mmf between points x and y is equal to the total mmf minus that required by the series path xcy; (4) the total flux in path xcy divides at points x and y so that one part passes into the xby path, and the other part into the xay path. An example will now be given to illustrate how this kind of circuit is handled quantitatively.

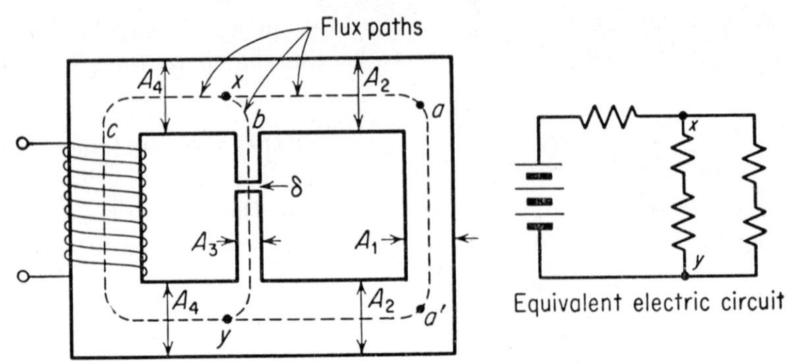

FIG. 66. Sketch illustrating a series-parallel magnetic circuit.

EXAMPLE 10. The following information is given for Fig. 66:

Magnetic-path lengths	*Magnetic-path areas*
$l_{xa} = l_{ya} = 7.5$ in.	$A_1 = 3$ sq in.
$l_{aa'} = l_{xy} = 6$ in.	$A_2 = 3.5$ sq in.
$l_{xcy} = 20$ in.	$A_3 = 1.1$ sq in.
$\delta = 0.035$ in.	$A_4 = 3.5$ sq in.

If the magnetic-core material is silicon steel (see Fig. 60 for magnetization curve), calculate the exciting-winding ampere-turns for a flux density of 95,000 lines per square inch in section A_1.

Solution

Step 1: For $B = 95{,}000$, $NI/l_{\text{in.}} = 65$.

$$(NI)_{aa'} = 65 \times 6 = 390$$

Step 2:

$$B_{xa} = B_{ya'} = 95{,}000 \times \frac{3}{3.5} = 81{,}500 \text{ lines per square inch}$$

For $B = 81{,}500$, $NI/l_{\text{in.}} = 17$.

$$(NI)_{xa} + (NI)_{ya'} = 17 \times 15 = 255$$

Step 3:

$$(NI)_{xy} = 390 + 255 = 645$$

Step 4: To determine the flux through the shunt magnetic path xby, the trial-and-error method must be used, because the known 645 amp-turns acts across a series circuit of iron and air in which the flux density is unknown. After several trials it was found that the flux density in section A_3 must be 55,000 lines per square inch to fulfill the 645-amp-turn requirement. Thus

$$(NI)_\delta = 0.313 \times 55{,}000 \times 0.035 = 603$$

and for $B = 55{,}000$, $NI/l_{\text{in.}} = 7$.

$$(NI)_{xby} = 603 + (7 \times 6) = 645 \qquad (Check)$$

Step 5: The total flux in path xcy is

$$\Phi_t = (95{,}000 \times 3) + (55{,}000 \times 1.1) = 345{,}500 \text{ maxwells}$$

$$B_{xcy} = \frac{345{,}000}{3.5} = 98{,}500 \text{ lines per square inch}$$

For $B = 98{,}500$, $NI/l_{\text{in.}} = 90$. Therefore

$$(NI)_{xcy} = 90 \times 20 = 1{,}800$$

Step 6:

$$\text{Total } NI = 645 + 1{,}800 = 2{,}445$$

Exciting-winding Wire Size and Turns. After determining the number of ampere-turns that must be used for the exciting winding of an electromagnet, it is necessary to find an appropriate number of turns of a standard wire size which, when connected to an available source of emf, will yield the proper magnetic excitation; moreover, this combination of wire size and turns must be so selected that the winding will not be heated excessively under normal operating conditions. Assuming that the number of ampere-turns NI has been found and that the impressed voltage E is known, it will first be necessary to estimate (from the magnetic-core dimensions) the winding height h of the coil and the average length of each turn ALT (see Fig. 67). Since coils are usually wound on a form, dipped in an insulating varnish, and baked before the electromagnet is assembled, the winding-height dimension, slightly less than the pole core, and the inside dimensions of the coil, slightly more than the peripheral dimensions of the core, are known. Also, the winding thickness w is generally limited to about 1 to 2 in. to prevent excessive internal hot-spot coil temperatures.

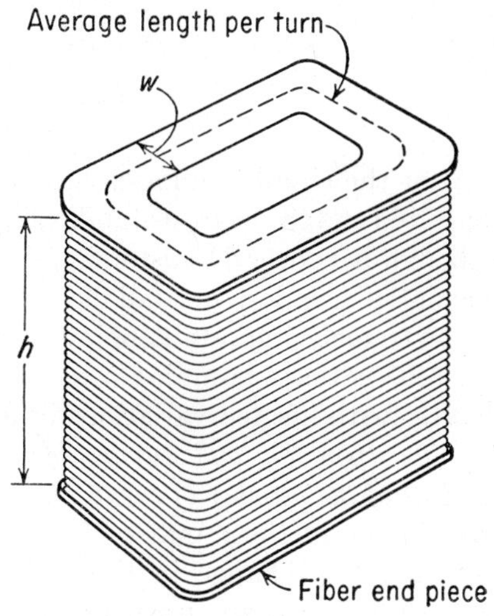

FIG. 67. Exciting coil for an electromagnet.

With the foregoing information of NI, ALT, and E known, the following derived equation will indicate how the wire size is determined: By Eq. (6), Chap. 2,

$$R = \rho \frac{l}{CM}$$

If ρ is specified in ohm–circular mils per *inch* of wire length, it will have a value of *one* if it is assumed that the winding material is copper at a temperature of 60°C; l will, of course, be given in *inches* of length of the exciting coil. But the total winding length is

$$l = N \times \text{ALT}$$

It follows, therefore, that

$$R = \frac{N \times \text{ALT}}{CM}$$

Since, by Ohm's law, $R = E/I$, the two values of resistance may be set equal to each other; thus

$$\frac{N \times \text{ALT}}{CM} = \frac{E}{I}$$

from which, by rearrangement of terms, the circular-mil area of copper may be computed from the equation

$$CM = \frac{NI \times \text{ALT}}{E} \tag{49}$$

After the circular-mil area has been found, Table 4 (page 24) should be consulted and the nearest standard wire size to this area should be selected, although it is usually customary to choose the next *larger* wire when the calculated size does not fall close to a standard number. An interesting and extremely important point that should be noted in connection with Eq. (49) is that, assuming a reasonably fixed value of ALT (it will vary slightly with limited variations in w) and a given voltage E, *the wire size depends upon the total number of ampere-turns* NI, *and is definitely independent of the number of turns* N. This latter condition prevails because any change in the number of turns of a given size of wire results in a corresponding change in the resistance of the coil, which, in turn, is accompanied by an inverse change in the current; the ampere-turns, therefore, remain constant no matter how many turns are used. However, since $P = I^2R$, the coil heating will increase as the number of turns of the given wire is diminished, and vice versa.

After the wire size is chosen, the next step is to calculate the number of turns of wire that can be placed in the winding-space area hw. This may be readily done by consulting tables published by wire manufacturers that give data concerning layer-wound (not random-wound) coils. For example, if n represents the number of wires of a given size and insulation that can be wound per inch when laid side by side, the total number of turns N that can be put into the coil will be *approximately* $nh \times nw$ or n^2hw; with allowances made for end turns, insulating paper, and the like, the actual number of turns may be somewhat less than this.

EXAMPLE 11. A coil of wire is to be wound on a form $2\frac{1}{4}$ by 2 in. to fit over a slightly smaller iron core. If the coil height h is to be 5.5 in. and the winding depth w must not exceed 1.5 in., calculate the wire size and number of turns in the coil if it is to develop 2,445 amp-turns when connected to a source of 110 volts.

Solution

$$\text{ALT} = 2(2.25 + 1.5) + 2(2 + 1.5) = 14.5 \text{ in. (approx)}$$

$$CM = \frac{2{,}445 \times 14.5}{110} = 322$$

From Table 4, No. 25 AWG wire has an area of 320 cir mils.

Referring to a manufacturers' wire table it is found that it is possible to wind 35 turns of No. 25 insulated wire to the inch. This means that each layer will have approximately $35 \times 5.5 = 192$ wires—say 190—and there will be $35 \times 1.5 = 52$ layers—say 50. The total number of turns will therefore be

$$N = 190 \times 52 = 9{,}880$$

To check the number of ampere-turns for this 9,880-turn coil of No. 25 wire,

$$R = \frac{9{,}880 \times 14.5}{320} = 447 \text{ ohms}$$

and

$$I = \frac{110}{447} = 0.246 \text{ amp}$$

from which $NI = 9{,}880 \times 0.246 = 2{,}430$ amp-turns (good agreement).

Leakage Flux. The primary function of all electromagnetic apparatus is to create flux that follows *prescribed* paths. Since ferromagnetic cores have permeabilities that may reach values of several thousand (see Fig. 61), the lines of force are, for the most part, confined to definite magnetic circuits that are mainly made up of iron. The *useful magnetic flux*, as the latter is called, is, however, accompanied by some lines of force that pass from the lateral surfaces of one pole to that of others through intervening air; such stray flux, usually called *leakage flux*, is a comparatively small per cent of the useful flux in well-designed electromagnets. Figure 68 illustrates the general core and winding proportions of three U-type electromagnets, and shows, in a rather general way, how the leakage flux may be partially controlled. Note particularly that designs such as Fig. 68*a*, where the poles are long and close together, will be subject to a larger percentage of leakage flux than those, like Fig. 68*c*, in which the poles are short and far apart. Moreover, where the main magnetic path (or paths) contain series air gaps, there will be an added tendency to create leakage flux; this is true because useful- and leakage-

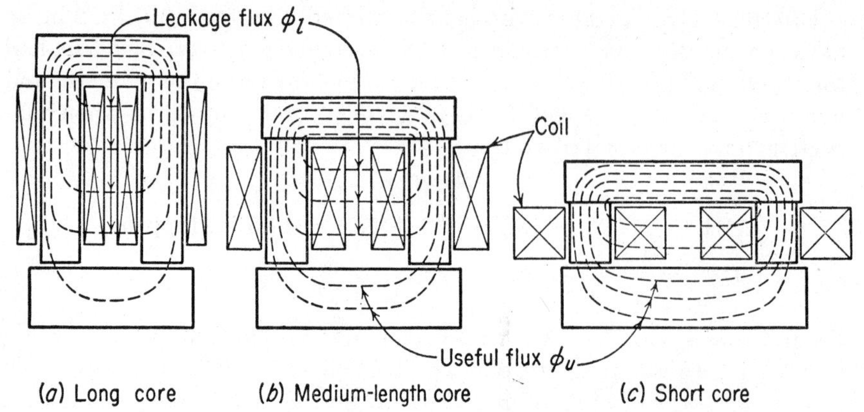

FIG. 68. U-type electromagnets showing different degrees of leakage flux.

flux paths are always in parallel, which means that the respective magnitudes of flux are inversely proportional to the corresponding reluctances.

Leakage flux is often difficult to calculate because it is set up in magnetic paths consisting of iron and air having indefinite dimensions. It is for this reason that estimates, based on experience with such matters, must generally be made when it becomes necessary to determine the value of the stray magnetism. In some cases where a high degree of accuracy is desired, it is possible to employ special kinds of flux maps that are drawn in accordance with well-developed practices. A term that is frequently used to indicate the extent to which leakage flux exists in a magnetic circuit is *leakage factor*, symbolized by LF; it is defined by the equation

$$\text{LF} = \frac{\Phi_u + \Phi_l}{\Phi_u} \tag{50}$$

where Φ_u = useful flux
Φ_l = leakage flux

Referring again to Fig. 68, it will be observed that the yoke must accommodate the total flux, consisting of the useful flux Φ_u and the leakage flux Φ_l; the pole cores, on the other hand, carry maximum values of flux near the yoke surface and progressively diminishing numbers of lines of force as the latter proceed toward open ends where they come in contact with the armature. This means, therefore, that flux densities in the various sections of the magnetic circuit must be based on existing values of flux. In or near the yoke the flux is $(\Phi_u + \Phi_l)$, at the pole ends and in the armature Φ_u, and in the pole core approximately $[\Phi_u + (\Phi_l/2)]$.

Fringing of Flux in an Air Gap. When lines of force pass from one ferromagnetic surface to another through an air gap they tend to spread out, or "fringe," from the pole faces. This effect, which becomes more pronounced as the air gap is lengthened, increases the area between pole faces and thereby lessens the average air-gap flux density. Figure 69 illustrates the flux-fringing action in two kinds of air gap. In Fig. 69*a* the desire is to create an intensely concentrated field between pole tips, while in Fig. 69*b* the intention is to reduce the flux density gradually in the spaces immediately adjacent to the pole tips. Since the number of ampere-turns required for an air gap is a direct function of the flux density ($NI = 0.313B_{in.}\delta$), it should be clear that the enlarged air-gap area must be properly determined if a reasonable calculation is to be made. It is, nevertheless, true that such computations, like those of leakage flux, must

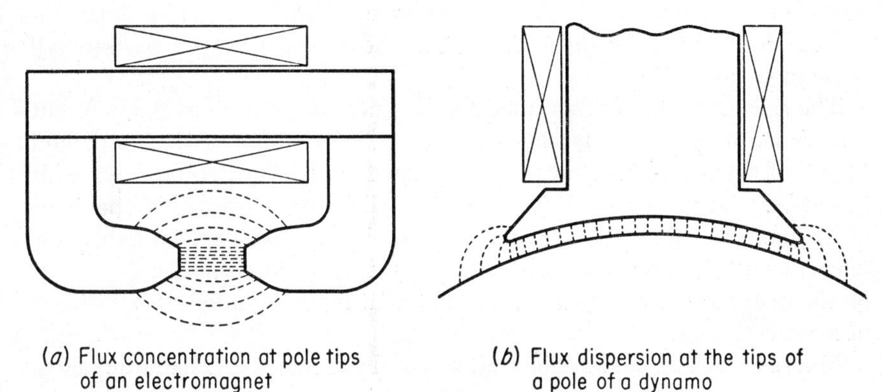

(*a*) Flux concentration at pole tips of an electromagnet

(*b*) Flux dispersion at the tips of a pole of a dynamo

FIG. 69. Sketch showing types of flux fringing.

rely upon reasonable estimates based on experience, if the results are to be reliable.

EXAMPLE 12. The following dimensions are given in connection with a U-type electromagnet (see Fig. 62): pole core = 2 by 3 in.; yoke = 2.25 by 3.25 in.; armature core = 2.25 by 3.5 in.; δ = 0.125 in. If the leakage factor LF = 1.2, and the flux fringes out on all sides in the air gap to a width equal to the air-gap length, calculate the average flux densities in the various portions of the magnetic circuit for an air-gap flux of 450,000 maxwells.

Solution

$$\Phi_l = (1.2 \times 450{,}000) - 450{,}000 = 90{,}000 \text{ maxwells}$$

$$B_y = \frac{450{,}000 + 450{,}000}{2.25 \times 3.5} = 73{,}900 \text{ lines per square inch}$$

$$B_a = \frac{450{,}000}{2.25 \times 3.5} = 57{,}200 \text{ lines per square inch}$$

$$B_p = \frac{450{,}000 + 45{,}000}{2 \times 3} = 82{,}500 \text{ lines per square inch}$$

$$B_{gap} = \frac{450{,}000}{(2 + 0.25) \times (3 + 0.25)} = 61{,}500 \text{ lines per square inch}$$

Hysteresis. One of the interesting peculiarities of ferromagnetic substances is that its previous history determines, in part, the extent to which it will be magnetized upon the application or removal of a magnetizing force; this implies that the magnetic strength, i.e., flux density, will depend upon (1) whether or not the specimen was previously magnetized before the mmf was applied or removed, (2) whether the mmf is applied to increase or decrease the flux, and (3) at what point on the magnetization curve (see Fig. 60) the change in mmf is initiated. The factors responsible for the stated conditions are saturation, previously discussed, and the so-called retentive property of magnetic substances. The latter is responsible for the *residual magnetism* and is, in fact, the basis of all permanent magnets.

The *retentivity*, or residual flux density, not only will vary for different materials, but will also be determined by such factors as the shape and length of the specimen, and the maximum flux density before the mmf is removed. Hardened steel, for example, will retain more than 75 per cent of its maximum flux when strongly magnetized, though considerably less when low maximum densities are used; soft iron in the form of a short bar, on the other hand, will be a weak permanent magnet under all conditions of magnetization.

Referring to Fig. 59, assume that a toroid of some good magnetic material is completely demagnetized. If a test is performed to determine the relation between flux density and magnetizing force (in ampere-turns per inch), data may be obtained to plot a complete loop similar to that of Fig. 70. As the magnetizing force is increased from zero in a *positive direction*, the graph of $B_{\text{in.}}$ vs. $NI/l_{\text{in.}}$ follows a so-called *virgin curve;* this is the typical magnetization curve similar to Fig. 60. Assuming that the iron is brought up to a rather high value of flux density $+B_m$, the curve will descend along the upper portion of the loop as the magnetizing force is slowly brought down to zero; at this latter point, with no applied mmf, the flux density in the specimen will be the residual value $+B_{\text{in.}r}$. To demagnetize the toroid completely it will next be necessary to apply a *negative* mmf, and when its value reaches the so-called *coercive force*, $B_{\text{in.}}$ will be zero. Further negative increases in mmf will magnetize the core in a *negative direction*, and at a numerical value of $-(NI)_m$, equal to the positive value $+(NI)_m$, the negative flux density $-B_{\text{in.}m}$ will be numerically equal to the positive flux density $+B_{\text{in.}m}$. The loop is then completed by first reducing the magnetizing force to zero, at which point the negative residual flux density $-B_{\text{in.}r}$ is reached, and then proceeding along the underside to the positive value of coercive force and the positive maximum flux density $B_{\text{in.}m}$. The outside envelope of the closed curve is called a *hysteresis loop* and is extremely important in calculations involving energy losses in iron when alternating current is used to magnetize and

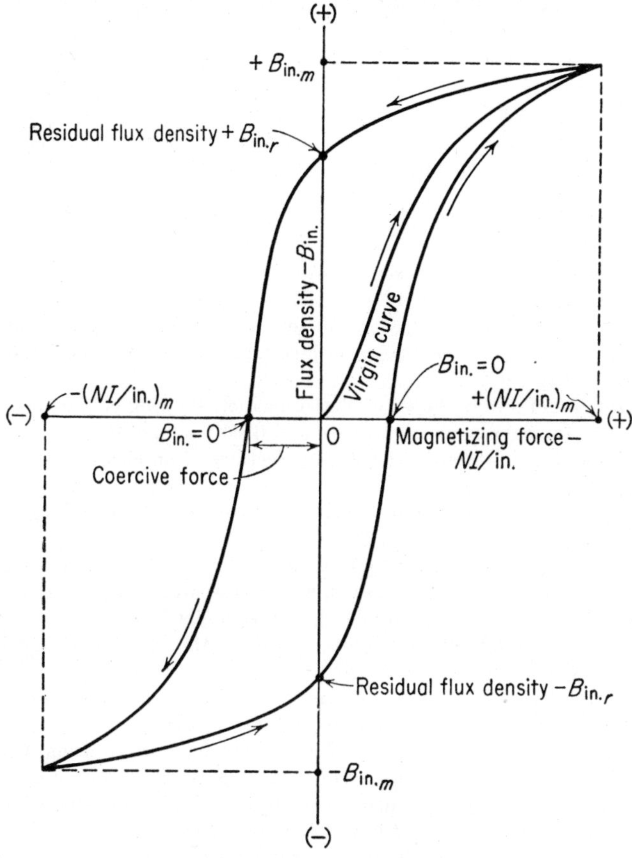

FIG. 70. Hysteresis loop.

demagnetize the material periodically, first in one direction and then in the other. The term *hysteresis* is applied to the phenomenon whereby the magnetic effect, i.e., the creation of flux, lags behind the magnetizing force.

Questions

1. What three terms in magnetic circuits may be likened to those in the Ohm's law equation for electric circuits?
2. State Ohm's law for magnetic circuits.
3. List several important differences between ferromagnetic- and electric-circuit operation.
4. Explain why flux-density changes that result from mmf changes depend upon the extent to which a ferromagnetic substance is initially magnetized.
5. What difficulties are sometimes encountered in making flux-density calculations in magnetic circuits consisting of iron and air in series?
6. Upon what factors does the reluctance of a magnetic material depend?
7. Why is it desirable to use air as a basis of comparison when rating the magnetic conductivity of ferromagnetic substances?

8. What is meant by *saturation*, referring to a magnetic substance?
9. How does the Weber-Ewing theory explain the phenomenon of saturation?
10. Explain the general shape of important portions of the magnetization curve.
11. Why is it generally desirable to work ferromagnetic materials at densities that are above the "knee" of the magnetization curve?
12. Concerning its ability to create flux, upon what four factors does the *quality* of a ferromagnetic substance depend?
13. Define *permeability*.
14. In terms of permeability explain why it is generally desirable to have as little air in a magnetic circuit as possible.
15. Explain why the slope of the *permeability* vs. *flux-density curve* is constant for air and variable for a ferromagnetic material.
16. Upon what factors does the tractive force of an electromagnet depend?
17. What assigned property of magnetic flux explains the tractive force in the air gap of an electromagnet?
18. Make sketches of several types of electromagnet, showing coil arrangements and flux paths. Indicate some advantages and disadvantages of each type.
19. How are the flux densities in the various sections of an electromagnet related to each other?
20. When is it necessary to employ a trial-and-error method in solving a magnetic circuit? Explain carefully.
21. Make sketches showing several kinds of unsymmetrical magnetic circuits. (These should include parallel, parallel-series, and series-parallel circuits.)
22. Outline the general procedure in solving an unsymmetrical series-parallel magnetic circuit, assuming a flux density in one section of the circuit and showing how to determine the required ampere-turns.
23. Explain carefully why the required size of wire in an exciting winding is, for the most part, dependent upon the number of ampere-turns.
24. Explain carefully why the number of ampere-turns in an exciting winding is, in general, independent of the number of turns of a given size of wire.
25. How is the average length of each turn determined in an exciting winding?
26. Why is it desirable to restrict the width of an exciting winding?
27. Given the wire size and the winding space of an exciting winding, how is the number of turns determined?
28. Distinguish between *useful flux* and *leakage flux*.
29. Explain why and how leakage flux alters the flux-density distributions in a magnetic circuit.
30. Why is it often difficult to calculate the magnitude of the leakage flux?
31. Define *leakage factor*. What values can it have?
32. What is meant by *flux fringing?* When is it most pronounced? least pronounced?
33. When the flux density in a given specimen of iron is to be altered, what will its final value depend upon?
34. Define *residual magnetism*. What determines the magnitude of the residual flux?
35. What is meant by the term *retentivity?*
36. What kinds of material are likely to retain a large per cent of the magnetism when the excitation is removed? a small per cent of the magnetism?
37. What is meant by *coercive force?*
38. Define *hysteresis*. Under what conditions is hysteresis particularly important?

Problems

1. Calculate the flux in a magnetic circuit that has a reluctance of 0.06, if the 2,500-turn exciting winding carries 2.5 amp.

2. How many ampere-turns are required to set up a flux density of 80,000 lines per square inch in a 15-in. length of silicon steel that has a permeability of 1,600?
3. What air-gap length will require the same number of ampere-turns as in Prob. 2, if an equal flux density is to be set up?
4. A cast-steel toroid has an average diameter of 6 in. and a circular section whose area is 0.45 sq in. If the 800-turn exciting coil must carry 0.32 amp to produce a flux of 27,000 maxwells, calculate the permeability of the steel.
5. A series magnetic circuit consists of a ring of steel of uniform cross section in which there is an air gap of 1/16 in. If the total mmf is 1,830 gilberts, of which 20 per cent is required for the iron, calculate flux density.
6. A U-type electromagnet has two 750-turn exciting coils, one on each leg, connected in series. When the winding carries 1.53 amp the magnetic-circuit flux is 360,000 maxwells. Calculate the total reluctance.
7. How many ampere-turns will be required to set up an air-gap flux density of 75,000 lines per square inch, if each of the air gaps in a U-type electromagnet has a length of 0.06 in. and the iron portions of the magnetic circuit are assumed to take 15 per cent of the total mmf?
8. The exciting winding on a U-type electromagnet develops 2,200 amp-turns, of which 74 per cent is required to overcome the reluctance of two 0.04-in. air gaps. If the area of each gap is 4.0 sq in., calculate the flux in the magnetic circuit.
9. The total flux in the center pole of a symmetrical E-type electromagnet (see Fig. 63) is 403,000 maxwells. If the area of the center-pole air gap is 6.5 sq in., the area of each outer-pole air gap is 3.5 sq in., and each air gap has a length of 0.035 in., calculate the number of ampere-turns on the exciting coil, assuming that the iron portions of the magnetic circuit require 22 per cent of those needed for the air gaps.
10. Calculate the tractive force exerted by a symmetrical U-type electromagnet if the flux density in each of the 8.25 sq in. air gaps is 52,000 lines per square inch.
11. For what flux densities, in Prob. 10, will the electromagnet exert forces of (*a*) 310 lb, (*b*) 930 lb?
12. The following information is given in connection with a symmetrical U-type electromagnet: area per pole face = 1.78 sq in.; total turns on exciting winding = 2,610; resistance of exciting winding = 17.8 ohms. (*a*) Calculate the pull exerted by the electromagnet when the winding is connected directly to a 24-volt source, under which condition each of the air gaps between pole face and armature is 1/4 in. (*b*) What resistance should be connected in series with the winding after the armature has moved to the pole faces to shorten the air gaps to 1/16 in., assuming that the tractive effort is to remain the same as in (*a*)?
13. A symmetrical E-type electromagnet (see Fig. 63) must exert a tractive force of 600 lb. How many ampere-turns must be developed by the exciting winding, given the following particulars: $A_c = 3.9$ sq in., $A_o = 1.95$ sq in., $\delta = 1/16$ in.?
14. The pole-face areas of a symmetrical E-type electromagnet are $A_c = 6$ sq in.; $A_o = 3.25$ sq in. Calculate the force exerted by the electromagnet if the flux density under the center pole face is 48,000 lines per square inch.
15. Referring to Fig. 64, neglect the reluctance of the iron portions of the magnetic circuit and calculate the flux densities in the two air gaps, given that $NI = 3{,}500$ amp-turns, $\delta_A = 0.15$ in., and $\delta_B = 0.22$ in.
16. What will be the flux in the iron section under the exciting winding in Prob. 15, if the air-gap areas are $A_A = 3.5$ sq in., and $A_B = 4.25$ sq in.
17. Referring to Fig. 65, assume that the reluctance of the iron under the exciting winding is negligible, and that the number of ampere-turns required for the iron of paths *A* and *B* is 15 per cent of their respective air-gap ampere-turn require-

ments. If $\delta_A = 0.08$ in., $\delta_B = 0.12$ in., and $B_{in.A} = 45{,}000$ lines per square inch, calculate (*a*) the number of ampere-turns on the exciting winding, (*b*) the flux density $B_{in.B}$.

18. Referring to Fig. 65, calculate the flux density in the iron under the exciting winding, given the following information: reluctance of path $A = 0.15$, reluctance of path $B = 0.08$, exciting-winding ampere-turns = 2,500, cross-sectional area of iron under the winding = 2.25 sq in. (Neglect the mmf required for the iron under the winding between points x and y.)

19. Using the same given data as those listed under Example 10, page 128, calculate the required number of ampere-turns for a *cast-steel* electromagnet and a flux density of 97,000 lines per square inch in section A_1.

20. A 4,600-amp-turn coil for an electromagnet is to be wound over a 3.25- by 4.5-in. rectangular form and is to be excited from a 24-volt source. If the winding width is not to exceed 1.5 in., calculate the proper size of wire that should be used.

21. How many ampere-turns would the winding of Prob. 20 produce if it were constructed in two equal halves of the same wire size and connected *in parallel* to (*a*) a 24-volt source, (*b*) a 12-volt source?

22. The air-gap flux under the pole face of a dynamo (see Fig. 69*b*) is 6.2×10^6 maxwells. If the pole-core dimensions (under the exciting winding) are 8.5 by 9 in. and the leakage factor is 1.15, calculate (*a*) the flux density at the section of the pole core where it is bolted to the yoke ring, (*b*) the average pole-core flux density.

CHAPTER 7

DIRECT-CURRENT INSTRUMENTS AND MEASUREMENTS

General Types and Uses of Measuring Instruments. Experimental testing is undertaken to verify rules, principles, or laws, or to determine how a piece of equipment behaves under operating conditions. Obviously, the information or data that are obtained from tests should be accurate and trustworthy; valid conclusions cannot be reached if the data are questionable. Many factors are responsible for the accuracy of the results of an experiment, but probably the most important of these is the precision of the electrical instruments used.

The two most commonly employed types of instrument in d-c circuit testing are ammeters and voltmeters; from the indications on such instruments, properly inserted in circuits, it is possible to calculate the power ($P = EI$) and the resistance ($R = E/I$). Direct-reading instruments are sometimes used to measure the resistances of circuits; these are ohmmeters, Wheatstone bridges, and megohmmeters, the latter for the determination of extremely high values of resistance and particularly insulation resistance. For the measurement of low values of emf with an extremely high degree of accuracy, and especially when the instrument must not draw current from the source of voltage that is measured, a potentiometer must be used. In a-c testing, for the measurement of power (watts), it is generally necessary to include a wattmeter; the latter, a sort of combination voltmeter-ammeter, may, and sometimes does, measure power in d-c circuits. All electrical instruments can be made to have any desirable range, and they are frequently constructed to have several ranges. In still other designs an instrument may be used as an ammeter *or* a voltmeter, the change from one to the other being readily accomplished by turning a selector switch.

Permanent-magnet Moving-coil Instrument. The arrangement most common to present-day instruments for the measurement of current (amperes) and electromotive force (volts) is the *permanent-magnet moving-coil mechanism.* Generally referred to as the *D'Arsonval* movement, it represents the efforts of many persons over a period of more than 140 years of development. Based upon the application of fundamental principles of electric and magnetic circuits, it embodies numerous ingenious designs. Among those who should be cited for major contributions to this important phase of electrical instrumentation are the following: Oersted (1819), who discovered the relation between a current of electricity and magnetism; Faraday (1821), who demonstrated that a current-carrying conductor would move when placed in a magnetic field; Ampère (1821), who worked out the mathematical laws that govern the strengths of currents; Sturgeon (1836), who first demonstrated that a current-carrying coil of wire would move (or rotate) if suspended in a magnetic field; Kelvin (1867), who placed a soft-iron core in the center of the coil to shorten the air gap and thereby increase the sensitivity (deflection per unit current) of the device; D'Arsonval (1881), who, having developed the first practical measuring device, patented an instrument of this type; Weston (1888), who discovered that the factors that govern the permanency of a magnetic circuit are associated with the *circuit* rather than the magnet, added soft-iron pole pieces to the magnet and current-carrying control springs, and made the first commercial permanent-magnet moving-coil instruments.

Although there have been no changes in theory and design since 1888 when Weston introduced his basically sound device, instruments of this type have been so greatly improved since that time that they now give a pointer deflection of about 5½ in. for a current of 0.005 ma (0.000005 amp) instead of the 1888 value of about 10 ma (0.01 amp).

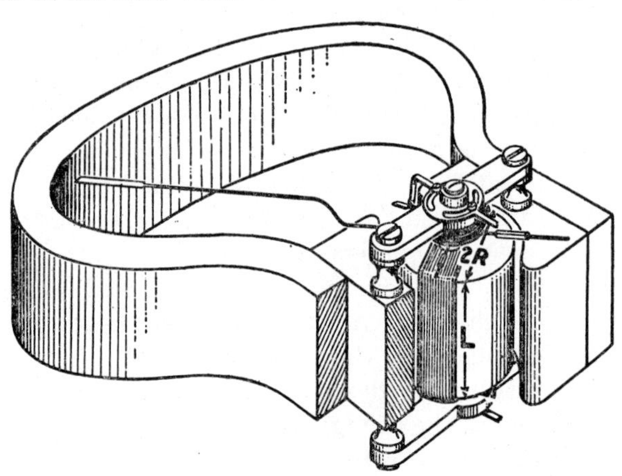

Fig. 71. Constructional details of D'Arsonval movement. (*Weston Electrical Instrument Corp.*)

Figure 71 illustrates the general constructional arrangement of the various parts of a modern type of D'Arsonval instrument. The assembly shows a coil of very fine wire wound on an extremely light aluminum frame accurately suspended in a magnetic field that is provided by a permanent magnet; the latter may be tungsten steel, cobalt steel, or

Alnico. Since the degree of permanency of the magnet is an important factor in the *sustained* accuracy of such an instrument, this feature has been thoroughly investigated. Among other things, it was found that permanency is related to proper aging of such magnets and is directly proportional to the length of the magnet steel and the cross-sectional area of the air gap, and inversely proportional to the cross-sectional area of the magnet steel and the length of the air gap. These basic principles are so well recognized that instrument manufacturers follow them carefully in their designs. Of particular significance in this respect is that it is customary to give the magnet its greatest length by making it follow the outside shape of the enclosing case.

The moving coil is suspended by two short pointed shafts fastened to the top and bottom of the frame, the ends of which rest in V-type sapphire bearings. In such double-pivoted instruments flat coil springs, wound in opposite directions and similar to watch hairsprings, are attached to the shaft extensions previously mentioned; the springs serve two important functions, namely, (1) as lead-in wires to conduct current into and out of the moving coil, and (2) to provide the countertorque against which the movement is calibrated. When the zero setting is made, both springs are given initial deflections so that they act against each other. An illustration showing the complete moving-coil assembly is shown in Fig. 72.

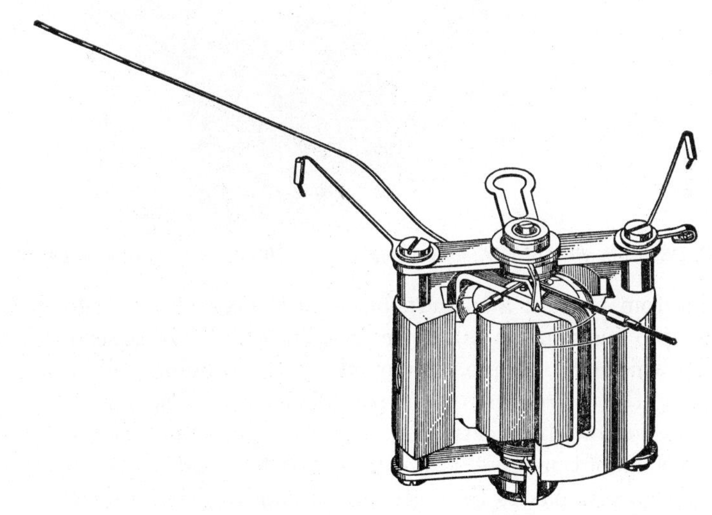

Fig. 72. Details of the moving-coil assembly. (*Weston Electrical Instrument Corp.*)

When current is passed through the suspended coil, torque is developed; moreover, if the current is in the proper direction with respect to the magnetic polarities of the permanent-magnet poles, an *upscale* deflection will result. Since the force tending to turn the coil is proportional to the strength of the magnet and the ampere-turns in the moving element, the torque, i.e., turning moment, is proportional to both factors and is given by the equation

$$T = 0.2BNI \times Rl \tag{51}$$

where T = torque, dyne-cm
B = flux density in air gap, lines per square centimeter
I = moving-coil current, amp
R = radius of moving coil, cm (see Fig. 71)
l = axial length of moving coil, cm (see Fig. 71)

A Model 1 Weston instrument that has a movement weighing about 2 gm will develop a torque of approximately 3½ dyne-cm per deg of deflection.

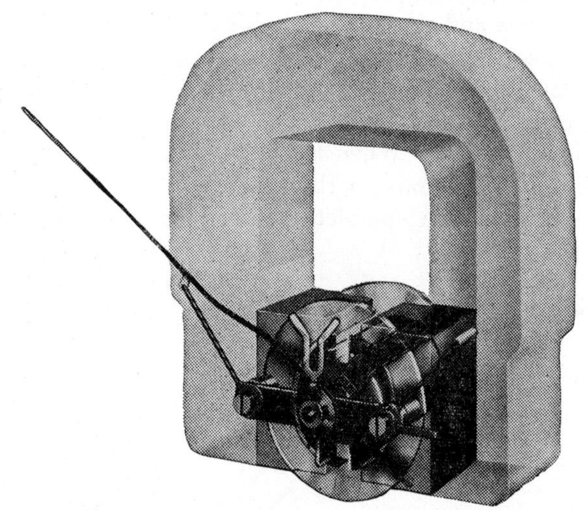

Fig. 73. Phantom view of D'Arsonval instrument. (*Weston Electrical Instrument Corp.*)

A phantom view of a modern permanent-magnet moving-coil (D'Arsonval-type) instrument is shown in Fig. 73. It is basically a *torque motor* in which the torque developed by the moving coil, Eq. (51), is opposed by the restraining torque provided by spiral springs. Analyzing the torque actions by electromagnetic theory, assume that the polarity of the permanent magnet is *north* on the left and *south* on the right. When no current passes through the moving coil, it is set at rest at an angle of about 45° with the vertical; in this position the light aluminum pointer fastened to the coil is adjusted to zero on the calibrated scale. Now then, if current is made to pass through the coil so that its direction is away from the observer at the top of the coil and toward the observer on the bottom of the coil, torque will be developed to produce *clockwise* rotation. This comes about because the two magnetic fields, i.e., the permanent-magnet field and the moving-coil field, tend to combine into a single *resultant* magnetic field having the greatest possible strength; the coil, therefore, swings around in an attempt to get its lines of force parallel to, and in the same direction as, the permanent-magnet field. The moving coil will, of course, come to rest when the electromagnetic force exerted upon it is exactly balanced by the restraining force created by the loaded (wound-up) springs. The term *torque motor* is therefore appropriate for an electrical instrument because motor action is developed during the upswing period, and sustained torque steadies the coil against the spring tension after the pointer reaches the position that is a measure of the coil current.

Instrument Damping. The fact that the turns of wire of the moving coil are wound upon an aluminum (a metal) frame means that the latter will exert a braking action upon the assembly as it revolves through the magnetic field. This braking or *damping* effect results from generated emf's in the metal frame *as it turns* through the very field that is responsible for the original motion. Since the generated voltage in the short-circuited frame is always in such a direction as to set up an mmf that tends to oppose the motion, the coil moves the pointer upscale slowly, and without overshooting its final deflected position; such damping is therefore effective in preventing oscillations that would normally result from the oppositely directed forces exerted by the spiral springs and the moving coil.

Direct-current Ammeters and Voltmeters. Both types of instrument are essentially alike, being constructed from foundation assemblies previously discussed; they *differ only in the manner in which an external resistor is connected with respect to the moving-coil element.* An extremely low value of current is permitted to pass through the suspended coil which, with its attached pointer, turns through an angle that is directly proportional to the current; the pointer moves over a calibrated scale to indicate either amperes or volts. A good *ammeter* has an extremely *low resistance;* a good *voltmeter* has a comparatively *high* resistance. This implies, of course, that when an ammeter is placed in *series* in a circuit it incurs a low voltage drop (its resistance is low), and when a voltmeter is connected *across* (in parallel with) a circuit it draws very little current (its resistance is high); in either case, it is important to understand that, when either type of instrument is inserted in a circuit for measurement purposes, *it must alter that circuit as little as possible.* In the D'Arsonval type of d-c instrument, very widely used, full-scale deflection usually occurs when the voltage across its terminals is 0.05 volt (50 mv). If the moving-coil resistance is 2.5 ohms, its current must not exceed $0.05/2.5 = 0.02$ amp. Under this condition a 5-amp ammeter, for example, must have a shunt connected *across* its terminals that must carry the difference between the maximum permissible 5-amp line current and the 0.02-amp instrument coil current, or 4.98 amp. The shunt resistance must therefore be (0.05/4.98) = 0.01004 ohm, an extremely low value. If the instrument is to be used as a voltmeter having a full-scale deflection of, say, 150 volts, the moving coil must be connected *in series* with a resistor capable of causing a voltage drop of (150 − 0.05) volts, or 149.95 volts, when a 150-volt source is applied to the series combination; the resistor must therefore have an ohmic value of (149.95/0.02) = 7,497.5 ohms, a comparatively high value. A voltmeter of this construction would then be

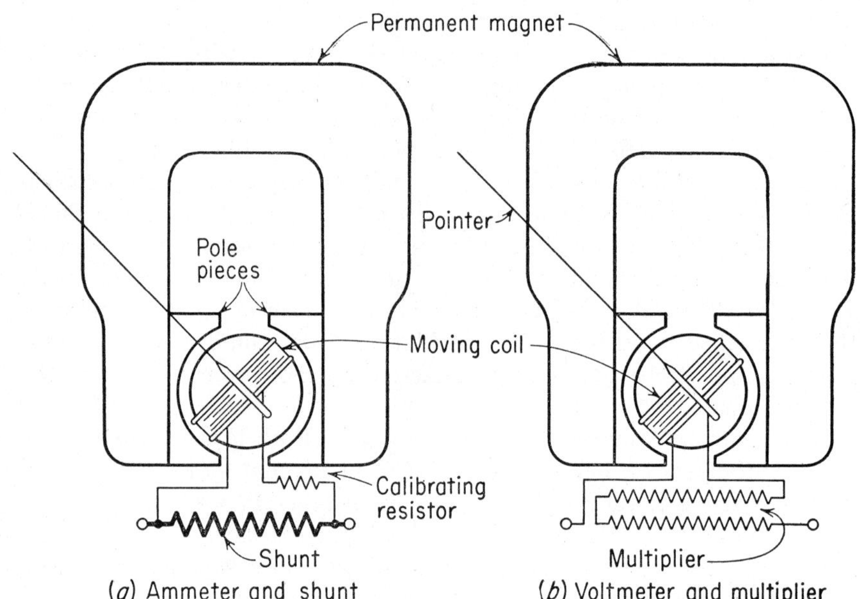

FIG. 74. Sketches illustrating internal connections of ammeter and voltmeter.

referred to as a 50-*ohms-per-volt* instrument. Figure 74*a* illustrates how a resistance—called a *shunt*—is connected *across* the moving coil and its series calibrating resistor when the instrument is constructed for ammeter service; Fig. 74*b* shows how a resistance—called a *multiplier*—is connected in *series* with the moving coil when the instrument is used as a voltmeter.

In ammeters of the smaller ranges, up to about 25 amp, shunts are generally placed inside the case. For ranges above 25 amp externally connected shunts are generally used because they become too large and develop an excessive amount of heat for internal mounting. Figure 75 shows two constructions of ammeter shunt that are applied externally; the 50-mv notation on each one indicates that the pointer will deflect full scale under the condition that rated current passes through the instrument with 0.05 volt impressed across its terminals.

Multipliers for voltmeters are constructed in various forms depending on the application, and are nearly always placed inside the cases. Self-

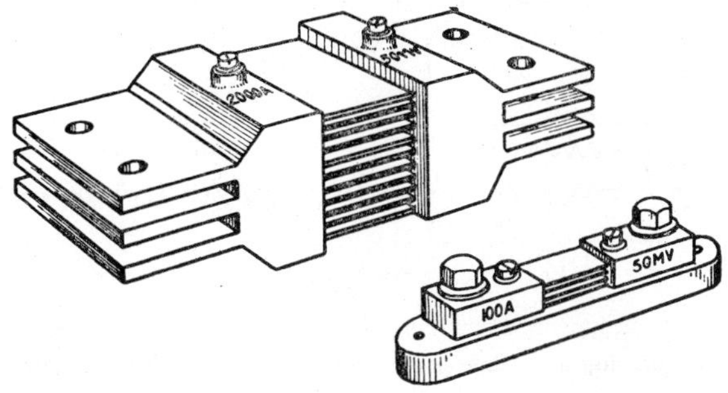

FIG. 75. Sketches illustrating external types of shunt. (*Weston Electrical Instrument Corp.*)

contained voltmeter ranges use small compact spools for the more sensitive mechanisms and larger units placed on cards for those requiring more current. All series resistors in which the generated heat is more than the amount that the instrument case can radiate must be external.

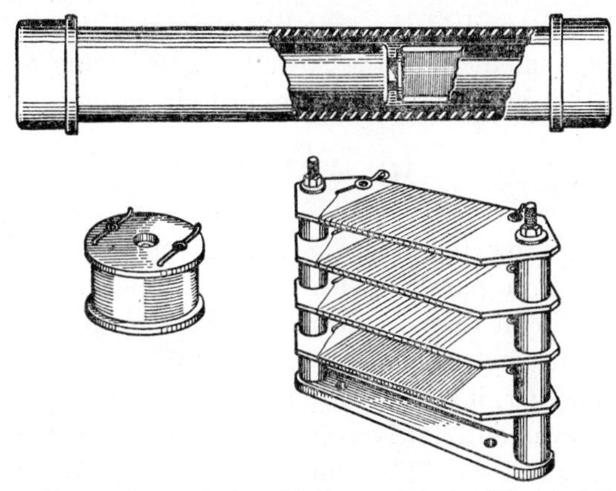

FIG. 76. Sketches illustrating typical multipliers. (*Weston Electrical Instrument Corp.*)

Figure 76 shows several multiplier constructions. The one at the top is a special tubular resistor filled with an inert compound, sealed, and electrostatically shielded, to ensure long life at high voltages in humid or salt atmospheres; the lower left sketch is a spool-wound resistor, while the lower right illustration represents a set of "carded" resistors for a multi-range voltmeter. Series resistors are usually wound with wire of such alloys as Manganin or constantan because changes in temperature will not appreciably affect their resistance values.

When it becomes necessary to extend the range of a *given* voltmeter whose total resistance is R_I, an externally connected multiplier of resistance R_M must be used. This arrangement of series resistances results in a division of the total impressed voltage V into two parts, namely,

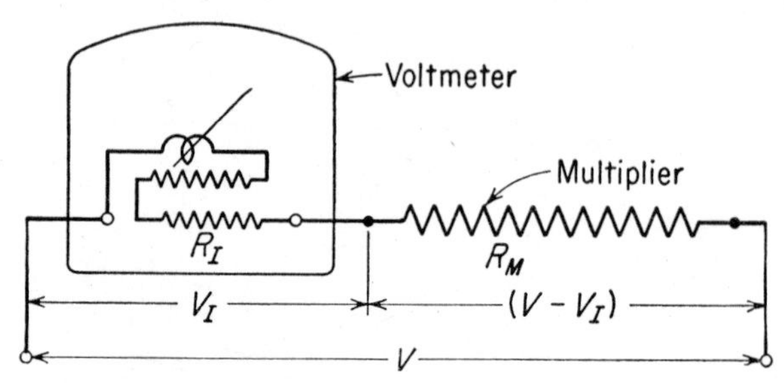

FIG. 77. Circuit showing a voltmeter connected in series with an external multiplier.

$(V - V_I)$ and V_I; moreover, these voltage drops are directly proportional to their respective resistance magnitudes. Thus, referring to Fig. 77,

$$\frac{R_M}{R_I} = \frac{(V - V_I)}{V_I} = \frac{V}{V_I} - 1$$

Since the ratio (V/V_I) is the factor by which the voltmeter indication V_I must be multiplied to yield the true line voltage V, it may be replaced by the more convenient MF, the so-called *multiplying factor*. Writing the above equation in a more desirable form, it becomes

$$\text{MF} = \frac{R_M}{R_I} + 1 \tag{52}$$

It is also possible to extend the range of a given ammeter by connecting an external shunt in parallel with the instrument. This practice is generally more difficult than a voltmeter-range change because the resistances involved are extremely low and contact resistances are often disturbing. However, if special care is taken to construct the shunt and calibrate the instrument, fairly accurate results may be obtained. In making such a shunt it should be remembered that (1) the instrument and shunt resistances R_I and R_{SH} are inversely proportional to the respective currents, and (2) the size of the wire used in the shunt must be sufficiently large to carry the shunted current without undue heating.

A number of examples will now be given to illustrate the principles of ammeters and voltmeters.

EXAMPLE 1. A D'Arsonval-type instrument (see Fig. 71) has a moving coil containing 60½ turns of wire, wound over a frame having a radius $R = 0.4$ in. and an axial length $L = 1.25$ in. If the air-gap flux density is radial and uniform and has a value of 4,800 lines per square inch, calculate the torque developed for a full-scale deflection, if the coil current under this condition is 15 ma (0.015 amp).

Solution

Before proceeding with a solution, using Eq. (51), it will be necessary to convert the values given in inch units to centimeter units, thus:

$$R = 0.4 \times 2.54 = 1.016 \text{ cm}$$
$$L = 1.25 \times 2.54 = 3.175 \text{ cm}$$
$$B = \frac{4{,}800}{6.45} = 745 \text{ lines per square centimeter}$$

Therefore

$$T = 0.2 \times 745 \times 60.5 \times 0.015 \times 1.016 \times 3.175 = 435 \text{ dyne-cm}$$

EXAMPLE 2. If full-scale deflection in Example 1 occurs for a coil rotation of 75°, calculate the torque per degree of deflection.

Solution

$$T \text{ per deg} = \frac{435}{75} = 5.8 \text{ dyne-cm per deg}$$

EXAMPLE 3. The moving coil of a D'Arsonval-type instrument has a resistance of 1.8 ohms and deflects full scale when an emf of 54 mv is applied to its terminals. Calculate (*a*) the resistance of a shunt that will give a full-scale deflection for a line current of 10 amp; (*b*) the resistance of a multiplier that will convert the instrument to a 75-volt voltmeter.

Solution

(*a*) Moving-coil current for full-scale deflection $= I_I = \dfrac{0.054}{1.8}$

$$= 0.03 \text{ amp}$$

$$\text{Resistance of shunt} = R_{SH} = \frac{0.054}{10 - 0.03} = 0.0057 \text{ ohm}$$

(*b*) Total resistance of instrument and multiplier $= \dfrac{75}{0.03} = 2{,}500$ ohms

$$\text{Resistance of multiplier} = R_M = 2{,}500 - 1.8 = 2{,}498.2 \text{ ohms}$$

EXAMPLE 4. A 150-volt voltmeter has a total resistance between terminals of 15,000 ohms (100 ohms per volt). (*a*) If a resistance of 7,500 ohms is connected in series with the instrument what is the multiplying factor MF? (This is the factor by which the instrument indication must be multiplied to give the true line voltage.) (*b*) What resistance should be connected in series with the instrument if the multiplying factor is to be 4? (The instrument will thus be converted into a 600-volt voltmeter.)

Solution

(*a*) $$\text{MF} = \frac{7{,}500}{15{,}000} + 1 = 1.5 \text{ [see Eq. (52)]}$$

(*b*) $$\text{MF} = 4 = \frac{R_M}{15{,}000} + 1$$

$$R_M = 45{,}000 \text{ ohms}$$

Multirange Instruments. The foregoing should make it clear that the usefulness of measuring instruments may be extended by providing them with several internal shunts or multipliers, or both; they then become *multirange instruments*, because each shunt or multiplier, properly connected to the moving coil, enlarges the calibrated scale by a different amount. The important point to remember in this connection is that full-scale deflection occurs when maximum permissible current passes through the moving coil and that this moving-coil current must not be exceeded whether the instrument is equipped with a shunt (in which event it becomes an ammeter) or a multiplier (under which condition it serves as a voltmeter). This implies, of course, that (1) when used as an ammeter the shunt always bypasses a definitely exact proportion of the total current, and (2) when used as a voltmeter the multiplier always incurs a definitely exact proportion of the total voltage drop. For example, if full-scale deflection occurs when the instrument potential drop is 50 mv and its current is 0.02 amp, a shunt must bypass 4.98 amp if the instrument is to be used as a 5-amp ammeter, or a multiplier must incur a voltage drop of 149.95 volts if it is to serve as a 150-volt voltmeter.

Multirange Ammeter. The internal wiring connections and other details of a triple-range d-c ammeter are shown in Fig. 78. Note particularly that there are three shunts R_A, R_B, and R_C. When the 1.5-amp range is used, between the *plus* and 1.5-amp terminals, the series circuit consisting of the moving coil and its calibrating resistor is paralleled (shunted) by $(R_A + R_B + R_C)$; under this condition a maximum line current of 1.5 amp will divide so that a major part will pass through the shunt and the remaining *correct* value of current will pass through the coil to give full-scale deflection. For the 3-amp range, between the *plus* and 3-amp terminals, the series circuit consisting of R_A, the moving coil and its calibrating resistor is shunted by $(R_B + R_C)$; under this condition a maximum line current of 3 amp will divide so that a still larger part will pass through the shunt and the remaining *correct* value of current (exactly the same value as for the 1.5-amp range) will pass through the coil to give full-scale deflection. Finally, for the 15-amp range, between the *plus* and 15-amp terminals, the series circuit consisting of R_B, R_A, the moving coil, and its calibrating resistor is paralleled by R_C only; under this condi-

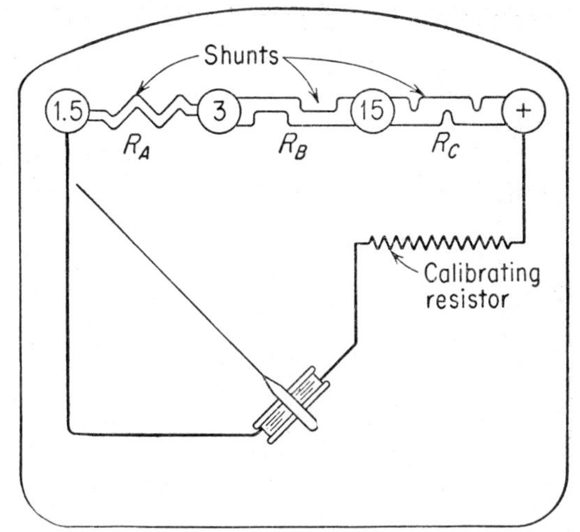

FIG. 78. Triple-range ammeter showing internal connections.

tion a maximum line current of 15 amp will divide so that most of the current will pass through R_C and the remaining *correct* value of current (exactly the same value as for the 1.5- and 3-amp ranges) will pass through the coil to give full-scale deflection. For line currents smaller than 1.5, 3, or 15 amp the deflections will, of course, be proportional to the current magnitudes on each of the respective ranges.

The material generally employed for ammeter shunts is the alloy *Manganin;* it is ideally suited for this purpose because it has a comparatively high specific resistance, good current-carrying capacity, and a negligibly small temperature-resistance coefficient. This latter property is extremely important because the accuracy of the instrument can be maintained only if the resistance of the shunt does not change with wide variations in temperature.

Multirange Voltmeter. Figure 79 shows the internal connections for a triple-range d-c voltmeter. Comparing it with the triple-range ammeter of Fig. 78, it will be observed that the shunts that parallel the moving coil are replaced by multipliers, i.e., series resistors. Assuming that full-scale deflection occurs when the moving coil is connected to a 50-mv source, it should be clear that (1) when the instrument is to be used as a 15-volt voltmeter (plus and 15-volt terminals) the R_C multiplier must incur a 14.95-volt drop for full-scale deflection; (2) when the instrument is to be used as a 150-volt voltmeter (plus and 150-volt terminals) the series combination of $(R_C + R_B)$ multipliers must incur a 149.95-volt drop for full-scale deflection; (3) when the instrument is to be used as a 300-volt voltmeter (plus and 300-volt terminals) the series combination of $(R_C + R_B + R_A)$ multipliers must incur a 299.95-volt drop for full-scale deflection. In each case the multiplier must absorb the difference between the maximum permissible line potential and 50 mv required by the moving coil. Obviously, for line voltages of less than 15, 150, and 300 volts the deflections will be proportional to the voltage magnitudes on each of the respective ranges.

Multiplier material must have a comparatively low temperature-resistance coefficient (for accuracy at varying temperatures) and a rather

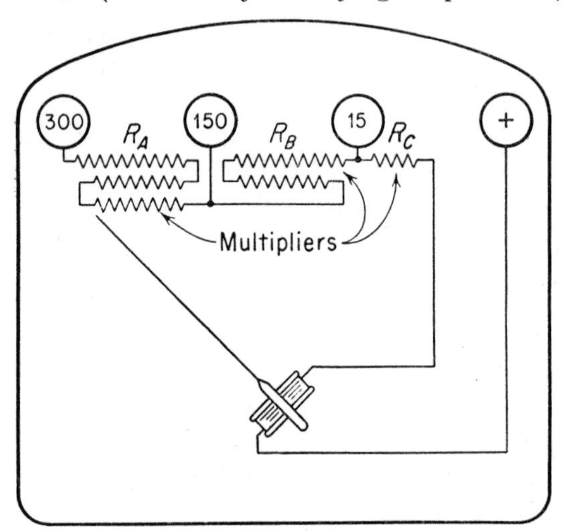

FIG. 79. Triple-range voltmeter showing internal connections.

high resistivity. The latter is particularly important here because multiplier resistances are usually large; for a given resistance the multiplier occupies less space as the resistivity increases. The alloy *Nichrome* possesses the properties indicated and is therefore generally used for this purpose.

Multirange Volt-ammeter. An instrument is sometimes designed to be used either as an ammeter *or* a voltmeter and may, moreover, have several ranges for both the current and voltage scales. Such an arrangement is shown in Fig. 80, in which three current ranges and two voltage ranges are indicated. Connections must, of course, be made to the proper instrument terminals in compliance with maximum current (load) and voltage (source) conditions. Note particularly that amperes will be registered when the insulated button is in the normal position shown; for a voltage measurement it is necessary to press the spring-loaded button. Being a combination instrument it is somewhat more difficult to calibrate than single-purpose measuring devices.

The Electrodynamometer Instrument. Although power in d-c circuits is generally measured by using an ammeter and a voltmeter ($P = EI$ watts) a special type of electrodynamometer instrument may be employed to do so directly. Consisting of a stationary set of coils that is

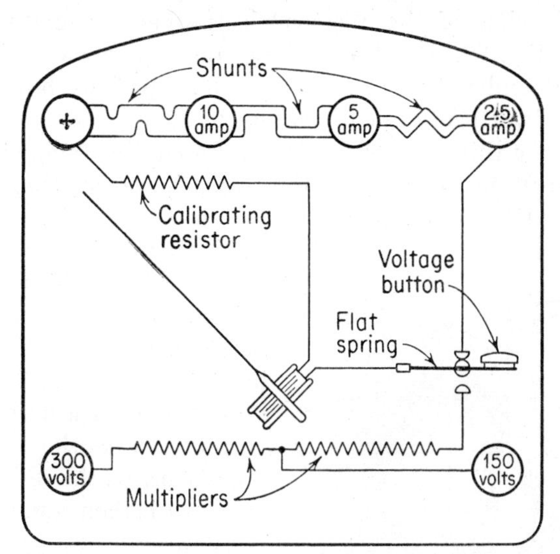

FIG. 80. Multirange volt-ammeter showing internal connections.

connected like an ammeter to carry the load current and a movable coil with an attached pointer that is connected like a voltmeter to give a measure of the line potential, it produces a turning moment when two components of flux, acting at an angle with respect to each other, are created. Since the current coils and the potential coil must establish fluxes that are directly proportional to the line amperes and the line

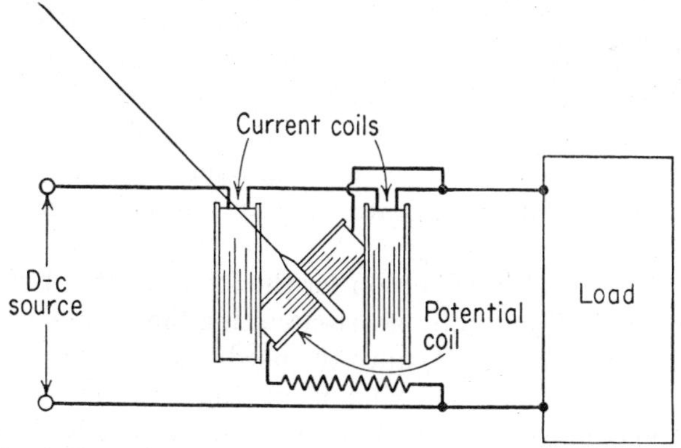

FIG. 81. Sketch illustrating a wattmeter, with internal wiring, connected to a load.

voltage, no iron is used in the wattmeter. A sketch illustrating the coil arrangement and the manner in which the instrument is connected to measure power is given in Fig. 81. Note that a pair of stationary heavy-wire coils is placed on both sides of a tilted and carefully balanced movable many-turn coil; the latter, of course, carries the pointer that moves over a calibrated scale.

A phantom view of the Weston electrodynamometer mechanism is illustrated in Fig. 82. It clearly shows the arrangement and mounting of the current and potential elements, and especially how the latter is set in a pair of vertically lined bearings.

Instruments of this type are also made for current (ammeter) and voltage (voltmeter) measurements; they are, however, employed almost exclusively for the measurement of power in a-c circuits.

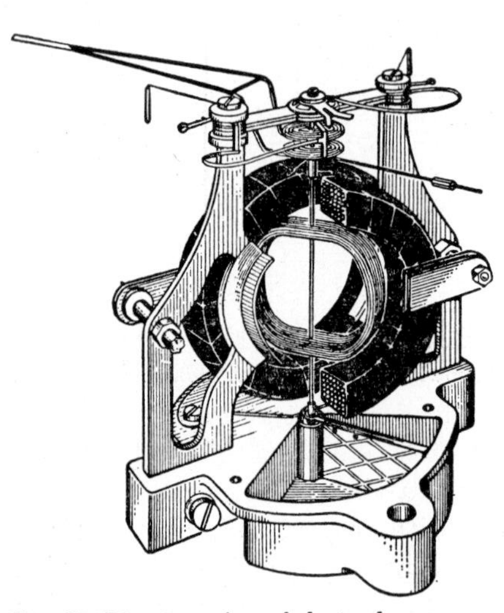

FIG. 82. Phantom view of electrodynamometer mechanism for a wattmeter. (*Weston Electrical Instrument Corp.*)

Ohmmeters. For the determination of resistance in a d-c circuit it is customary to employ the voltammeter method. The procedure, illustrated by Fig. 9, page 40, involves the measurement of the current *through* the resistor and the voltage *across* the resistor; the ratio of E to I is then equal to the circuit resistance.

A more convenient method, although somewhat less accurate, makes use of a direct-reading *ohmmeter*. This self-contained instrument has two externally mounted open-circuited terminals that are internally connected in series with a small dry-type battery and a fixed limiting resistor; a calibrating rheostat, directly in parallel with the movement, completes the internal connections. After the ohmmeter is calibrated, as described below, the unknown resistor is connected to the instrument's terminals, whereupon the needle is deflected to indicate directly the ohmic value of the unknown unit.

Figure 83 shows a wiring diagram for the instrument. Before it is put to use, it must be calibrated by short-circuiting the terminals and adjusting the calibrating rheostat R_C until the needle gives a "zero" deflection; the latter zero-resistance marking is at the extreme right, because, representing maximum current, it results from an external resistance of zero ohms. Now then, if the short circuit is removed and an unknown resistor R_X is connected to the terminals, the needle will receive a smaller upscale deflection that, on the previously calibrated scale, indicates the resistance in ohms. In fact, if the terminals are left open-circuited the needle will remain at the extreme left to indicate infinite resistance.

Since the accuracy of the deflection, for a given value of R_X, depends upon the condition of the dry cell, compensation for aging and use must be provided by the calibrating rheostat; this simple *shunt* rheostat merely provides an easy means of adjusting the sensitivity of the ohmmeter.

A serious disadvantage of the instrument is that its ohmic range, over a comparatively short scale, is from zero to infinity. This makes the ohmmeter quite inaccurate for deflections that are somewhat less than

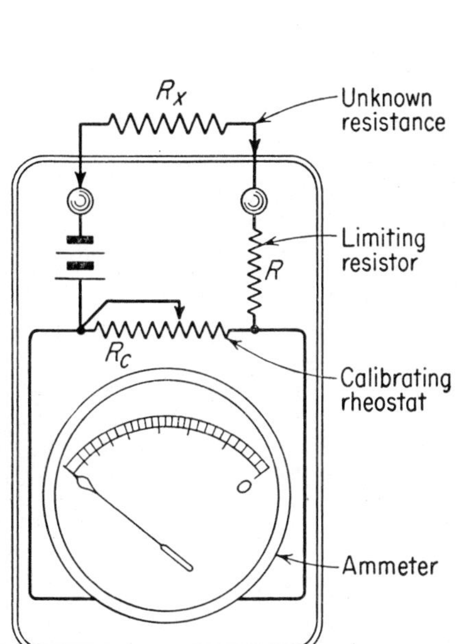

FIG. 83. Internal wiring connections of an ohmmeter.

FIG. 84. Photograph of a wide-range ohmmeter. (*Weston Electrical Instrument Corp.*)

10 per cent of full scale. Figure 84 depicts a widely used type of ohmmeter.

EXAMPLE 5. The moving coil of the instrument in an ohmmeter (see Fig. 83) has a resistance of 2.5 ohms and deflects full scale on 40 mv. When the ohmmeter terminals are short-circuited, the calibrating rheostat must be adjusted to 10 ohms to give a "zero" needle deflection. If the battery emf is 3 volts, calculate (*a*) the resistance of the limiting resistor R; (*b*) the current through the moving coil and the per cent full-scale deflection if an external resistance, R_X, of 250 ohms is connected across the ohmmeter's terminals. Neglect the internal resistance of the battery.

Solution

(*a*) With the terminals short-circuited, the current through the limiting resistor R is the sum of the currents through the moving coil and the calibrating rheostat. Thus

$$I_R = \frac{0.04}{2.5} + \frac{0.04}{10} = 0.02 \text{ amp}$$

Since the voltage drop across the limiting resistor is

$$E_R = 3 - 0.04 = 2.96 \text{ volts}$$

it follows that

$$R = \frac{2.96}{0.02} = 148 \text{ ohms}$$

(*b*) With 250 ohms connected across the instrument's terminals the total circuit resistance is

$$R_t = 250 + 148 + \frac{2.5 \times 10}{12.5} = 400 \text{ ohms}$$

The total circuit current will therefore be

$$I_R = \frac{3}{400} = 0.0075 \text{ amp}$$

and the moving-coil current will be

$$I_{mc} = 0.0075 \times \frac{10}{(10 + 2.5)} = 0.006 \text{ amp}$$

Hence

$$\text{Deflection} = \frac{0.006}{0.016} \times 100 = 37.5 \text{ per cent}$$

The Wheatstone Bridge. When four resistors are connected in *parallel-series*, as shown in Fig. 85*a*, the *potential difference* between x and y will be zero if the voltage drops across R_X and R_A are equal; under this

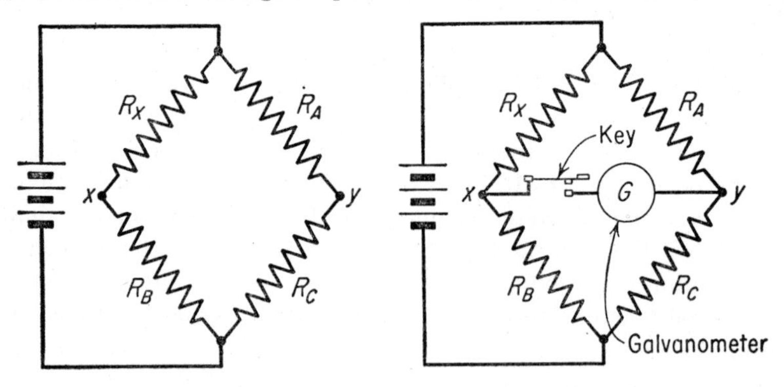

Fig. 85. Circuits illustrating derivation of a Wheatstone bridge.

condition the voltage drops across R_B and R_C will also be equal. In equation form, these statements become

$$I_1 R_X = I_2 R_A \qquad \text{and} \qquad I_1 R_B = I_2 R_C$$

If the first equation is divided by the second,

$$\frac{I_1 R_X}{I_1 R_B} = \frac{I_2 R_A}{I_2 R_C}$$

from which

$$R_X = \left(\frac{R_B}{R_C}\right) R_A \tag{53}$$

Since, as indicated above, zero potential difference exists between x and y, a conductor joining these two points will carry no current. This suggests the possibility, therefore, of connecting a delicate instrument between points x and y to determine whether or not the condition given by Eq. (53) is fulfilled; the arrangement is shown in Fig. 85*b* with a *bridge*, consisting of a delicate instrument—a *galvanometer*—and a key connecting points x and y. First proposed by Wheatstone for the measurement of resistance, it is called a *Wheatstone bridge*. In practice it is customary to have one set of standard resistances that may be adjusted to give a desired *ratio* of R_B to R_C in the decimal system (i.e., 0.001, 0.01, 0.1, 1.0, 10, 100, etc.) and another variable *standard* resistance representing R_A. By properly manipulating the dials corresponding to the *ratio arm* and the variable resistance it is possible to *balance the bridge;* under this condition the galvanometer will show zero deflection and the value of R_X may be determined by Eq. (53). While the bridge is being balanced, the experimenter should exercise care to prevent violent deflections of the pointer. As the bridge approaches a balance, when resistance R_A is varied, the needle will swing to the left or right (zero is at the center of the scale in the type of galvanometer generally used); after some practice the operator will know whether to increase or decrease R_A to obtain a balance.

EXAMPLE 6. Referring to Fig. 85*b*, determine the value of R_X if the bridge is balanced when $R_B/R_C = 0.1$ and $R_A = 68$.

Solution

$$R_X = 0.1 \times 68 = 6.8 \text{ ohms}$$

The Varley Loop. An interesting and useful practical application of the Wheatstone bridge is concerned with the location of grounded faults in cables. When the insulation around a conductor in any part of a transmission system breaks down it must be repaired as quickly as possible if safe and satisfactory electrical service is to be maintained. The first step is, obviously, to locate the so-called *ground* (within a reasonable distance of the actual point of failure), and this is accomplished quite accurately by the *Varley-loop* procedure.

Referring to Fig. 86, assume that a cable is grounded at point x, an unknown distance d ft from the beginning. A second cable of the same size and length, but completely intact (it generally acts with another conductor to form a *pair* in a two-wire transmission line), is then looped to the first cable at the far end. Connections are completed by joining the looped cables to three arms of a Wheatstone bridge and a SPDT switch as shown.

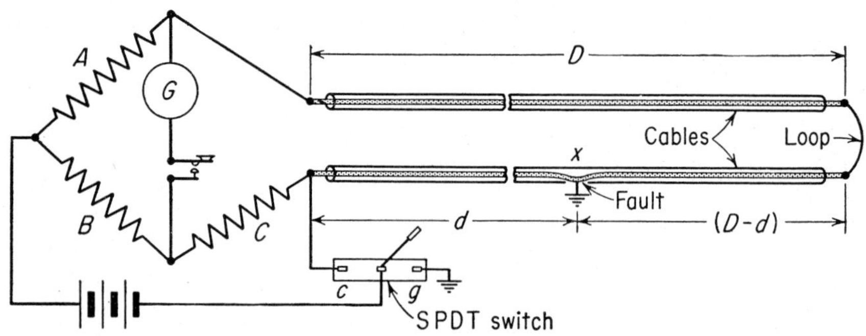

FIG. 86. Varley-loop circuit diagram for the location of the distance to a grounded cable.

The first, or preliminary, step is to determine the total resistance R of both lengths of cable in series. To do this it is merely necessary to close the SPDT switch to the left—point c—in which event resistance R becomes the fourth, or unknown, arm of the bridge; when the latter is balanced,

$$\frac{A}{B} = \frac{R}{C} \quad \text{and} \quad R = \frac{AC}{B}$$

In the second step the SPDT switch is closed to the *ground* side, i.e., point g, and a bridge balance is again obtained. Under this condition,

$$\frac{A}{B} = \frac{rD + r(D - d)}{C + rd} = \frac{r(2D - d)}{C + rd}$$

where D = transmission-line length, ft
r = resistance, ohms per ft of conductor

Solving for the distance to the fault,

$$d = \frac{2rBD - AC}{r(A + B)}$$

Since it is desirable to eliminate the value of r from the above formula, its equivalent, in terms of R and D, will be substituted ($r = R/2D$). Therefore

$$d = \frac{2(R/2D)BD - AC}{(R/2D)(A + B)}$$

from which
$$d = \frac{2D}{R}\left(\frac{BR - AC}{A + B}\right) \tag{54}$$

Equation (54) is greatly simplified if the ohmic values of A and B are made equal to each other; under this condition,

$$d_{(A=B)} = \frac{D}{R}(R - C) \tag{55}$$

EXAMPLE 7. A Varley loop (Fig. 86) is used to locate a grounded fault in a cable 3,700 ft long. After two similar cables are looped as indicated, the SPDT switch is closed to point c to determine the value of R; when a balance is obtained, $A = 10$, $B = 100$, and $C = 12.6$. Upon closing the SPDT switch to the right, with the same settings of A and B, the bridge is balanced for a value of $C = 9.3$. Determine the distance to the fault.

Solution

$$R = \frac{AC}{B} = \frac{10 \times 12.6}{100} = 1.26 \text{ ohms}$$

$$d = \frac{2 \times 3{,}700}{1.26}\left(\frac{100 \times 1.26 - 10 \times 9.3}{10 + 100}\right) = 1{,}760 \text{ ft}$$

The Slide-wire Bridge. A convenient simplification of the Wheatstone bridge is the so-called *slide-wire* bridge. In practice the ratio arm, represented in Fig. 85 by R_B/R_C, is replaced by a Manganin or german silver wire of *uniform* cross section exactly 100 cm long; the latter is laid on an accurately divided meter scale and tightly stretched between a pair of heavy copper terminals. A specially constructed key that fits neatly over the scale may be moved along the wire where contact may be made with the latter to complete the shunt circuit between points x and y of Fig. 87. The fact that the resistance per unit length of wire is constant means that the *wire-resistance ratios* are equal to corresponding *wire-length ratios*. Thus, if l is the entire length of the wire, i.e., 100 cm, and S is the distance from the zero end of the scale to the point where the key is depressed for a balanced bridge, it follows that

$$\frac{R_X}{R} = \frac{l - S}{S} = \frac{(100 - S)}{S} = \left(\frac{100}{S} - 1\right)$$

from which
$$R_X = R\left(\frac{100}{S} - 1\right) \tag{56}$$

If resistor R is a standard whose value may be adjusted to be approximately equal to the unknown resistor, the bridge will be in balance when the key is near the middle of the slide wire; under this condition wire

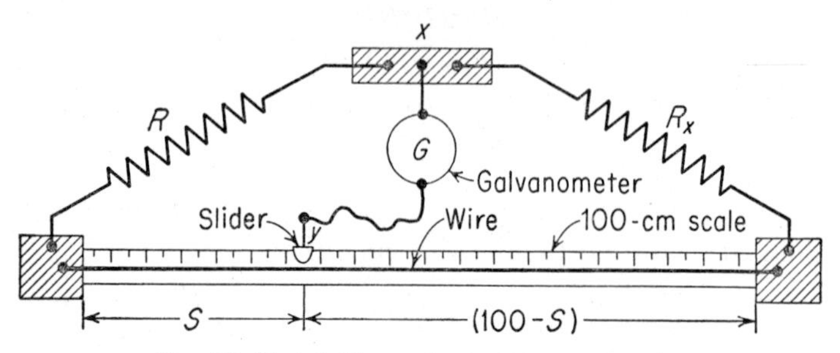

Fig. 87. Sketch illustrating a slide-wire bridge.

irregularities will tend to cancel, and, because a length ratio is used, the value of R will be more accurate.

Example 8. Using a slide-wire bridge a balance is obtained when R, the standard, is 80 ohms and the key is 62.5 cm from the zero end of the scale; i.e., S = 62.5 cm. Calculate the value of R_X.

Solution

$$R_X = 80\left(\frac{100}{62.5} - 1\right) = 48 \text{ ohms}$$

High-resistance Measurements. *Voltmeter Method.* It is sometimes necessary to determine by measurement the insulation resistance of electrical machines or cables, the ohmic values of high-resistance radio components, and others; many excellent precision devices, such as megohmmeters and special bridges, have been developed for this purpose. Although descriptions and operation of the latter are beyond the scope of this book, a simple procedure that employs a high-resistance voltmeter will be considered.

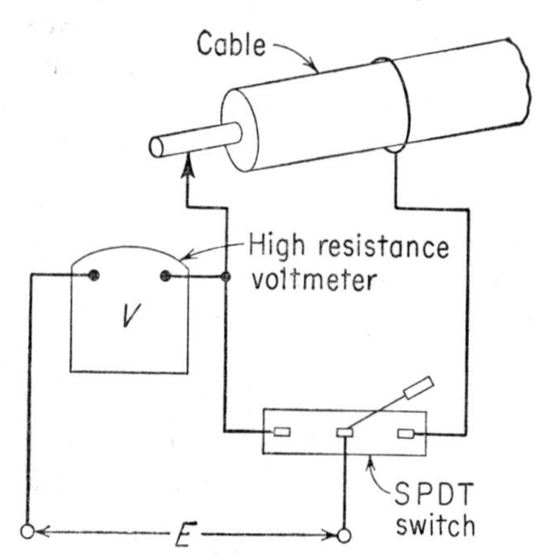

Fig. 88. Circuit diagram to measure the insulation resistance of a cable.

For reasonably good accuracy it is necessary to have a 150- or 300-volt voltmeter that has a resistance of 1,000 ohms per volt; such voltmeters, having resistances of 150,000 or 300,000 ohms, are widely used, and their internal resistances are usually given on the calibrated scale or case.

Referring to the diagram of Fig. 88, which shows the wiring connections for the measurement of the insulation resistance of a cable between conductor and surrounding cover (e.g., a lead sheath), the procedure is as follows: (1) the blade of the SPDT switch is closed to the left to measure the line voltage E; (2) the switch is then closed to the right, whereupon the voltmeter registers its *own* voltage drop E_v. Since the voltage drop across the cable insulation resistance is $(E - E_v)$, it follows that, for a simple series circuit,

$$\frac{(E - E_v)}{E_v} = \frac{R}{R_v}$$

from which

$$R = \left(\frac{E}{E_v} - 1\right) R_v \tag{57}$$

To measure the insulation resistance, between conductor and ground, of an electrical machine a similar procedure is followed; the leads shown connected to the cable in Fig. 87 would then be joined to any conductor (or commutator in the case of a d-c armature) and the grounded frame.

EXAMPLE 9. A 150,000-ohm voltmeter is connected in series with the insulating material of a motor (between a conductor and the frame), and then to a previously measured 114-volt d-c source. If the voltmeter deflection indicates that the voltage drop across its own 150,000-ohm resistance is 6 volts, calculate the insulation resistance.

Solution

$$R = \left(\frac{114}{6} - 1\right) 150{,}000 = 2{,}700{,}000 \text{ ohms, or } 2.7 \text{ megohms}$$

Questions

1. What types of instrument are generally used for d-c measurements? for a-c measurements?
2. How is the resistance of a circuit, or of part of a circuit, determined by the voltammeter method? Explain.
3. Name several types of *direct-reading* instrument used for the measurement of resistance.
4. What purpose is served by a potentiometer? Is it a precision instrument?
5. What important fundamental principles are involved in the operation of a permanent-magnet type of instrument?
6. Upon what factors does the permanency of a magnet depend? Which are *directly proportional* factors? *inversely proportional* factors?
7. What materials are generally used for permanent magnets?
8. Describe the construction of the moving coil of a D'Arsonval type of instrument.
9. Upon what factors does the developed torque of an electrical instrument depend?
10. How is the moving coil set with respect to the permanent-magnet field?
11. Why is damping generally necessary in a measuring instrument? How is this effected in the D'Arsonval type of instrument?

12. How do the permanent-magnet and moving-coil fields react with respect to each other to develop torque? Explain carefully.
13. What fundamental differences exist between ammeters and voltmeters?
14. What is a *shunt?* a *multiplier?*
15. How does a shunt limit the moving-coil current in an ammeter?
16. How does a multiplier limit the moving-coil current in a voltmeter?
17. What is the relative resistance of a good ammeter? a good voltmeter? Explain why, for each type of instrument.
18. Explain why the insertion of an instrument in a circuit tends to alter the conditions in the circuit. Indicate how such alteration may be minimized.
19. Is it possible to extend the range of a given ammeter or voltmeter? Explain carefully.
20. Make simple sketches showing how shunts and multipliers are applied in measuring instruments.
21. What materials are generally used for shunts and multipliers?
22. Explain why a very low shunt resistance greatly increases the range of an ammeter.
23. Explain why a very high multiplier resistance greatly increases the range of a voltmeter.
24. What is a *multirange ammeter?* a *multirange voltmeter?* a *volt-ammeter?*
25. For a full-scale deflection, what current must be bypassed by the shunt of an ammeter?
26. For full-scale deflection, what voltage drop must be incurred by the multiplier of a voltmeter?
27. What is meant by the *multiplying factor* MF of a voltmeter?
28. Describe the construction of the electrodynamometer type of instrument.
29. Under what operating conditions is it desirable to use an electrodynamometer type of instrument in preference to a D'Arsonval unit?
30. Describe the construction of an ohmmeter.
31. Why is it possible to calibrate an ohmmeter in terms of ohm units?
32. In an ohmmeter, why is the zero-resistance marking at the extreme right?
33. In an ohmmeter, why is the marking at the extreme left given as *infinite ohms?*
34. Why must an ohmmeter be calibrated before use? Explain carefully.
35. Why is a resistance measurement, made with an ohmmeter, less accurate than one made by the volt-ammeter method?
36. How is it possible to use an ohmmeter to make a continuity test?
37. Describe a simple Wheatstone-bridge circuit.
38. What type of measuring instrument is used in a Wheatstone bridge? Where is its zero marking?
39. Is it possible to use a pair of headphones in place of a measuring instrument in a Wheatstone bridge? Explain.
40. What is meant by a ratio dial in a Wheatstone bridge? Explain why this is a convenient arrangement.
41. Describe the procedure in balancing a Wheatstone bridge.
42. Explain why the *Varley loop* is fundamentally a Wheatstone bridge.
43. Describe the procedure that must be followed to locate a ground fault in a cable by the Varley-loop method.
44. Describe a slide-wire bridge and explain why, and under what conditions, it is fundamentally a Wheatstone bridge.
45. In using a slide-wire bridge where is it desirable to have the slider when a balance is obtained? Explain why.
46. Why is a high-resistance voltmeter desirable when used to measure very high values of resistance? Describe the procedure for doing this.

Problems

1. The moving coil of a D'Arsonval-type instrument has $80\frac{1}{2}$ turns of wire that are wound over a frame having an axial length of 1.5 in. and a width of $\frac{7}{8}$ in. If the permanent magnet produces a uniform air-gap flux density of 5,000 lines per square inch, and full-scale deflection of 75° occurs when the current is 12 ma, calculate the torque per degree of deflection.
2. If the calibrated scale of Prob. 1 is assumed correct, what per cent error will result if the permanent magnet suffers a loss of 300 maxwells per square inch?
3. A millivoltmeter has a resistance of 2.5 ohms and deflects full scale on 50 mv. (*a*) What should be the resistance of a shunt if the instrument is to be used as a 1-amp ammeter? (*b*) Repeat part (*a*) neglecting the moving-coil current.
4. Using the given data of Prob. 3, calculate the resistance of a multiplier if the instrument is to be used as a 150-volt voltmeter.
5. Repeat Prob. 4 neglecting the voltage drop across the moving coil.
6. A D'Arsonval-type instrument has a resistance of 3.5 ohms. If a 0.0028-ohm shunt is connected across its terminals and full-scale deflection occurs when the line current is 25 amp, calculate (*a*) the instrument current, (*b*) the current in the shunt.
7. If a resistance of 3,746.5 ohms is connected in series with the instrument of Prob. 6, determine the voltage that may be impressed across the combination to give full-scale deflection.
8. A 75-volt voltmeter has a resistance of 7,500 ohms. What will be the multiplying factor of the instrument if a resistance is connected in series having a value of (*a*) 7,500 ohms, (*b*) 22,500 ohms, (*c*) 18,000 ohms?
9. A 3-volt voltmeter has a resistance of 300 ohms. Calculate the total resistance of a multiplier, and the points at which it should be tapped, so that its range may be extended to 15, 150, and 300 volts.
10. A 150-volt voltmeter has a resistance of 16,000 ohms. When connected to a source of emf slightly greater than 150 volts the deflection is a little off scale. A resistance of 1,500 ohms is then connected in series with the instrument, whereupon it deflects 141 volts. Calculate the voltage of the source.
11. A 15,000-ohm 150-volt voltmeter is connected in series with a 17,500-ohm 150-volt voltmeter and the combination is used to measure the emf of a source. If the 15,000-ohm instrument gives a deflection of 102 volts, determine the reading on the 17,500-ohm voltmeter and the line voltage.
12. What maximum source voltage can be measured by the series combination of voltmeters of Prob. 11?
13. An ohmmeter has a 1.8-ohm instrument that gives full-scale deflection on 54 mv. When the ohmmeter terminals are short-circuited the calibrating rheostat (see Fig. 83) must be adjusted to 13.5 ohms to give "zero" needle deflection. If the battery emf is 1.5 volts, calculate (*a*) the ohmic value of the limiting resistor, (*b*) the per cent of full-scale deflection if an external resistance of 41.1 ohms is connected to the ohmmeter's terminals.
14. What will be the per cent deflection if the external resistance in Prob. 13 is doubled, i.e., 82.2 ohms?
15. If the ratio arm of a Wheatstone bridge is set at 10 and the variable standard resistance is adjusted to 168.2 ohms, calculate the resistance of the unknown resistor.
16. A 4,250-ft length of cable has a ground. To locate the fault the following data are obtained from a Varley-loop test: with the SPDT switch at c (see Fig. 86), a balance is obtained when $A = 10$, $B = 1{,}000$, and $C = 116$; with the switch

thrown to the grounded side g, $C = 72.6$ for the balanced bridge, A and B remaining the same as before. What is the distance to the cable ground?

17. Using a slide-wire bridge (see Fig. 87) what should be the setting of R in a standard decade box (an arrangement of standard resistors having values based on the decimal system) if the unknown resistance is about 180? 62? 0.87?

18. A 150,000-ohm voltmeter is connected in series with the insulating materials of a d-c armature winding (between the commutator and the shaft). If the voltmeter registers a deflection of 4.5 volts when the line potential is 117 volts, determine the resistance of the insulation in megohms.

CHAPTER 8

INDUCTANCE AND ELECTROMAGNETIC INDUCTION

Closing and Opening Electric Circuits. In a d-c circuit the only *opposition* offered to the flow of a continuous (steady) current is the equivalent resistance of all the conducting parts used in constructing the electric circuit. The laws, theorems, and rules previously studied in Chaps. 3 and 4 are applicable only to circuits in which the currents are in the steady state; they *are not valid during periods of current change*, and particularly *while* the current is rising to its ultimate value when a circuit is energized, or decaying to zero when a circuit is deenergized. The changes indicated may, and usually do, take place in an exceedingly short period of time, but it is nevertheless true that the conditions that then prevail are often as important, or even more so, than those that are finally established.

The manner in which the current will change during transient periods will depend, for the most part, upon the magnetic properties of the circuit. If, for example, very little magnetism is created by a current flow, practically no energy is stored in a magnetic field; under this condition the current rises abruptly, and almost instantaneously, to its steady-state value. In Fig. 89*a*, which applies to an 11-ohm nonmagnetic device, the current is observed to rise almost instantly to 10 amp when an emf of 110 volts is suddenly impressed by the closing of the switch. However, when the same resistor is coiled around a high-permeability, closed-magnetic core, the 10-amp current value is reached in about ½ sec (see Fig. 89*b*), because time is required to store the considerable magnetic energy in the magnetic substance. To expect an instantaneous rise in current as in Fig. 89*a*, where negligible magnetic energy is stored, would imply that the power, i.e., the rate at which energy is supplied to the coil, would have to be infinite; this is an obvious impossibility. The same reasoning applies to the opening of a circuit in which stored magnetic energy must be dissipated; here the current of 10 amp dies to zero in about ½ sec (see Fig. 89*c*). A circuit in which the current *lags* behind the application or removal of the emf is said to be *inductive*.

While the current is rising to its ultimate E/R value as in Fig. 89*b*, magnetic energy is continually being stored in the magnetic substance at

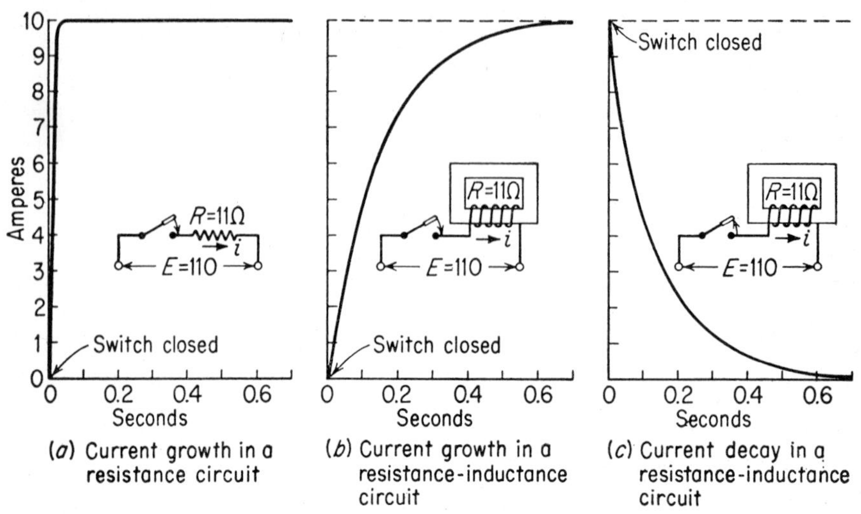

FIG. 89. Current vs. time relations in resistance and inductance circuits.

a progressively diminishing rate. Moreover, since every incremental increase in current represents a corresponding increase in magnetic energy, it follows that the latter tends to prevent the current from rising in value. This is similar to the condition that exists when a rubber tire is pumped up; as the stored energy in the rubber increases, it acts to prevent a further building up of air pressure in the tire although forced by considerable pressure from an air pump. In other words, it is only during the energy-storing period that opposition is developed to a change, i.e., an increase, in current; after that period has elapsed, the current is stabilized at its Ohm's law value. Further, when the circuit is opened and the emf is suddenly removed as in Fig. 89*c*, the current is prevented from dying out instantly because the stored magnetic energy cannot be released and restored to the circuit instantly; the current decreases *gradually* to zero as shown.

If an inductive d-c circuit is intermittently closed and opened by a simple interrupter, such as the "make-and-break" device of the ignition system in an automobile, the current curve would be made up of a succession of alternately repeating curves like Fig. 89*b* and *c*. If the interrupter operated every second, the current would repeatedly rise and fall, to 10 amp and zero, respectively, with successive "makes" and "breaks." However, if the interrupter had a shorter period of operation of, say, 0.1 sec, the current would never reach 10 amp or drop to zero but would vary between two intermediate values.

Self-inductance. The property of any electric circuit that opposes a *change* in the value of the current is known as self-inductance, or briefly *inductance*. This is the property that is responsible for the lag of the current behind the impressed voltage, and where, as in Fig. 89*b*, time must elapse before the current reaches its E/R value, or, as in Fig. 89*c*, the current decays to zero. If the circuit conditions are such that it takes the current a comparatively long time to change from zero to its ultimate value, or to drop from some definite value to zero, the inductance is large with respect to the resistance. On the other hand, if the current makes a complete change in an exceedingly short time, the resistance is large with respect to the inductance; the latter may, under certain conditions, be considered negligible. Note particularly that the *circuit conditions* determine the current behavior during the transient period; the time lag is affected by neither the final E/R value nor the voltage. The *inductance property* is analogous to inertia in a mechanical system; in the electric circuit the current lags behind the applied voltage, whereas in the mechanical system, such as the automobile or rotating flywheel, the motion lags behind the applied force.

In electric circuits the inductance property manifests itself through the creation, or induction, of an *opposing voltage* whose value generally changes from instant to instant. At the instant a switch is closed in a highly inductive d-c circuit, the opposing *induced* emf is practically equal to the impressed voltage; under this condition the current is zero because the *net* voltage in the circuit is zero. As the current proceeds to rise to its ultimate value, the countervoltage, i.e., the induced voltage, diminishes, and this in turn is accompanied by progressively larger values of current. Finally, when the current has reached its E/R value, the countervoltage is zero, so that opposition to change is no longer present. Understand that when the current is changing, there is opposition to such change; when the current is steady, no such opposition can be created.

Now, *if the current changes at the rate of one ampere per second and, as a result of such change, the induced opposing emf is one volt, the circuit is said to possess unit inductance, or one henry.* Assuming a total current change of I amp in t sec, the *average* induced emf will be given by the equation

$$E_{av} = L\left(\frac{I}{t}\right) \qquad \text{volts} \tag{58}$$

where L = inductance, henrys.

Remembering that inductive circuits always involve magnetic lines of force linking with turns of wire N it is also possible to express the average induced voltage E_{av} in terms of the rate of change of flux through the coil. Representing the product of Φ and N by flux *linkages,* where unit flux linkage is 1 maxwell linking with 1 turn of wire, it is known, and has been experimentally proved, that *the average induced emf is directly proportional to the rate of change of flux linkages.* Using practical units, this statement may be written in equation form as follows:

$$E_{av} = \frac{N\Phi}{t \times 10^8} \tag{59}$$

Setting the two voltages of Eqs. (58) and (59) equal to each other,

$$L\left(\frac{I}{t}\right) = \frac{N\Phi}{t \times 10^8}$$

from which

$$L = \frac{N\Phi}{I \times 10^8} \quad \text{henrys} \tag{60}$$

Since inductance depends, for the most part, upon the construction and arrangement of the electric- and magnetic-circuit elements of a device, its value, in henrys, may be related to numerical quantities that involve physical properties, or specifically, factors responsible for magnetic flux. When the latter, given by Eq. (44) (Chap. 6, page 115), is substituted in Eq. (60), the inductance becomes

$$L = \frac{N}{I \times 10^8} \times \frac{0.4\pi N I \mu A}{l} = \frac{0.4\pi N^2 A \mu}{l \times 10^8} \quad \text{henrys} \tag{61}$$

It is important to note, in Eq. (61), that inductance is a function not only of the area and permeability of the core, but also of the *square* of the number of turns; all factors are, of course, measures of the amount of flux that is created, although the *turns* term is most effective in this respect. It is well to remember this when the inductance property of a coil must be altered.

Equation (61) also indicates that a magnetic-core device will have varying values of inductance if it operates over a wide range of flux densities; this is true because the permeability μ varies considerably with flux density (see Fig. 61). It is for this reason that inductance calculations must be made for particular values of operating current, which, in turn, determines the magnitudes of B and μ. However, where the core material is *nonmagnetic*, Eq. (61) holds for all values of exciting current, because the permeability is unity.

EXAMPLE 1. A 1,500-turn solenoid produces 600,000 maxwells when excited by a current of 2.5 amp. Calculate (*a*) the flux linkages, (*b*) the inductance.

Solution

(*a*) Flux linkages $= 1{,}500 \times 600{,}000 = 9 \times 10^8$

(*b*) $$L = \frac{9 \times 10^8}{2.5 \times 10^8} = 3.6 \text{ henrys}$$

EXAMPLE 2. If 300 turns are removed from the solenoid of Example 1, calculate the inductance and the flux that will be created, assuming the same current and no change in permeability.

Solution

$$L_{1,200} = L_{1,500} \times \frac{(1{,}200)^2}{(1{,}500)^2} = 3.6 \times 0.64 = 2.3 \text{ henrys}$$

Since, by Eq. (60), Φ is directly proportional to L and inversely proportional to N, for a constant value of current,

$$\Phi_{1,200} = 600{,}000 \times \frac{2.3}{3.6} \times \frac{1{,}500}{1{,}200} = 480{,}000 \text{ maxwells}$$

EXAMPLE 3. A 1,250-turn coil is uniformly wound over the non-magnetic core of a toroid whose average diameter is 4 in., and cross-sectional area is 0.45 sq in. Calculate the inductance of the toroid.

Solution

$$L = \frac{0.4\pi \times (1{,}250)^2 \times (0.45 \times 6.45)}{(\pi \times 4 \times 2.54) \times 10^8} = 0.00178 \text{ henry}$$

EXAMPLE 4. A group of electromagnets that create flux in a d-c generator—the *field circuit*—has an inductance of 15 henrys. If the 2.6-amp excitation is interrupted in 0.04 sec by the opening of the field switch, what average voltage is induced in the winding?

Solution

$$E_{av} = 15 \times \frac{2.6}{0.04} = 975 \text{ volts}$$

Current Growth in Inductive Circuits. It is customary to represent a simple coil as though the properties of resistance and inductance were separate; the inductance is, moreover, regarded as "perfect" in the sense that it is *lumped* in the coil, rather than being distributed, and that all magnetic energy stored in the field could be restored to the electric circuit. An arrangement such as this, i.e., an *R-L* circuit, is shown in Fig. 90 connected in series with a battery and a switch. At the instant the switch is suddenly closed, at $t = 0$, the current i is zero; this is because an abrupt current change cannot occur in an inductive circuit. The result is that the current changes differentially, i.e., by extremely small amounts, with differential elements of time as it proceeds toward its ultimate E/R value. Designating a differential current change by di, and a differential time change by dt, the *rate* of current change is di/dt. Now then, since any current change in an inductive circuit is accompanied by an emf that

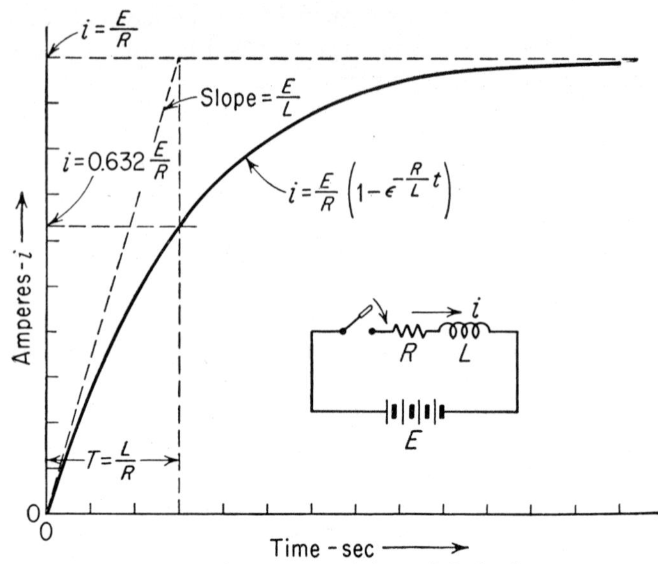

Fig. 90. Current growth in an R-L circuit.

opposes the impressed voltage and is numerically equal to the product of the inductance and the rate of current change [Eq. (58)], it follows, by Kirchhoff's law, that

$$E = iR + L\frac{di}{dt}$$

This is a so-called differential equation, involving as it does rapidly changing values of current (represented by the lower-case i) and rates of current change. It is well to note that at $t = 0$, when $i = 0$, the iR drop is zero, under which condition the induced emf $L\,di/dt = E$; also, when i reaches its E/R value, $L\,di/dt = 0$. When the above equation is solved for the current by the calculus,

$$i = \frac{E}{R}(1 - \epsilon^{-(R/L)t}) \qquad (62)^1$$

where ϵ is the Naperian logarithmic base $= 2.718$.

A typical graph of this exponential form of equation is shown in Fig. 90. Note that the current reaches its E/R value when the exponential term is zero, and this occurs theoretically at infinite time; practically, this condition is reached in a comparatively short time.

Inductive circuits are often compared with one another on the basis of the rapidity with which the currents tend to rise after the switch is closed. One standard of comparison is a time unit equal to L/R. This is desig-

[1] See Appendix 1H for derivation.

nated as the *time constant* of the circuit and is represented by capital letter T. Substituting $L/R = T$ for t, Eq. (62) becomes

$$i_T = \frac{E}{R}\{1 - \epsilon^{-[(R/L)\times(L/R)]}\} = \frac{E}{R}\left(1 - \frac{1}{\epsilon^{+1}}\right) = 0.632\frac{E}{R}$$

This indicates that the current will rise to 63.2 per cent of its ultimate E/R value in L/R sec after the switch is closed.

The *initial* rate of current change is also an important measure of a circuit's inductive property. If, for reasons of comparison, it is assumed that the current continues to change at its *initial* rate and reaches its ultimate value in $T = L/R$ sec, it follows that

$$\left(\frac{di}{dt}\right)_{\text{at } t=0} = \frac{E/R}{L/R} = \frac{E}{L} \tag{63}$$

The latter statement is obviously true because the rate of current change at any point on a curve (at $t = 0$ in this case) is the ratio of the ordinate to the abscissa of the tangent line at that point.

In summarizing, the following points can be made in connection with the *time constant* of a *current-growth* inductive circuit:

1. It is equal to L/R sec.
2. It is the time in seconds that is required for the current to rise to 63.2 per cent of its ultimate E/R value.
3. It is the time in seconds that would be required for the current to reach its ultimate E/R value if the initial rate of change E/L were maintained.

In an R-L circuit, it is extremely important to understand that increasing values of inductance L have a tendency to *reduce* the initial rate of rise of current as well as *retard* the current's growth; they have absolutely no effect upon the final E/R value. Moreover, when a circuit possesses the property of inductance it always acts as an open circuit at the instant a switch is closed; the current cannot change abruptly and is therefore exactly the same at $t = 0$ as it is just before. On the other hand, an increase in R does not affect the *initial* rate of rise of current although it does accelerate the current's growth to a *lower* E/R value. The foregoing points are illustrated by the graphs in Figs. 91 and 92. Figure 91 shows three R-L current-growth curves for which the values of inductance are L, $2L$, and $3L$, and the resistances R and voltages E are the same; observe particularly the change in the initial rates of rise of current, and that the same E/R value of current is reached in progressively increasing intervals of time. Figure 92 represents three typical current-growth curves for resistance values of R, $1.5R$, and $3R$, and constant values of L and E; note that the initial rates of current change are unaltered while

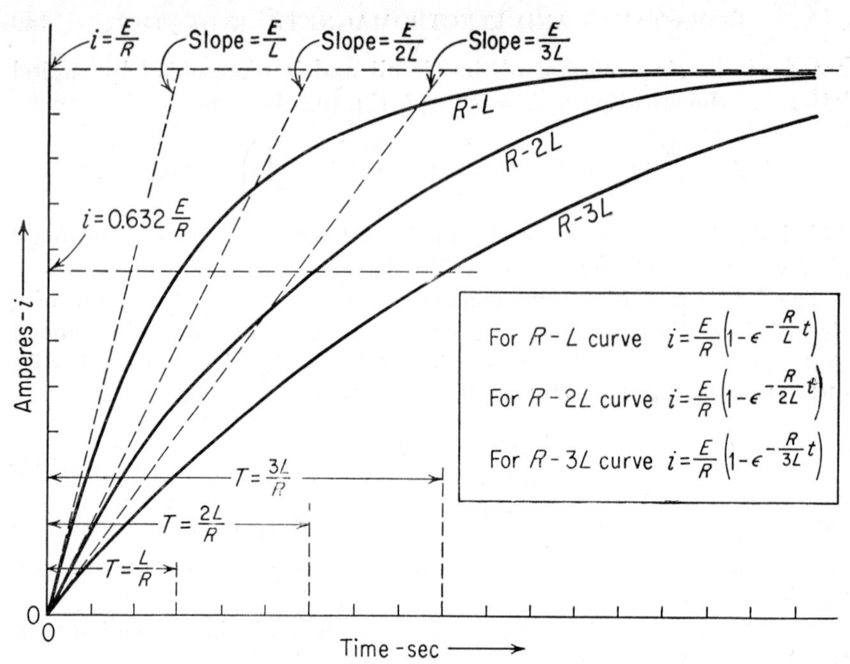

FIG. 91. Graphs illustrating the effect upon current growth when inductance is changed in an R-L circuit.

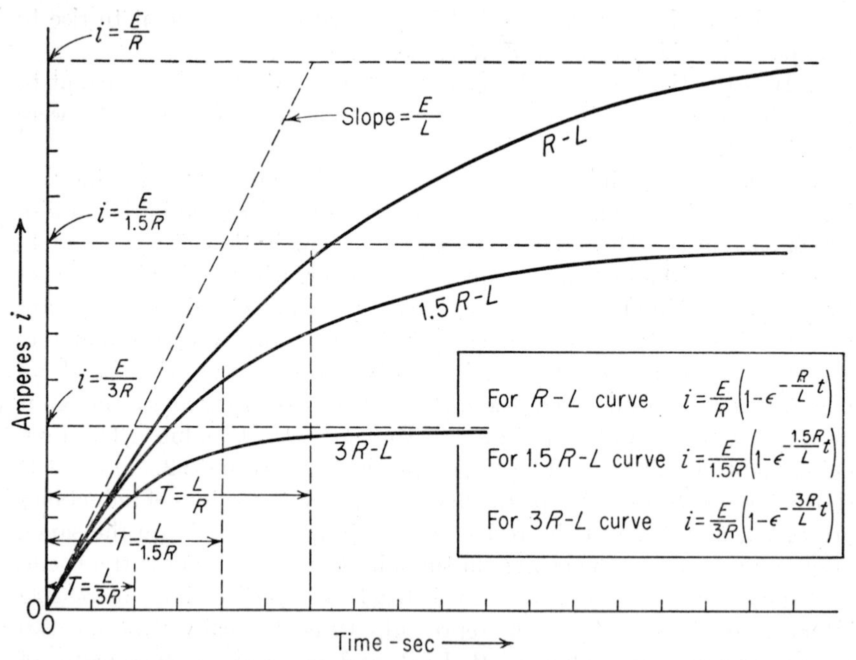

FIG. 92. Graphs illustrating the effect upon current growth when resistance is changed in an R-L circuit.

the lower values of E/R are reached in progressively shorter periods of time.

EXAMPLE 5. A relay has a resistance of 240 ohms and an inductance of 0.6 henry. When 48 volts is suddenly impressed across the device, determine (*a*) the equation of the current-growth curve, (*b*) the initial rate of current increase, (*c*) the time constant, (*d*) the current at the instant corresponding to the time constant, (*e*) the current at 0.00125 sec from the closing of the switch.

Solution

(*a*) $i = \frac{48}{240}[1 - \epsilon^{-(240/0.6)t}] = 0.2(1 - \epsilon^{-400t})$ amp

(*b*) At $t = 0$:

$$\frac{di}{dt} = \frac{E}{L} = \frac{48}{0.6} = 80 \text{ amp per sec}$$

(*c*) $T = \frac{0.6}{240} = 0.0025$ sec

(*d*) At $t = T = 0.0025$ sec:

$$i_T = 0.632 \times 0.2 = 0.1264 \text{ amp}$$

(*e*) $i = 0.2(1 - \epsilon^{-400 \times 0.00125}) = 0.2(1 - \epsilon^{-0.5}) = 0.2\left(1 - \frac{1}{\sqrt{\epsilon}}\right)$

$$= 0.0796 \text{ amp}$$

EXAMPLE 6. The initial rate of current rise in an R-L circuit is 300 amp per sec when 120 volts is suddenly impressed. What is the inductance of the circuit?

Solution

$$L = \frac{E}{di/dt} = \frac{120}{300} = 0.4 \text{ henry}$$

EXAMPLE 7. If the circuit resistance of Example 6 is 30 ohms, calculate the rate of current change when the current is 2.6 amp.

Solution

$$E = iR + L\frac{di}{dt} = (2.6 \times 30) + 0.4\frac{di}{dt} = 120$$

$$\frac{di}{dt} = \frac{120 - 78}{0.4} = 105 \text{ amp per sec}$$

Current Decay in Inductive Circuits. Just as the current rises *exponentially* to its E/R value when an R-L circuit is energized, so does the current decay *exponentially* when a similar circuit is deenergized; i.e., current cannot rise or fall abruptly when a circuit possesses inductive properties. Figure 93 shows three types of circuit arrangement in which the current may be made to drop to zero from its initial I_0 value. Considering Fig. 93*a* first, a fundamental though impractical circuit, it is obvious that the current is $i = I_0 = E/R$ just before and at the instant the switch is closed. Also, when the switch *is* closed, it becomes a short circuit across both the battery and the R-L circuit; the fuse therefore

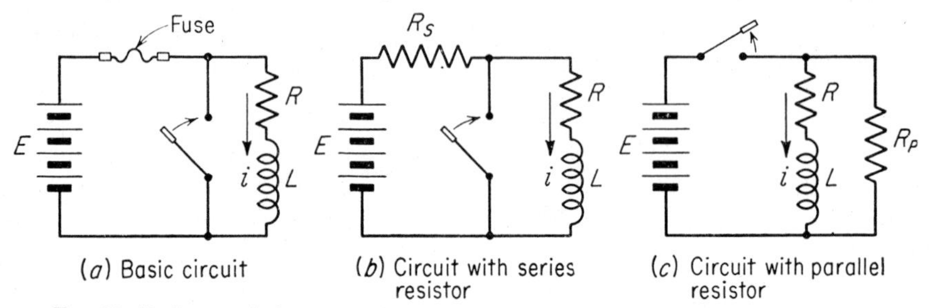

FIG. 93. Resistance-inductance circuits in which the currents decay exponentially.

blows, and, because the circuit voltage is zero, the current i decays exponentially to zero. Writing a differential equation for the circuit under consideration, it should be clear that, at any time t,

$$0 = iR + L\frac{di}{dt}$$

When this equation is solved for the current by the calculus,

$$i = I_0\epsilon^{-(R/L)t} \tag{64}$$

where I_0 = initial current, i.e., *inductive-circuit current just before it starts to decay*

R = *total resistance of circuit in which current is decaying*

Equation (64) must be used with care and in accordance with the definitions given for I_o and R. Thus,

For circuit 93*a*: $$i = \frac{E}{R}\epsilon^{-(R/L)t} \qquad (64a)^1$$

For circuit 93*b*: $$i = \frac{E}{(R + R_s)}\epsilon^{-(R/L)t} \qquad (64b)^1$$

For circuit 93*c*: $$i = \frac{E}{R}\epsilon^{-[(R+R_p)/L]t} \qquad (64c)^1$$

where R_s = *series* line resistance of Fig. 93*b*

R_p = *parallel* resistance of Fig. 93*c*

A time-constant criterion is used for current decay, as for current growth; i.e., $T = L/R$. The time constant is always the reciprocal of

[1] See Appendix 1I for derivation.

the constant term in the exponential of Eqs. (64*a*), (64*b*), and (64*c*); thus, for Fig. 93*a* and *b* it is L/R, and for Fig. 93*c* it is $L/(R + R_P)$. When the proper time constant is substituted in the appropriate equation,

$$i_T = I_0 \times \frac{1}{\epsilon} = 0.368 I_0$$

This merely indicates that the current will decay to 36.8 per cent of its original value in T sec; in other words, the current will make a 63.2 per cent change in T sec.

Concerning the initial rate of current change, this, by reasoning similar to that applied to current growth, is $-(E/L)$.

Summarizing, the following points can be made in connection with the time constant of a *current-decay* inductive circuit:

1. It is equal to L/R, using the proper value of R.
2. It is the time in seconds that is required for the current to decay to 36.8 per cent of its original value.
3. It is the time in seconds that would be required for the current to decay to zero if the initial rate of change $-(E/L)$ were maintained.

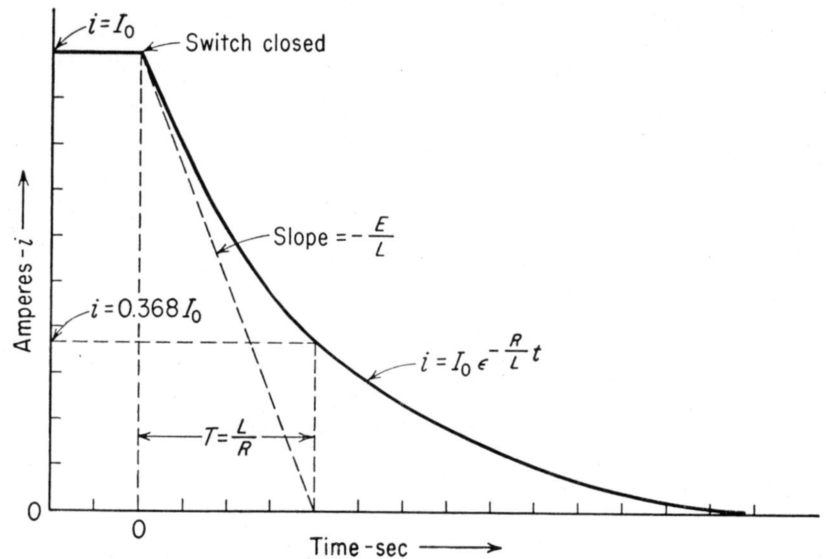

FIG. 94. Current decay in basic *R-L* circuit (see Fig. 93*a*).

A typical current-decay curve is illustrated in Fig. 94. For the basic circuit of Fig. 93*a* the current is $I_0 = E/R$ just before and at the instant the switch is closed; the current then proceeds to drop rapidly, and at $T = L/R$ it is $0.368 I_0$. For a circuit similar to Fig. 93*b* the initial current would be $I_0 = E/(R + R_S)$, and the time constant $T = L/R$. It would be necessary to *open* the switch in Fig. 93*c* to cause current decay; under this condition $I_0 = E/R$ and $T = L/(R + R_P)$.

EXAMPLE 8. In the circuit of Fig. 93*a*, $R = 12$ ohms, $L = 0.8$ henry, and $E = 24$ volts. (*a*) Write the equation for current decay after the switch is closed. Calculate (*b*) the time constant and the current at $t = T$, (*c*) the current at $t = 0.0222$ sec. (*d*) Determine the initial rate of current change.

Solution

(*a*) $$i = \frac{24}{12}\epsilon^{-(12/0.8)t} = 2\epsilon^{-15t}$$

(*b*) $$T = \frac{0.8}{12} = 0.0667 \text{ sec}$$

$$i_T = 0.368 \times 2 = 0.736 \text{ amp}$$

(*c*) $$i \text{ (at } t = 0.0222) = 2 \times \epsilon^{-15\times 0.0222} = 2 \times \epsilon^{-0.333} = \frac{2}{\sqrt[3]{\epsilon}} = 1.43 \text{ amp}$$

(*d*) $$\frac{di}{dt} \text{ (at } t = 0) = -\frac{24}{0.8} = -30 \text{ amp per sec}$$

EXAMPLE 9. Divide the 12-ohm resistance of Example 8 into two equal resistances of 6 ohms each. With the circuit elements arranged as in Fig. 93*b*, with $R = 6$, $R_S = 6$, $L = 0.8$, and $E = 24$, solve as before.

Solution

(*a*) $$i = \frac{24}{12}\epsilon^{-(6/0.8)t} = 2\epsilon^{-7.5t}$$

(*b*) $$T = \frac{0.8}{6} = 0.133 \text{ sec}$$

$$i_T = 0.368 \times 2 = 0.736 \text{ amp}$$

(*c*) $$i \text{ (at } t = 0.0222) = 2 \times \epsilon^{-7.5\times 0.0222} = 2\epsilon^{-0.167} = \frac{2}{\sqrt[6]{\epsilon}} = 1.69 \text{ amp}$$

(*d*) $$\frac{di}{dt} \text{ (at } t = 0) = -\frac{12}{0.8} = -15 \text{ amp per sec}$$

EXAMPLE 10. Rearrange the circuit elements of Example 9 to appear like Fig. 93*c*. With $R = 6$, $R_P = 6$, $L = 0.8$, and $E = 24$, solve as before for conditions after the switch is *opened*.

Solution

(*a*) $$i = \frac{24}{6}\epsilon^{-(12/0.8)t} = 4\epsilon^{-15t}$$

(*b*) $$T = \frac{0.8}{12} = 0.0667 \text{ sec}$$

$$i_T = 0.368 \times 4 = 1.472 \text{ amp}$$

(c) $i \text{ (at } t = 0.0222) = 4\epsilon^{-15\times0.0222} = 4\epsilon^{-0.333} = \dfrac{4}{\sqrt[3]{\epsilon}} = 2.86 \text{ amp}$

(d) $\dfrac{di}{dt} \text{ (at } t = 0) = -\dfrac{24}{0.8} = -30 \text{ amp per sec}$

Current Growth between Two Finite Values. In the operation of certain relays, i.e., electromagnets used in control circuits, it is sometimes desirable to insert or remove an external series resistor *while* the current is rising. When this is done the current grows along one exponential curve

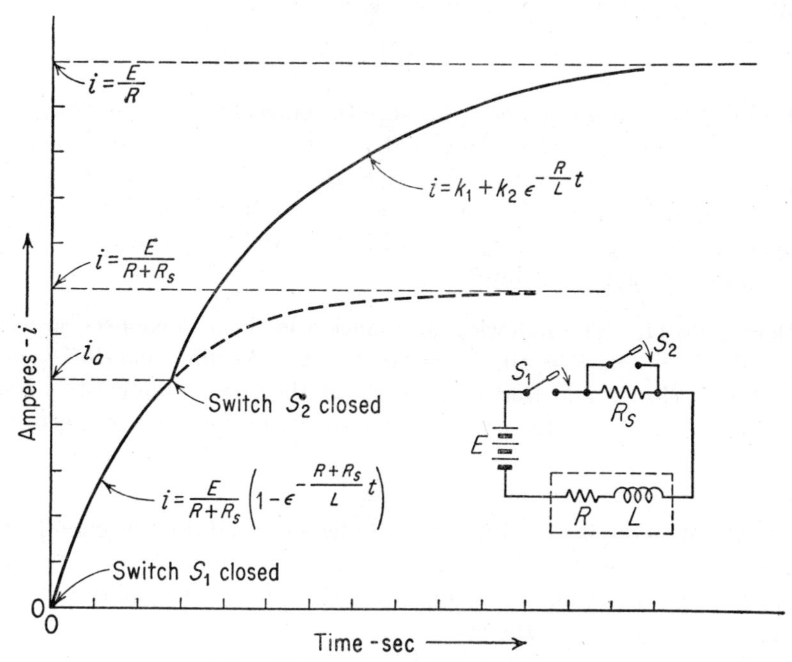

FIG. 95. Current growth in two steps.

for a short period of time and, after the external resistor is "cut in" or "cut out," proceeds to grow along a second—a different—exponential curve. Figure 95 illustrates an *R-L* circuit in which the relay is energized in two stages. When switch S_1 is closed, the current increases along the lower curve to the point where switch S_2 is closed or opened; the current then proceeds along the upper curve to its ultimate value. (The broken line is a continuation of the lower i vs. t relationship, with S_2 unoperated.)

If S_2 is assumed to be open at the instant S_1 is closed, the current equation for the first step becomes

$$i_1 = \frac{E}{R + R_S}\{1 - \epsilon^{-[(R+R_S)/L]t}\}$$

Written in a more *general form,*

$$i = k_1 + k_2\epsilon^{-\alpha t}$$

where $k_1 = k_2 = E/(R + R_S)$ and $\alpha = (R + R_S)/L$. Note particularly that $k_1 = k_2$ *only* under the condition that $i = 0$ when $t = 0$; at $t = 0$, $\epsilon^{-[(R+R_S)/L]t} = 1$ and $i = 0$; at $t = \infty$, $\epsilon^{-[(R+R_S)/L]t} = 0$ and $i = E/(R + R_S)$.

Analyzing the current equation for the second step, i.e., for the time interval *after* S_2 is closed, the current equation is

$$i_2 = k_1 + k_2\epsilon^{-(R/L)t}$$

where k_1 *is no longer equal to* k_2, because the current does *not* start at zero for the upper curve. Assuming that $t = 0$ at the instant S_2 is closed, i (at $t = 0$) $= i_a$ and i (at $t = \infty$) $= E/R$. With the latter two conditions known it is a simple matter to evaluate k_1 and k_2 and hence write the equation for the upper curve. Examples will now be given to illustrate the foregoing procedure.

Example 11. The following information is given in connection with Fig. 95: $E = 120$, $R = 40$, $R_S = 20$, $L = 2$. Assume that S_2 is open when S_1 is closed, and that S_2 is closed at the instant the current $i_2 = i_a = 1.2$ amp. Write the equations for the two steps of current growth.

Solution

Step 1: When S_1 is closed $i_1 = 0$. Under this condition the circuit acts as though the total resistance as $(R + R_S) = 60$ ohms, and the inductance $L = 2$. The values of k_1 and k_2 are therefore each equal to $^{120}/_{60} = 2$, and $\alpha = {}^{60}/_{2} = 30$. Hence

$$i_1 = 2 - 2\epsilon^{-30t} = 2(1 - \epsilon^{-30t})$$

Step 2: When S_2 is closed $i_2 = i_a = 1.2$. Under this condition k_1 is *not* equal to k_2; also $\alpha = {}^{40}/_{2} = 20$. Thus

$$i_2 = k_1 + k_2\epsilon^{-20t}$$

To evaluate k_1 set $t = \infty$; this makes $k_2\epsilon^{-20t} = 0$ and $i_2 = k_1 = {}^{120}/_{40} = 3$. At $t = 0$, $i_2 = i_a = 1.2$ and $\epsilon^{-20t} = 1$. Thus $1.2 = 3 + k_2$, from which $k_2 = -1.8$. Hence

$$i_2 = 3 - 1.8\epsilon^{-20t}$$

Example 12. Solve Example 11 assuming that S_2 is initially closed and that it is *opened* when i_1 reaches a value of 1.2 amp.

Solution

The first current equation may be written by inspection. This is

$$i_1 = {}^{120}\!/_{40}(1 - \epsilon^{-(40/2)t}) = 3(1 - \epsilon^{-20t})$$

The general expression for the second current is

$$i_2 = k_1 + k_2\epsilon^{-(60/2)t} = k_1 + k_2\epsilon^{-30t}$$

When $t = \infty$,

$$k_2\epsilon^{-30t} = 0 \qquad \text{and} \qquad i_2 = k_1 = {}^{120}\!/_{60} = 2$$

When $t = 0$,

$$\epsilon^{-30t} = 1 \qquad \text{and} \qquad i_1 = i_a = 1.2$$

Therefore $\quad 1.2 = 2 + k_2 \qquad$ and $\qquad k_2 = -0.8$

Hence $\quad i_2 = 2 - 0.8\epsilon^{-30t}$

Magnetic-field Energy. During the period when a current is rising in the coil of an electromagnet, energy is expended (1) to heat the exciting winding and (2) *to establish the magnetic field.* After the current has reached its ultimate value, electric energy continues to heat the coil, but no further energy is required for the magnetic field; the energy supplied to the latter is *stored energy,* i.e., *potential energy,* in which respect it may be likened to the energy of the water in an elevated storage tank. The *magnetic-field energy* is eventually restored to the electric circuit as kinetic energy when the current is permitted to decay from its E/R value to zero; under this condition heating may take place in the circuit resistance, and/or arcing may occur at the switch contacts.

To determine the total amount of energy stored in a magnetic field, in watt-seconds, or joules, it is necessary to sum up, i.e., integrate, a gradually changing series of differential elements of energy, each one represented by a product of differential quantities of induced voltage e, current i, and time dt; each differential element of energy is therefore equal to

$$dw = ei\,dt \qquad \text{joules}$$

Since e is an induced voltage and is equal to $L(di/dt)$,

$$dw = \left(L\frac{di}{dt}\right) i\,dt = Li\,di$$

When this differential equation is solved by the calculus it becomes

$$W = \frac{1}{2}LI^2 \qquad \text{joules} \tag{65}$$[1]

where I, in amperes, is the total *change* in current. When the current starts at $i = 0$ at $t = 0$, the total current change is $I = E/R$ amp; if, on

[1] See Appendix 1J for derivation.

the other hand, the current changes between two finite values I_1 and I_2, the total energy change is

$$W = \frac{1}{2}LI_2^2 - \frac{1}{2}LI_1^2 = \frac{1}{2}L(I_2^2 - I_1^2) \quad \text{joules} \qquad (65a)^1$$

EXAMPLE 13. How much magnetic-field energy is stored in each of the poles of a generator if 8×10^5 maxwells are produced by a current of 2.6 amp in a 2,200-turn coil? (Assume constant permeability.)

Solution

$$L = \frac{N\Phi}{I \times 10^8} \frac{2{,}200 \times 8 \times 10^5}{2.6 \times 10^8} = 6.76 \text{ henrys}$$

$$W = \frac{1}{2} \times 6.76 \times (2.6)^2 = 22.8 \text{ joules}$$

EXAMPLE 14. How much energy is restored to the electric circuit if the current, in Example 13, is quickly reduced to 1.3 amp?

Solution

$$W = \frac{1}{2} \times 6.76 \times [(2.6)^2 - (1.3)^2] = 17.1 \text{ joules}$$

Under this condition the energy still remaining in the magnetic field is $(22.8 - 17.1) = 5.7$ joules.

Mutual Induction and Transformer Action. The flux produced by the current through a coil in free space always spreads out more or less uniformly and symmetrically to form closed magnetic paths. Any of the flux thus created that passes directly through a second coil is said to be *mutual* to both coils and is called *mutual flux*. Moreover, when the mutual flux changes in magnitude or direction, a voltage will be *induced* in the second coil, and the emf resulting is therefore a voltage of *mutual induction*. Mutual induction always implies that two coils are coupled magnetically, a condition that prevails when some or all of the flux passes *through* both coils at the same time.

It should be clear that fundamentally the induced emf in the second coil—the so-called *secondary*—results because its flux linkages change, although the change is occasioned, in the first place, by a current change in the coil that is excited—the so-called *primary*. The induced emf of mutual induction in the secondary is often referred to as a *transformer voltage*, and the action that creates the emf is known as *transformer action*.

Transformer action takes place in any d-c system of coupled circuits when a switch is opened or closed, but its more important application is

[1] See Appendix 1J for derivation.

in connection with the operation of a-c apparatus, such as transformers and induction motors. In such electrical equipment one coil or set of coils is connected directly to an a-c source so that the current and the accompanying flux automatically change periodically in both magnitude and direction. And since the flux linkages in the coupled coil or set of coils change, a voltage is induced in it by transformer action. Furthermore, the frequency of the induced emf, represented by two complete alternations, will be *exactly* the same as the impressed primary voltage. If the secondary-coil terminals are now connected to an electrical unit, i.e., a load, current will exist. Thus, electrical energy can be transferred from one electric circuit to another electric circuit by transformer action even though there is absolutely no metallic connection between the two. The whole remarkable process of energy transfer takes place in accordance with the *principle of electromagnetic induction*, first discovered in 1831 by Michael Faraday.

Mutual Inductance and Coefficient of Coupling. It is important to understand that an induced voltage in a coil results from a change in flux linkages in the coil and is, moreover, independent of the *cause* of the flux-linkage change. In a single-coil circuit the induced emf is said to be a *voltage of self-induction*, and it always acts to oppose a current change in its *own* winding; when coils are mutually coupled the induced emf in the secondary is said to be a *voltage of mutual induction*, which in turn tends to establish a secondary current whose action is to oppose a flux change. Now then, *if the current changes in the primary at the rate of one ampere per second and, as a result of such change, the induced emf in the secondary is one volt, the coupled coils are said to possess unit mutual inductance.* Assuming a total primary-current change of I_P amp in t sec, the *average* induced secondary emf will therefore be given by the equation

$$E_{S_{av}} = M\left(\frac{I_P}{t}\right) \quad \text{volts} \tag{66}$$

As in the derivation of Eq. (59) the average induced secondary voltage can also be expressed in terms of the rate of change of flux linkages in the coil. Written in this way,

$$E_{S_{av}} = \frac{N_S\Phi_S}{t \times 10^8} \tag{67}$$

Setting the two voltages of Eqs. (66) and (67) equal to each other, and solving for mutual inductance,

$$M = \frac{N_S\Phi_S}{I_P \times 10^8} \quad \text{henrys} \tag{68}$$

This equation states that the mutual inductance existing between a pair of coils is proportional to the flux linkages in the secondary per ampere in the primary.

If the secondary circuit is closed, it too will carry current while an induced emf is being induced in it; also, the flux created in the secondary will link with the primary and *to the same extent.* Since the latter condition indicates that the mutual inductance between secondary and primary is exactly equal to its value between primary and secondary, it follows that

$$M = \frac{N_P\Phi_P}{I_S \times 10^8} \quad \text{henrys} \tag{69}$$

The next step in this analysis of mutual induction introduces a term known as *coefficient of coupling*. This, represented by the symbol K, is defined as the fractional part of the flux in one winding that links with the other. Thus, it is possible to express the flux that *links* with the secondary in terms of the flux that is *created* in the primary; i.e., $\Phi_S = K\Phi_P$. A similar relationship can also be written for the flux that *links* with the primary in terms of the flux that is *created* in the secondary; i.e., $\Phi_P = K\Phi_S$. Substituting the two values of flux in Eqs. (68) and (69),

$$M = \frac{N_S(K\Phi_P)}{I_P \times 10^8} \quad \text{and} \quad M = \frac{N_P(K\Phi_S)}{I_S \times 10^8}$$

Multiplying the two values of mutual inductance and rearranging terms,

$$M^2 = K^2\left(\frac{N_P\Phi_P}{I_P \times 10^8}\right)\left(\frac{N_S\Phi_S}{I_S \times 10^8}\right)$$

But each of the quantities in the brackets is the respective value of self-inductance [see Eq. 60]; it follows, therefore, that

$$M^2 = K^2L_PL_S$$

from which

$$K = \frac{M}{\sqrt{L_PL_S}} \tag{70}$$

This important equation indicates that the coefficient of coupling may also be defined on the basis of mutual and self-inductances; stated in this way, *it is equal to the ratio of the mutual inductance to the geometric mean of the self-inductances of the individual coils.*

The coefficient of coupling between two coils can have values between *zero* and *unity;* the zero limit implies that *no* flux links primary and secondary, while the unity limit indicates that *all* the flux passes completely through *both* coils. Moreover, the degree to which magnetic coupling exists depends upon the following: (1) the closeness of the coils with respect to each other, (2) whether or not the coils are linked by a common magnetic core, (3) the permeability of the core material if the linking takes place through a common ferromagnetic substance, and (4) the angle between the magnetic axes of the two coils when no common magnetic substance links the coils.

Terms that are sometimes used in connection with this aspect of magnetic coupling are "tight," "close," and "loose." Power transformers are, for example, coupled very tightly by placing them upon a common magnetic core of high permeability and as close together as insulation thicknesses permit. The reason for such construction is the fact that the induced voltage in the secondary depends, among other things, upon the number of lines of force, created by the primary, that pass *through* the secondary. In other cases, as in certain communication systems, where it is desirable to prevent the feeding of electromagnetic energy from one electric circuit to another, the coils are widely separated and with their magnetic axes at right angles.

Figure 96 illustrates three degrees of coupling between coils A and B. Where the flux is confined to a good magnetic core to link the coils

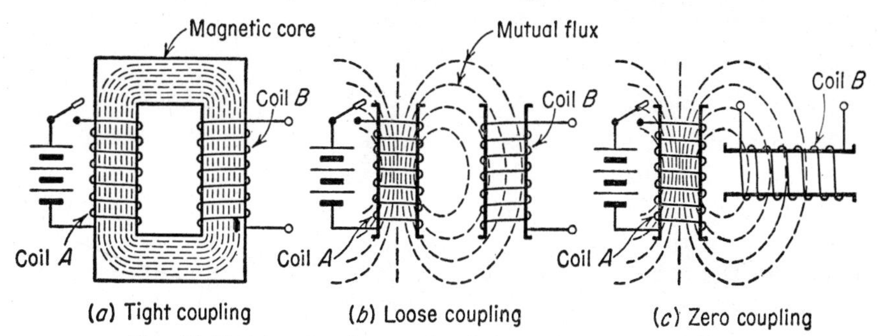

FIG. 96. Sketches showing varying degrees of magnetic coupling.

completely, as in Fig. 96a, the coefficient of coupling is practically unity. A similar pair of coils will, however, be linked by a comparatively small part of the flux created by A (Fig. 96b) if there is no common core; under this condition the coefficient of coupling will be rather small. Finally, when the two coils, in free space, are placed with their magnetic axes at right angles (Fig. 96c), no part of the established flux passes through the secondary; the coefficient of coupling is therefore zero in this case.

EXAMPLE 15. The mutual inductance between a pair of coupled coils is 0.25. If the self-inductances of the individual units are 0.2 and 0.5 henry, calculate the coefficient of coupling.

Solution

$$K = \frac{0.25}{\sqrt{0.2 \times 0.5}} = 0.79$$

EXAMPLE 16. The reluctance of the magnetic circuit that links two series-connected coils is 0.002, and the coefficient of coupling is 0.35. If coils A and B have 500 and 800 turns, respectively, and the current is 1.2 amp, calculate (*a*) the self-inductances of the individual coils, (*b*) the mutual inductance between the coils.

Solution

$$(a)\ \Phi_A = \frac{0.4\pi \times 500 \times 1.2}{0.002} = 377{,}000 \text{ maxwells}$$

$$\Phi_B = \frac{0.4\pi \times 800 \times 1.2}{0.002} = 603{,}000 \text{ maxwells}$$

$$L_A = \frac{N_A \Phi_A}{I \times 10^8} = \frac{500 \times 377{,}000}{1.2 \times 10^8} = 1.57 \text{ henrys}$$

$$L_B = \frac{N_B \Phi_B}{I \times 10^8} = \frac{800 \times 603{,}000}{1.2 \times 10^8} = 4.02 \text{ henrys}$$

$$(b)\ M = \frac{N_B \times (K\Phi_A)}{1.2 \times 10^8} = \frac{N_A \times (K\Phi_B)}{1.2 \times 10^8}$$

$$= \frac{800 \times (0.35 \times 377{,}000)}{1.2 \times 10^8} = \frac{500 \times (0.35 \times 603{,}000)}{1.2 \times 10^8} = 0.88$$

also

$$M = K\sqrt{L_A L_B} = 0.35\sqrt{1.57 \times 4.02} = 0.88 \qquad (Check)$$

Magnetically Coupled Coils Connected in Series. When two coils are connected in series to a source of emf they obviously carry the same current. Each one establishes flux that links not only with its own turns but also with those of the other coil. Moreover, if the two coils are wound in the *same* direction so that their magnetic polarities *aid* one another, the mutual inductance of each one with respect to the other acts additively with the self-inductances of the individual units. On the other hand, if coils are wound in *opposite* directions their fluxes tend to nullify, and the mutual inductance of each one with respect to the other acts subtractively with the self-inductances of the individual units. Remembering that M between coils A and B is always equal to M between B and A, it follows that

$$L_{\text{additive}} = L_A + L_B + 2M \tag{71}$$

and

$$L_{\text{subtractive}} = L_A + L_B - 2M \tag{72}$$

Equations (71) and (72) may be applied experimentally to the determination of the mutual inductance between a pair of coils. If the total inductance is first found for the aiding connection and then, by interchanging the leads on one of the coils, for the opposing connection, the mutual inductance may be evaluated by the equation

$$M = \frac{L_{\text{additive}} - L_{\text{subtractive}}}{4} \tag{73}$$

The foregoing formula is readily derived by subtracting (72) from (71) to eliminate L_A and L_B.

EXAMPLE 17. Using the data of Example 16, calculate the total inductance for the aiding and opposing connections.

Solution

$$L_{\text{additive}} = 1.57 + 4.02 + (2 \times 0.88) = 7.35 \text{ henrys}$$
$$L_{\text{subtractive}} = 1.57 + 4.02 - (2 \times 0.88) = 3.83 \text{ henrys}$$

A special, but important, way to arrange two coils is to wind them with identical numbers of turns, in opposite directions, and couple them so tightly that the coefficient of coupling is unity. Under such conditions $M = L_A = L_B$, and the total inductance is $L_{\text{subtractive}} = L_A + L_B - 2M = 0$. The effect of such a combination of coils is, of course, zero flux, since each turn carrying current in one direction has a corresponding nullifying turn that carries current in the opposite direction. An assembly such as this is generally referred to as a *noninductive coil* and is used where it is desired to have the current change almost instantaneously when a circuit is energized or deenergized.

Lenz's Law and Direction of Induced Voltage. The fact that an induced emf always tends to oppose the very action that is responsible for its creation—the action being a flux change—means that the secondary of a pair of coupled coils must (1) try to establish flux in opposition to an increasing primary flux, or (2) try to establish flux to sustain a decreasing

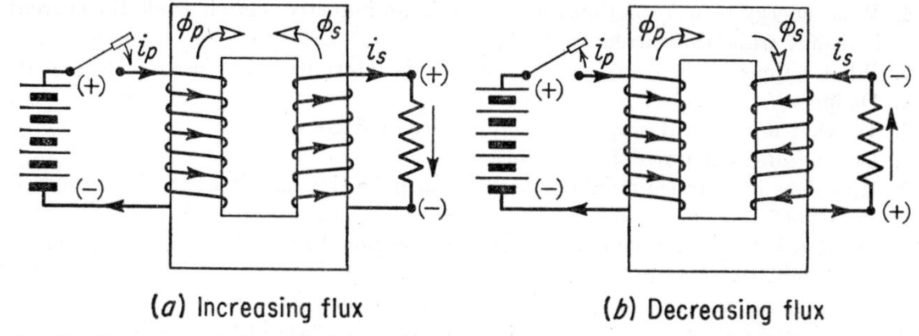

FIG. 97. Sketches showing polarities of induced voltages, and directions of current and flux to illustrate Lenz's law.

primary flux. Thus, for example, if the switch is closed as in Fig. 97*a*, the primary flux Φ_P will build up in the core in a clockwise direction; while the primary current is changing, and *only* then, the induced secondary voltage will be directed as shown, i.e., to produce a current i_S that will establish a counterclockwise flux Φ_S. On the other hand, if the switch is opened as in Fig. 97*b*, the induced secondary voltage will be directed to produce a current i_S that will attempt to *sustain* the existing primary flux. It follows, therefore, that the secondary current *direction* is determined by whether the switch is closed or opened. In Fig. 97*a*, for switch closing, the polarities of the secondary terminals are plus (+) at the top and minus (−) at the bottom; in Fig. 97*b*, for switch opening, the polarities of the secondary terminals are plus (+) at the bottom and minus (−) at the top.

The general principle that summarizes the foregoing discussion was first given by H. L. Lenz. Known as *Lenz's law*, it may be stated as follows: *In all cases of electromagnetic induction the current set up by an induced voltage tends to create flux whose direction opposes any change in the existing flux.*

If the battery of Fig. 97 is replaced by an a-c source, the current in the exciting coil—the primary—will be continually changing in both magnitude and direction. Under this condition the *induced voltage* in the secondary coil will be alternating and will, at every instant, be opposite in direction to the impressed voltage on the primary. When used in this way, an a-c electromagnet, containing a primary exciting coil and a load-delivering secondary coil, is called a transformer.

Questions

1. Under what conditions do d-c circuits obey the general laws, theorems, and rules studied in Chaps. 3 and 4? When are such principles not applicable?

2. What property must a circuit possess if the current is to rise instantly to its ultimate value when a switch is closed? if the current rise is delayed?

3. What is meant by an *inductive circuit?*

4. What energy transformation takes place in an inductive circuit while the current is rising? while the current is decaying?

5. What happens when an inductive circuit is intermittently closed and opened?

6. Define *self-inductance.*

7. To what mechanical property is inductance analogous?

8. Define unit inductance, i.e., a henry.

9. How does inductance manifest itself in an inductive circuit when the current is changing?

10. To what is the average induced voltage proportional when the current is changing in an inductive circuit?

11. Define *inductance* in terms of flux linkages and current.

12. How is the inductance of a coil affected by an increase in the number of turns? by an increase in the cross-sectional area of the core? by the kind of core material?

13. Why does the inductance of a magnetic device change for varying values of current if the core is a ferromagnetic substance?

14. What is meant by "lumped" constants, referring to resistance and inductance?

15. In setting up general equations, why is it necessary to employ differential quantities for circuits undergoing transient changes?

16. What is meant by an exponential equation?

17. Define *time constant* in three ways, for current growth.

18. What is the effect upon the time constant in an *R-L* circuit when *R* is changed? when *L* is changed?

19. What is the effect upon the ultimate current in an *R-L* circuit when *R* is changed? when *L* is changed?
20. When is the current change a maximum in an inductive current-growth circuit?
21. How does the current decay in an inductive circuit?
22. When is the current change a maximum in an inductive, current-decay circuit?
23. Define *time constant* in three ways, for current decay.
24. Draw two general types of circuit for current decay, and write the exponential equation for each.
25. Write the *general equation* for the current growth in a circuit when the current changes between two finite values.
26. Into what forms of energy is the electrical energy converted while the current is growing in an inductive circuit?
27. When the current decays in an inductive circuit what happens to the stored magnetic energy?
28. Under what conditions is a voltage of mutual induction developed?
29 What is meant by *transformer action?*
30. Under what conditions is transformer action most pronounced? least pronounced?
31. Define *mutual inductance.*
32. Define *unit mutual inductance.*
33. What is meant by the term *coefficient of coupling* when referring to magnetic coupling?
34. Under what conditions are coils said to be tightly coupled? loosely coupled?
35. Define *coefficient of coupling* in terms of mutual and self-inductance.
36. Upon what factors does the coefficient of coupling depend?
37. When magnetically coupled coils are connected in series, how must they be wound if the total inductance is to be a maximum? a minimum?
38. Under what conditions is the total inductance of two mutually coupled coils zero? Give reasons for your answer.
39. State Lenz's law.
40. Carefully explain how the polarity of the induced secondary voltage is determined when two coils are magnetically coupled.

Problems

1. What is the inductance of a 780-turn solenoid which establishes 420,000 maxwells when the current is 4.1 amp?
2. If the coil of Prob. 1 has a 50 per cent tap, what is the inductance between either end and the tapped point?
3. What would be the inductance of the solenoid in Prob. 1 between the 50 per cent tap and a junction that connects the two ends of the coil?
4. How many additional turns should be added to the solenoid of Prob. 1 if the inductance is to be 1.0 henry?
5. A 1,300-turn toroid has a cast-iron core whose average length and area are 22 in. and 0.75 sq in., respectively. If the current variation causes the permeability to vary between 230 and 600, calculate the inductance range of the toroid.
6. An inductive circuit has a resistance of 40 ohms and an inductance of 0.5 henry. If an emf of 120 volts is suddenly impressed, (*a*) write the equation for current growth, (*b*) calculate the time constant T and the current at the instant T.
7. What is the initial rate of current change in Prob. 6?
8. For the given data of Prob. 6, calculate the current at 0.00625 sec from the closing of the switch.

9. An electromagnet has a resistance of 400 ohms and an inductance of 0.64 henry. If 48 volts is suddenly impressed, calculate (*a*) the initial rate of current change and the induced emf at $t = 0$, (*b*) the induced emf and the rate of current rise when $i = 0.07$ amp.

10. If a 250-ohm noninductive resistance is connected in parallel with the electromagnet of Prob. 9, what will be the line current (*a*) at the instant the switch closes, (*b*) when the induced emf in the inductance is 16 volts?

11. Write the equation for current growth in the line in Prob. 10.

12. The initial rate of current change in an inductance coil is 1,500 amp per sec when a certain emf is suddenly impressed. If an external resistance equal to the coil resistance is connected in series and one-half the original voltage is applied to the circuit, what is the initial rate of current change?

13. Referring to Fig. 93*b*, $R_S = 14$, $R = 56$, and $L = 80$ mh. If the circuit is in a steady-state condition with the switch open and a voltage of 112 volts impressed, (*a*) write the equation for current decay after the switch is closed. Calculate (*b*) the time constant and the current at $t = T$, (*c*) the initial rate of current change, (*d*) the current at $t = 0.000476$ sec.

14. Referring to Fig. 93*c*, $R_P = 24$, $R = 56$, and $L = 80$ mh. If the circuit is in a steady-state condition with the switch closed, and a voltage of 112 volts is impressed, (*a*) write the equation for current decay after the switch is opened. Calculate (*b*) the time constant and the current at $t = T$, (*c*) the initial rate of current change.

15. A series circuit consists of a 32-ohm resistor, an 8-ohm resistor, and a 1.2-henry inductance connected to a 120-volt source. A switch is connected across the 32-ohm resistor to short-circuit it while the circuit is in a steady-state condition. At the instant the switch is opened to permit the circuit current to drop, what is the induced emf in the inductance and the rate of current change?

16. The field circuit of a 125-volt d-c generator has a resistance of 50 ohms and an inductance of 12.3 henrys. A discharge resistor of 144 ohms is connected directly across the field winding at the instant the main switch is opened. What voltage appears at the winding terminals at $t = 0$, and what is the initial rate of current change?

17. What should be the ohmic value of a discharge resistor for the generator field of Prob. 16 if the maximum field voltage is not to exceed twice its rated emf?

18. Each of the six poles of d-c generator creates 2.3×10^6 maxwells when 3.7 amp passes through its 1,260 turns. Calculate the total magnetic-field energy stored in the poles.

19. If the field current in Prob. 18 is quickly decreased to 3 amp, determine the energy that is returned to the electric circuit, and the energy still remaining in the magnetic field.

20. For the field of Prob. 18, calculate the winding current when each pole stores 60 joules of magnetic energy.

21. Two magnetically coupled coils have self-inductances of 0.43 and 0.36 henry. If the mutual inductance between them is 0.28 henry, calculate the coefficient of coupling.

22. If the two coils of Prob. 21 could be perfectly coupled (i.e., $K = 1$), what would be the mutual inductance between the coils?

23. Two coils *A* and *B* are magnetically coupled. When connected in series-aiding, the total inductance is 0.137 henry, and when connected in series-opposing the total inductance is 0.085 henry. Calculate the mutual inductance between coils and the self-inductance of each coil if the coefficient of coupling is 0.242.

24. A coil A, having a resistance of 25 ohms and a self-inductance of 1.4 henrys, is magnetically coupled to a coil B whose resistance and self-inductance are 10 ohms and 0.9 henry, respectively. If the coefficient of coupling between coils is 0.715, calculate the induced emf in each coil at the instant 120 volts is impressed across coil A.

25. What voltage is induced in coil B of Prob. 24 at the instant the current in coil A is 1.2 amp?

26. Two similar coils are magnetically coupled. The total inductance is 0.9 henry when they are connected in series-aiding and 0.54 henry when in series-opposing. Determine the mutual inductance between coils, the self-inductance of each coil, and the coefficient of coupling.

CHAPTER 9

CAPACITANCE AND DIELECTRIC CIRCUITS

Static Electricity. Circuits in which electrons are in constant motion are *dynamic circuits,* and the phenomenon associated with electrons in motion is often referred to as *dynamic electricity.* Moreover, when the electron flow is unidirectional only it is called *direct-current dynamic electricity,* or briefly *direct current;* this aspect of the broad subject of electric circuits has been considered in the foregoing chapters.

Electric circuits may, however, be established in which an electrical potential difference is applied to a pair (or pairs) of completely insulated enlarged metallic surfaces so that negative charges (electrons) are removed from one surface and are deposited on the other; one surface thus acquires an excess of electrons and becomes *negatively charged,* while the other, suffering a deficiency of an equal number of electrons, becomes *positively charged.* Electric charge accumulated in this way is regarded as *direct-current static electricity,* or briefly *static electricity.*

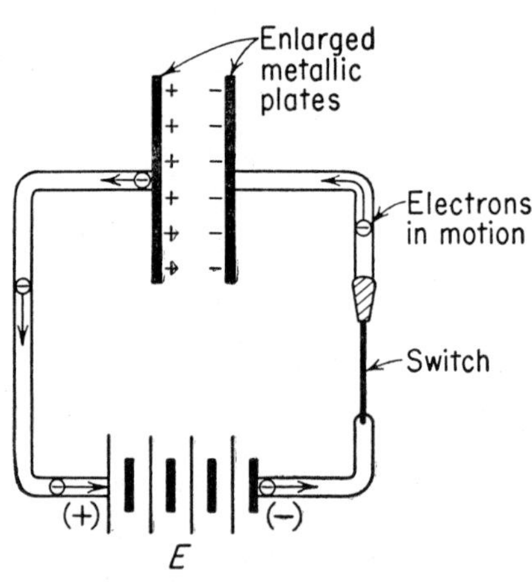

FIG. 98. Plates being charged by a battery.

The fact that dynamic electricity (electrons in motion) becomes static electricity when electric charges are accumulated and brought to rest on appropriate surfaces implies, of course, that both are fundamentally the same. Moreover, the existence of static charge results only after a period of electron motion, i.e., dynamic electricity, during which time charges "pile up" on the surfaces until the potential of each, plus or minus, becomes equal to the potential difference of the source. This is illustrated by Fig. 98 in which two plates are shown insulated from each other and connected to a battery through a switch. Assuming the plates to be neutral (uncharged) before the circuit is energized, closing the switch will immediately result in a motion of electrons as indicated. Initially the potentials of the plates differ from the source potential by voltage E, and this results in a sudden rise in current (electron motion). As one plate loses negative electrons and becomes positively charged, and the other plate acquires negative electrons to become negatively charged, the plate and battery potentials tend to equalize; the current, therefore, continues to drop from its initial maximum value until it ultimately becomes zero. The charged plates then have the same potential as the battery, as a result of which the circuit is said to be in a static condition.

Charging a Capacitor. The arrangement of two enlarged plates that are separated by an insulating medium (Fig. 98) constitutes a *capacitor*, and the property which permits it to accumulate and store electric charge is called *capacitance*. The extent to which a capacitor may be charged will depend upon the way in which it is constructed—this involves such details as plate dimensions and separation, and kind of insulation material—and the electric potential to which it is subjected. For a given capacitor, however, the charge Q in coulombs is obviously proportional to the applied voltage E. Representing the proportionality factor by the symbol C'—this is the capacitance of the capacitor in farad units, to be considered in the next section—the relationship between charge, voltage, and capacitance may be expressed by the equation

$$Q = C'E \tag{74}$$

Since the extent to which a certain capacitor becomes charged is determined by the voltage that is applied to its terminals, it should be clear that the maximum charge is limited by the highest permissible voltage across the insulation *before* the latter breaks down and becomes conducting. In practice it is generally desirable to keep the voltage per unit of insulation thickness somewhat below known breakdown potentials for the purpose of maintaining reasonable factors of safety; this is especially important with solid insulation materials such as paper, mica, porcelain, rubber, plastics, varnished fibers, etc., because failure due to excessive voltage results in complete destruction of the capacitor.

EXAMPLE 1. A 50-μf capacitor (1 μf $= 10^{-6}$ farad) is connected to a 240-volt source. (*a*) What charge will ultimately appear on the plates? (*b*) If the current is maintained at a constant value of 30 ma during the charging period, how long will it take to charge the capacitor?

Solution

(*a*) $$Q = (50 \times 10^{-6}) \times 240 = 0.012 \text{ coulomb}$$

(*b*) Since $Q = It$,

$$t = \frac{0.012}{0.03} = 0.4 \text{ sec}$$

EXAMPLE 2. The breakdown potential of a certain grade of insulation paper is 750 volts per mil. Assuming a factor of safety of 2.5, what is the maximum permissible voltage across a capacitor whose paper thickness is 3 mils?

Solution

$$E = \frac{750}{2.5} \times 3 = 900 \text{ volts}$$

EXAMPLE 3. A 40-μf capacitor is connected to a 600-volt source and is completely charged in 1.5 sec. If, during the charging period, the current diminishes linearly with time from its initial maximum value to zero, what is the instantaneous maximum value of the current?

Solution

$$Q = (40 \times 10^{-6}) \times 600 = 0.024 \text{ coulomb}$$

Since $Q = \frac{1}{2} I_{max} t$ (in this case),

$$I_{max} = \frac{2 \times 0.024}{1.5} = 0.032 \text{ amp}$$

Although the charging of a capacitor involves no net change in its electron content, there is, nevertheless, an actual transfer of electrical energy from the battery to the capacitor. This may be readily demonstrated by carefully removing the insulated ends from the battery terminals after the capacitor is charged and then bringing the bared wires together; a sudden arcing snap will indicate that the stored energy is released. Or, if the bared wire ends are quickly touched to the terminals of a suitable incandescent lamp, the latter will light up for a brief instant. This phenomenon, impressive as it may appear, is not especially unique or different from many commonplace operations such as the winding of a clock spring, the setting of a spring trap, the cocking of a rifle, or the elastic deformation of a rubber tube when a tire is pumped up. In the latter example, it is, however, well to remember that the stored energy is accompanied by an actual increase in substance, whereas no material change takes place in capacitor charging.

Capacitance. Any combination of conductors and insulators that is capable of storing electric charge is a capacitor; moreover, its ability to do so is characterized by the surface area of the conductors and, what is most important, the kind of material and thickness of the insulating material. The latter, called the *dielectric*, not only will determine how much charge can be stored on each unit of area of the metallic surfaces but will indicate what maximum voltage can be applied to the capacitor before breakdown occurs (see Example 2). Furthermore, the shape, thickness, or kind of terminal plates used in the construction of the capacitor have no particular significance so long as they make good contact with the dielectric.

Two arrangements of insulation and the metal plates it separates are generally found in practice. In one of these (Fig. 99*a*) layers of dielectric material are sandwiched between sheets of metal, after which one group of alternate plates is joined to form one terminal and an adjacent group of alternate plates is connected to serve as the other terminal; in a second construction, the so-called rolled type, two narrow, thin strips of metal foil (usually aluminum) and two slightly wider strips of thin paper are interleaved and rolled to the desired size, as indicated by Fig. 99*b*.

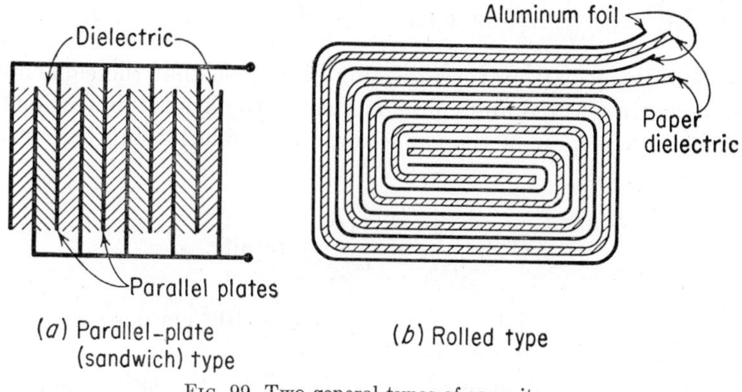

FIG. 99. Two general types of capacitor.

As previously stated, the kind and thickness of dielectric are especially important in determining how much charge can be stored on unit area of metal per volt. Comparing the charge-storing ability of capacitors employing solid or liquid insulations with that of an *equivalent* capacitor, i.e., one with equal dimensions with an *air* dielectric, it is found that the former are substantially better than the latter; that is, using air as a basis of reference (similar to the practice of rating magnetic substances in terms of permeability) practical solid and liquid dielectrics are 2 to 10 times as good. Thus, for example, if a sheet of glass is inserted to fit exactly between two layers of metal it is found that the capacitance is about 5.4 to 9 times as much as it would be with the glass removed. Other dielectrics, such as mica, paper, porcelain, and certain liquids, like oil, show similar increases in capacitance over air. Indices of the "ability" of a dielectric to store charge, in terms of air (which is arbitrarily given a value of unity), are *dielectric constant, permittivity,* and *specific inductive capacity;* they all refer to the *ratio* of the capacitance of a capacitor with the given dielectric material with respect to a capacitor of *equivalent* dimensions using air as a dielectric. A list of some of the more commonly used dielectric materials and their corresponding dielectric constants is given in Table 9.

TABLE 9. TABLE OF DIELECTRIC CONSTANTS

Material	*Dielectric constant k*	*Material*	*Dielectric constant k*
Bakelite	4.5–5.5	Paper	2–3.5
Castor oil	4.7	Paraffin	2.1–2.5
Chlorinated diphenyl	4.95	Polystyrene	2.6
Fiber	2.5–5	Porcelain	5.7–7
Glass	5.5–9	Pressboard, oiled	5
Gutta-percha	3.3–4.9	Rubber	2–4
Isolantite	6.1	Steatite	5.9
Mica	2.5–6.6	Water	81
Oil	2.2–4.7	Wood	2.5–7.7

It should be clear from the foregoing discussion that the capacitance, in conveniently selected units, may be related to physical dimensions and the dielectric constant of the capacitor. This relationship has, in fact, been shown to be

$$C' = \frac{10^9}{4\pi c^2} \times \frac{kA'}{d'} \qquad \text{farads}$$

where c = velocity of light, cm per sec = 3×10^{10} cm per sec
k = dielectric constant (see Table 9)
A' = total cross-sectional area of the dielectric path between contact surfaces of plates, sq cm
d' = thickness of the dielectric, cm

Using *inch* units for area A and thickness d, substituting the numerical value for c, and writing the capacitance C in microfarads, the above equation becomes

$$C = \left[\frac{10^9}{4\pi(3 \times 10^{10})^2}\right]\left[\frac{k(A \times 6.45)}{d \times 2.54}\right] \times 10^6$$

whence

$$C = \frac{2.25kA}{d \times 10^7} \qquad \mu\text{f} \tag{75}$$

EXAMPLE 4. A parallel-plate capacitor is constructed by cementing, using shellac, sheets of 6- by 8-in. aluminum to 8- by 10-in. glass plates that are 0.05 in. thick. One set of alternate metal sheets is then connected to form one electrode, and another set of joined alternate plates forms the other electrode (see Fig. 99a). If 150 metal and 149 glass plates are used, calculate the capacitance of the capacitor, assuming a dielectric constant of 6.2 for glass.

Solution

$$C = \frac{2.25 \times 6.2 \times 149 \times 6 \times 8}{0.05 \times 10^7} = 0.2\ \mu\text{f}$$

EXAMPLE 5. A rolled type of capacitor (see Fig. 99*b*) is to be constructed using strips of aluminum foil 3 in. wide and waxed paper 4 mils thick that is slightly wider. If it is desired to have a capacitance of 1.5 μf, what should be the length of each of the two strips of aluminum foil and the two strips of paper? Assume a dielectric constant of 2.5 for paraffined paper.

Solution

$$1.5 = \frac{2.25 \times 2.5 \times (2l \times 3)}{0.004 \times 10^7}$$

$$l = \frac{1.5 \times 0.004 \times 10^7}{2.25 \times 2.5 \times 2 \times 3} = 1{,}780 \text{ in., or } 148 \text{ ft}$$

Rolled capacitors are rather commonly employed in low-voltage applications such as telephone systems and some radio receivers, although they are not satisfactory for noninductive circuits. Where space requirements are especially important, an entirely different class of so-called *electrolytic* capacitors is widely used; these have extremely thin dielectric materials that are formed by electrochemical action on specially prepared aluminum or tantalum foil. *Electrolytics* of 5 to 20 μf not much larger than a small finger are frequently found in many kinds of electronic equipment, such as radios and hearing aids. For high-voltage circuits it is generally necessary to employ oil-immersed capacitors or those containing noninflammable liquid dielectrics such as chlorinated diphenyl. Variable capacitors as applied to radio tuners are constructed so that one set of aluminum plates may be rotated in air to sandwich between, and expose varying areas to, a fixed set of plates.

Capacitors in Parallel. It is frequently necessary to interconnect several capacitors (as with resistors) for the purpose of obtaining a value of equivalent capacitance that is different from that of an available single unit, and/or to limit the voltages across two or more units to acceptable maximum potentials. To do this, two basic types of connection, and combinations of them, are used, namely, the *parallel* connection and the *series* connection.

Consider Fig. 100, which illustrates a group of capacitors connected in parallel. Since the *same* voltage E is impressed across all capacitors, the charges on the individual units are, respectively,

$$Q_1 = C_1E \qquad Q_2 = C_2E \qquad Q_3 = C_3E \qquad \text{etc.}$$

Moreover, the total charge is equal to

$$Q_t = Q_1 + Q_2 + Q_3 + \cdots$$

and this is also equal to the product of a so-called *equivalent capacitance* C_{eq} and the voltage E:

$$Q_t = C_{eq} \times E$$

Equating the foregoing relationships,

$$C_{eq} \times E = C_1E + C_2E + C_3E + \cdots = (C_1 + C_2 + C_3 + \cdots)E$$

from which $$C_{eq} = C_1 + C_2 + C_3 + \cdots \tag{76}$$

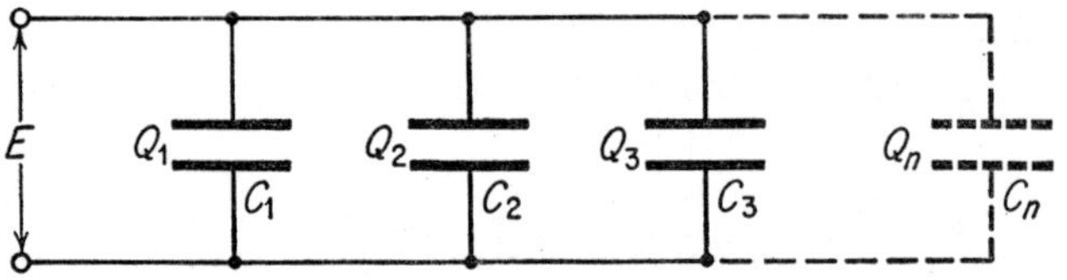

FIG. 100. A parallel-capacitor circuit.

Equation (76) indicates, therefore, that *the equivalent capacitance of a number of capacitors that are connected in parallel is equal to the sum of the individual units.*

EXAMPLE 6. Four capacitors having values of capacitance that are, respectively, 2, 3, 5, and 8 μf are connected in parallel and to a 120-volt d-c source. Calculate (*a*) the equivalent capacitance of the group, (*b*) the charge on each capacitor, (*c*) the total charge on the group.

Solution

(*a*) $C_{eq} = 2 + 3 + 5 + 8 = 18\ \mu\text{f}$

(*b*) $Q_2 = 2 \times 10^{-6} \times 120 = 2.4 \times 10^{-4}$ coulomb

$Q_3 = 3 \times 10^{-6} \times 120 = 3.6 \times 10^{-4}$ coulomb

$Q_5 = 5 \times 10^{-6} \times 120 = 6.0 \times 10^{-4}$ coulomb

$Q_8 = 8 \times 10^{-6} \times 120 = 9.6 \times 10^{-4}$ coulomb

(*c*) Total charge $Q_t = 21.6 \times 10^{-4}$ coulomb

Also $Q_t = 18 \times 10^{-6} \times 120 = 21.6 \times 10^{-4}$ coulomb

Capacitors in Series. When several capacitors are connected in series as in Fig. 101, (1) the equivalent capacitance is *less* than that of the smallest unit, and (2) the impressed emf E is divided among the capacitors so that the individual voltage drops are *inversely proportional* to their respective capacitances. The following analysis will show these statements to be valid.

When the circuit of Fig. 101 is energized as indicated, plate a will be *positively* charged to potential $+E$ and plate b will receive a corresponding charge of $-E$. As a result of this charging action, and assuming all capacitors to be perfectly insulated, plate a' will immediately take on an equal negative charge, while plate b' will assume an equal positive charge. Moreover, since plates a' and c', joined by lead x, are completely isolated from the source and must therefore have a *net* charge of zero, it follows that plate c' will become *positively* charged to exactly the *same* extent as plate a' is negatively charged. Applying the same reasoning to lead y and plates b' and d' which it joins, plate d' will acquire an *equal* negative charge. The fact that plate c' is positively charged means, of course that

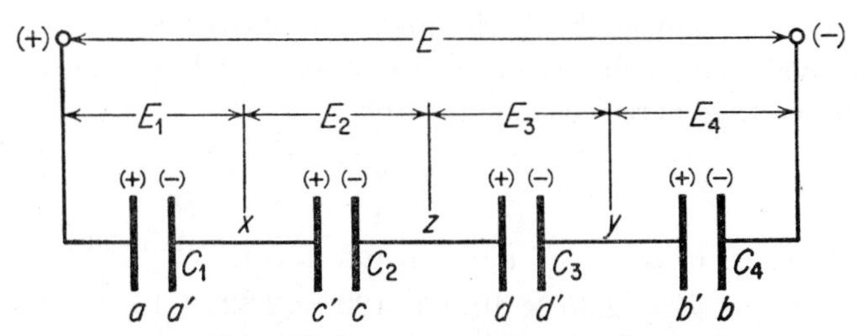

FIG. 101. A series-capacitor circuit.

plate c will become its negative counterpart; also plate d will assume a positive charge because it is the mate of plate d'. This leaves the region involving plates c and d, joined by lead z, neutral, as it should be. The significant point to recognize in this discussion is that *all plates in a series capacitor circuit acquire exactly the same charge*, albeit not the same polarities.

Recognizing the situation that capacitors C_1, C_2, C_3, and C_4 of Fig. 101 all have the same charge, it is proper to say that

$$Q = C_1E_1 = C_2E_2 = C_3E_3 = C_4E_4$$

from which

$$E_1 = \frac{Q}{C_1} \qquad E_2 = \frac{Q}{C_2} \qquad E_3 = \frac{Q}{C_3} \qquad \text{and} \qquad E_4 = \frac{Q}{C_4}$$

Also, for this series circuit,

$$E = E_1 + E_2 + E_3 + E_4 = \frac{Q}{C_{eq}}$$

Equating the proper foregoing equations, it follows that

$$\frac{Q}{C_{eq}} = \frac{Q}{C_1} + \frac{Q}{C_2} + \frac{Q}{C_3} + \frac{Q}{C_4} = Q\left(\frac{1}{C_1} + \frac{1}{C_2} + \frac{1}{C_3} + \frac{1}{C_4}\right)$$

from which $$C_{eq} = \frac{1}{(1/C_1) + (1/C_2) + (1/C_3) + 1/C_4} \qquad (77)$$

Note that this equation for the equivalent capacitance of a group of series-connected capacitors is similar in form to the equivalent resistance of a group of parallel-connected resistors.

Another important relationship that is indicated by the individual voltage equations for E_1, E_2, E_3, and E_4 is that any ratio of two voltages is *inversely* proportional to the corresponding capacitance ratio. Thus

$$\frac{E_1}{E_2} = \frac{C_2}{C_1} \qquad \frac{E_2}{E_3} = \frac{C_3}{C_2} \qquad \frac{E_3}{E_4} = \frac{C_4}{C_3} \qquad \frac{E_4}{E_1} = \frac{E_1}{C_4} \qquad \text{etc.}$$

EXAMPLE 7. Three capacitors having capacitances of 5, 8, and 10 μf, respectively, are connected in series and to a 120-volt source. Calculate (*a*) the equivalent capacitance of the group, (*b*) the charge on each capacitor, (*c*) the voltage across each capacitor.

Solution

$$(a) \quad C_{eq} = \frac{1}{1/5 + 1/8 + 1/10} = \frac{1}{0.2 + 0.125 + 0.1} = 2.35\ \mu\text{f}$$

$$(b) \quad Q = C_{eq} \times E = 2.35 \times 10^{-6} \times 120 = 2.82 \times 10^{-4}\ \text{coulomb}$$

$$(c) \quad E_1 = \frac{2.82 \times 10^{-4}}{5 \times 10^{-6}} = 56.4\ \text{volts}$$

$$E_2 = \frac{2.82 \times 10^{-4}}{8 \times 10^{-6}} = 35.3\ \text{volts}$$

$$E_3 = \frac{2.82 \times 10^{-4}}{10 \times 10^{-6}} = 28.2\ \text{volts}$$

Note that $E = 120 = 56.4 + 35.3 + 28.2$. Also observe that $E_1/E_2 = C_2/C_1 = 1.6$; $E_1/E_3 = C_3/C_1 = 2$; $E_2/E_3 = C_3/C_2 = 1.25$.

EXAMPLE 8. Three capacitors having capacitances of 12, 15, and 18 μf, respectively, are connected in series. If the voltage drop across any one of them must not exceed 150 volts, what is the maximum permissible potential difference of the source?

Solution

Since the maximum voltage drop will always exist across the *smallest* capacitor in a series combination, $E_{12} = 150$ volts. Therefore

$$E_{15} = (12/15)150 = 120$$

$$E_{18} = (12/18)150 = 100\ \text{volts}$$

Hence $$E = 150 + 120 + 100 = 370\ \text{volts max}$$

When two capacitors are connected in series, and this is frequently the case in practice, the equivalent capacitance is equal to the product of their individual capacitances divided by their sum. Thus

$$C_{ab} = \frac{C_a \times C_b}{C_a + C_b} \tag{78}$$

EXAMPLE 9. The equivalent capacitance of two capacitors in series is 6 μf, and the impressed emf across the combination is 600 volts. If one of them has a capacitance of 24 μf, calculate the value of the other, and the voltage drops across the individual units.

Solution

$$6 = \frac{24 \times C}{24 + C}$$

$$144 + 6C = 24C$$

$$C = \frac{144}{18} = 8 \ \mu\text{f}$$

$$E_8 = 600 \times \frac{24}{32} = 450 \text{ volts}$$

$$E_{24} = 600 \times \frac{8}{32} = 150 \text{ volts}$$

Parallel and Series Capacitor Interconnections. Several capacitors are sometimes interconnected to yield desired equivalent values of capacitance and/or to limit the maximum voltage across a particular unit in the

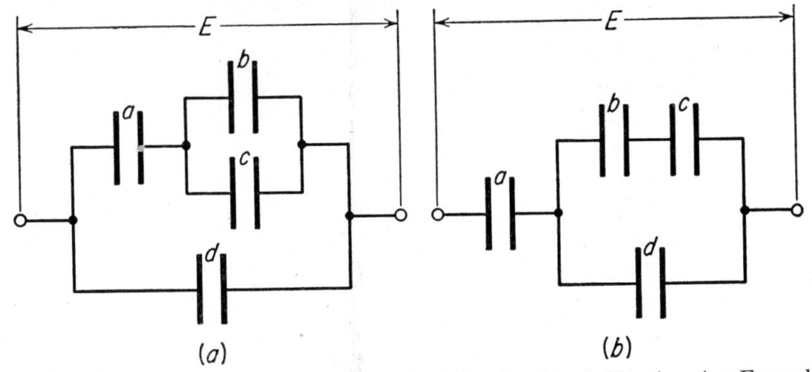

FIG. 102. Two arrangements of capacitors in parallel and series combinations (see Examples 10 and 11).

combination. Although such circuits often appear to be complex their treatment is exactly similar to those given for simple parallel and series arrangements when they are analyzed by elemental sections. Referring to Fig. 102, which shows two arrangements of four capacitors, and applying the rules developed in the foregoing articles, it is clear that, for Fig. 102*a*,

$$C_{bc} = C_b + C_c \qquad C_{abc} = \frac{C_a \times C_{bc}}{C_a + C_{bc}} \qquad C_{eq} = C_{abc} + C_d$$

For Fig. 102*b*,

$$C_{bc} = \frac{C_b \times C_c}{C_b + C_c} \qquad C_{bcd} = C_{bc} + C_d \qquad C_{eq} = \frac{C_a \times C_{bcd}}{C_a + C_{bcd}}$$

Concerning voltage drops across individual units, these may be determined by procedures previously given, to illustrate which two examples are considered.

EXAMPLE 10. Referring to Fig. 102*a*, assume the following values for the capacitors shown: $C_a = 12\ \mu f$, $C_b = 6\ \mu f$, $C_c = 30\ \mu f$, $C_d = 19\ \mu f$. Calculate (*a*) the equivalent capacitance of the entire combination, (*b*) the voltages across the individual capacitors for a line potential of 600 volts.

Solution

(*a*)

$$C_{bc} = 6 + 30 = 36\ \mu f$$

$$C_{abc} = \frac{12 \times 36}{12 + 36} = 9\ \mu f$$

$$C_{eq} = 9 + 19 = 38\ \mu f$$

(*b*)

$$E_{19} = 600 \text{ volts}$$

$$E_a = 600 \times \frac{36}{48} = 450 \text{ volts}$$

$$E_b = E_c = 600 \times \frac{12}{48} = 150 \text{ volts}$$

EXAMPLE 11. Referring to Fig. 102*b* and assuming the same values as those given in Example 10, calculate (*a*) the equivalent capacitance of the entire combination, (*b*) the voltages across the individual capacitors for a line potential of 600 volts.

Solution

(*a*)

$$C_{bc} = \frac{6 \times 30}{6 + 30} = 5\ \mu f$$

$$C_{bcd} = 5 + 19 = 24\ \mu f$$

$$C_{eq} = \frac{12 \times 24}{12 + 24} = 8\ \mu f$$

(*b*)

$$E_{12} = 600 \times \frac{24}{36} = 400 \text{ volts}$$

$$E_{19} = 600 \times \frac{12}{36} = 200 \text{ volts}$$

$$E_6 = 200 \times \frac{30}{36} = 166.7 \text{ volts}$$

$$E_{30} = 200 \times \frac{6}{36} = 33.3 \text{ volts}$$

Multiple-dielectric Capacitors. In some types of high-voltage equipment electrical conductors or plates are separated by one or more kinds of insulation material; these constructions obviously constitute capacitors in which charges are stored. To forestall the possibility of breakdown of such equipment from insulation failure it is necessary to maintain *voltage gradients*, i.e., volts per unit thickness across the dielectrics below certain maximum values. Although tests upon practical materials used in electrical circuits and machines indicate that the breakdown potentials vary somewhat with temperature, humidity, and shape, Table 10 lists acceptable values of so-called dielectric strengths in terms of volts per mil for a number of dielectrics. In applying these experimental data to the design of high-tension apparatus it is customary to apply reasonable factors of safety.

TABLE 10. DIELECTRIC STRENGTHS OF INSULATING MATERIALS

Material	*Dielectric strength, volts per mil*	*Material*	*Dielectric strength, volts per mil*
Air.......	76	Paper.....	250–650
Bakelite..	150–500	Paraffin...	190
Ebonite...	760–2,800	Porcelain..	100–250
Fiber.....	50	Rubber....	400–1,270
Glass.....	760–3,800	Slate......	7.5
Mica.....	760–5,600	Water.....	380
Oil.......	100–500	Wood... .	25–75

When the space between two metallic plates is occupied by two or more different insulating materials, the arrangement may, in effect, be regarded as comprising a group of two or more capacitors connected in series. This means that, with voltage applied to the plates, zero net charge will exist at each surface boundary between any pair of dielectrics; fictitious metallic plates may thus be thought to occupy each boundary level. Moreover, since all the assumed series capacitors have exactly the *same* area it will be convenient to use a *relative capacitance* term, symbolized by $\mathcal{C}$, to represent each of the series capacitors; written in equation form,

$$\mathcal{C} = \frac{Kk}{d}$$

where K is a constant that stands for the numerical quantity $2.25A/10^7$ in Eq. (75). This formula simplification for capacitance, where A is treated as part of a constant term, makes it possible to determine the several relative capacitances of the series combination, after which the proper voltage and relative-capacitance *ratios* may be equated, and the voltage gradients computed.

Several examples will now be given to illustrate the foregoing analysis.

EXAMPLE 12. Referring to Fig. 103, which illustrates two dielectric materials a and b between a pair of plates connected to a source whose voltage is E, compute the voltage gradients G across the insulating materials given the following information: k_a (mica) $= 4.5$; k_b (glass) $= 6.4$; $d_a = 0.025$ in.; $d_b = 0.06$ in.; $E = 16{,}000$ volts.

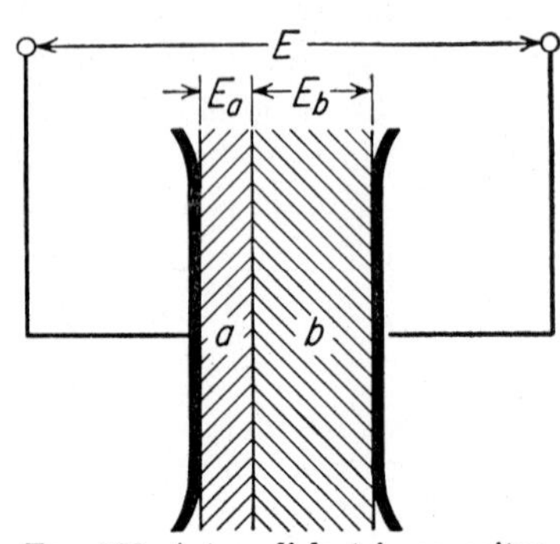

FIG. 103. A two-dielectric capacitor.

Solution

$$\mathcal{C}_a = \frac{K \times 4.5}{0.025} = 180K$$

$$\mathcal{C}_b = \frac{K \times 6.4}{0.06} = 140K$$

$$E_a = 16{,}000 \times \frac{140K}{320K} = 7{,}000 \text{ volts}$$

$$E_b = 16{,}000 \times \frac{180K}{320K} = 9{,}000 \text{ volts}$$

$$G_a = \frac{7{,}000}{25} = 280 \text{ volts per mil}$$

$$G_b = \frac{9{,}000}{60} = 150 \text{ volts per mil}$$

EXAMPLE 13. The following particulars are given in connection with the three-part dielectric capacitor of Fig. 104: k_a (mica) $= 4.5$; k_b (porcelain) $= 6.25$; k_c (paper) $= 2.5$; $d_a = 0.075$ in.; $d_b = 0.25$ in.; $d_c = 0.025$ in. Calculate the voltage gradient across each of the dielectrics if 40,000 volts is impressed across the combination.

Solution

$$\mathcal{C}_a = \frac{K \times 4.5}{0.075} = 60K$$

$$\mathcal{C}_b = \frac{K \times 6.25}{0.25} = 25K$$

$$\mathcal{C}_c = \frac{K \times 2.5}{0.025} = 100K$$

$$\mathcal{C}_{bc} = \frac{25K \times 100K}{25K + 100K} = 20K$$

$$E_a = 40{,}000 \times \frac{20}{80} = 10{,}000 \text{ volts}$$

$$E_{ab} = 40{,}000 - 10{,}000 = 30{,}000 \text{ volts}$$

$$E_b = 30{,}000 \times \frac{100}{125} = 24{,}000 \text{ volts}$$

$$E_c = 30{,}000 \times \frac{25}{125} = 6{,}000 \text{ volts}$$

$$G_a = \frac{10{,}000}{75} = 133 \text{ volts per mil}$$

$$G_b = \frac{24{,}000}{250} = 96 \text{ volts per mil}$$

$$G_c = \frac{6{,}000}{25} = 240 \text{ volts per mil}$$

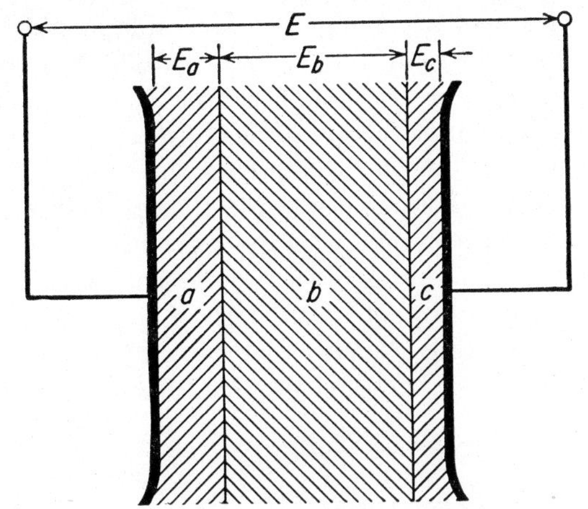

FIG. 104. A three-dielectric capacitor.

EXAMPLE 14. A three-dielectric capacitor (Fig. 104) is made up with a ⅛-in. pane of glass sandwiched between two sheets of paper each of which is 30 mils thick. If the potential gradients across the glass and paper must not exceed 300 and 100 volts per mil, respectively, what is the maximum permissible applied emf? Assume dielectric constants of 6 for glass and 3 for paper.

Solution

$$\mathcal{C}_g = \frac{K \times 6}{0.125} = 48K$$

$$\mathcal{C}_p = \frac{K \times 3}{0.03} = 100K$$

Maximum permissible voltage across paper is

$$E_p = 100 \times 30 = 3{,}000 \text{ volts}$$

Under this condition

$$E_g = 3{,}000 \times \frac{100K}{48K} = 6{,}250 \text{ volts}$$

and the voltage gradient across the glass is

$$G_g = \frac{6{,}250}{125} = 50 \text{ volts per mil}$$

Therefore

$$E = 2E_p + E_g = 2 \times 3{,}000 + 6{,}250 = 12{,}250 \text{ volts}$$

If the problem had been solved assuming a maximum gradient of 300 volts per mil to exist across the glass, the line potential would have been 73,500 volts with a paper gradient of 600 volts per mil.

Capacitance of a Cable. A high-voltage cable in which a cylindrical sheath, usually lead, surrounds a centrally located conductor and intervening insulation is, in reality, a capacitor; in such construction the internal surface of the outer sheath is one of the metallic conductors while the outside surface of the wire represents the other conductor. Considering unit length of cable, that is, 1 in., the capacitance between inner and outer conductors theoretically comprises an infinite number of capacitors in *series*, the one adjacent to the outer sheath having the largest value; this is true because, per unit length of cable, the inner capacitor has an area $2\pi r_1 \times 1$, while the outer capacitor has an area $2\pi r_2 \times 1$ (see Fig. 105). This implies, therefore, that the capacitance of an elemental

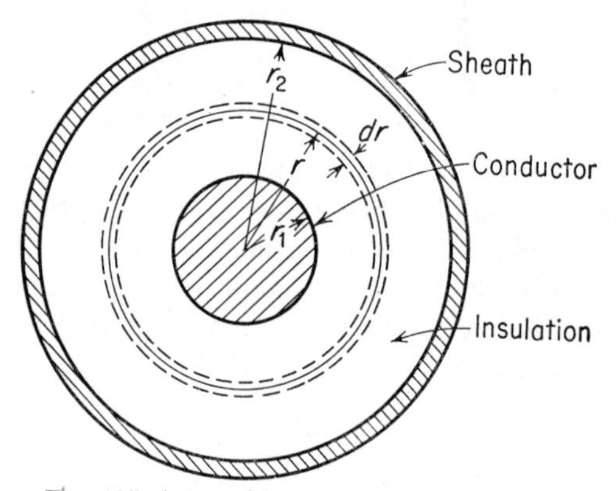

FIG. 105. A capacitor represented by a cable.

capacitor at radius r from the center and having differential dielectric thickness dr will be

$$dC = \frac{2.25K \times 2\pi r}{10^7\ dr}$$

Since, as previously stated, the imagined capacitors are in series, it will be convenient to write the reciprocal of the foregoing equation for the purpose of summing up, i.e., integrating, an infinite number of capacitors whose values increase progressively from the inside to the outside. Thus

$$\frac{1}{dC} = \frac{10^7\ dr}{2.25k \times 2\pi r}$$

Now then, when this differential equation is integrated by the calculus between the limits of r_1 and r_2, it becomes

$$\frac{1}{C} = \frac{10^7}{14.1k} \log_\epsilon \frac{r_2}{r_1}$$

and the equivalent capacitance of the cable, being its reciprocal, is

$$C = \frac{14.1k}{10^7 \log_\epsilon (r_2/r_1)} \qquad \mu\text{f per in.}$$

Written in more desirable terms, i.e., in microfarads per mile and logarithms to the base 10,

$$C = \frac{14.1k}{10^7 \times 2.3 \log_{10} (r_2/r_1)} \times 12 \times 5{,}280$$

whence
$$C = \frac{0.0388k}{\log_{10} (r_2/r_1)} \quad \mu\text{f per mile} \qquad (79)^1$$

EXAMPLE 15. A lead-sheath cable for underground service has a copper conductor (diameter = 0.204 in.) surrounded by a 0.16-in. wall of rubber insulation. Assuming a dielectric constant of 3.5 for rubber, calculate the capacitance of cable per mile of length.

Solution

$$C = \frac{0.0388 \times 3.5}{\log_{10} (0.262/0.102)} = \frac{0.1358}{0.41} = 0.331 \ \mu\text{f per mile}$$

Charging Current in a Resistance-Capacitance (R-C) Circuit. When a series resistance-capacitance circuit is connected to a d-c source current will flow to charge the capacitor. However, the *rate* at which charge is deposited on the plates will vary with time, being a maximum at the instant the circuit is energized (at $t = 0$), i.e., when maximum potential difference exists between source and plates, and zero after a theoretically long period of time (at $t = \infty$), i.e., when source and plate potentials are equalized. Now then, since *rate of motion of charge*, that is, coulombs per second, is defined as current [see Eq. (1), page 4], it should be clear that the charging *current* will be a maximum at the instant the circuit is first energized and zero after the capacitor is fully charged; the current is, in fact, equal to E/R at t = zero, and zero at t = infinity. (In practical circuits a capacitor is charged in a comparatively short time.) Considered another way, these statements imply that *a capacitor acts like a short circuit at* $t = 0$ *and like an open circuit at* $t = \infty$.

Further analyzing the *current-time* relations in an R-C circuit (Fig. 106) in which a capacitor is charged, it can be seen that the varying current i will involve a resistance-voltage drop $e_R = (E/R)R = E$ at $t = 0$ and $e_R = 0$ at $t = \infty$. This means that the voltage e_C across the capacitor will vary between $e_C = 0$

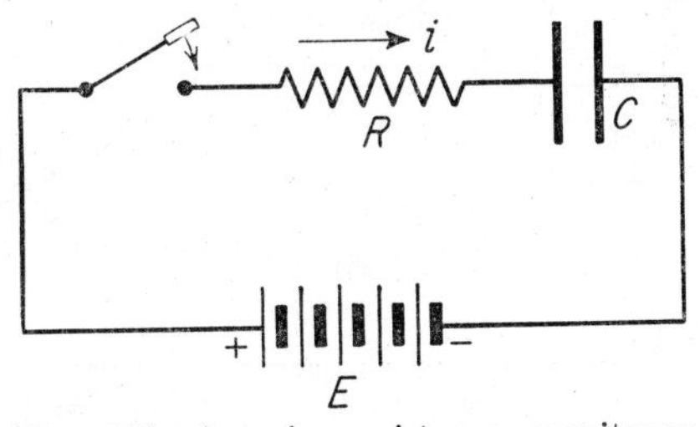

FIG. 106. A series resistance-capacitance (R-C) circuit, in which a capacitor is charged.

[1] See Appendix 1K for derivation.

at $t = 0$ and $e_C = E$ at $t = \infty$. To put the foregoing in equation form and in general terms,

$$e_C = E - iR$$

But the voltage e_C across the capacitor is, at any instant of time, equal to q/C, where C is given in *farads* and the equation is expressed for varying values of charge and voltage. Also, q represents the accumulated charge in coulombs between the time the circuit is energized and any time t; this is therefore a summation (an integration) of charge and differential elements of time and may be represented by $\int i\,dt/C$. Making the proper substitutions,

$$E = iR + \int_0^t \frac{i\,dt}{C}$$

which, by the calculus, may be solved for the instantaneous value of current in the circuit; this becomes

$$i = \frac{E}{R}\epsilon^{-t/RC} \qquad (80)^{1}$$

A typical graph of this exponential form of equation is shown in Fig. 107. Note particularly that the current rises to its E/R value at the

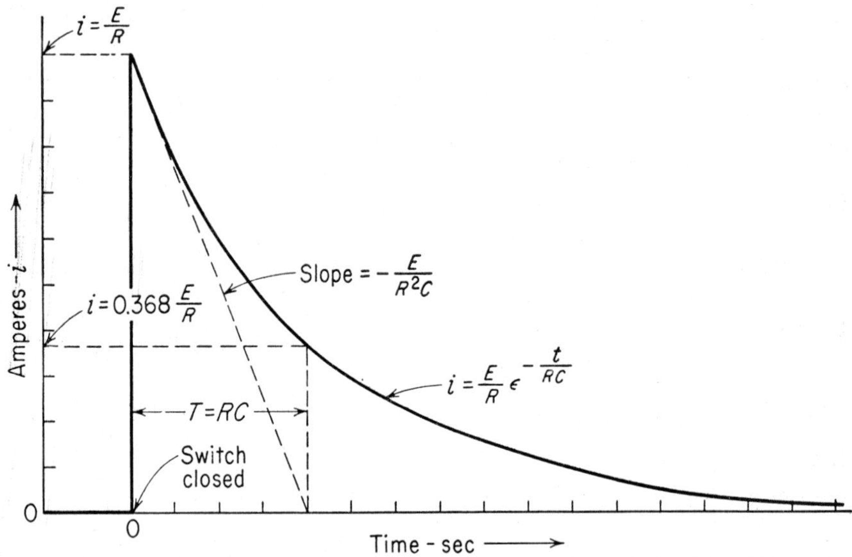

FIG. 107. Current vs. time relationship in a basic R-C circuit (see Fig. 106).

instant the switch is closed, i.e., when the exponential term becomes unity at $t = 0$, and drops to zero when the exponential term becomes zero at the theoretical time $t = \infty$.

[1] See Appendix 1L for derivation.

As with inductive circuits (Chap. 8), capacitive circuits are often compared on the basis of the rapidity with which the current drops from its initial instantaneous value after the switch is closed. One standard of comparison is a time unit equal to RC. This is designated as the *time constant* of the circuit and is represented by the capital letter T. Substituting RC for $t = T$, Eq. (80) becomes

$$i_T = \frac{E}{R} \epsilon^{-RC/RC} = \frac{E}{R} \epsilon^{-1} = \frac{E}{R} \times \frac{1}{\epsilon} = 0.368 \frac{E}{R}$$

This indicates that the current will drop to 36.8 per cent of its initial E/R value in RC sec after the switch is closed.

Another important measure of a circuit's capacitive property is the *initial rate of current change*. If for reasons of comparison it is assumed that the current continues to change at its *initial rate*, i.e., its *maximum rate*, and becomes zero in $T = RC$ sec, it follows that

$$\left(\frac{di}{dt}\right)_{\text{at } t=0} = \frac{E/R}{-RC} = -\frac{E}{R^2C} \tag{81}$$

where di/dt is the rate of current change in amperes per second and C is expressed in *farads*. This is obviously true because the rate of current change at any point on a *current-time* curve (at $t = 0$ in this case) is the ratio of the ordinate to the abscissa of the tangent line at that point.

In summarizing, the following points can be made in connection with the *time constant* of *current decay* in a capacitive circuit:

1. It is equal to RC sec.
2. It is the time in seconds that is required for the current to drop to 36.8 per cent of its initial E/R value.
3. It is the time in seconds that would be required for the current to drop to zero if the initial rate of change $-E/R^2C$ were maintained.

In an R-C circuit, it is extremely important to understand that increasing the value of C tends to *reduce* the initial rate of drop of current as well as to *retard* the current's decay; it has absolutely no effect upon the initial E/R value. Moreover, when the circuit possesses the property of capacitance it behaves like a short circuit at the instant a switch is closed; the current changes abruptly because the capacitor is initially uncharged and, therefore, offers no counter emf to oppose the potential of the source. However, as charge accumulates on the capacitor its potential increases progressively until, being equal to and opposing the emf of the source, the current drops to zero. Increasing values of R, on the other hand, have the effect of retarding the current decay as well as reducing both the initial current *and* the initial rate of drop of current. The foregoing points are well illustrated by the accompanying graphs. Figure 108 shows three R-C current-decay curves for which the values of capacitance

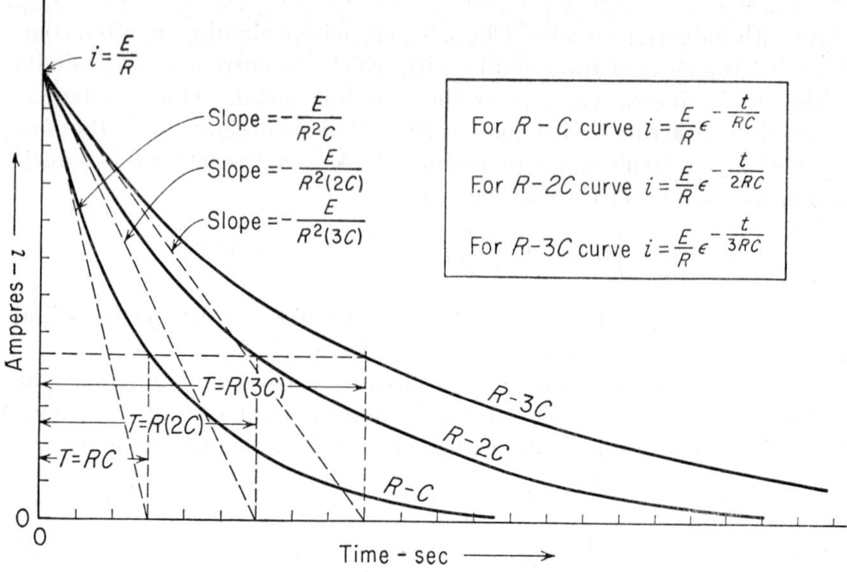

FIG. 108. Graphs illustrating the effect upon current decay when capacitance is changed in an R-C circuit.

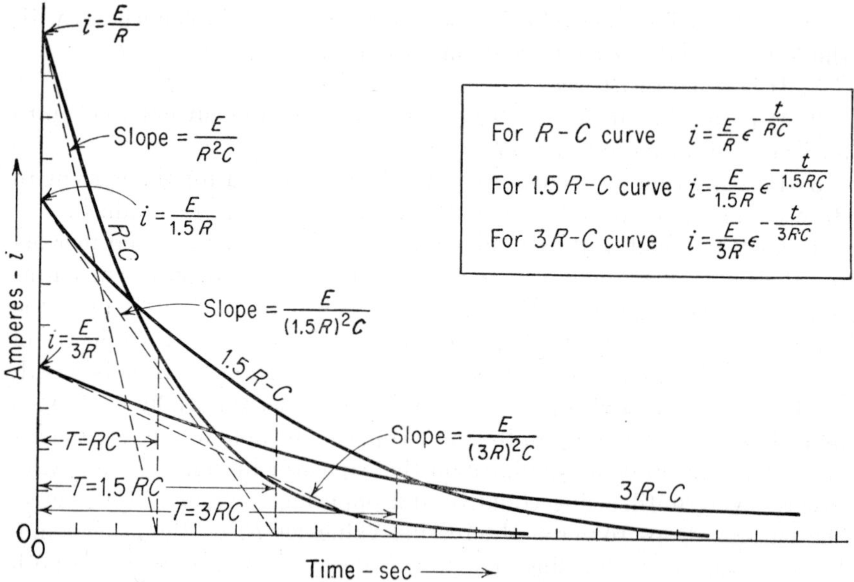

FIG. 109. Graphs illustrating the effect upon current decay when resistance is changed in an R-C circuit.

are C, $2C$, and $3C$, and the resistances R and voltages E are the same. Observe particularly the change in the initial rates of decay of current, and the fact that, starting with the same E/R value, the current decays to zero in progressively increasing intervals of time. Figure 109 represents three typical current-decay curves for resistance values of R, $1.5R$, and $3R$, and constant values of C and E; note that, while retarding the current decay, the initial current and the initial rate of current change are reduced with progressively increasing values of resistance.

EXAMPLE 16. A 50-μf capacitor is connected in series with a 150,000-ohm resistor. If this combination is then energized by a 120-volt d-c source, (*a*) what is the current at the instant the switch is closed, (*b*) what is the time constant of the circuit, (*c*) what current will be charging the capacitor at the instant $t = RC$?

Solution

(*a*) $$i = \frac{120}{150{,}000} = 0.0008 \text{ amp, or } 0.8 \text{ ma}$$

(*b*) $$T = RC = 150{,}000 \times 50 \times 10^{-6} = 7.5 \text{ sec}$$

(*c*) $$i = 0.368 \frac{E}{R} = 0.368 \times 0.0008 = 0.000294 \text{ amp, or } 0.294 \text{ ma}$$

EXAMPLE 17. For the circuit of Example 16, calculate (*a*) the initial rate of current change, (*b*) the charging current 3.75 sec from the closing of the switch.

Solution

(*a*) $$\left(\frac{di}{dt}\right)_{\text{at } t=0} = -\frac{120 \times 10^3}{(150{,}000)^2 \times 50 \times 10^{-6}} = -\frac{120 \times 10^3}{(150)^2 \times 10^6 \times 50 \times 10^{-6}}$$
$$= -\frac{120}{1{,}125} = -0.1067 \text{ ma per sec}$$

(*b*) $$i = \frac{120}{150{,}000} \epsilon^{-(3.75/7.5)} = 0.0008 \times \frac{1}{\epsilon^{0.5}}$$
$$= 0.000487 \text{ amp, or } 0.487 \text{ ma}$$

EXAMPLE 18. The current in a 600-volt series R-C circuit is to be limited to a maximum of 30 ma, and the time constant is to be 4 sec. Calculate the values of R and C.

Solution

$$R = \frac{600}{0.03} = 20{,}000 \text{ ohms}$$

$$4 = 20{,}000 \times C \times 10^{-6}$$

$$C = \frac{4 \times 10^6}{20{,}000} = 200 \ \mu\text{f}$$

EXAMPLE 19. A series *R-C* circuit has a time constant of 6 sec, and when connected to a certain d-c source has an initial rate of current change of 0.3 ma per sec. How will these values be affected if (*a*) the resistance is doubled, (*b*) the resistance is halved, (*c*) the capacitance is doubled, (*d*) the capacitance is halved?

Solution

(*a*)
$$T = 2 \times 6 = 12 \text{ sec}$$
$$\frac{di}{dt} = -\frac{1}{4} \times 0.3 = -0.075 \text{ ma per sec}$$

(*b*)
$$T = 0.5 \times 6 = 3 \text{ sec}$$
$$\frac{di}{dt} = -4 \times 0.3 = -1.2 \text{ ma per sec}$$

(*c*)
$$T = 2 \times 6 = 12 \text{ sec}$$
$$\frac{di}{dt} = -\frac{1}{2} \times 0.3 = -0.15 \text{ ma per sec}$$

(*d*)
$$T = 0.5 \times 6 = 3 \text{ sec}$$
$$\frac{di}{dt} = -2 \times 0.3 = -0.6 \text{ ma per sec}$$

Discharge Current in a Resistance-Capacitance (R-C) Circuit. After a capacitor is charged the potential difference between its terminal plates is exactly equal to the voltage of the source E to which it is connected; the energy stored in the capacitor will then be $\frac{1}{2} CE^2$, as will be shown subsequently. Assuming the capacitor to be perfect in respect to its ability to prevent loss of charge, it will retain the stored energy indefinitely if disconnected from the source; on the other hand, if the disconnected capacitor is short-circuited or has its terminals connected across a resistor, the charge will be dissipated, under which condition the capacitor is said to be discharged.

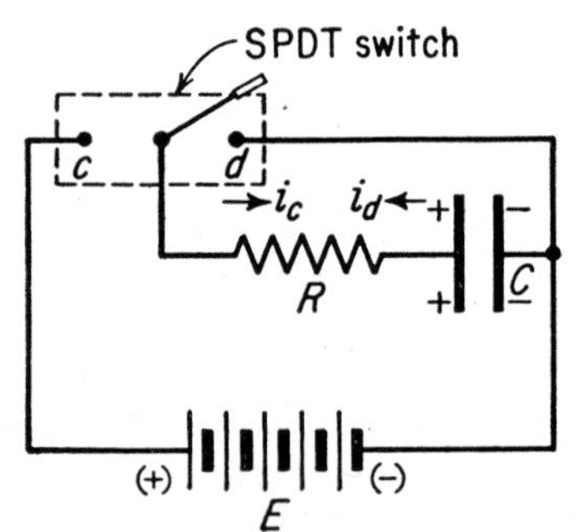

FIG. 110. A series resistance-capacitance (*R-C*) circuit connected for charging and discharging.

Referring to Fig. 110, assume that the SPDT switch is closed to the charge *c* side; the battery will then send a current i_c through resistor R to charge the capacitor in accordance with Eq. (80), and after a reasonable period of time has elapsed the capacitor will be charged to potential E. If the switch is next closed to the discharge side *d*, the capacitor, acting as a diminishing source of emf, will send a current i_d through the resistor R in the *reverse* direction, doing so until all the original stored energy represented by $\frac{1}{2} CE^2$ is dissipated. Moreover, since the potential difference between the terminal plates is a maximum at the instant the switch is thrown to d, the current i_d will be a maximum and equal to E/R; after the capacitor is completely discharged, the current i_d will, of course, become zero, because the voltage across the resistor, i.e., the plate potential difference, will be zero. During the discharge period the capacitor voltage e_C will, at every instant, be equal to $-e_R$; equating these continually varying values of voltage in terms of equivalent quantities,

$$\frac{q}{C} = -iR$$

But, as shown in the previous section, the charge q at any given time t may be represented by a summation, an integration of instantaneous charges $i\,dt$. Thus

$$iR + \int_0^t \frac{i\,dt}{C} = 0$$

which, by the calculus, may be solved for the discharge current in the circuit consisting of R and C; this becomes

$$i = -\frac{E}{R}\epsilon^{-t/RC} \qquad (82)[1]$$

Note particularly that the current-discharge equation has the same form as that given for capacitor charge [Eq. (80)] with the exception that one is the negative of the other. This confirms the foregoing analysis in which it was stated that the discharge current, opposite in direction to the charging current, is a progressively diminishing one that starts at an E/R value and eventually becomes zero. It should be clear, therefore, that the graphical relationship between i and t is exactly similar to that shown in Fig. 107 for the charging of a capacitor; furthermore, the time constant $T = RC$ and the initial rate of current change given by Eq. (81) apply equally well here.

Charging and Discharging Capacitors in Complex Circuits. It is sometimes necessary to interconnect one or more capacitors in combination with several resistors to form a complex circuit. When this is done and the circuit is energized from a d-c source, it is well to remember that the final current in the capacitor branch will always be zero, because under this condition the capacitor always acts like an open circuit. The initial capacitor current is, however, quite another matter, and must be determined on the basis of *how the capacitor is connected* in the circuit and whether it is being *charged* or *discharged*. Although the degree of circuit

[1] See Appendix 1M for derivation.

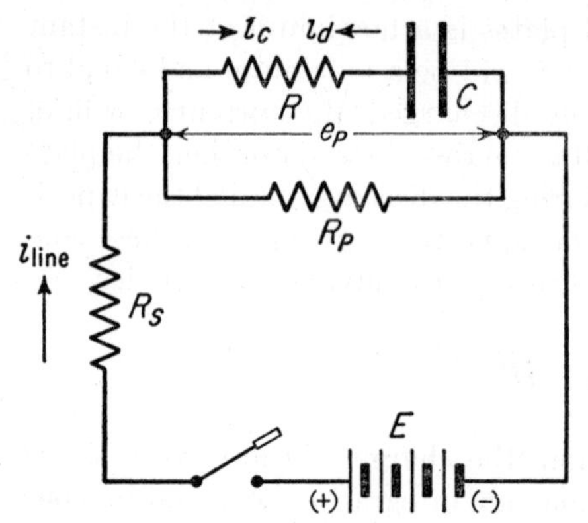

FIG. 111. A series-parallel circuit arrangement in which a capacitor may be charged or discharged.

complexity may vary somewhat, the resulting actions may be analyzed quite readily if the capacitor is assumed to behave like a short circuit at $t = 0$, and the initial capacitor voltage is determined.

Consider Fig. 111, which illustrates a typical series-parallel circuit and in which it is desired to determine the initial capacitor current on both charge and discharge. Assuming the capacitor to be in an uncharged condition when the switch is open, the voltage across the *R-C* branch will be e_P at the instant the switch is closed; also, since the capacitor acts like a short circuit at $t = 0$,

$$e_{P_c} = E \times \frac{(R_P \times R)/(R_P + R)}{R_S + [(R_P \times R)/(R_P + R)]}$$

The initial *charging* current will therefore be

$$i_{c_0} = \frac{e_{P_c}}{R}$$

The final capacitor-branch current will, of course, be zero.

Assuming next a steady-state condition with the switch closed, the voltage across resistor R_P will be

$$e_{P_d} = E \times \frac{R_P}{R_S + R_P}$$

because the capacitor acts like an open circuit. However, at the instant the switch is *opened* to discharge the capacitor, the latter behaves like a short circuit; the *discharge* current will therefore be

$$i_{d_0} = \frac{e_{P_d}}{R_P + R}$$

A numerical example will now be solved to illustrate the foregoing.

EXAMPLE 20. The following data are given in connection with Fig. 111: $E = 120$ volts, $R_S = 40$, $R_P = 80$, $R = 240$, $C = 50$ μf. (*a*) For the charging condition, calculate the initial capacitor-branch current, and the initial line current; (*b*) for the discharging condition, calculate the initial capacitor-branch current, and the initial line current.

Solution

(*a*) $$i_{P_c} = 120 \times \frac{(80 \times 240)/(80 + 240)}{40 + [(80 \times 240)/(80 + 240)]} = 120 \times \frac{60}{100} = 72 \text{ volts}$$

$$i_{c_0} = \frac{72}{240} = 0.3 \text{ amp}$$

$$i_{\text{line}_0} = \frac{120}{100} = 1.2 \text{ amp}$$

(*b*) $$e_{P_d} = 120 \times \frac{80}{80 + 40} = 80 \text{ volts}$$

$$i_{d_0} = \frac{80}{80 + 240} = 0.25 \text{ amp}$$

$$i_{\text{line}_0} = 0$$

Energy Stored in a Capacitor. The fact that a capacitor stores electric charge (coulombs) to develop a potential difference between electrodes when it is connected to a source of emf implies that energy is transferred to it from the source. However, unlike a resistor circuit in a steady-state condition where the voltage and current are constant and in which the energy in watt-seconds is EIt [see Eq. (14), Chap. 3], the energy delivered to a capacitor changes differentially during its entire charging period; it varies at a progressively *increasing* rate from zero to a maximum and then proceeds to vary progressively at a *diminishing* rate from a maximum to zero. During an extremely short period of time dt immediately following the closing of the switch, the charging current i is at a maximum value, i.e., E/R, but the capacitor voltage e_C is zero; the differential energy dw will therefore be zero ($dw = 0 \times Edt/I = 0$). Also, during a differentially small period of time dt after the capacitor is completely charged the capacitor voltage will be at a maximum value, i.e., E, but the charging current i is zero; the differential energy dw will again be equal to zero ($dw = E \times 0 \times dt = 0$). Between these two extreme differential periods of time, however, the capacitor voltage and charging current will *both* have finite, though rapidly changing, values; this implies, of course, that finite differential amounts of energy will be delivered to the capacitor, first at an increasing rate until a maximum is reached, and then at a decreasing rate until the charging process is completed. Moreover, theoretical analysis indicates that maximum energy is delivered to the capacitor during a differentially small period when the capacitor voltage e_C equals the voltage drop e_R across the resistor.

The foregoing discussion is graphically illustrated by Fig. 112. Starting with the familiar *charging current* vs. *time* curve, i.e., i vs. t, observe that the *resistance-voltage drop* vs. *time* relationship, i.e., e_R vs. t, is essentially similar in form, because the $iR = e_R$ voltage drop is directly pro-

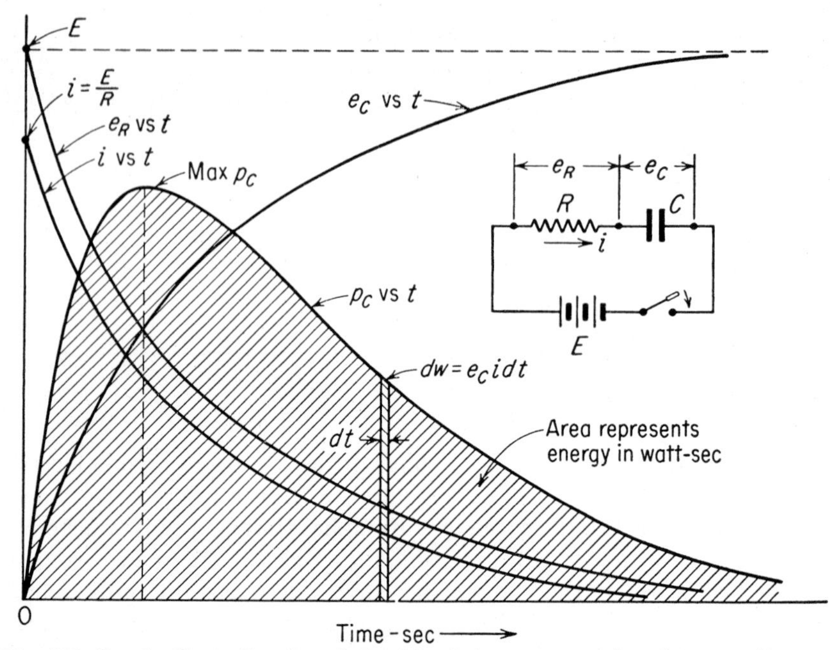

FIG. 112. Graphs illustrating the relationships between current i, resistance voltage e_R, capacitor voltage e_C, and capacitor power p_C with respect to time, in an R-C circuit that is being charged.

portional to the current at every instant of time. Furthermore, since the capacitor voltage is equal to $E - e_R$, it should be clear that the *capacitor-voltage* vs. *time* curve, i.e., e_C vs. t, must have a *rising* exponential shape as shown. Finally, the capacitor power, being at any instant equal to the product of e_C and i, yields the curve shown as p_C vs. t; note particularly that maximum power occurs when $e_C = e_R$, a point that was made in the preceding paragraph.

Proceeding with the analysis to determine how *much* energy is eventually stored in a capacitor, it should first be stated that, since a differential amount of energy is correctly represented by a small "sliver" of area under the p_C vs. t curve, i.e., $dw = e_C\, i\, dt$, the summation (integration) of an infinite number of such areas will yield the total number of watt-seconds. Remembering that

$$e_C = \int_0^t \frac{i\, dt}{C}$$

the expression for current is

$$i = \frac{1}{C}\frac{de_C}{dt}$$

when the first equation is differentiated. Interpreted in words, this states that the charging current i is directly proportional to the *rate* at which the voltage changes across the capacitor. Thus, referring to Fig. 112, at $t = 0$ when the capacitor voltage is changing by a maximum amount, the current i is a maximum, i.e., E/R; also, at $t = \infty$ when there is no change in capacitor voltage, the current i is zero. The instantaneous capacitor power, being equal to the product of capacitor voltage and charging current, becomes

$$p_C = e_C \times \frac{1}{C}\frac{de_C}{dt}$$

and the differential amount of energy is

$$dw = \frac{1}{C} e_C \frac{de_C}{dt} dt = \frac{1}{C} e_C \, de_C$$

When the last equation is properly integrated by the calculus to yield the total area under the p_C vs. t curve,

$$W = \frac{1}{2} CE^2 \qquad \text{watt-sec} \tag{83}$$

where C is in farads and E is in volts.

EXAMPLE 21. How much energy is stored in a 25-μf capacitor connected to a 600-volt d-c source?

Solution

$$W = \frac{1}{2} \times 25 \times 10^{-6} (600)^2 = 4.5 \text{ watt-sec}$$

EXAMPLE 22. If it requires 5 watt-sec to charge a capacitor with 0.04 coulomb, calculate the necessary d-c voltage and the size of unit in microfarads.

Solution

$$C = \frac{0.04}{E}$$

and $$5 = \frac{1}{2} CE^2 = \frac{1}{2}\left(\frac{0.04}{E}\right) E^2 = 0.02E$$

Therefore $$E = \frac{5}{0.02} = 250 \text{ volts}$$

and $$C = \frac{0.04}{250} = 0.00016 \text{ farad, or } 160 \ \mu\text{f}$$

Questions

1. Distinguish between *static* and *dynamic electricity*.
2. Explain how dynamic electricity may become static electricity.

3. Describe a capacitor, and explain how it may be charged.
4. Upon what factors does the charge on a capacitor depend?
5. What is meant by the breakdown voltage, referring to a capacitor?
6. Explain why there is no net change in electron content in a circuit in which a capacitor is charged.
7. How is it possible to demonstrate that energy is transferred from a battery to a capacitor when it is charged?
8. Upon what factors does the capacitance of a capacitor depend?
9. What is meant by the term *dielectric*, and how does it affect the capacitance of a capacitor?
10. Describe the so-called *interleaved* (*sandwich*) and *rolled* types of capacitor.
11. What is meant by the term *dielectric constant*, and how does it affect the capacitance of a capacitor?
12. What are *electrolytic* capacitors, and where are they commonly used?
13. How are variable capacitors constructed?
14. What is meant by *equivalent capacitance*, referring to a group of interconnected capacitors?
15. How is the equivalent capacitance of a group of parallel-connected capacitors determined?
16. How is the equivalent capacitance of a group of series-connected capacitors determined?
17. When a group of capacitors are connected in series, what is the net charge on the plates that are joined together? on each of the plates that is connected to the d-c source? Give reasons for your answers.
18. Explain why all plates in a series-connected group of capacitors acquire the same charge when connected to a d-c source.
19. What is the equivalent capacitance of a group of series-connected capacitors in terms of any one of them? Why?
20. When a group of series-connected capacitors is energized by a d-c source, what is the relationship between the voltage drops across the individual units?
21. What is the equivalent capacitance of a pair of series-connected capacitors having different values? the same value?
22. When a capacitor is constructed with several dielectric materials between terminal plates, how should it be regarded when calculating the value of the equivalent capacitance?
23. What is meant by the term *relative* capacitance, referring to a multiple-dielectric capacitor?
24. Define the term *voltage* gradient. Why is this particularly important in multiple-dielectric capacitors?
25. Explain how the voltage gradients across the various dielectrics may be determined in a multiple-dielectric capacitor.
26. Why is a lead-sheath cable a capacitor? What are its terminal plates?
27. Assuming a given conductor size and dielectric material in an underground cable, what is the effect upon the capacitance if the over-all diameter is increased? the length of the cable is increased? Give reasons for your answers.
28. In a simple *R-C* circuit that is connected to a d-c source, what is the value of the charging current at the instant the switch is closed? after the circuit has been energized for an extremely long time?
29. In a simple *R-C* circuit that is connected to a d-c source, what are the voltage drops across the resistor and capacitor at the instant the switch is closed? after the circuit has been energized a long time?

30. What is the typical form of equation for the charging current in an R-C circuit? How does this equation compare with that for an R-L circuit?

31. Define the time constant in terms of the circuit parameters; in terms of the value of charging current at some instant of time; in terms of the initial rate of current change.

32. What is the initial rate of current change in a simple R-C circuit in terms of circuit constants?

33. How is the time constant affected by an increase in R? by an increase in C?

34. How is the initial rate of current change affected by an increase in R? by an increase in C? by an increase in E?

35. When a capacitor is discharged, what is the direction of the circuit current with respect to the charging current?

36. Explain why a capacitor that is discharging acts as a diminishing source of emf.

37. What is the typical form of equation for the discharge current in an R-C circuit?

38. What is the value of the discharge current at the instant an R-C circuit is short-circuited, assuming that the capacitor is originally charged?

39. Explain how a capacitor stores energy when it is charged.

40. When a capacitor is being charged in a simple R-C circuit, what is the differential energy during the short period following the closing of the switch? during the short period at the end of the charging period? Give reasons for your answers.

41. How much energy is stored in a capacitor when it is connected to a d-c source? Does the value of the resistance in the circuit have any effect upon the amount of stored energy? Explain carefully.

42. How is the amount of energy stored in a capacitor affected by the capacitance of the capacitor? by the applied d-c voltage?

Problems

1. A 60-μf capacitor is connected to a 250-volt d-c source. (*a*) Calculate the final charge that will appear on the plates. (*b*) If the current is maintained at a constant value of 25 ma during the first half of its charge and at 15 ma during the remainder of the charge, calculate the time it will take to charge the capacitor completely.

2. A constant source of direct current is used to charge a 50-μf capacitor. If the current diminishes uniformly from an initial value of 40 ma to zero in 0.8 sec, what is the voltage of the source?

3. How many electrons are stored on one of the electrodes of a 75-μf capacitor when it is charged from a 125-volt source?

4. A capacitor is charged at a constant current of 2.5 ma. If its emf is 500 volts at the end of 15 sec, calculate the capacitance of the capacitor.

5. The capacitance between a pair of parallel plates in air is 0.0002 μf. When the plates are immersed in a certain grade of insulating oil the capacitance is raised to 0.00072. What is the dielectric constant of the oil?

6. Calculate the capacitance of a parallel-plate capacitor that consists of 80 glass plates, each one 0.045 in. thick, and 81 sheets of 6.5- by 7.5-in. aluminum foil tightly cemented to the glass. One set of alternate metal sheets is connected to form one electrode and the remaining metal sheets are joined to become the second electrode. Assume a dielectric constant of 6 for glass.

7. How many glass and aluminum sheets of the sizes given in Prob. 6 would be necessary to construct a capacitor having a capacitance of 0.5 μf?

8. A capacitor of the rolled-type construction consists of two strips of 3.25-in.-wide aluminum foil, each 210 ft long, and two strips of 3.5-mil waxed paper slightly wider. Assuming a dielectric constant of 2.4 for waxed paper, calculate the capacitance.

9. What length of aluminum foil and 4-mil paper strips having the dimensions given in Prob. 8 should be used to construct a rolled type of capacitor if the capacitance is to be 2 μf?

10. Three capacitors have capacitance values of 3, 6, and 18 μf, respectively. What will be the equivalent capacitance when they are connected (*a*) in parallel, (*b*) in series?

11. What three values of equivalent capacitance are possible if two of the capacitors of Prob. 10 are used at a time and are connected (*a*) in *parallel*, (*b*) in *series?*

12. What three values of equivalent capacitance are possible if the three capacitors of Prob. 10 are connected in *series-parallel?*

13. What three values of equivalent capacitance are possible if the three capacitors of Prob. 10 are connected in *parallel-series?*

14. Two capacitors having capacitance values of 8 and 24 μf, respectively, are connected in series and to a 120-volt d-c source. Calculate the charge on, and the voltage across, each one.

15. After the capacitors of Prob. 14 are charged in series, they are carefully disconnected from the source and connected in parallel. Assuming no leakage of charge, calculate the charge on each one and the voltage across the combination.

16. Three capacitors having capacitances of 30, 37.5, and 50 μf, respectively, are connected in series and to a 600-volt d-c source. Calculate (*a*) the equivalent capacitance of the combination, (*b*) the charge on each capacitor, (*c*) the voltage across each capacitor.

17. After the capacitors of Prob. 16 are charged in series they are carefully disconnected from the source and connected in parallel. Assuming no leakage of charge, calculate (*a*) the charge on each capacitor, (*b*) the equivalent capacitance of the combination, (*c*) the voltage across the combination.

18. What capacitance should be connected in series with a 12-μf capacitor if the equivalent capacitance is to be 4 μf?

19. A 65-μf capacitor is to be connected in series with another unit whose voltage drop must not exceed 390 volts when 600 volts is impressed across the combination. What should be the capacitance of the added unit, and what is the equivalent capacitance of the combination?

20. The following data are given in connection with Fig. 102*a*: $C_a = 30\ \mu$f, $C_b = 20\ \mu$f, $C_c = 40\ \mu$f, $C_d = 10\ \mu$f, $E = 240$ volts. Calculate (*a*) the equivalent capacitance of the combination, (*b*) the voltages across the individual capacitors.

21. If the capacitors of Prob. 20 are connected in *series* and to a 240 volt d-c source, calculate (*a*) the equivalent capacitance, (*b*) the voltage drops across the individual capacitors.

22. If the capacitors of Prob. 20 are connected in *parallel* and to a 240-volt source, calculate (*a*) the equivalent capacitance of the combination, (*b*) the charge deposited on each capacitor.

23. The following data are given in connection with Fig. 102*b*: $C_a = 30\ \mu$f, $C_b = 10\ \mu$f, $C_c = 40\ \mu$f, $C_d = 12\ \mu$f, $E = 250$ volts. Calculate (*a*) the equivalent capacitance of the combination, (*b*) the voltages across the individual capacitors.

24. How should the four capacitors of Prob. 20 be connected to yield an equivalent capacitance of 25 μf?

25. A two-dielectric capacitor (see Fig. 103) consists of a 3/16-in. thickness of Bakelite and a 1/8-in. thickness of pressboard. If their dielectric constants are, respectively, 4.7 and 5.0, calculate the voltage gradients across the two insulation materials when the capacitor is subjected to an emf of 25,000 volts.

26. What maximum voltage can be impressed across the capacitor of Prob. 25 if the pressboard voltage gradient is not to exceed 100 volts per mil? What will be the Bakelite voltage gradient under this condition?

27. A potential of 3,500 volts is impressed across a pair of plates that has an air separation of 0.065 in. (*a*) What is the voltage gradient across the air dielectric? (*b*) If a sheet of glass having a thickness of 0.045 in. and a dielectric constant of 6.5 is inserted between the plates, what will be the voltage gradient in the remaining air space? Will the air break down under this condition?

28. A three-dielectric capacitor (see Fig. 104) is made up of a ¼-in. thickness of porcelain, sandwiched between a 50-mil thickness of paper on one side and a 30-mil thickness of rubber on the other. If 40,000 volts is impressed across the plates on the outside of the insulating materials, calculate the voltage gradient across each dielectric. Assume dielectric constants of 6 for porcelain, 2.5 for paper, and 3 for rubber.

29. Calculate the capacitance of a 5-mile length of underground lead-sheath cable that has a No. 2 B&S gage conductor (diameter = 0.257 in.) surrounded by a 0.25-in. thickness of rubber insulation ($k = 3.6$).

30. For what length of the cable in Prob. 29 will the capacitance be 0.5 μf?

31. A 62.5-μf capacitor is connected in series with a 200,000-ohm resistor and to a 250-volt d-c source. (*a*) Write the expression for the charging current following the closing of the switch. (*b*) What is the initial charging current? (*c*) Calculate the time constant and the charging current at $t = T$.

32. What will be the initial rate of current change for the circuit of Prob. 31?

33. If a 20,000-ohm resistor is substituted for the one in Prob. 31, calculate (*a*) the initial current, (*b*) the time constant, (*c*) the initial rate of current change.

34. If a 125-μf capacitor is substituted for the one in Prob. 32, calculate (*a*) the initial current, (*b*) the time constant, (*c*) the initial rate of current change.

35. Find the values of R and C in a 600-volt series R-C circuit in which the charging current in milliamperes varies in accordance with the equation $i = 24\epsilon^{-0.5t}$.

36. A series R-C circuit is to have an initial charging current of 4 ma and a time constant of 3.6 sec when connected to a 120-volt d-c source. Calculate the values of R and C.

37. A 100-μfd capacitor is connected in series with a 150-volt voltmeter that has a resistance of 1,000 ohms per volt. Calculate the reading on the voltmeter at the instant when t equals the time constant following the closing of the switch that impresses 120 volts on the circuit.

38. After the capacitor in Prob. 37 is completely charged, it is discharged across the resistance of the voltmeter. What will be the reading on the voltmeter 5 and 7.5 sec after the capacitor starts to discharge?

39. Referring to Fig. 111, the following data are given: $R_S = 50$, $R_P = 100$, $R = 300$, $C = 75$ μf, $E = 250$ volts. (*a*) For the charging condition, calculate the initial charging current, the initial rate of change of charging current, and the initial line current; (*b*) for the discharging condition, calculate the initial capacitor-branch current, the initial rate of change of discharge current, and the initial line current.

40. Calculate the energy stored in a 2-μf capacitor when connected to a 1,500-volt d-c source.

41. A 600-volt d-c source is impressed across two capacitors, 15 and 30 μf, in series. How much energy is stored in each one?

42. A capacitor that was previously charged to a potential of 240 volts is connected in series with a 500-ohm resistor and, through a switch, to a 120-volt d-c source. Calculate the two possible values of initial current.

43. A series *R*-*C* circuit consists of a 20-μf capacitor and a 500-ohm resistor. When it is connected to a 125-volt d-c source, what is the maximum power delivered to the circuit and the current at which this maximum power occurs?

Part II

ELECTRICAL CIRCUITS
ALTERNATING CURRENT

CHAPTER 10

SINUSOIDAL VOLTAGES AND CURRENTS

General Aspects of Direct- and Alternating-current Systems. More than 90 per cent of electrical energy is *generated* by a-c machines. This is not to say that all the energy is used in this form; indeed, a great portion of the energy is converted to direct current for use in many types of industry, in railway transportation, on the farm, in communication systems (telephones, telegraphs, and radio), and in the home. A substantial part of the gigantic electrochemical industry, for example, depends upon direct current for such electrolytic processes as electroplating, electrorefining (copper, gold, and other precious metals), electrotyping, the production of aluminum, and the manufacture of fertilizers. Also, many motor applications such as elevators, printing presses, many kinds of machine tools, and certain kinds of steel-mill equipment are generally superior when operated by d-c systems. In these and others, the incoming alternating current must be converted to direct current.

The advantages of a-c generation are, however, apparent when it is recognized that it can be accomplished economically in large power plants that may be located where fuel and water are abundant. Moreover, generators and associated equipment may be large, an important matter in so far as cost per kilowatt is concerned; also transmission over networks of high-voltage lines to distant load centers is entirely practicable. The industrial applications of alternating current are, of course, widespread. These include the many types of induction motor, ranging in size from the mighty midgets to the giants employed in wind tunnels and reclamation projects, transformer equipment used in connection with welders and many kinds of control devices, communication systems, and many others.

It should be emphasized that electrical energy is, for the most part, generated as alternating current even though it may finally develop as direct current. This is particularly true in the d-c generator where the current in the armature winding, the source of the energy, is actually alternating current; in such a machine the *generated* alternating current is commutated, i.e., rectified, by a commutator and brushes to become direct current. Significantly, the limitation imposed upon the size of d-c generators, about 10,000 to 15,000 kw, results from the fact that commutators and brushes must be provided to rectify generated alternating currents in rotating armatures; this requirement is not present in a-c generators where armature windings are commonly placed in stationary cores.

Still another important difference between d-c and a-c systems concerns the transmission and distribution potentials. Since it is not feasible to raise or lower the voltages in d-c systems, energy must be transmitted from generator to consumer at essentially the same emf as it is generated; this is usually restricted to such low values as 250, 600, and 1,500 volts, a condition that limits both the amount and distance of transmission. These limitations are definitely not imposed upon a-c systems where efficient transformer equipment is used to raise or lower the voltage as required. In a typical a-c system, for example, the generated emf of 13,800 volts might be raised to 132,000 volts for long-distance transmission, say 100 miles, where in several successive step-down phases the so-called secondary lines might operate at 13,000, 6,600, 2,300, 230, and 115 volts. These changes are, of course, made to save copper, reduce copper loss, and provide some element of safety.

Generation of Alternating EMFs. A voltage can be developed in a coil of wire in one of three ways; these are (1) by changing the flux through the coil, (2) by moving the coil through a magnetic field so that flux cutting results, and (3) by altering the direction of the flux with respect to the coil. In the first of these the voltage is said to be an *induced emf* and, in accordance with Faraday's law, its magnitude at any instant of time is given by the equation

$$e = N \frac{d\Phi}{dt} \times 10^{-8} \qquad \text{volts} \tag{84}$$

where N = number of turns in the coil
$d\Phi/dt$ = *rate* at which the flux, in maxwells, changes through the coil

Note particularly that, by this method of developing an emf, there is no physical motion of coil or magnet; the current through the exciting coil that is responsible for the magnetism is altered to change the flux through the coil in which the voltage is induced. By the second or third method there is actual physical motion of coil or magnet, although in altered positions of coil or magnet there is an actual change of flux through the coil. A voltage developed in either of these ways is said to be a *generated emf* and is given by the equation

$$e = Blv \times 10^{-8} \qquad \text{volts} \tag{85}$$

where B = flux density, lines per square inch
l = length of the wire, in., that is moved relative to the flux
v = velocity of the wire, in. per sec, with respect to the flux

In the a-c generator relative motion does actually occur between moving magnets and stationary coils, or vice versa, so that it is proper to regard the voltages developed in such a machine as *generated* emfs. Figure 113 illustrates an extremely elementary a-c generator in which a single-turn coil *mabdcn* may be moved through a magnetic field created by two magnet poles N and S. The ends of the coil are fastened to two collectors x and y upon which rest two stationary brushes that are connected to a load resistor AB. In the position shown, for clockwise rotation of the coil, coil side *ab* is moving vertically upward to *cut* maximum flux under *south* pole S, while coil side *cd* is moving vertically downward

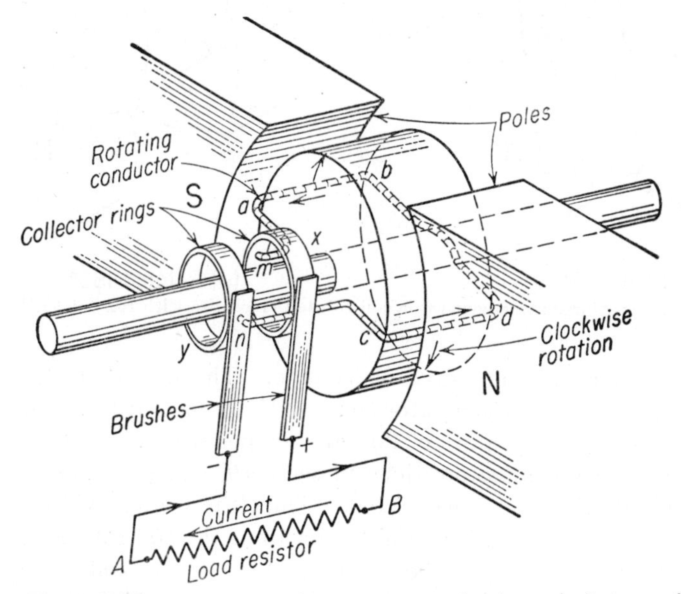

Fig. 113. Elementary two-pole a-c generator showing a single-turn coil.

to *cut* maximum flux under *north* pole N. After the coil is rotated one-quarter of a revolution to the position shown in Fig. 114*a* the coil sides will cut *no* flux and no voltage is generated. As the coil proceeds to rotate, coil side *ab* will cut flux under a *north* pole while coil side *cd* will cut flux under a *south* pole; with this change in the polarity of the fluxes that are cut by the conductors reversal in brush potential will occur. Moreover, when the coil is in the position shown in Fig. 114*b*, maximum voltage will be generated, although, as previously indicated, in a direction opposite to that shown in Fig. 113. This discussion should therefore emphasize two important points in connection with the rotation of a coil of wire through a fixed magnetic field, namely, (1) that the voltage changes from instant to instant and (2) that the electrical polarity plus (+) and minus (−), changes with altering positions under *north* and *south* poles. In the actual a-c generator it is the general practice to rotate a set of poles that is placed concentrically within a cylindrical core containing many coils of wire. However, what has been said concerning a moving coil inside of a pair of stationary poles applies equally well to the rotating-poles construction; in both arrangements there is *relative* motion of one element with respect to the other.

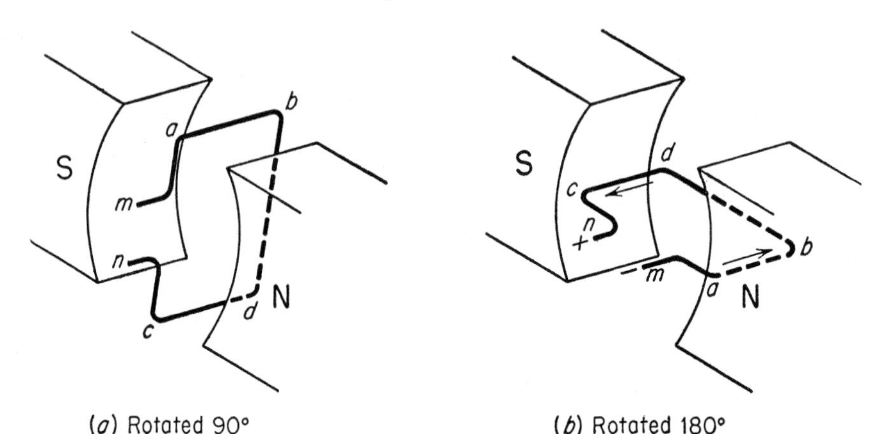

FIG. 114. Alternating-current generator coil rotated clockwise with respect to that shown in Fig. 113.

Generation of a Sine Wave of Voltage. The fact that the voltage developed in a coil of a generator changes (1) in magnitude from instant to instant as varying values of flux are cut per second and (2) in direction as coil sides change positions under *north* and *south* poles, implies that an alternating emf is generated. Thus, the voltage will be a maximum for Fig. 113 and will diminish to zero as the coil rotates clockwise toward the position illustrated by Fig. 114*a*; as the coil continues to rotate clockwise toward the position shown by Fig. 114*b* the polarities will change from $+m \; -n$ to $-m \; +n$. In the general case, assuming *uniform flux-density distribution* between *north* and *south* poles, the generated voltage in a coil located $\alpha°$ from the vertical (Fig. 115) will be

$$e = E_m \sin \alpha \tag{86}$$

The reason for this relationship between instantaneous voltage e and maximum voltage E_m is that a coil side such as a, moving tangentially to a circle as indicated, *cuts* lines of force in proportion to its *vertical component of motion.* If vector length ay represents a constant rotating velocity, it should be obvious that vector xy is, at the instant shown, its vertical component; the vector length ax is the horizontal component and implies that motion in this direction involves no flux-cutting action. Since the velocity ratio $xy/ay = \sin \alpha$ is also a measure of the voltage in

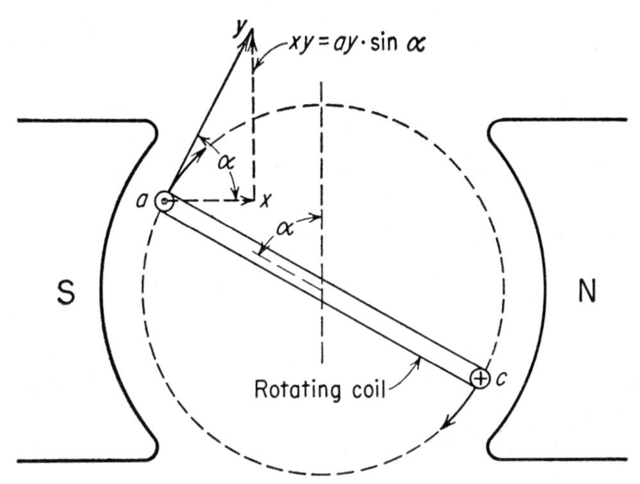

FIG. 115. A rotating coil illustrating that the generated voltage is proportional to sin x.

coil side a with respect to the maximum voltage (when the coil is located horizontally) it follows that sin α is a varying proportionality factor that equates e to E_m.

Equation (86) may be used to determine a succession of generated-voltage values in a coil as it rotates through a complete revolution. Such a list, computed for a selected set of angular displacements from the vertical (with poles located to create a uniform *horizontal* field of *flux*) is given in the Table 11.

TABLE 11

North pole				South pole			
Deg	Voltage	Deg	Voltage	Deg	Voltage	Deg	Voltage
0	0	90	$+E_m$	180	0	270	$-E_m$
15	$0.259E_m$	105	$0.966E_m$	195	$-0.259E_m$	285	$-0.966E_m$
30	$0.500E_m$	120	$0.866E_m$	210	$-0.500E_m$	300	$-0.866E_m$
45	$0.707E_m$	135	$0.707E_m$	225	$-0.707E_m$	315	$-0.707E_m$
60	$0.866E_m$	150	$0.500E_m$	240	$-0.866E_m$	330	$-0.500E_m$
75	$0.966E_m$	165	$0.259E_m$	255	$-0.966E_m$	345	$-0.259E_m$
90	$+E_m$	180	0	270	$-E_m$	360	0

A more convenient way of representing Eq. (86) is to draw a graph to illustrate the smooth variation of voltage with respect to the angular position of the coil; such a graph is called a *sine wave*. Since the wave repeats itself it is *periodic;* in this respect each *complete* succession of values is called a *cycle*, while each positive *or* negative half of the cycle is referred to as an *alternation* (see Fig. 116).

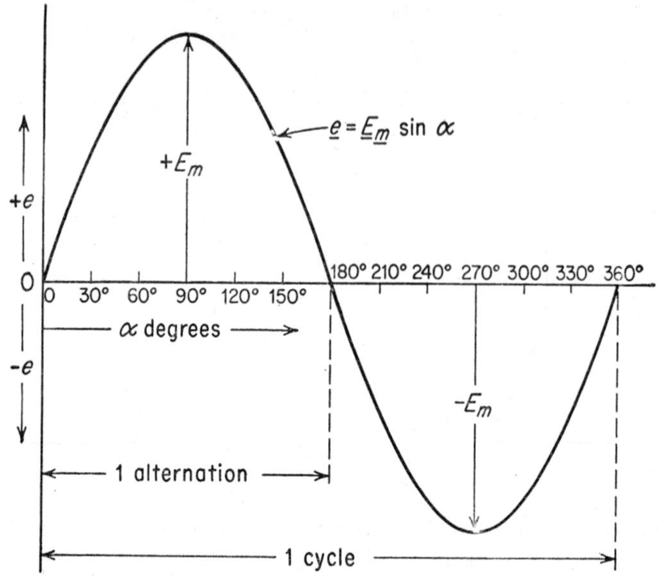

FIG. 116. A sinusoidal voltage wave.

The foregoing can now be summarized by defining *an alternating voltage* as *an emf that varies in magnitude and direction periodically.* Moreover, when the emfs are proportional to the trigonometric sine function, it is referred to as a *sinusoidal alternating voltage.*

Although this discussion will be restricted, for the most part, to sinusoidal waves, it should be stated that periodic waves frequently do not follow this ideal shape. Under such conditions they are called *nonsinusoidal* waves and, for the purposes of analysis, may be regarded as made up of a so-called *fundamental* sine wave and one or more superimposed sine waves that vary more rapidly and are called *harmonics.* The study of nonsinusoidal waves is considered in a later chapter.

Frequency and Electrical Degrees. An a-c generator, usually called an *alternator,* having two poles will develop one cycle of voltage variations for each revolution of the rotating element of the machine, i.e., armature winding or field poles. If rotation occurs at the rate of one revolution per second (rps) then the voltage wave is said to have a *frequency* of one cycle per second (cps). Obviously, the greater the speed the higher will be the frequency; thus, at 3,600 rpm (60 rps) the frequency will be 60 cps. Now then, since each cycle is developed for *one pair of poles,* it should be clear that a multipolar alternator will generate $P/2$ cps per revolution, and the frequency will be $(P/2) \times$ (rps) cycles per second. Indicating the rotating speed in the more convenient units of rpm, rps becomes rpm/60; thus

$$f = \frac{P \times \text{rpm}}{120} \tag{87}$$

As will be shown later, it is desirable to represent one complete cycle as occurring in 360°, whether or not the alternator has two poles or is multipolar. This means that the number of *cycle degrees* in a circle, called *electrical degrees*, is $P/2 \times$ (mechanical degrees). Thus, for example, if the machine has 2 poles, 4 poles, 6 poles, or P poles, there will be, respectively, 360, 720, 1,080, or $P/2 \times$ mech deg in a circle; i.e., elec deg = mech deg $\times$ $(P/2)$.

EXAMPLE 1. The maximum value of the sinusoidal voltage wave generated in one coil of an alternator is 12 volts. How many electrical degrees from the zero point in the cycle (increasing positively) will the voltage be (*a*) +8.5 volts, (*b*) −8.5 volts?

Solution

(*a*)

$$8.5 = 12 \sin \alpha$$

$$\alpha = \sin^{-1} \frac{8.5}{12} = \sin^{-1} 0.707 = 45°$$

The voltage will also be +8.5 volts at (180 − 45°) = 135°.

(*b*) The negative values of voltage occur between 180 and 360°. The voltage will therefore be −8.5 volts at (180 + 45°) = 225° and (360 − 45°) = 315°.

EXAMPLE 2. An alternator has 6 poles. (*a*) At what speed must the machine be driven to develop 60 cycles? 25 cycles? (*b*) What frequency is developed if the speed is 1,000 rpm? 1,600 rpm?

Solution

(*a*)

$$\text{Speed at 60 cycles} = \frac{120 \times 60}{6} = 1{,}200 \text{ rpm}$$

$$\text{Speed at 25 cycles} = \frac{120 \times 25}{6} = 500 \text{ rpm}$$

(*b*)

$$f_{1,000} = \frac{6 \times 1{,}000}{120} = 50$$

$$f_{1,600} = \frac{6 \times 1{,}600}{120} = 80$$

Commercial alternators designed for power service generate, for the most part, at 60, 25, and 50 cycles; odd frequencies such as 16⅔, 30, 40, and 80 cycles are sometimes found in isolated installations. A good portion of the United States has standardized at 60 cycles, with some 50-cycle systems in the Far West, and 25 cycles in the Niagara Falls district. In Europe and Asia much of the electrical energy is generated and used at 50 cycles. For special purposes, such as the operation of electric locomotives, low frequencies are desirable; the New York, New Haven & Hartford Railroad and the Norfolk & Western Railway, for example, have found 25 cycles satisfactory.

Modern alternators, especially those of the large high-speed type, have two or four poles. Thus, for 60-cycle systems, speeds would be 3,600 and 1,800 rpm, respectively; for 50 cycles, such machines would operate at 3,000 and 1,500 rpm. Alternators designed for 25-cycle service invariably have two poles and run at a speed of 1,500 rpm. In low-head hydroelectric plants speeds must necessarily be low, and this generally means alternators with a great many poles; it is not uncommon to find water-turbine-driven alternators with as many as 60 poles, which, for 60 cycles, would require a speed of 120 rpm.

Sinusoidal Alternating Currents. When a voltage that varies sinusoidally is impressed across a resistor of constant ohmic value, the current will be directly proportional to the emf at every instant of time. This implies that

$$i = \frac{e}{R} = \frac{E_m \sin \alpha}{R} = I_m \sin \alpha$$

where $I_m = E_m/R$. It is for this reason that the current wave is also sinusoidal; moreover, since the current and voltage vary simultaneously and in unison, being zero, a positive maximum, a negative minimum, etc., at exactly identical instants of time, the current is said to be *in phase* with the voltage. Therefore, defining an *alternating current* in the same way as an alternating emf, it is *a current that varies in magnitude and direction periodically*. Thus, what was said about frequency and wave form applies equally to currents.

It is generally more desirable to express the angle, in the sine function of the current (or voltage) equation, in terms of radians. When this is done, $\alpha = \pi/2$ radians at 90°, $\alpha = \pi$ radians at 180°, $\alpha = 3\pi/2$ radians at 270°, and $\alpha = 2\pi$ radians at 360°. Also, since 1 cycle occurs in $1/f$ sec or 2π radians, it is proper to say that the angular velocity, whose symbol is ω, equals $2\pi/(1/f) = 2\pi f$ radians per second. Thus, the angle in *radians* at any instant of time t becomes $2\pi ft$, and the equation for the sinusoidal current becomes

$$i = I_m \sin 2\pi ft = I_m \sin \omega t$$

An identical equation for a voltage that is in phase with the current would, of course, be $e = E_m \sin 2\pi ft = E_m \sin \omega t$. Two such waves are shown in Fig. 117.

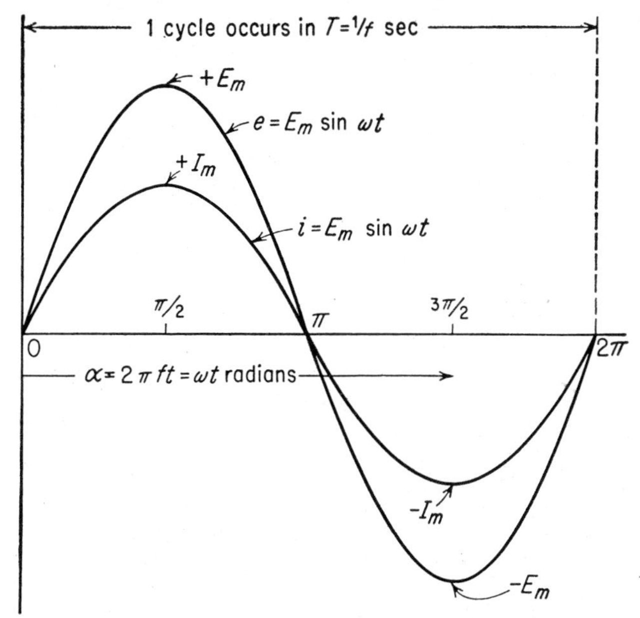

FIG. 117. Sinusoidal voltage and current waves in phase with each other.

EXAMPLE 3. A 60-cycle current has a maximum value of 6.5 amp. What will be the instantaneous value of current (*a*) 0.0025 sec after the wave passes through zero in a positive direction, (*b*) 0.01042 sec after the wave passes through zero in a positive direction?

Solution

(*a*) $i = 6.5 \sin (2\pi \times 60 \times 0.0025) = 6.5 \sin (0.3\pi) = 5.25$ amp

(*b*) $i = 6.5 \sin (2\pi \times 60 \times 0.01042) = 6.5 \sin (1.25\pi) = -4.6$ amp

EXAMPLE 4. What is the angular velocity ω for a 60-cycle circuit? a 25-cycle circuit? a 50-cycle circuit?

Solution

$$\omega_{60} = 2\pi \times 60 = 377 \text{ radians per second}$$
$$\omega_{25} = 2\pi \times 25 = 157 \text{ radians per second}$$
$$\omega_{50} = 2\pi \times 50 = 314 \text{ radians per second}$$

The Alternating-current Ampere. It will be recalled (Chap. 3, under the heading, Chemical Effect) that a d-c ampere is defined as the unvarying current that deposits 0.001118 gm of silver per second when passed through an electrolytic cell of standard specifications. Obviously, such a definition could not apply to an a-c ampere because the net chemical deposit per cycle would be zero in such a cell; each negative half of the cycle would nullify the effect of its corresponding positive half. Also, a d-c ammeter placed in a circuit to measure such a current would register zero because, indicating the *average value* over successive cycles, the *average current* of each positive and negative alternation is zero; actually, the pointer of a d-c ammeter will be observed to vibrate rapidly about the zero mark when inserted in an a-c circuit.

Since the energy of the current passing through a resistor is converted to heat *regardless of its direction,* it is this effect—the heating effect—that has been adopted, in part, to define an a-c ampere. Also, it is desirable to relate the a-c ampere to a standardized unit, and this leads to its comparison with the d-c ampere. Stated in words, therefore, an *a-c ampere is* defined as *the current which, passing through a resistance of given ohmic value, produces heat at the same rate as a d-c ampere.*

In order to determine the current that is *effective* in producing heat in a resistor during each alternation (the heating effect is the same for the negative as well as the positive half of each cycle) it is well to remember (1) that the current varies sinusoidally and (2) that the heating effect is proportional to the *square* of the current [Eq. (16), Chap. 3]. Thus, for some current i passing through a resistor for a differential time period of dt sec,

$$dH = ki^2\,dt = k(I_m \sin \omega t)^2\,dt = kI_m^2 \sin^2 \omega t\,dt$$

The total amount of heat developed in one-half of a cycle is therefore a summation—an integration—of a succession of differential elements of heat; it may be represented by the equation

$$H_{t/2} = kI_m^2 \int_0^{t/2} \sin^2 \omega t\,dt$$

where $t/2$ is the time required for one-half of a cycle. Note particularly that this equation for $H_{t/2}$ is actually *proportional* to the area under the i^2 curve for one alternation (see Fig. 118). It follows then that the average value of $i^2 \times t/2$, the *squared value of the current that is effective in producing heat,* is

$$I_{\text{eff}}^2 = \frac{I_m^2}{t/2} \int_0^{t/2} \sin^2 \omega t\,dt$$

Hence, the *effective value of the current* becomes

$$I_{\text{eff}} = I_m \sqrt{\frac{2}{t} \int_0^{t/2} \sin^2 \omega t\,dt}$$

When the last equation is properly integrated it yields

$$I_{\text{eff}} = \frac{I_m}{\sqrt{2}} = 0.707 I_m \qquad (88)^1$$

[1] See Appendix 1N for derivation.

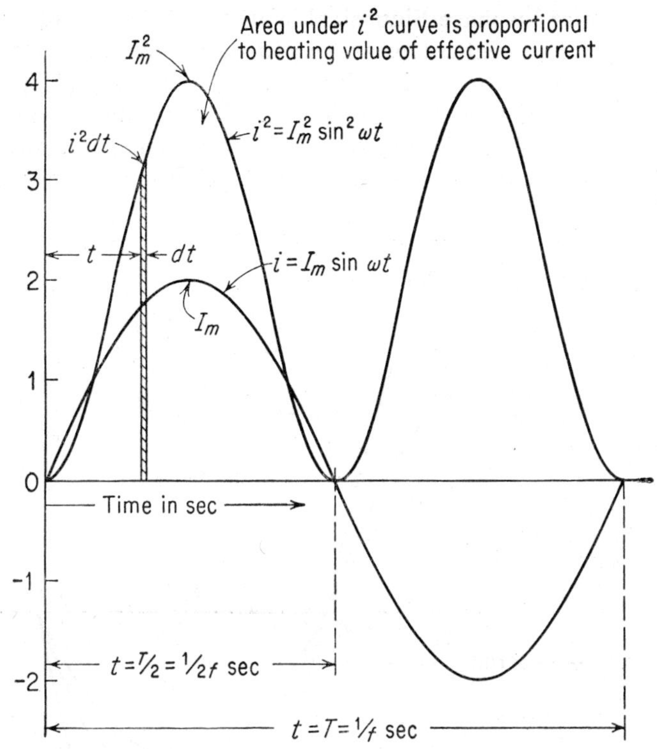

FIG. 118. Sinusoidal current and current-squared waves.

In deriving Eq. (88) it will be noted that it was necessary to take the square *r*oot of the *m*ean (average) value of the *s*quared current wave. This has led to the term *rms* value for the effective value of the alternating current; it will be used frequently in these discussions. Moreover, since this current is always implied in a-c circuits, and a-c ammeters are generally calibrated to indicate rms values, it is not customary to use the subscript eff; effective currents will hereafter be designated simply by the symbol I.

Since an effective current of I amp through a resistance of R ohms requires an effective emf of E volts, it follows that $E = E_m/\sqrt{2} = 0.707\, E_m$.

EXAMPLE 5. A sinusoidal voltage wave having an effective value of 120 volts is impressed across a 50-ohm resistor. Calculate the rms and maximum values of the current.

Solution

$$I = 120/50 = 2.4 \text{ amp}$$
$$I_m = 2.4 \times \sqrt{2} = 3.39 \text{ amp}$$

Summation of In-phase Sinusoidal Waves. When two or more sinusoidal voltage or current waves are *in phase* and have the *same frequency* they may be added to yield a sine wave of the *same frequency*. The *resultant* wave will then have a maximum value that is equal to the arithmetical sum of the maximum values of the component waves. Figure 119 illustrates such a summation for two current waves; note that

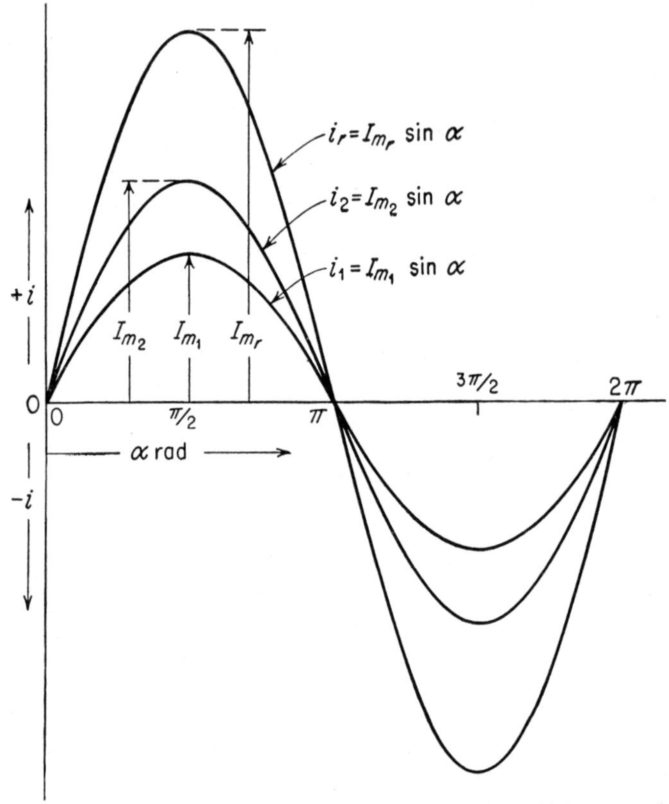

FIG. 119. Graphs showing the summation of two in-phase sinusoidal waves of the same frequency.

the resultant wave, obtained by a *point-by-point* summation, is in phase with, and has the same frequency as, the component waves. It follows, therefore, that

$$E_{m_r} = E_{m_1} + E_{m_2} + E_{m_3} + \cdots$$

and

$$I_{m_r} = I_{m_1} + I_{m_2} + I_{m_3} + \cdots$$

These equations may be expressed in *effective* terms by dividing both sides of either one by $\sqrt{2}$; thus

$$E = E_1 + E_2 + E_3 + \cdots$$

and

$$I = I_1 + I_2 + I_3 + \cdots$$

Many a-c circuits contain similar units, such as resistors, that are connected in series or parallel. Under such conditions the frequency and wave shapes are the same for all circuit elements, and this means that (1) *effective voltage* drops in a series circuit may be added to give the total rms value, and (2) the effective *currents* in the individual branches of a parallel circuit may be added to give the total rms value. The treatment of a-c circuits is, *in this respect*, no different from that of d-c circuits.

EXAMPLE 6. Three resistors having ohmic values that are, respectively, 9, 12.5, and 16 ohms are connected in series to a sinusoidal source of emf whose effective voltage is 120. Calculate the current through the circuit and the voltage drops across the individual resistors.

Solution

$$I = \frac{120}{9 + 12.5 + 16} = \frac{120}{37.5} = 3.2 \text{ amp}$$
$$E_9 = 9 \times 3.2 = 28.8 \text{ volts}$$
$$E_{12.5} = 12.5 \times 3.2 = 40 \text{ volts}$$
$$E_{16} = 16 \times 3.2 = 51.2 \text{ volts}$$
$$E = E_9 + E_{12.5} + E_{16} = 28.8 + 40 + 51.2 = 120 \text{ volts} \qquad (\textit{Check})$$

EXAMPLE 7. Four incandescent lamps (resistors) having ratings of 50, 60, 75, and 100 watts, respectively, are connected in parallel and to a sinusoidal emf whose effective voltage is 120. Calculate the current through each lamp and the total current.

Solution

$$I_{50} = {}^{50}\!/_{120} = 0.416 \text{ amp}$$
$$I_{60} = {}^{60}\!/_{120} = 0.5 \text{ amp}$$
$$I_{75} = {}^{75}\!/_{120} = 0.625 \text{ amp}$$
$$I_{100} = {}^{100}\!/_{120} = 0.833 \text{ amp}$$
$$I_t = 0.417 + 0.5 + 0.625 + 0.833 = 2.375 \text{ amp}$$

Summation of Out-of-phase Sinusoidal Waves. When two or more sinusoidal voltage or current waves are *out of phase* but have the same *frequency*, they may be added to yield a sine wave of the *same frequency*. However, a point-by-point summation will *not* yield a maximum value for the resultant wave that is the arithmetical sum of the maximums of the individual waves; the reason is that the maximum values of the individual waves do *not* occur at the same instants of time. This implies, therefore, that the rms value of the resultant wave is *not* equal to the sum of the effective values of the component waves; it is, in fact, always *less* than the arithmetical sum, and may be as little as the arithmetical difference when the waves are as much as 180° (π radians) out of phase.

Figure 120 shows a graphical construction of a summation of two like-frequency sinusoidal voltage waves. Note particularly that the maximum value of the resultant wave is less than the arithmetical sum of the component waves and is moreover displaced with respect to the latter, occupying a position somewhere between the two.

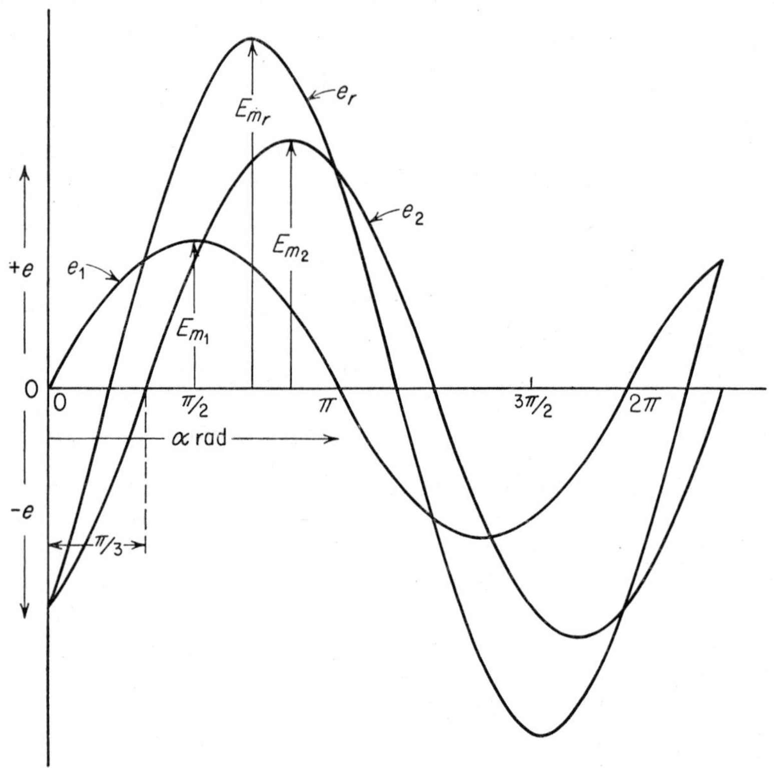

FIG. 120. Graphs showing the summation of two out-of-phase sinusoidal waves of the same frequency.

To determine the *magnitude* of the effective value of the resultant of two like-frequency sinusoidal waves, the following equation may be used:

$$R = \sqrt{(A + B\cos\Theta)^2 + (B\sin\Theta)^2} \tag{89}$$

where A and B = rms values of component waves
Θ = angular displacement between A and B, elec deg
R = rms value of resultant wave

EXAMPLE 8. Two units, connected in parallel, are energized by an a-c source. If the component currents are 12 and 16 amp, respectively, and the corresponding sinusoidal waves are out of phase by 60 elec deg, calculate the rms value of the total current.

Solution

$$I = \sqrt{[12 + (16 \times \cos 60°)]^2 + (16 \times \sin 60°)^2}$$
$$= \sqrt{400 + 192} = 24.4 \text{ amp}$$

Although a-c circuits will be analyzed more rigidly and in some detail in the following chapters, mention should be made here to indicate why the waves of voltages and/or currents are displaced with respect to each other. Among the several reasons are (1) the generator or transformers that supply power may develop out-of-phase emfs; (2) electric circuits may consist of combinations of resistance, inductance, and capacitance, each of which displays special properties; (3) various types of a-c machine loads possess unique characteristics with regard to phase-angle displacements.

Voltages and Currents as Vectors. In the analysis of a-c circuits, it is often necessary to perform mathematical operations that involve out-of-phase voltages and/or currents. The solution of such problems, frequently complex, inaccurate, and time-consuming when wave-drawing procedures are employed, is greatly facilitated by the so-called *vector* method, a discussion of which follows.

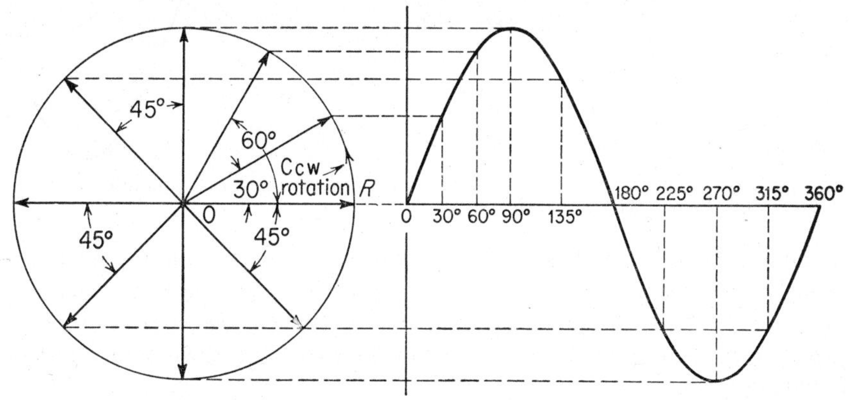

Fig. 121. Graph illustrating the construction of a sine wave from a vector rotating counterclockwise at uniform speed.

Referring to Fig. 121, consider radius OR to be a *vector* rotating at uniform speed in a *counterclockwise* direction. (A vector is a quantity that possesses the property of direction as well as magnitude.) If the *vertical components* of this vector, in its successive positions, are projected horizontally to intersect vertical lines that are erected at corresponding angular distances measured along the x axis, the intersecting points will trace a sine wave. Observe particularly that each vertical component, which is equal to $R \sin \alpha$, fulfills Eq. (86), where R represents the maximum value of a quantity such as voltage or current; in the diagram shown points are plotted for 30, 60, 90, 135, 180, 225, 270, 315, and 0 or 360°. It should also be noted that the positive half of the wave occurs between 0 and 180°, while the negative alternation exists between 180 and 360°.

Next, if two rotating vectors such as I_{m_1} and I_{m_2}, differing in phase position by Θ°, are plotted simultaneously, the sine waves will appear like those shown in Fig. 122. Note that the latter are displaced by exactly the same number of electrical degrees as are the originally drawn rotating vectors. The next step, the important one in this discussion, is to determine the sum of the two vectors. This may be done as follows: (1) draw a parallelogram formed by the original two rotating vectors; (2) draw the diagonal of the parallelogram from the origin; (3) using the

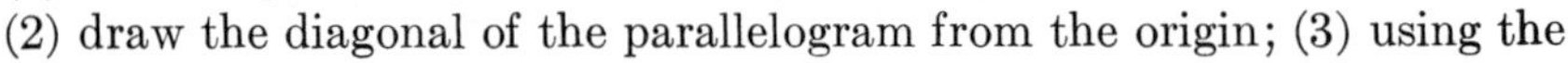

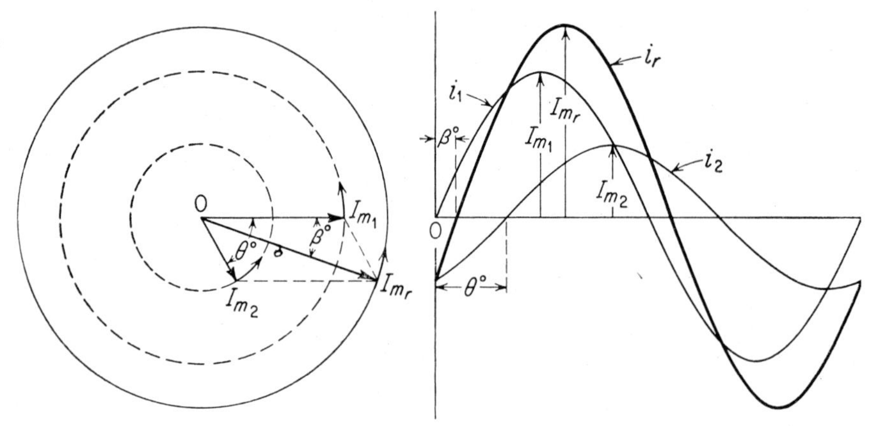

FIG. 122. Graphs illustrating the construction to determine the vector sum of two vectors that are out of phase with each other.

diagonal as a rotating vector, proceed to construct the sine wave as previously described. When this is accomplished it will be found that *the diagonal of the parallelogram is the maximum value of the summation of the two waves;* it is, in fact, the *vector sum* of the two rotating vectors. Put in equation form,

$$\dot{I}_{m_r} = \dot{I}_{m_1} + \dot{I}_{m_2}$$

where the dots above the symbols indicate vector quantities. If both sides are divided by $\sqrt{2}$, the above equation is reduced to effective values: thus

$$\dot{I}_r = \dot{I}_1 + \dot{I}_2$$

Further inspection of Fig. 122 indicates that the resultant vector is displaced β° from the x axis.

Another important point that must be made concerns the question of *lag* or *lead.* Since *counterclockwise rotation* of vectors is assumed, the adopted convention, it is proper to say that I_2 *lags behind* I_1 or that I_1 leads I_2; also I_r lags behind I_1 and leads I_2. These designations are based on the fact that, starting at 0°, (1) the maximum value of I_1 occurs ahead of I_2 and I_r, (2) the maximum value of I_r occurs ahead of I_2 and behind I_1, and (3) the maximum value of I_2 occurs behind I_1 and I_r.

Considering I_1 as the *reference vector* (the reference is generally taken along the x axis), the angle $\beta°$ may be determined by dividing the *sum* of the horizontal components by the resultant vector; this is $\cos \beta$. Thus

$$\cos \beta = \frac{I_1 + I_2 \cos \Theta}{I_r}$$

The foregoing rules, developed in terms of currents I, are, of course, applicable to vector voltages; they will later be shown to apply equally well to other quantities that involve resistors, inductors, and capacitors.

EXAMPLE 9. The voltage drops across two series-connected units A and B are 60 and 90 volts, respectively. Assuming E_A to be the reference vector, calculate the resultant voltage and the angle it makes with the x axis reference (*a*) if E_B lags behind E_A by 90°, (*b*) if E_B leads E_A by 60°.

Solution

(*a*) Since the two voltages are out of phase by 90°, the resultant voltage, the diagonal of the parallelogram, is

$$E_r = \sqrt{(60)^2 + (90)^2} = 108 \text{ volts}$$

Also, $\cos \beta = 60/108 = 0.555$, from which $\beta = 56.3°$ lagging behind E_A.

$$(b) \quad E_r = \sqrt{[60 + (90 \cos 60°)]^2 + [(90 \sin 60°)]^2} = \sqrt{(105)^2 + (78)^2} = 130.8 \text{ volts}$$

Also, $\cos \beta = 105/130.8 = 0.803$, from which $\beta = 36.5°$ leading E_A.

EXAMPLE 10. Three load units A, B, and C are connected in parallel and take currents that are respectively 12, 10, and 15 amp. Assuming I_A to be the reference vector, I_B leads I_A by 30° and I_C lags behind I_A by 65°. Calculate the total (resultant) current and the angle it makes with the x axis.

Solution

Referring to Fig. 123, which represents a general vector diagram for the summation of three vectors, note (*a*) that vector A has no vertical component, (*b*) that vector B has a positive (above the x axis) vertical component, (*c*) that vector C has a negative (below the x axis) vertical component, (*d*) that all have positive (to the right) horizontal components.

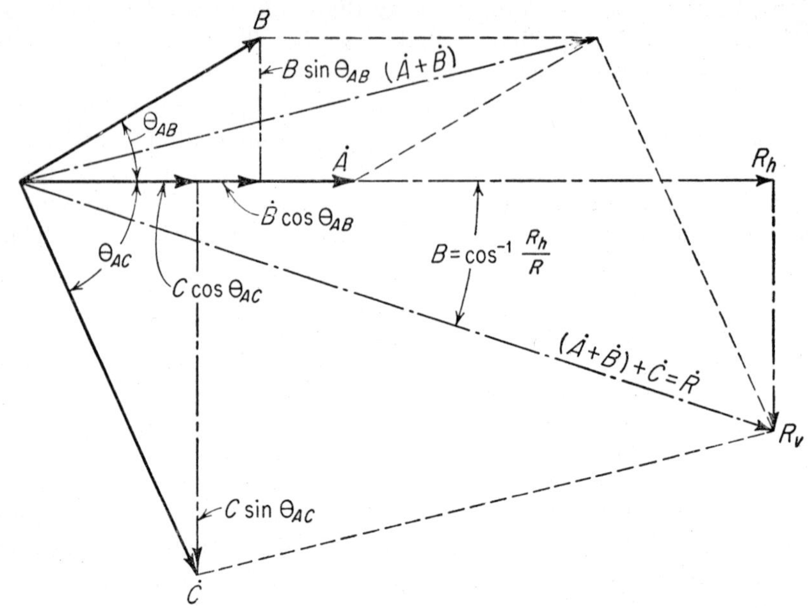

FIG. 123. Vector diagram illustrating the summation of vectors A, B, and C.

Since $I_r = \sqrt{I_h^2 + I_v^2}$, where I_h and I_v are, respectively, *total* horizontal and vertical components, it will be desirable to determine the latter values first. Thus,

$$I_h = 12 + 10 \cos 30° + 15 \cos 65° = 12 + 8.66 + 6.34 = 27$$

and

$$I_v = 0 + 10 \sin 30° - 15 \sin 65° = +5 - 13.6 = -8.6$$

Therefore

$$I_r = \sqrt{(27)^2 + (8.6)^2} = 28.3 \text{ amp}$$

Note that I_v is, in this example, a *negative* number; this implies that I_r *lags behind* I_A, the reference vector, by

$$\beta° = \cos^{-1} \frac{I_h}{I_r} = \cos^{-1} \frac{27}{28.3} = \cos^{-1} 0.954 = 17.3°$$

EXAMPLE 11. A certain type of alternator (a so-called three-phase machine) generates three *equal* sinusoidal emfs E_{OA}, E_{OB}, and E_{OC} that are exactly 120 elec deg out of phase with one another; this implies that the three vector voltages must be drawn radially outward from a common point O, with the angle between any two vectors equal to 120°. Calculate the vector sum of the three voltages.

Solution

Assuming E_{OA} to be the reference vector, with E_{OB} lagging behind E_{OA} by 120° and E_{OC} leading E_{OA} by 120°,

$$E_h = E_{OA} \cos 0° + E_{OB} \cos (-60°) + E_{OC} \cos (+60°)$$
$$= E - 0.5E - 0.5E = 0$$
$$E_v = E_{OA} \sin 0° + E_{OB} \sin (-60°) + E_{OC} \sin (+60°)$$
$$= 0 - 0.866E + 0.866E = 0$$

Therefore $$E_r = 0$$

Questions

1. List several applications in which direct current is desirable or necessary.
2. Under what conditions is it advantageous to generate alternating current in preference to direct current?
3. Indicate some of the industrial applications of alternating current.
4. What kind of current is actually generated in a d-c generator? Explain carefully.
5. Why are transmission voltages in a-c systems generally higher than those in d-c systems? Explain carefully.
6. What three methods may be used to develop a voltage?
7. Distinguish between an induced emf and a generated emf.
8. State Faraday's law.
9. Explain how an alternating voltage is generated in a coil of wire when it is rotated between the poles of a magnet.
10. Under what conditions will a sinusoidal voltage be generated in a coil of wire that rotates in a magnetic field?
11. What is a *sine wave?* Explain how such a wave is drawn graphically.
12. Accurately define an *alternating current.*
13. What is a *nonsinusoidal wave?* How may it be regarded?
14. Define a *cycle;* an *alternation.*
15. What is meant by the term *frequency?*
16. When referring to an alternator, what factors determine the frequency in cycles per second? Explain.
17. What is meant by *electrical degrees?* How do electrical degrees differ from *mechanical* degrees? Under what conditions are the two equal? unequal?
18. What are the common frequencies used in this country?
19. How many poles are generally used in modern high-speed steam-turbine-driven alternators?
20. Why is it necessary to use alternators with large numbers of poles when they are driven by low-head water turbines?
21. Write a general expression for a sinusoidal current; a sinusoidal voltage. Define all symbols properly.
22. How many electrical degrees are there in a radian?
23. Define *angular velocity,* using electrical terms.
24. What is the duration of 1 cycle, in seconds?
25. Define an *a-c ampere.*
26. Define a *d-c ampere,* and explain why an a-c ampere cannot be defined in this way.
27. Why is the a-c current often referred to as the *effective value?* the *rms value?*
28. What is the rms value of a sinusoidal current in terms of the maximum value?

29. What is the effective value of a sinusoidal voltage in terms of the maximum value? Why?
30. What is the resultant voltage in a series circuit comprising two or more sinusoidal voltages (or voltage drops) that are *in phase?* Give reasons for your answer.
31. What is the resultant current in a parallel circuit comprising two or more sinusoidal currents that are *in phase?*
32. What is the wave shape that results from the sum of two like-frequency sinusoidal voltage or current waves?
33. Why is the resultant current or voltage of two like-frequency sinusoidal waves that are in series but out of phase, not their arithmetical sum? Give reasons for your answer.
34. Under what conditions may voltage and current waves be out of phase?
35. What is a *vector?* How does it differ from a quantity that may be scaled (a scalar) only? List several nonelectrical vectors; scalars.
36. How can it be shown that a radius, rotating at constant speed, will trace out a sinusoidal wave?
37. How is it possible to determine the vector sum of two electrical quantities such as voltages or currents?
38. Explain the meaning of such terms as *lag* and *lead.* Upon what direction of vector rotation are these terms based?
39. How is the angular displacement of the resultant quantity determined with respect to some reference vector?
40. What is the vector sum of three equal sinusoidal voltages that are out of phase by 120°?
41. If two equal sinusoidal voltages are out of phase 90°, what is their vector sum?

Problems

1. Calculate the average voltage induced in a coil of 300 turns through which the flux changes from 250,000 to 20,000 maxwells in 0.15 sec.
2. How many turns of wire are there in a coil in which 35.7 volts are induced when the flux through it increases uniformly at the rate of 3×10^6 maxwells per second?
3. A square coil, 2 in. on a side, has 240 turns of wire and is placed between the poles of a magnet that are slightly more than 2 in. apart. If the horizontally directed field has a uniform flux density of 1,800 maxwells per square inch and the coil is rotated from a vertical plane to a horizontal plane in 0.05 sec, calculate the average generated voltage.
4. A voltage wave has the equation $e = 170 \sin \alpha$. Calculate the instantaneous values of voltage for the following angles: 30°, 60°, 75°, 105°, 135°, 180°, 270°, and 330°.
5. A current wave has the equation $i = 21.2 \sin \alpha$. At what angles will the instantaneous values of current be the following: 7.25 amp, 15 amp, 19.9 amp, 13.6 amp, −13.6 amp, −19.9 amp, −12.2 amp?
6. An alternator has 8 poles. (*a*) At what speed must it be driven to develop 60 cycles? 25 cycles? 50 cycles? 40 cycles? (*b*) What frequency will be developed if the speed is 825 rpm? 1,350 rpm? 1,800 rpm? 450 rpm?
7. What are the frequencies of the following sinusoidal waves: (*a*) $e = E_m \sin 377t$, (*b*) $i = I_m \sin 157t$, (*c*) $e = E_m \sin 314t$?
8. A 25-cycle sinusoidal emf wave has a maximum value of 340 volts. Determine the instantaneous values of emf (*a*) 0.007 sec after the wave passes through zero in a positive direction, (*b*) 0.01 sec after the wave passes through zero in a negative direction.

9. Calculate the effective currents in circuits in which the maximum values of the sinusoidal current waves are 8.4 amp, 22.8 amp, 65 ma.

10. The rms value of the voltage in a 60-cycle circuit is 115 volts. Write the equation for the sinusoidal wave.

11. The in-phase sinusoidal currents in the parallel branches of a circuit have the following equations: $i_1 = 17 \sin 377t$, and $i_2 = 22.6 \sin 377t$. (*a*) Write the equation for the summation (the resultant) of the two waves; (*b*) calculate the effective currents in the individual branches, and the resultant current.

12. A 117-volt 60-cycle source is connected to a series circuit consisting of three resistors. If the ohmic values of the latter are 20, 30, and 40 ohms, respectively, calculate the current through the circuit and the voltage drop across each resistor.

13. Three incandescent lamps (resistors) are connected in parallel, and to a 115-volt 60-cycle source. If the lamp ratings are 75, 100, and 150 watts, (*a*) calculate the rms value of the resultant current, (*b*) write the equation for the resultant current.

14. A resistance load of 4 ohms is connected to a 220-volt 60-cycle line which leads back to the source through a pair of wires, the resistance of each of which is 0.08 ohm. What is the voltage at the source?

15. Two loads are connected in parallel to an a-c source and take currents of 10 and 40 amp, respectively. If the sinusoidal waves of the component currents are out of phase by 30 elec deg, calculate the resultant current.

16. Two equal voltages are out of phase with respect to each other by 90 elec deg. If their vector sum is 311 volts, calculate the rms value of each one.

17. The resultant value of two currents that are out of phase with each other by 60 elec deg is 70 amp. If one of them is 50 amp, what is the other?

18. Each of two alternator windings generate 1,270 volts and may be interconnected to add at an angle of 60 or 120 elec deg. What are the two possible resultant voltages?

19. An a-c source delivers current to two loads *A* and *B* that are connected in parallel. If the *A*-load current of 25 amp leads the *B*-load current of 42.2 amp by 45 elec deg, (*a*) calculate the resultant current, and (*b*) determine the angle between the resultant current and an assumed *A*-current reference.

20. The following information is given in connection with an a-c source that delivers current to three loads in parallel: $I_A = 20$ amp; $I_B = 12$ amp and lags behind I_A by 30 elec deg; $I_C = 32$ amp and leads I_A by 60 elec deg. Using I_A as the reference vector, determine the resultant current and the angle between it and I_A.

CHAPTER 11

RESISTANCE (R), INDUCTANCE (L), AND CAPACITANCE (C) CIRCUITS

Basic Types of Circuit. The study of circuits involves three basic types of units and four possible series combinations of them. The latter, in turn, may be arranged in many kinds of parallel, series-parallel, parallel-series, or other complex circuits.

Figure 124 illustrates the fundamental circuits in which a voltage E (rms value of a sinusoidal wave) is impressed across a resistor R, an inductor L, and a capacitor C. In each case a current I will be established that will depend upon the magnitude of E and corresponding ohmic

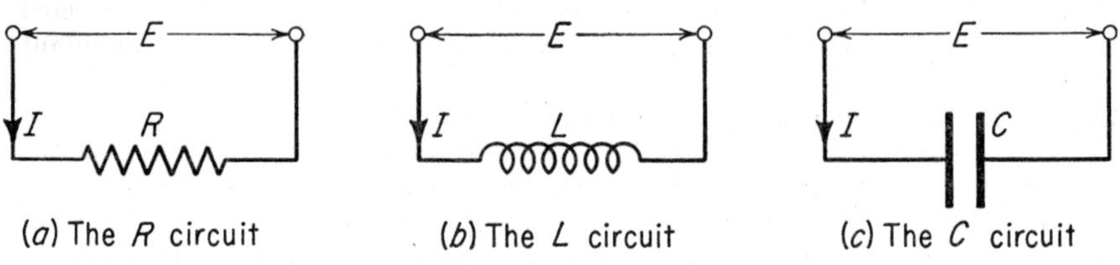

FIG. 124. Three basic types of circuit.

values represented by the units. As will be shown later certain multiplying factors are used to convert L in henrys and C in microfarads to ohms.

Another important point that should be made in connection with the basic circuits is that a sinusoidal wave of current will be established in R and C branches if the voltage wave is sinusoidal; the L-branch current wave will be sinusoidal only when the magnetic circuit contains no iron, or, in general, when hysteresis is not present.

Four possible series combinations of R, L, and C are shown in Fig. 125. The wave form of current will, as before, be sinusoidal, assuming, of course, that a sine wave of voltage is impressed and the circuit elements are ideal.

Before proceeding with a detailed analysis of a-c circuits it will be desirable to make several important generalizations concerning the actions of ideal circuit parameters such as R, L, and C.

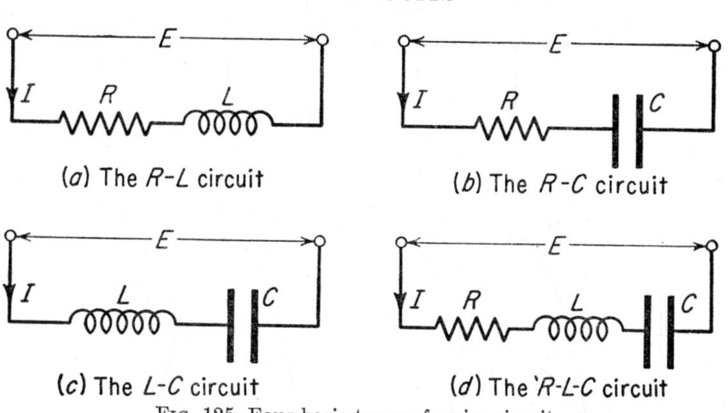

FIG. 125. Four basic types of series circuit.

1. The behavior of a pure resistor in an a-c circuit is exactly similar to that in a d-c circuit. The laws governing resistors in d-c systems may therefore be applied to a-c circuits, assuming, of course, that rms values of voltage and current are used. Also, current and voltage vectors are always in phase in resistor circuits.

2. A pure inductor in an a-c circuit takes a current that lags behind the impressed emf by exactly 90 elec deg. Storing and releasing equal amounts of electromagnetic energy during successive quarter cycles, the average energy per cycle involved in such a circuit is zero; this means that the average power delivered to an inductor is zero.

3. A perfect capacitor in an a-c circuit takes a current that leads the impressed emf by exactly 90 elec deg. Storing and releasing equal amounts of electrostatic energy during successive quarter cycles, the average energy per cycle involved in such a circuit is zero; this means that the average power delivered to a capacitor is zero.

The Resistance Circuit. When a sinusoidal emf $e = E_m \sin \omega t$ is impressed across a fixed resistor of R ohms, the current, at any instant of time, will be $i = E_m/R \sin \omega t$ (see Fig. 126*a*). Since $E_m/R = I_m$, the maximum value of the resulting sinusoidal current, the current equation is $i = I_m \sin \omega t$. Comparing the voltage and current relationships it should be clear that the waves are in phase with each other; i.e., e and i are zero simultaneously and increasing in the same direction, and corresponding positive and negative maximum values occur simultaneously. This is clearly illustrated in Fig. 126*b*. Moreover, the fact that the *waves* are in phase with each other means that the *rms values* of the voltage and current are likewise in phase. *Drawing an effective voltage vector with an open arrowhead and an effective current vector with a closed arrowhead*, the conventional method that distinguishes currents from voltages, this in-phase relationship is shown in Fig. 126*c*.

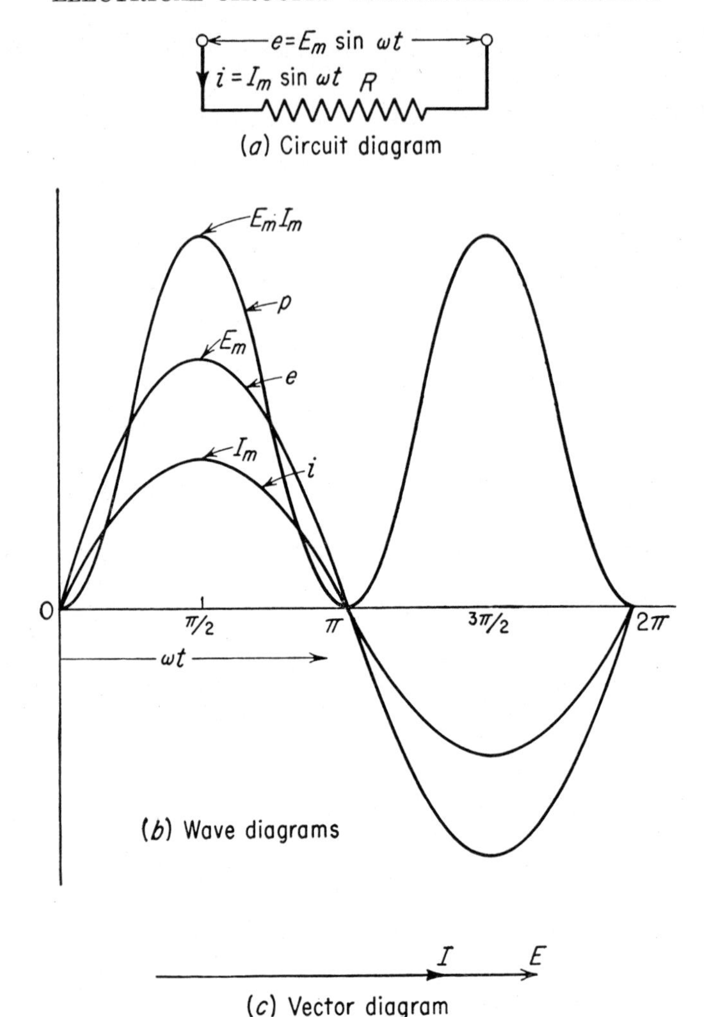

FIG. 126. Diagrams illustrating conditions in a resistor circuit.

Figure 126*b* also shows a power curve drawn by plotting point-by-point products of e and i. Note particularly that (1) it is a double-frequency wave in relation to the voltage or current variation, (2) its maximum instantaneous value is $E_m I_m$, and (3) it lies completely above the x axis to indicate that power is always *positive*, i.e., from source to resistor. Expressing the instantaneous power by the formula $p = ei$, it becomes

$$p = (E_m \sin \omega t)(I_m \sin \omega t) = E_m I_m \sin^2 \omega t$$

when the proper substitutions are made. Since $\sin^2 \omega t = \frac{1}{2} - \frac{1}{2} \cos 2\omega t$ the equation may be rewritten in the following form:

$$p = E_mI_m\left(\frac{1}{2} - \frac{1}{2}\cos 2\omega t\right) = \left(\frac{E_mI_m}{2}\right) - \left(\frac{E_mI_m}{2}\cos 2\omega t\right)$$

It is interesting to observe that the power delivered to a resistor may be regarded as made up of two components, one of which, $E_mI_m/2$, is constant in magnitude, and the other varying cosinusoidally at twice the frequency of the voltage or current. Or, to put it another way, the cos $2\omega t$ term is supposedly superimposed upon a constant term to cause the instantaneous power to change periodically between zero and $+E_mI_m$

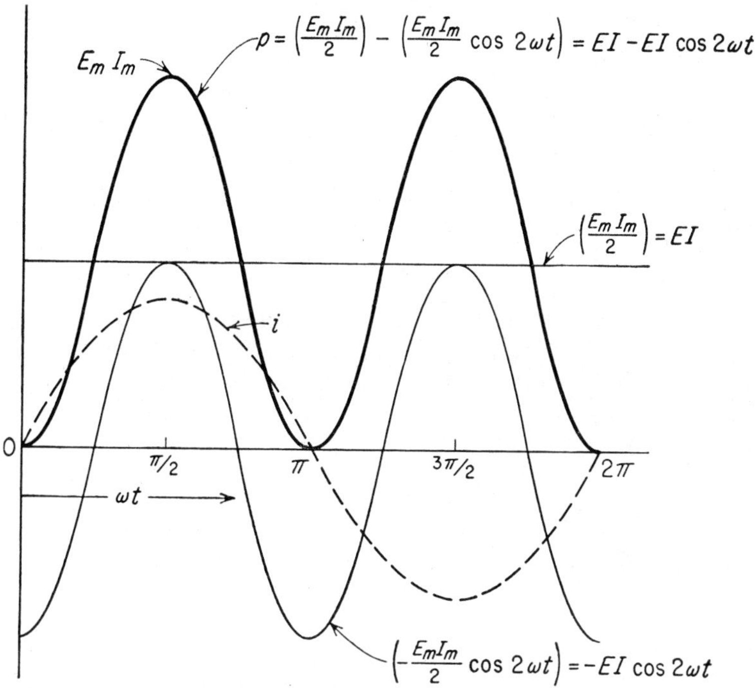

FIG. 127. Graphs illustrating the power wave and its components in a resistor circuit.

values. Figure 127 illustrates the actual power wave (as shown in Fig. 126) and its presumed components as given in the foregoing equation.

Analysis of Fig. 127 indicates that the average power *per cycle* that is represented by the cos $2\omega t$ term is zero, because the positive and negative halves of each cycle of a cosine (or sine) function cancel each other. This means, of course, that the constant term, represented by $E_mI_m/2$, is the average power delivered to the resistor. Or, in equation form,

$$P_{av} = \frac{E_mI_m}{2} = \frac{E_m}{\sqrt{2}} \times \frac{I_m}{\sqrt{2}} = EI \tag{90}$$

Equation (90) indicates, therefore, that the *average power* in a pure resistance circuit is given by the product of the rms values of voltage and current; it is, in this respect, similar to the conditions that exist in a d-c circuit.

Example 1. An incandescent-lamp load, generally considered to be made up of resistors, takes 4.8 kw from a 120-volt a-c source. Calculate (*a*) the total current, (*b*) the instantaneous maximum value of power, (*c*) the resistance of the load.

Solution

(*a*) $$I = \frac{P}{E} = \frac{4{,}800}{120} = 40 \text{ amp}$$

(*b*) $$P_{\text{max}} = (\sqrt{2}\,E)(\sqrt{2}\,I) = 2EI = 2 \times 4{,}800 = 9{,}600 \text{ watts}$$

(*c*) $$R = \frac{E}{I} = \frac{120}{40} = 3 \text{ ohms}$$

The Inductance Circuit. When a sinusoidal voltage is impressed across a pure inductance (Fig. 128*a*) (the resistance of the coil is considered to be negligibly small), the current wave will also be sinusoidal. However, unlike the pure resistance circuit in which e and i are in phase, the current will *lag behind* the voltage by $\pi/2$ radians or 90 elec deg; the following analysis will verify this statement. It was shown in Chap. 8 (under the heading, Current Growth in Inductive Circuits) that a direct current builds up in an *R-L* circuit in accordance with the equation $E = iR - L\,di/dt$. This basic relationship is equally applicable to a-c circuits, and in this section, where R is zero and the impressed emf is a sinusoidal function, it becomes

$$e = E_m \sin \omega t = L \frac{di}{dt}$$

where L = inductance of the coil, henrys
di/dt = rate at which the current is changing

Since $\sin \omega t$ is a maximum when $\omega t = \pi/2$ radians (i.e., 90 elec deg), the above formula is fulfilled at $\pi/2$ radians only when di/dt is a maximum or when the current i is zero (the current changes by its maximum amount when it passes through zero). This implies, therefore, that i is zero when e is a maximum, and that i is a maximum when e is zero; in other words, *the voltage and current waves are out of phase by $\pi/2$ radians or 90 elec deg.*

Rewriting the foregoing equation in terms of current change,

$$di = \frac{E_m}{L} \sin \omega t \, dt$$

Both sides may now be readily integrated by the calculus to yield

$$i = -\frac{E_m}{\omega L} \cos \omega t$$

$e = E_m \sin \omega t$
$i = I_m \sin(\omega t - \pi/2)$ L

(a) Circuit diagram

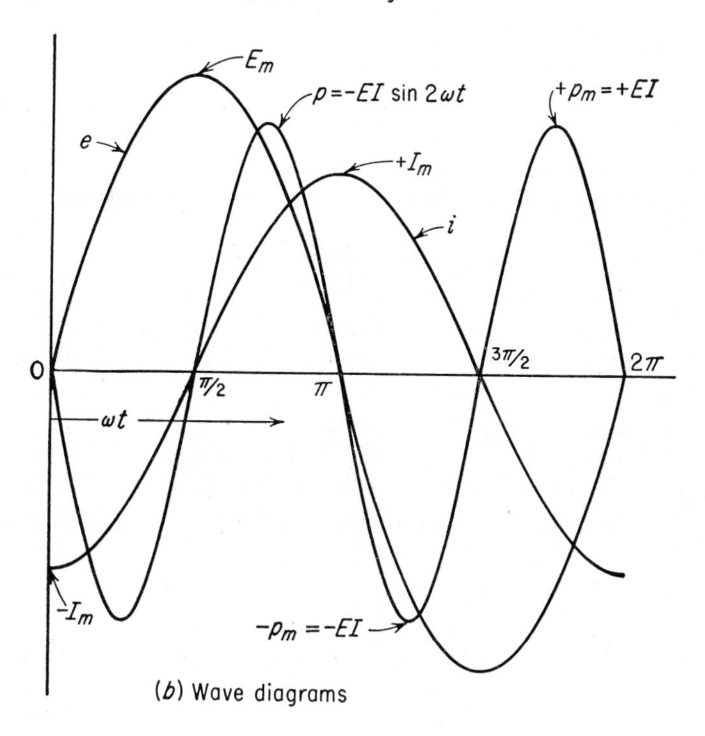

(b) Wave diagrams

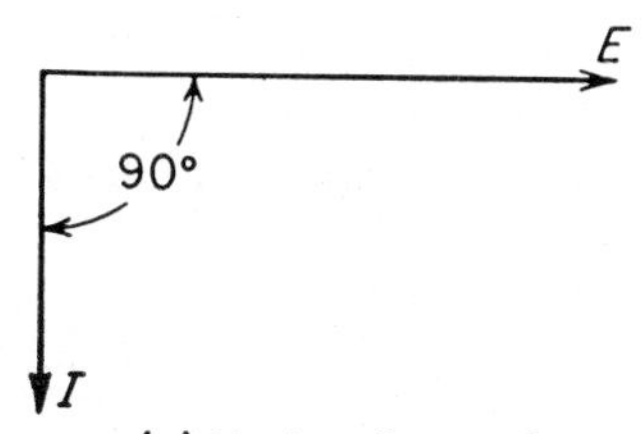

(c) Vector diagram

FIG. 128. Diagrams illustrating conditions in an inductor circuit.

But $\cos \omega t = \sin(\pi/2 - \omega t)$. Hence

$$i = \frac{E_m}{\omega L} \sin\left(\omega t - \frac{\pi}{2}\right) \tag{91}$$ [1]

This basic formula for the L circuit shows not only that the current is out of phase with the voltage by $\pi/2$ radians, but that because a *negative*

[1] See Appendix 10 for derivation.

sign precedes the $\pi/2$, the current *lags* behind the voltage. Figure 128*b* clearly illustrates this relationship between e and i and indicates that (1) when $\omega t = 0$, $i = -E_m/\omega L = -I_m$; (2) when $\omega t = \pi/2$, $i = 0$; (3) when $\omega t = \pi$, $i = +E_m/\omega L = +I_m$; and (4) when $\omega t = 3\pi/2$, $i = 0$.

The very useful *vector diagram* indicating that the *current I lags behind the voltage E* is shown in Fig. 128*c*.

The next step is to identify the units of ωL in the relationship $E_m/\omega L = I_m$. Dividing both sides of the latter equation by $\sqrt{2}$ and rearranging terms it becomes $\omega L = E/I$. But the ratio of volts (E) to amperes (I) always yields ohms. It follows, therefore, that ωL must be in ohm units. Thus, representing ωL by the symbol X_L and applying the term *inductance reactance* to it,

$$X_L = \omega L = 2\pi f L \qquad \text{ohms} \tag{92}$$

Figure 128*b* also shows a power curve drawn by plotting point-by-point products of e and i. Note particularly that (1) it is a double-frequency wave in relation to the voltage or current variation, (2) its maximum instantaneous values are $+E_mI_m/2 = +EI$ and $-E_mI_m/2 = -EI$, and (3) the average power per cycle is zero because there is just as much positive power (to the inductor to build up a magnetic field) as negative power (to the source when the electromagnetic energy is dissipated). Expressing the instantaneous power by the formula $p = e \times i$, it becomes

$$p = (E_m \sin \omega t)(-I_m \cos \omega t) = -E_mI_m(\sin \omega t)(\cos \omega t)$$

But $(\sin \omega t)(\cos \omega t) = \sin 2\omega t/2$. Therefore

$$p = -\frac{E_mI_m}{2} \sin 2\omega t = -\frac{E_m}{\sqrt{2}} \times \frac{I_m}{\sqrt{2}} \sin 2\omega t = -EI \sin 2\omega t$$

It is interesting to note that this equation verifies the statements previously made, that the power varies at twice the voltage or current frequency, and that the maximum values of power are $+EI = +E_mI_m/2$ and $-EI = -E_mI_m/2$. It also proves that *the average power in an inductive circuit is zero,* because the average value of a sine wave over one complete cycle is zero.

Example 2. An inductance of 0.106 henry is connected to a 120-volt 60-cycle source. Calculate (*a*) the inductive reactance, (*b*) the current in the circuit, (*c*) the average power taken by the inductor, (*d*) the maximum power delivered to the inductor or returned to the source. Write the equations for (*e*) the current, and (*f*) the power.

Solution

(*a*) $$X_L = 2\pi f L = 2\pi \times 60 \times 0.106 = 40 \text{ ohms}$$

(*b*) $$I = \frac{E}{X_L} = \frac{120}{40} = 3 \text{ amp}$$

(*c*) $$P_{av} = 0$$

(*d*) $$p_{max} = EI = 120 \times 3 = 360$$

(*e*) $$i = \frac{E_m}{\omega L} \sin\left(\omega t - \frac{\pi}{2}\right) = 3\sqrt{2} \sin\left(377t - \frac{\pi}{2}\right)$$

(*f*) $$p = -EI \sin 2\omega t = -120 \times 3 \sin 2 \times 377t = -360 \sin 754t$$

The Capacitance Circuit. When a capacitor is connected to a sinusoidal source of emf (Fig. 129*a*), it will continually go through periods of charge and discharge and will, moreover, undergo periodic polarity changes. Also, the current variations will be sinusoidal but, unlike the pure resistance circuit in which e and i are in phase, the current will *lead* the voltage by $\pi/2$ radians or 90 elec deg. The following analysis will verify this statement.

It was shown in Chap. 9 (under the heading, Charging Current in an *R-C* Circuit) that, in accordance with Kirchhoff's law,

$$E = iR + \int_0^t \frac{i\,dt}{C}$$

where E is the impressed d-c voltage and iR and $\int_0^t i dt/C$ are, respectively, the voltages across the resistor and the capacitor. This equation applies equally well to an a-c circuit in which the impressed emf is sinusoidal and, when R is zero, becomes

$$E_m \sin \omega t = \int_0^t \frac{i\,dt}{C} = \frac{1}{C}\int_0^t i\,dt$$

But the term $\int_0^t i\,dt$ merely represents, in mathematical form, the accumulation or summation of charge q in time interval t. Thus

$$q = CE_m \sin \omega t$$

However, the *rate* at which charge is *changing* on the capacitor, i.e., dq/dt, depends upon the rate at which the voltage is changing, and the latter is a maximum when the voltage is going through zero, i.e., at $t = 0$, and zero when the voltage is a maximum, i.e., at $t = \pi/2$ radians. In other words, the rate of change of charge is $\pi/2$ radians (90 elec deg) out of phase with the voltage. This is shown to be mathematically valid if, by the calculus, the foregoing equation is differentiated; when this is done,

$$\frac{dq}{dt} = \omega CE_m \cos \omega t$$

Since dq/dt is the current i at any instant and $\cos \omega t = \sin(\omega t + \pi/2)$, the final form for the capacitance current in an a-c circuit is

$$i = \omega CE_m \sin\left(\omega t + \frac{\pi}{2}\right) \tag{93}$$

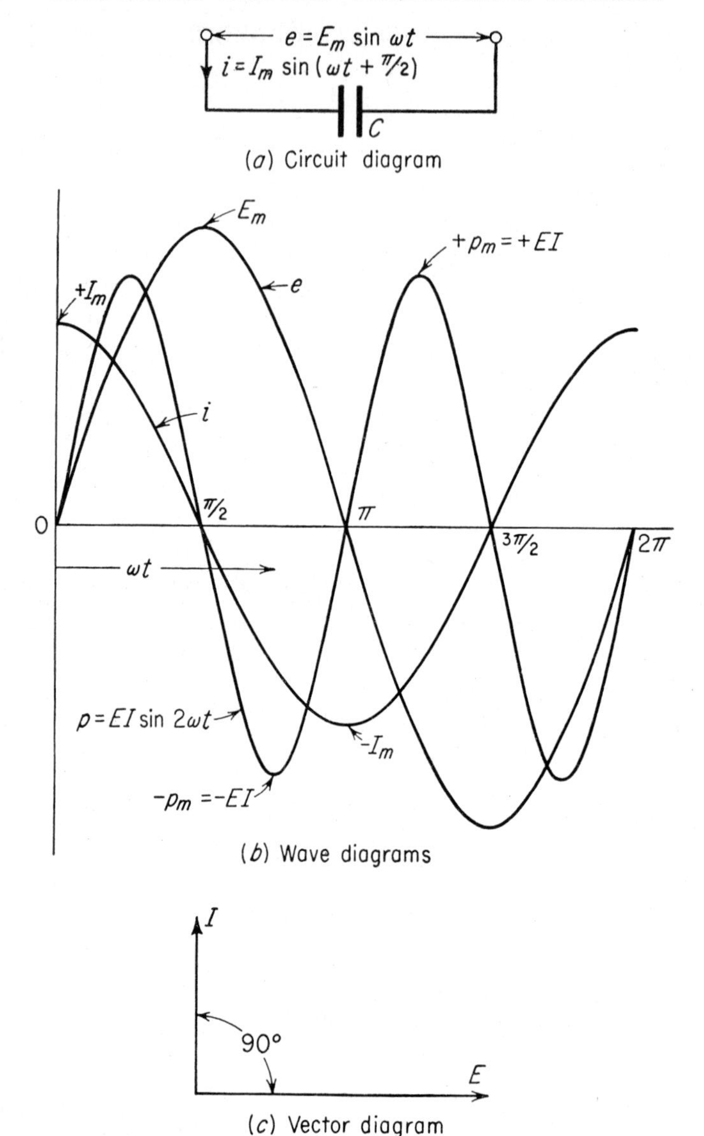

FIG. 129. Diagrams illustrating conditions in a capacitor circuit.

This basic formula for the C circuit shows not only that the current is out of phase with the voltage by $\pi/2$ radians, but that, because a *positive sign* precedes the $\pi/2$, the current *leads* the voltage. Figure 129*b* clearly illustrates this relationship between e and i and indicates that (1) when $\omega t = 0$, $i = \omega C E_m = +I_m$; (2) when $\omega t = \pi/2$, $i = 0$; (3) when $\omega t = \pi$, $i = -\omega C E_m = -I_m$; and (4) when $\omega t = 3\pi/2$, $i = 0$.

The extremely useful *vector diagram* indicating that *the current I leads the voltage E* is shown in Fig. 129*c*.

Since Eq. (93) is a general sine-wave formula, it should be clear that the ωCE_m product, preceding the sine term, is equal to the maximum current I_m. Thus

$$I_m = \omega CE_m$$

Dividing both sides of the latter equation by $\sqrt{2}$ and rearranging terms, $(1/\omega C) = E/I$. But the ratio of volts (E) to amperes (I) always yields ohms. It follows, therefore, that $(1/\omega C)$ must be in ohm units. Thus, representing $(1/\omega C)$ by the symbol $X_{C'}$ and applying the term *capacitive reactance* to it,

$$X_{C'} = \frac{1}{\omega C'} = \frac{1}{2\pi fC'} \qquad \text{ohms}$$

where C' is in farads. If capacitance C is expressed in the more convenient microfarad unit,

$$X_C = \frac{10^6}{2\pi fC} \qquad \text{ohms} \tag{94}$$

Figure 129*b* also shows a power curve drawn by plotting point-by-point products of e and i. Note particularly that (1) it is a double frequency in relation to the voltage or current variation, (2) its maximum instantaneous values are $+E_mI_m/2 = +EI$ and $-E_mI_m/2 = -EI$, and (3) the average power per cycle is zero because there is just as much positive power (to the capacitor to charge it) as negative power (to the source when the capacitor discharges). Expressing the instantaneous power by the formula $p = ei$, it becomes

$$p = (E_m \sin \omega t)(I_m \cos \omega t) = E_mI_m(\sin \omega t)(\cos \omega t)$$

But $(\sin \omega t)(\cos \omega t) = \sin 2\omega t/2$. Therefore

$$p = \frac{E_mI_m}{2} \sin 2\omega t = \frac{E_m}{\sqrt{2}} \times \frac{I_m}{\sqrt{2}} \sin 2\omega t = EI \sin 2\omega t$$

It is interesting to note that this equation verifies the statements previously made, namely, that the power varies at twice the voltage or current frequency, and that the maximum values of power are $+EI = +E_mI_m/2$ and $-EI = -E_mI_m/2$. It also proves that *the average power in a capacitive circuit is zero,* because the average value of a sine wave over one complete cycle is zero.

EXAMPLE 3. A 127-μf capacitor is connected to a 125-volt 50-cycle source. Calculate (*a*) the capacitive reactance, (*b*) the current in the circuit, (*c*) the average power taken by the capacitor, (*d*) the maximum power delivered to the capacitor or returned to the source. Write equations for (*e*) the current and (*f*) the power.

Solution

(*a*) $$X_C = \frac{10^6}{2\pi f C} = \frac{10^6}{2\pi \times 50 \times 127} = 25 \text{ ohms}$$

(*b*) $$I = \frac{E}{X_C} = \frac{125}{25} = 5 \text{ amp}$$

(*c*) $$P_{av} = 0$$

(*d*) $$p_m = EI = 125 \times 5 = 625 \text{ watts}$$

(*e*) $$i = \omega C E_m \sin\left(\omega t + \frac{\pi}{2}\right) = 5\sqrt{2} \sin\left(314t + \frac{\pi}{2}\right)$$

(*f*) $$p = EI \sin 2\omega t = 125 \times 5 \sin 314t = 625 \sin 314t$$

The Series Inductance-Capacitance (L-C) Circuit. Concerning the behavior of the three basic types of units, i.e., R, L, and C, in a-c circuits, the following aspects should be emphasized: (1) the current is *in phase* with the voltage in a resistance circuit, (2) the current *lags behind* the voltage by 90 elec deg in an inductance circuit, and (3) the current *leads* the voltage by 90 elec deg in a capacitance circuit. This implies, for example, that a series combination of L and C (Fig. 125*c*) might behave like an inductance *or* a capacitance, depending upon whether the inductive reactance X_L is greater than the capacitive reactance X_C, or vice versa. Thus, the equivalent reactance X_{eq} of an *L-C* circuit would be X_L minus X_C if the latter is less than the former, under which condition a 90 elec deg current lag would result; or the equivalent reactance X_{eq} would be X_C minus X_L if conditions were reversed, in which case the current would lead the voltage by 90 elec deg. There is, moreover, the possibility that X_L might equal X_C, in which event the inductive and capacitive effects would cancel; a special condition such as this is said to produce *resonance*, a subject that will be considered in a subsequent chapter.

Remembering that X_L is *directly proportional* to the frequency [Eq. (92)] and that X_C is *inversely proportional* to the frequency [Eq. (94)], it should be clear that the behavior of a given series *L-C* circuit is altered when the frequency is changed; not only does the current vary when this is done, but, with a sufficiently large frequency change, it is quite possible to reverse the lag or lead relationship.

Analysis of Eqs. (92) and (94) also indicates that different effects are produced in a constant-frequency series *L-C* circuit when the inductance *or* the capacitance is changed. An increase in L *or* C will result in an over-all increase in the inductive reactance of such a circuit; a decrease in L *or* C will, on the other hand, result in an over-all increase in the capacitive reactance of a similar circuit.

Several examples will now be given to illustrate the behavior of series *L-C* circuits.

EXAMPLE 4. A series circuit consisting of a 0.0795-henry inductor and a 177-μf capacitor is connected to a 120-volt 60-cycle source. Calculate (*a*) the equivalent reactance of the circuit, (*b*) the circuit current, indicating whether the latter lags or leads.

Solution

(*a*)

$$X_L = 2\pi \times 60 \times 0.0795 = 30 \text{ ohms}$$

$$X_C = \frac{10^6}{2\pi \times 60 \times 177} = 15 \text{ ohms}$$

$$X_{eq} = 30 - 15 = 15 \text{ ohms (inductive)}$$

(*b*)

$$I = \frac{120}{15} = 8 \text{ amp}$$

The current lags the voltage by 90 elec deg.

EXAMPLE 5. If a variable capacitor is substituted for the one in Example 4, what should be its value if an equal current is to lead the voltage? Assume all other conditions to remain unchanged.

Solution

It will be necessary to make $X_C = 30 + 15 = 45$ ohms. Therefore

$$C = \frac{10^6}{377 \times 45} = 59 \ \mu\text{f}$$

$$X_{eq} = 45 - 30 = 15 \text{ ohms (capacitive)}$$

EXAMPLE 6. A series circuit consisting of a 0.0795-henry inductor and a 177-μf capacitor is connected to a 120-volt variable-frequency source. At what frequency will the circuit take a *lagging* current of 4 amp?

Solution

$$X_{eq} = \frac{120}{4} = 30 \text{ ohms}$$

Also

$$X_{eq} = X_L - X_C$$

$$X_L = 2\pi f \times 0.0795 = 0.5f$$

$$X_C = \frac{10^6}{2\pi f} \times \frac{1}{177} = \frac{900}{f}$$

$$30 = 0.5f - \frac{900}{f}$$

from which

$$f^2 - 60f - 1{,}800 = 0$$

$$f = \frac{60 \pm \sqrt{3{,}600 + 7{,}200}}{2} = \frac{60 \pm 104}{2} = 82 \text{ cycles}$$

EXAMPLE 7. Solve Example 6 for a *leading* current of 4 amp.

Solution

$$X_{eq} = X_C - X_L = 30$$

$$X_C = \frac{900}{f}$$

and

$$X_L = 0.5f$$

$$30 = \frac{900}{f} - 0.5f$$

from which

$$f^2 + 60f - 1{,}800 = 0$$

$$f = \frac{-60 \pm \sqrt{3{,}600 + 7{,}200}}{2} = \frac{-60 \pm 104}{2} = 22 \text{ cycles}$$

EXAMPLE 8. A 5-μf capacitor is connected in series with a variable inductor to a 20-volt 796-cycle source. For what value of inductance will the current be (*a*) 2 amp lagging, (*b*) 2 amp leading?

Solution

(*a*)

$$X_{eq} = \frac{20}{2} = 10 \text{ ohms}$$

$$X_{eq} = X_L - X_C = 10$$

$$10 = 2\pi \times 796L - \frac{10^6}{2\pi \times 796 \times 5}$$

Therefore

$$L = \frac{10 + 40}{5{,}000} = 0.01 \text{ henry}$$

(*b*)

$$X_{eq} = \frac{20}{2} = 10 \text{ ohms}$$

$$X_{eq} = X_C - X_L = 10$$

$$10 = \frac{10^6}{2\pi \times 796 \times 5} - 2\pi \times 796L$$

Therefore

$$L = \frac{40 - 10}{5{,}000} = 0.006 \text{ henry}$$

The Series Resistance-Inductance (R-L) Circuit. Circuits possessing properties of resistance (opposition to current flow) *and* inductance (opposition to current change) are widely employed in practice. They may consist of simple coils in which the resistance and inductance effects are distributed and interdependent, or may be made up of two or more combinations of pure resistance and resistance-inductance coils. In all cases it is, however, convenient to represent the two properties separately, i.e., as though they were *lumped* as independent resistors and inductors; a basic circuit illustrating such a series resistance-inductance (R-L) combination, connected to an a-c source, is shown in Fig. 130*a*.

Assuming that the impressed emf wave is sinusoidal, the following points can be made about the circuit's behavior: (1) the *common current* will be sinusoidal, although not in phase with the line-voltage wave; (2) the voltage drop across the resistor—the IR drop—will be in phase with the current (see Fig. 126*c*); (3) the voltage drop across the inductor—the IX_L drop—will be 90 elec deg *ahead* of the current (see Fig. 128*c*); (4) the line voltage E will be the *vector sum* of the IR and IX_L voltage drops (the hypotenuse of a right triangle in this case). Using the common current vector as the reference, a customary practice for series circuits, the vector diagram of Fig. 130*b* shows the phase-angle relationships for the

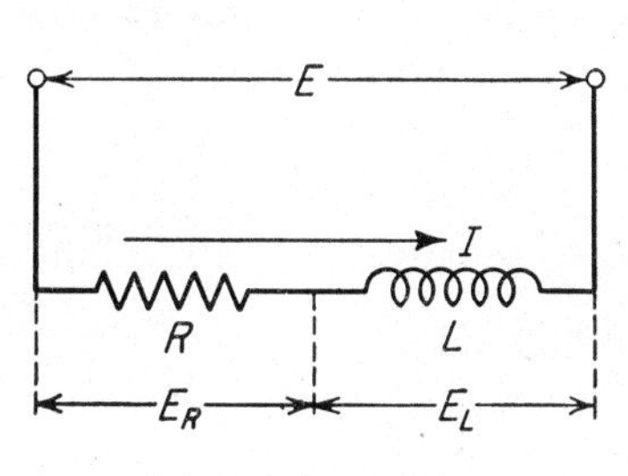

(*a*) Circuit diagram

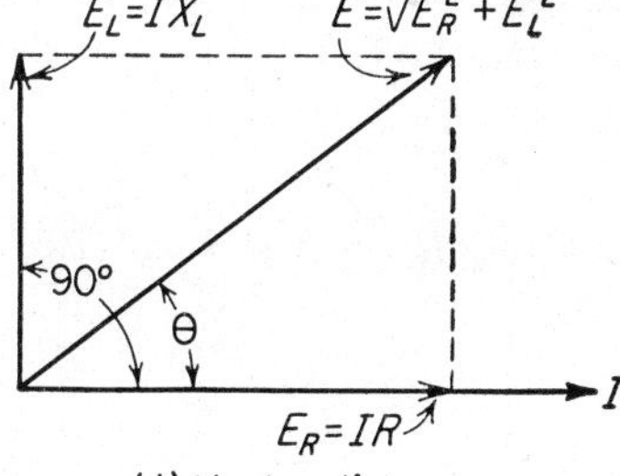

(*b*) Vector diagram

FIG. 130. Relations existing in a series resistance-inductance (R-L) circuit.

various parts of the circuit. Note that the phase angle between the current and the line voltage, i.e., angle Θ, is, as it should be, less than 90 and more than 0 elec deg; this results because the circuit parameters are neither pure resistances nor pure inductances.

Representing the equivalent opposition to current flow, a combination of R and X_L, by the symbol Z, and designating it as the *impedance* of the circuit,

$$E = I \times Z = \sqrt{E_R^2 + E_L^2} = \sqrt{(IR)^2 + (IX_L)^2} = I\sqrt{R^2 + X_L^2}$$

from which

$$Z = \sqrt{R^2 + X_L^2} \tag{95}$$

Also

$$\cos\Theta = \frac{E_R}{E} = \frac{IR}{IZ} = \frac{R}{Z} \tag{96}$$

Since $\cos\Theta$ indicates the *extent* to which the current is out of phase with the impressed emf it is an extremely important property of a circuit. As such it is usually called the circuit *power factor*, abbreviated PF; the reason for this designation should be clear from the following:

$$\text{PF} = \cos \Theta = \frac{R}{Z} = \frac{I^2R}{I^2Z} = \frac{P}{(IZ)(I)} = \frac{P}{EI} \tag{97}$$

and rearranged

$$P = EI \cos \Theta \qquad \text{watts} \tag{97a}$$[1]

Note particularly in Eq. (97*a*) that the circuit power is directly proportional to the power factor, which in turn can have values between 1.0 and 0. When the current is in phase with the voltage, $\Theta = 0$ and $\cos 0° = 1$; under this condition the circuit behaves like a pure resistance and $P = EI$ *volt-amperes* or watts. When the current is out of phase with the voltage by 90 elec deg, $\cos 90° = 0$; under this condition the circuit power is zero even though there is a finite value of EI *volt-amperes.*

EXAMPLE 9. A 240-volt 60-cycle source is connected to a coil of wire that has a resistance of 7.5 ohms and an inductance of 0.0477 henry. Calculate the following: impedance, current, power, power factor.

Solution

$$Z = \sqrt{R^2 + X_L^2} = \sqrt{(7.5)^2 + (2\pi \times 60 \times 0.0477)^2} = 19.5 \text{ ohms}$$

$$I = \frac{E}{Z} = \frac{240}{19.5} = 12.3 \text{ amp}$$

$$P = I^2R = (12.3)^2 \times 7.5 = 1{,}135 \text{ watts}$$

$$\text{PF} = \frac{P}{EI} = \frac{1{,}135}{240 \times 12.3} = 0.385 \text{ lagging}$$

Also

$$\text{PF} = \frac{R}{Z} = \frac{7.5}{19.5} = 0.385 \text{ lagging}$$

It will next be desirable to analyze the wave diagrams for a series *R-L* circuit. Referring to Fig. 131, observe that the current wave is shown to *lag behind* the reference voltage wave by Θ radians and that their respective equations are

$$e = E_m \sin \alpha$$

and

$$i = I_m \sin (\alpha - \Theta)$$

where α and Θ are, for convenience, expressed in radians. Also shown is the power wave which was drawn by plotting point-by-point products of e and i. Note particularly that (1) it is a double-frequency wave in relation to the voltage or current variation; (2) for each cycle, a larger portion of the wave lies *above* the x axis than below it, and this indicates that more power is delivered by the source to the coil (positive power) than by the coil back to the source (negative power); (3) the average

[1] See Appendix 1P for derivation.

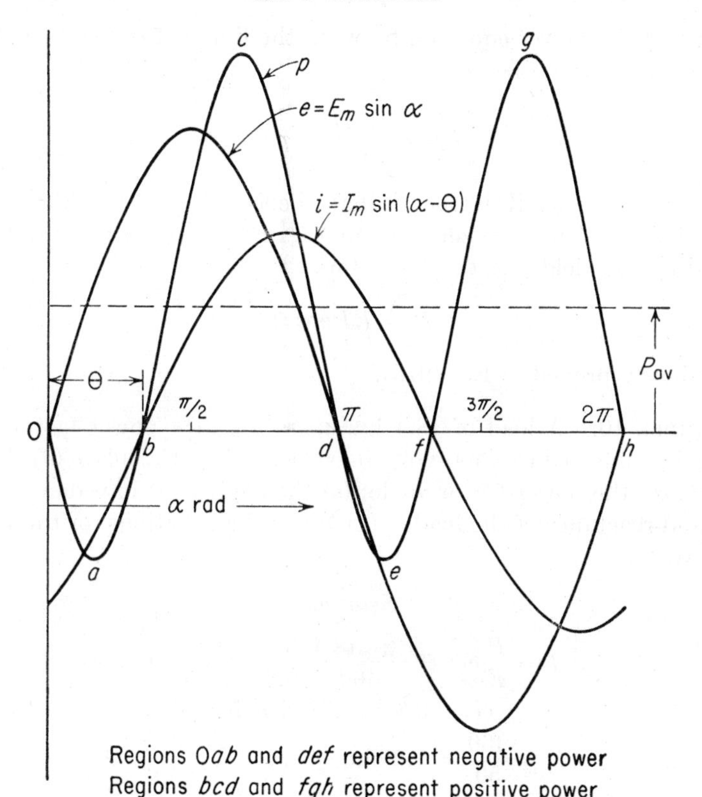

FIG. 131. Waves illustrating conditions in a resistance-inductance (*R-L*) circuit.

power, *above* the x axis, is exactly halfway between the maximum positive value and the maximum negative value.

Multiplying the foregoing two equations for e and i, the instantaneous power is

$$\begin{aligned} p &= E_m I_m \sin \alpha \sin(\alpha - \Theta) = E_m I_m \sin \alpha(\sin \alpha \cos \Theta - \cos \alpha \sin \Theta) \\ &= E_m I_m(\sin^2 \alpha \cos \Theta - \sin \alpha \cos \alpha \sin \Theta) \\ &= E_m I_m \left[\left(\frac{1}{2} - \frac{1}{2} \cos 2\alpha\right) \cos \Theta - \frac{\sin 2\alpha}{2} \sin \Theta\right] \\ &= \frac{E_m I_m}{2} [(1 - \cos 2\alpha) \cos \Theta - \sin 2\alpha \sin \Theta] \\ &= EI(\cos \Theta - \cos 2\alpha \cos \Theta - \sin 2\alpha \sin \Theta) \end{aligned}$$

The magnitude of the *average power* can be evaluated by determining the total area under the power curve *per cycle* (this includes both positive and negative portions) and then dividing by the base, i.e., 2π. This operation is best performed by the calculus by an integration—a summation—of the power equation between the limits of 0 and 2π and then division by 2π; thus

$$P_{av} = \frac{1}{2\pi} \int_0^{2\pi} p \, d\alpha$$

When this is done, it is found that the $\cos 2\alpha \cos \Theta$ term and the $\sin 2\alpha \sin \Theta$ term become zero; the first term becomes $2\pi \cos \Theta$ and, when divided by 2π, yields $\cos \Theta$. Therefore

$$P = EI \cos \Theta$$

as previously proved in Eq. (97*a*).

Example 10. A load of 18.4 kw operating at a power factor of 0.8 lagging is connected to a 460-volt 60-cycle source. Calculate (*a*) the load current; (*b*) the power-factor angle; (*c*) the equivalent impedance, resistance, and reactance of the load. (*d*) Write the equations for the voltage and current.

Solution

(*a*) $$I = \frac{P}{E} \cos \Theta = \frac{18{,}400}{460 \times 0.8} = 50 \text{ amp}$$

(*b*) $$\cos^{-1} 0.8 = 36.8 \text{ elec deg}$$

(*c*) $$Z = \frac{460}{50} = 9.2 \text{ ohms}$$

$$R = Z \cos \Theta = 9.2 \times 0.8 = 7.36 \text{ ohms}$$

$$X_L = \sqrt{(9.2)^2 - (7.36)^2} = 5.52 \text{ ohms}$$

(*d*) $$e = 460 \sqrt{2} \sin 2\pi \times 60t = 650 \sin 377t$$

$$i = 50 \sqrt{2} \sin \left(377t - \frac{36.8}{180} \pi\right) = 70.7 \sin (377t - 0.205\pi)$$

The Series Resistance-Capacitance (R-C) Circuit. A series circuit consisting of a resistor and a capacitor will, when connected to a sinusoidal source of emf, take current that is neither in phase with the voltage nor 90 elec deg out of phase with it; the current will, in fact, *lead* the voltage by an angle that is more than 0° and less than 90°.

Referring to Fig. 132, which shows a basic *R-C* circuit and a corresponding vector diagram, and assuming a sine wave of impressed voltage, the following points can be made concerning its behavior: (1) the *common current* will be sinusoidal, although not in phase with the line-voltage wave; (2) the voltage drop across the resistor—the IR drop—will be in phase with the current (see Fig. 126*c*); (3) the voltage drop across the capacitor—the IX_C drop—will be 90 elec deg *behind* the current (see Fig. 129*c*); (4) the line voltage E will be the *vector sum* of the IR and IX_C

voltage drops (the hypotenuse of a right triangle in this case). Again using the common current vector as the reference, the vector diagram of Fig. 132*b* shows the phase-angle relationships for the various parts of the circuit. Note that the phase angle between the current and the line voltage, i.e., angle Θ, is, as it should be, less than 90 and more than 0 elec deg; this results because the circuit parameters are neither pure resistances nor pure capacitances.

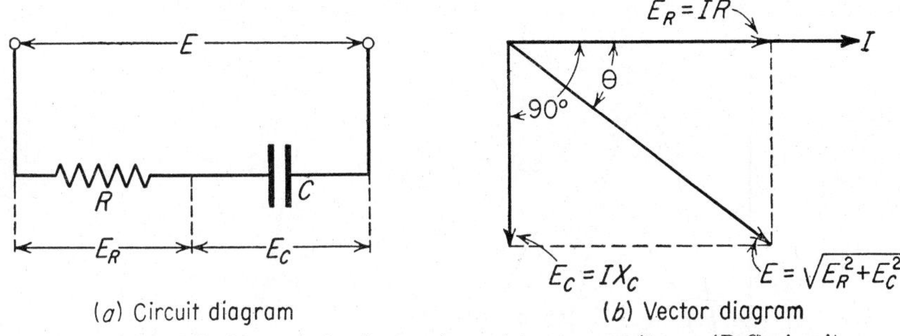

FIG. 132. Relations existing in a series resistance-capacitance (*R-C*) circuit.

Since the impressed voltage in *any* a-c circuit is always equal to the product of the equivalent impedance and the resulting current,

$$E = IZ = \sqrt{E_R^2 + E_C^2} = \sqrt{(IR)^2 + (IX_C)^2} = I\sqrt{R^2 + X_C^2}$$

from which

$$Z = \sqrt{R^2 + X_C^2} \tag{98}$$

Also, the same power-factor and power equations [Eqs. (97) and (97*a*)] apply equally to series *R-C* and to *R-L* circuits.

EXAMPLE 11. A 125-volt 25-cycle source is connected to a series circuit consisting of a 30-ohm resistor and a 159-μf capacitor. Calculate the following: impedance, current, power factor, power.

Solution

$$Z = \sqrt{R^2 + X_C^2} = \sqrt{(30)^2 + \left(\frac{10^6}{2\pi \times 25 \times 159}\right)^2}$$

$$= \sqrt{(30)^2 + (40)^2} = 50 \text{ ohms}$$

$$I = \frac{E}{Z} = \frac{125}{50} = 2.5 \text{ amp}$$

$$\text{PF} = \frac{R}{Z} = \frac{30}{50} = 0.6 \text{ leading}$$

$$P = EI \cos \Theta = 125 \times 2.5 \times 0.6 = 187.5 \text{ watts}$$

Also

$$P = I^2R = (2.5)^2 \times 30 = 187.5 \text{ watts}$$

The wave diagrams for a series *R-C* circuit are shown in Fig. 133. Note particularly that the current wave *leads* the reference voltage wave by Θ radians, and that their respective equations are

$$e = E_m \sin \alpha$$

and
$$i = I_m \sin (\alpha + \Theta)$$

where α and Θ are, for convenience, expressed in radians. Also shown is the power wave, which, as previously, was drawn by plotting point-by-

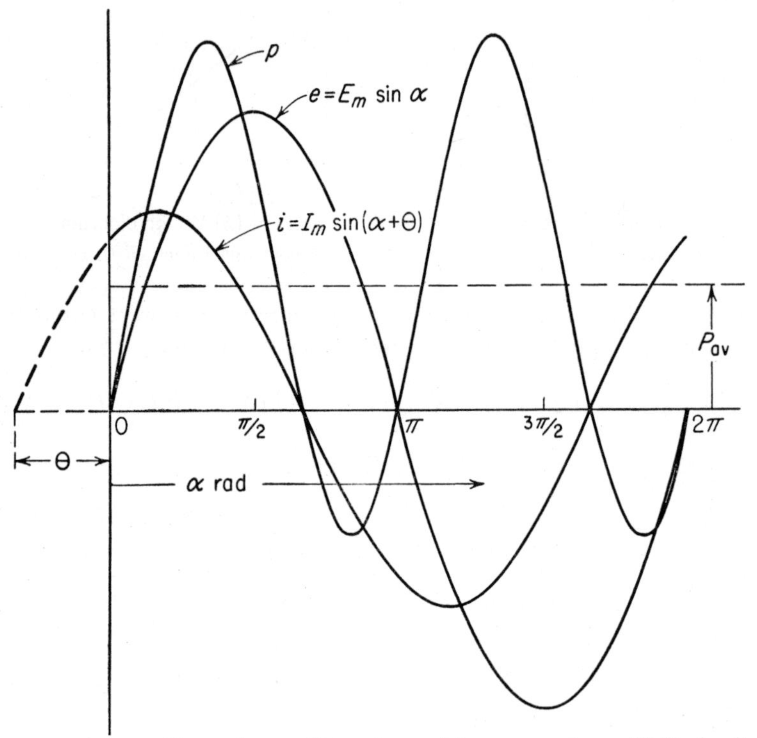

Fig. 133. Waves illustrating conditions in a resistance-capacitance (*R-C*) circuit.

point products of e and i. Comparing it with Fig. 132, observe that (1) it is a double-frequency wave in relation to the voltage or current variation; (2) for each cycle, a larger portion of the wave lies *above* the x axis than below it, and this indicates that more power is delivered by the source to heat the resistor and charge the capacitor (positive power) than by the discharge of the capacitor back to the source (negative power); (3) the average power, *above* the x axis, is exactly halfway between the maximum positive value and the maximum negative value.

Multiplying the foregoing two equations for e and i, the instantaneous power is

$$
\begin{aligned}
p &= E_m I_m \sin \alpha \sin (\alpha + \Theta) = E_m I_m \sin \alpha(\sin \alpha \cos \Theta + \cos \alpha \sin \Theta) \\
&= E_m I_m(\sin^2 \alpha \cos \Theta + \sin \alpha \cos \alpha \sin \Theta) \\
&= E_m I_m \left[\left(\frac{1}{2} - \frac{1}{2} \cos 2\alpha\right) \cos \Theta + \frac{\sin 2\alpha}{2} \sin \Theta\right] \\
&= \frac{E_m I_m}{2} [(1 - \cos 2\alpha) \cos \Theta + \sin 2\alpha \sin \Theta] \\
&= EI(\cos \Theta - \cos 2\alpha \cos \Theta + \sin 2\alpha \sin \Theta)
\end{aligned}
$$

To determine the equation for the average power in a series R-C circuit, the above relationship is treated by the calculus in the same way as was done in the previous section for the R-L circuit; i.e., when the general expression $P_{av} = (1/2\pi) \int_0^{2\pi} p \, d\alpha$ is solved mathematically, using the foregoing equation for p, it will be found to yield exactly the same formula as that given by Eq. (97*a*). It can therefore be stated that the average power in *any* a-c circuit served by a single a-c source is $P = EI \cos \Theta$.

EXAMPLE 12. A series resistance-capacitance (R-C) circuit is connected to a 230-volt 60-cycle source. If the power taken by the circuit is 4,800 watts and the voltage drop across the resistor is 115 volts, calculate (*a*) the current, (*b*) the power factor, (*c*) the circuit impedance, (*d*) the ohmic value of the resistor, (*e*) the capacitance of the capacitor. (*f*) Write the equations for the voltage and current.

Solution

(*a*) $$I = \frac{P}{E_R} = \frac{4{,}800}{115} = 41.7 \text{ amp}$$

(*b*) $$\text{PF} = \frac{P}{EI} = \frac{4{,}800}{230 \times 41.7} = 0.5 = \cos 60°$$

(*c*) $$Z = \frac{E}{I} = \frac{230}{41.7} = 5.51 \text{ ohms}$$

(*d*) $$R = \frac{E_R}{I} = \frac{115}{41.7} = 2.75 \text{ ohms}$$

(*e*) $$X_C = \sqrt{Z^2 - R^2} = \sqrt{(5.51)^2 - (2.75)^2} = 4.77 \text{ ohms}$$

$$C = \frac{10^6}{2\pi f X_C} = \frac{10^6}{377 \times 4.77} = 555 \ \mu\text{f}$$

(*f*) $$e = 230 \sqrt{2} \sin (2\pi \times 60t) = 325 \sin 377t$$

$$i = 41.7 \sqrt{2} \sin \left(2\pi \times 60t + \frac{60}{180} \pi\right) = 59 \sin \left(377t + \frac{\pi}{3}\right)$$

The Series Resistance-Inductance-Capacitance (R-L-C) Circuit. The behavior of a series circuit comprising all three kinds of units, i.e., resistance, inductance, and capacitance will depend upon the *relative* magnitudes of X_L and X_C. Remembering that inductive reactance and capacitive reactance act oppositely with respect to each other, it should be clear that the combination behaves (1) like an *R-L* circuit when X_L is greater than X_C, (2) like an *R-C* circuit when X_C is greater than X_L, and (3) like a pure resistance R when X_L equals X_C. The latter condition has a special significance and is said to produce *resonance* in the circuit; it will be considered in some detail in a separate chapter.

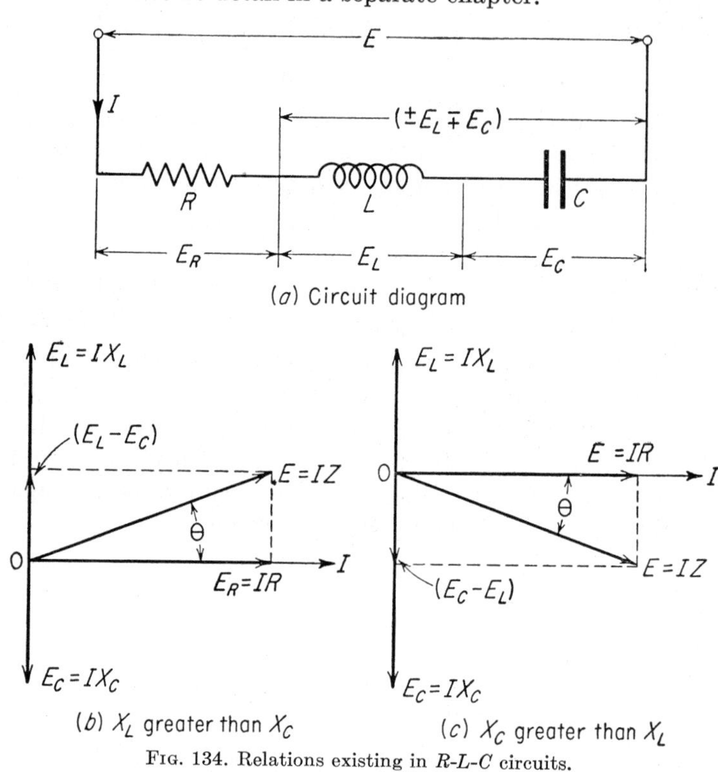

FIG. 134. Relations existing in *R-L-C* circuits.

Vector diagrams illustrating both the *R-L* and *R-C* conditions in an *R-L-C* circuit are shown in Fig. 134. Note that the voltage drops across the inductance and capacitance, i.e., IX_L and IX_C, respectively, are in *direct opposition*, their resultant is therefore an arithmetical difference, and this difference is combined with the IR drop vectorially to yield the total impressed voltage. The following equations relate the various quantities in such a circuit:

$$E = \sqrt{(IR)^2 + (\pm IX_L \mp IX_C)^2} \tag{99}$$

and

$$Z = \sqrt{R^2 + (\pm X_L \mp X_C)^2} \tag{100}$$

EXAMPLE 13. A series circuit consisting of an 80-ohm resistor, a 0.3-henry inductor, and a 50-μf capacitor is connected to a 120-volt 60-cycle source. Calculate the following: (*a*) equivalent impedance of the circuit, (*b*) current, (*c*) voltage drops across the several units, (*d*) power and power factor.

Solution

(*a*)
$$X_L = 2\pi \times 60 \times 0.3 = 113 \text{ ohms}$$
$$X_C = \frac{10^6}{2\pi \times 60 \times 50} = 53 \text{ ohms}$$
$$Z = \sqrt{(80)^2 + (113 - 53)^2} = 100 \text{ ohms}$$

(*b*)
$$I = \frac{120}{100} = 1.2 \text{ amp}$$

(*c*)
$$E_R = 1.2 \times 80 = 96 \text{ volts}$$
$$E_L = 1.2 \times 113 = 135.6 \text{ volts}$$
$$E_C = 1.2 \times 53 = 63.6 \text{ volts}$$

(*d*)
$$P = (1.2)^2 \times 80 = 115.2 \text{ watts}$$
$$\text{PF} = \frac{115.2}{120 \times 1.2} = 0.8 \text{ lagging}$$

EXAMPLE 14. It is desired to have the circuit of Example 13 take the same current and power but operate at a power factor of 0.8 leading. (*a*) For what value of capacitance will these conditions exist, assuming that impressed voltage, frequency, resistance, and inductance remain unchanged? (*b*) Calculate the voltage drop across the capacitance under this condition.

Solution

(*a*) Since the equivalent impedance of the circuit must remain unchanged,

$$Z = 100 = \sqrt{(80)^2 + (X_C - 113)^2}$$

from which
$$X_C = 173 \text{ ohms}$$

Hence
$$C = \frac{10^6}{2\pi \times 60 \times 173} = 15.3 \ \mu\text{f}$$

(*b*)
$$E_C = 1.2 \times 173 = 207.6 \text{ volts}$$

The Impedance Coil–Resistance (RL-R) Circuit. As was previously pointed out, a coil of wire possesses properties of resistance *and* inductance that are interdependent; in this respect it is therefore an *impedance* coil. To determine the resistance and inductance of such a coil it is sometimes desirable to connect a fixed resistance in series with the unit, measure the voltages E_Z, E_R, and E, and the current I, as shown in Fig. 135*a*, and proceed to make calculations in accordance with the following analysis and its accompanying vector diagram (Fig. 135*b*).

Using the current I as a horizontal reference vector, draw vector E_R in phase with it. With the tip of E_R as a center strike an arc upward using E_Z as a radius. Next, with the origin O as a center, swing another arc with E as a radius to intersect the impedance-voltage arc at point a. The lines from the ends of E_R to the point a will then represent the vectors E_Z and E. If a parallelogram is then completed as shown in Fig. 135*b* it will be noted that the power-factor angle of the *impedance*

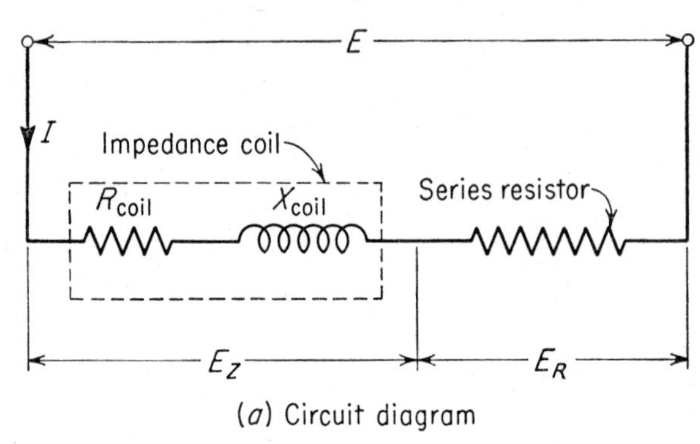

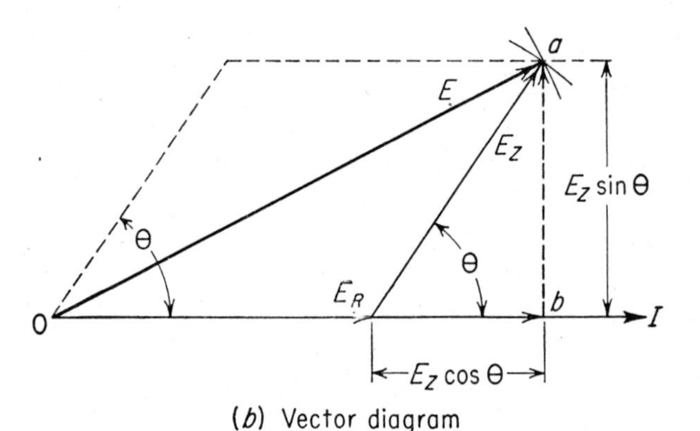

FIG. 135. Diagrams illustrating a series impedance coil–resistance (*RL-L*) circuit and its vector diagram.

coil is the angle Θ between the current vector and E_Z. Writing an expression for triangle *Oab*,

$$E^2 = (E_R + E_Z \cos \Theta)^2 + (E_Z \sin \Theta)^2$$
$$= E_R^2 + 2E_RE_Z \cos \Theta + E_Z^2(\cos^2 \Theta + \sin^2 \Theta)$$

But

$$(\cos^2 \Theta + \sin^2 \Theta) = 1$$

Therefore

$$\cos \Theta = \frac{E^2 - E_R^2 - E_Z^2}{2E_RE_Z}$$

After cos Θ is determined it is possible to evaluate the resistance and inductance of the coil by using the equations

$$R_{coil} = \frac{E_Z \cos \Theta}{I} \quad \text{and} \quad L_{coil} = \frac{E_Z \sin \Theta}{I \times 2\pi f}$$

EXAMPLE 15. A 115-volt 60-cycle source is connected to a series circuit consisting of a fixed resistor and an impedance coil. If the resistor- and coil-voltage drops are 55.4 and 80 volts, respectively, under which condition the current is 1.69 amp, calculate the resistance and inductance of the impedance coil.

Solution

$$\cos \Theta = \frac{(115)^2 - (55.4)^2 - (80)^2}{2 \times 55.4 \times 80} = \frac{3,755}{8,865} = 0.423$$

$$\Theta = 65°$$

$$\sin \Theta = 0.906$$

$$R_{coil} = \frac{80 \times 0.423}{1.69} = 20 \text{ ohms}$$

$$L = \frac{80 \times 0.906}{1.69 \times 377} = 0.114 \text{ henry}$$

Volt-amperes and Reactive Volt-amperes. It is customary to refer to an a-c load by using the term *volt-amperes*, abbreviated va; in systems involving considerable loads the larger unit, *kilovolt-amperes* (kva), is more desirable. Representing the product of volts and amperes, or kilovolts and amperes, it is, in a constant-potential system, a measure of such operational factors as current-carrying capacity of wires, heating effect in electrical equipment, ratings of machines, and others. Unlike the situation that exists in a d-c system where power and volt-amperes are identical, power in an a-c system can have any number of values from zero to EI. In fact, the well-labeled power-factor ($\cos \Theta$) term in Eq. (97*a*) indicates the *extent* to which volt-amperes (EI) become P (watts).

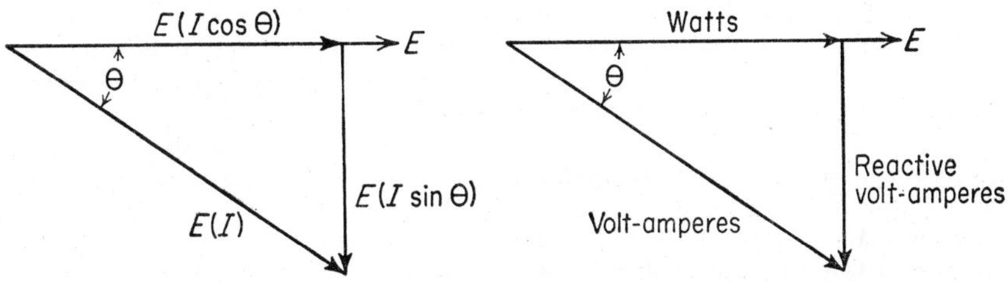

FIG. 136. Vector diagrams illustrating the relation between volt-amperes (EI), watts ($EI \cos \Theta$), and reactive volt-amperes ($EI \sin \Theta$) for a lagging power-factor load.

A convenient form of vector diagram that makes use of *volt-ampere* terms is shown in Fig. 136. If the horizontal reference vector is made to stand for watts ($P = EI \cos \Theta$), the volt-ampere vector ($EI = P/\cos \Theta$) may be drawn at the proper power-factor angle Θ with respect to the former. It follows, therefore, that the vertical component—the *quadrature component*—is $EI \sin \Theta$. The latter, acting adversely to lessen the power factor, is expressed as the *reactive volt-amperes*, abbreviated R-va or R-EI, or, for larger quantities, *reactive kilovolt-amperes*, abbreviated R-kva; the standardized units for these quantities are, respectively, var (from *v*olt-*a*mperes *r*eactive) and kvar. Also, dividing the reactive volt-amperes by EI gives the *reactive factor*, abbreviated RF. Thus

$$\text{RF} = \frac{\text{R-EI}}{EI} = \frac{EI \sin \Theta}{EI} = \sin \Theta \tag{101}$$

Moreover, since $\cos^2 \Theta + \sin^2 \Theta = 1$, $\sin \Theta = \sqrt{1 - \cos^2 \Theta}$; hence

$$\text{RF} = \sqrt{1 - (\text{PF})^2} \tag{101a}$$

EXAMPLE 16. A load of 250 kva, operating at a power factor of 0.86 lagging, is connected to a 2,300-volt a-c source. Calculate (*a*) power, (*b*) current, (*c*) reactive kilovolt-amperes, (*d*) reactive factor.

Solution

(*a*) $$\text{Power} = \text{kva} \times \text{PF} = 250 \times 0.86 = 215 \text{ kw}$$

(*b*) $$I = \text{kva} \times \frac{1{,}000}{E} = \frac{250 \times 1{,}000}{2{,}300} = 108.7 \text{ amp}$$

(*c*) $$\Theta = \cos^{-1} 0.86 = 30°41'$$

$$\sin 30°41' = 0.51$$

$$\text{R-kva} = \text{kva} \sin \Theta = 250 \times 0.51 = 127.5 \text{ kvar}$$

(*d*) $$\text{RF} = \sqrt{1 - (\text{PF})^2} = \sqrt{1 - (0.86)^2} = 0.51$$

Questions

1. List the basic types of units used in a-c circuits.

2. Under what condition will a pure inductance take a sinusoidal current when connected to a sinusoidal source of emf?

3. List four possible series combinations of resistance, inductance, and capacitance.

4. What general statements can be made concerning the behavior of resistance, inductance, and capacitance in a-c circuits?

5. What is the shape of the power wave in a pure-resistance circuit that is energized by a sinusoidal wave of voltage? What are the maximum and average values of power in such a circuit?

6. How is an incandescent-lamp load regarded in a-c circuits?

7. Answer Question 5 as applied to a pure-inductance circuit.

8. What is meant by the term *inductive reactance?* What are its units, and how is it computed?

9. What are the significance of *positive power* and *negative power* when referring to a pure-inductance circuit? Explain carefully.

10. Answer Question 5 as applied to a pure-capacitance circuit.

11. What is meant by the term *capacitive reactance?* What are its units, and how is it computed?

12. How does a change in frequency affect the inductive reactance? the capacitive reactance?

13. Explain the terms *lagging current* and *leading current.*

14. Answer Question 9 as applied to a pure-capacitance circuit.

15. How does a series inductance-capacitance circuit behave when X_L is greater than X_C? when X_C is greater than X_L?
16. Under what condition will resonance occur in a series inductance-capacitance circuit? In what three ways can this be accomplished?
17. What kind of power factor will exist in a series resistance-inductance circuit? Why?
18. Under what condition will the power factor of a series *R-L* circuit approach unity? zero? Explain carefully.
19. How are the voltage drops across R and X_L related in a series *R-L* circuit? How are these voltage drops related to the impressed emf?
20. What is meant by the term *impedance*, referring to a series *R-L* circuit?
21. Define *power factor*. What is its significance in an a-c circuit?
22. How much power is involved in a circuit in which the power factor is unity? is zero? is 0.5?
23. What is the significance of the negative power in the power wave of an *R-L* circuit? Explain carefully.
24. Assuming that the impressed emf wave in a series *R-L* circuit is $E_m \sin \alpha$, write the general expression for the current wave.
25. What kind of power factor will exist in a series resistance-capacitance circuit? Why?
26. Under what condition will the power factor of a series *R-C* circuit approach unity? approach zero? Explain carefully.
27. How are the voltage drops across R and X_C related in a series *R-C* circuit? How are these voltage drops related to the impressed emf?
28. What is the significance of the negative power in the power wave of an *R-C* circuit? Explain carefully.
29. Assuming that the impressed emf wave in a series *R-C* circuit is $E_m \sin \alpha$, write the general expression for the current wave.
30. What kind of power factor will exist in a series *R-C* circuit? Why?
31. How does a series *R-L-C* circuit behave when X_L is greater than X_C? when X_C is greater than X_L? when $X_L = X_C$?
32. What kinds of power factor exist in circuits indicated by Question 31?
33. Explain why it is possible for the voltage drops across X_L and/or X_C to be *greater* than the total impressed voltage in a series *R-L-C* circuit.
34. Explain the significance of the impedance coil–resistance series circuit. What kind of voltage, in relation to the resistance voltage, is measured across the impedance coil?
35. Define the terms *volt-amperes* and *reactive volt-amperes*.
36. What is the relationship of the reactive volt-amperes to the total volt-amperes in unity-power factor circuit? in a zero-power-factor circuit? in a circuit in which the power factor is 0.866?
37. What is meant by *reactive factor?* Express it as a trigonometric function. Express it in terms of the circuit power factor.

Problems

1. A large room is illuminated by twenty 150-watt lamps and thirty 100-watt lamps. If the circuit voltage is 116, calculate the total current.
2. Calculate the resistance of a load that takes 1,600 watts from a 220-volt source.
3. How much power is represented by a circuit in which the voltage and current equations are $e = 160 \sin 314t$ and $i = 42.5 \sin 314t$?
4. A coil of wire having negligible resistance and an inductance of 0.248 henry is connected to a 117-volt 50-cycle source. Calculate (*a*) the inductive reactance,

(*b*) the current, (*c*) the maximum power delivered to the inductor or returned to the source, (*d*) the average power. Write the equations for (*e*) the current and (*f*) the power.

5. At what frequency will a 0.016-henry inductor have an inductive reactance of 80 ohms?

6. What value of capacitance will have a capacitive reactance of 80 ohms at 796 cycles?

7. A 45-μf capacitor is connected to a 118-volt 60-cycle source. Calculate (*a*) the capacitive reactance, (*b*) the current, (*c*) the maximum power delivered to the capacitor or returned to the source, (*d*) the average power. Write equations for (*e*) the current and (*f*) the power.

8. What value of capacitance will have a capacitive reactance on 180 cycles that is equal to the 60-cycle inductive reactance of a 0.061-henry inductor?

9. At what frequency will the inductive reactance of a 0.0211-henry inductor be equal to the capacitive reactance of a 75-μf capacitor?

10. A series circuit consisting of a 30-μf capacitor and a 0.155-henry inductor is connected to a 120-volt 60-cycle source. Calculate the circuit current and indicate whether it lags behind or leads the voltage.

11. If a variable inductor is substituted for the one in Prob. 10, what should be its value if an equal current is to lag behind the voltage? Assume all other conditions to remain unchanged.

12. A series circuit consisting of a 0.398-henry inductor and a 212-μf capacitor is connected to a 125-volt variable-frequency source. At what frequency will the circuit take a lagging current of 2.5 amp?

13. Solve Prob. 12 for a leading current of 2.5 amp.

14. A 0.143-henry inductor is connected in series with a variable capacitor to a 208-volt 400-cycle source. For what value of capacitance will the current be (*a*) 1.04 amp lagging? (*b*) 1.04 amp leading?

15. A small a-c motor used in a washing machine is, in effect, an *R-L* circuit. If the machine takes 311 watts and 4.5 amp from a 115-volt source when operating normally, calculate its power factor.

16. A transformer takes 5,175 watts at a power factor of 0.85 when connected to a 2,300-volt distribution circuit. What is the current input?

17. In an a-c circuit the sinusoidal voltage and current waves have the following equations: $e = 170 \sin 314t$, $i = 28.4 \sin (314t - \pi/3)$. Calculate the following: (*a*) effective voltage and current, (*b*) frequency, (*c*) power factor, (*d*) power.

18. An impedance coil has a resistance of 20 ohms and an inductive reactance of 40 ohms. For what value of series resistance will the over-all power factor of the circuit be 0.6?

19. A series *R-L* circuit takes 371.2 watts at a power factor of 0.8 from a 116-volt 60-cycle source. What are the values of R and L?

20. What additional inductance should be inserted in series in the circuit of Prob. 19 if the over-all power factor is to be reduced to 0.5? What will be the current and power under this condition?

21. Two impedance coils A and B are connected in series to a 111-volt a-c source. Coil A has a resistance of 12 ohms and an inductive reactance of 16 ohms. Coil B has a resistance of 24 ohms and an inductive reactance of 10 ohms. Calculate the voltage drop across each coil.

22. An *R-L* circuit takes a current of 7 amp that lags behind the 231-volt source by 35 elec deg. Calculate the power factor, power, impedance, resistance, and inductive reactance of the circuit.

23. A resistor, in series with a 138-μf capacitor, is connected to a 60-cycle source. If the voltage drop across the capacitor is 115 volts and the power taken by the circuit is 922 watts, calculate (*a*) the circuit current, (*b*) the ohmic value of the resistor, (*c*) the line voltage, (*d*) the circuit power factor.

24. A series *R-C* circuit takes a current whose equation is $i = 0.85 \sin (754t + \pi/4)$ when connected to a source of emf having the equation $e = 340 \sin 754t$. Calculate (*a*) the values of Z, R, and X_C; (*b*) the capacitance of the capacitor; (*c*) the circuit power factor and power.

25. What should be the capacitance of a capacitor, in series with a 250-ohm resistor, that will limit the current to 1.2 amp when the circuit is connected to a 600-volt 60-cycle source? Also calculate the power and power factor under this condition.

26. A series circuit consists of a 66.2-μf capacitor and a variable resistor. For what two values of resistance will the power taken by the circuit be 172.8 watts, if the impressed 60-cycle emf is 120 volts?

27. A series *R-L-C* circuit consists of a 25-ohm resistor, a 0.221-henry inductor, and a 66.3-μf capacitor. For what 60-cycle impressed voltage will the current be 2.5 amp?

28. If the series circuit of Prob. 27 is connected to a 125-volt variable-frequency source, what will be the frequency at which the current is 5 amp? What will be the circuit power factor under this condition?

29. An impedance coil is connected in series with a fixed resistor, and a 120-volt 25-cycle source is then impressed across the combination. If the voltage drops across the coil and resistor are 70 and 80 volts, respectively, when the circuit current is 1.4 amp, calculate the resistance and inductance of the impedance coil.

30. The power input to an electric motor is 8.8 kw when operating normally from a 230-volt a-c source. If the current is 45 amp under this condition, calculate the power factor, reactive factor, and reactive kilovolt-amperes.

31. An a-c circuit takes a load of 160 kva at a lagging power factor of 0.75 when connected to a 460-volt source. Calculate the current, power factor, power, reactive kilovolt-amperes, and reactive factors.

32. A 46-kw 0.8-lagging–power-factor load is connected to the end of a short transmission line where the voltage is 230. If the line resistance and reactance are 0.06 and 0.08 ohm, respectively, calculate the voltage at the sending end.

CHAPTER 12

PARALLEL AND SERIES-PARALLEL CIRCUITS

Relations in Basic Parallel Circuits. Two or more of the elementary circuits considered in Chap. 11 may be connected in parallel as shown in Fig. 137. Since there are only three kinds of power factor at which any branch can operate, each one may be designated as a unity-power-factor, a lagging-power-factor, or a leading-power-factor load. Moreover, the over-all power factor of the combined load may have any value, and this

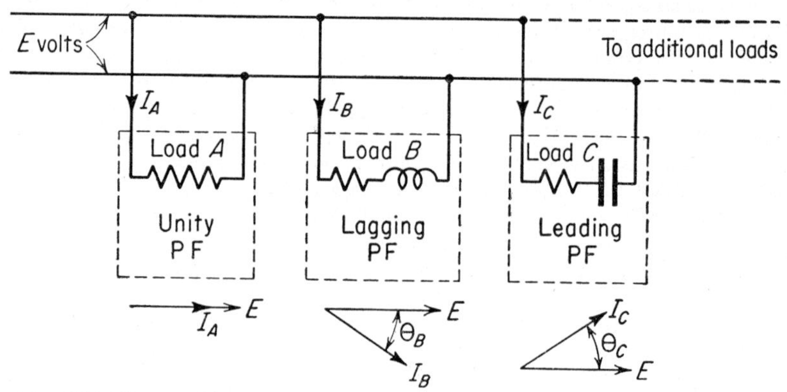

FIG. 137. Diagram illustrating three general types of load connected in parallel.

will depend not only upon the branch power factors but upon the magnitudes of the individual loads as well.

A composite vector diagram for the three general types of load is illustrated by Fig. 138. Note that the voltage vector, being common to all loads in a parallel circuit, is used as the horizontal reference, and the branch currents are drawn at the proper angles with respect to it. The total current is obviously the *vector sum* of the individual load currents, and this, in accordance with Fig. 138, is equal to

$$I_t = \sqrt{(I_A + I_B \cos \Theta_B + I_C \cos \Theta_C)^2 + (-I_B \sin \Theta_B + I_C \sin \Theta_C)^2}$$

In general terms this may, however, be expressed by the equation

$$I_t = \sqrt{(\Sigma I_h)^2 + (\Sigma I_v)^2} \tag{102}$$

where ΣI_h = *arithmetic sum* of the horizontal or in-phase components of current

ΣI_v = *algebraic sum* of the vertical or quadrature components of current

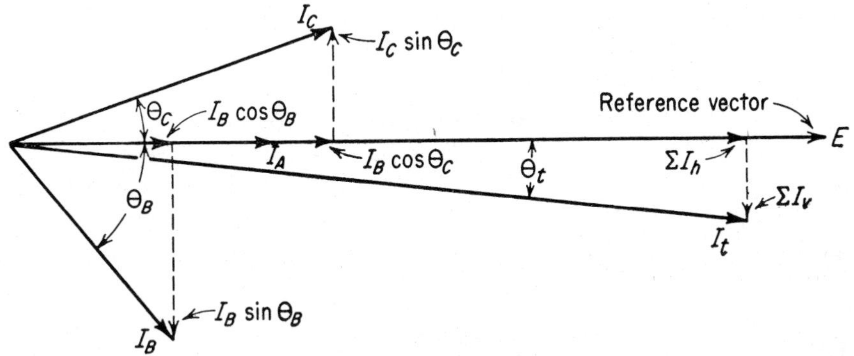

FIG. 138. Vector diagram showing how the total current is determined in a basic circuit consisting of three parallel branches.

The total power in such a circuit is equal to the product of the voltage E and the *in-phase component* of the total current, i.e., ΣI_h; thus

$$P_t = E\Sigma I_h = E(I_A + I_B \cos \Theta_B + I_C \cos \Theta_C) = P_A + P_B + P_C$$

Again, in general terms this may be expressed by the equation

$$P_t = \Sigma P \tag{103}$$

where ΣP is the *arithmetic sum* of the individual load powers.

Finally, the reactive volt-amperes are equal to the product of the voltage E and the *quadrature component* of the current; i.e., ΣI_v; thus

$$\text{R-va} = E\Sigma I_v = E(-I_B \sin \Theta_B + I_C \sin \Theta_C) = -(\text{R-va})_B + (\text{R-va})_C$$

In general terms this may be expressed by the equation

$$(\text{R-va})_t = \Sigma(\text{R-va}) \tag{104}$$

where Σ(R-va) is the *algebraic sum* of the individual-load reactive-volt-ampere values.

EXAMPLE 1. The following information is given in connection with three loads that are connected in parallel to a 230-volt a-c line: load A = 4.6 kw at unity power factor; load B = 11.5 kva at a lagging power factor of 0.62; load C = 5.52 kw at a leading power factor of 0.8. Calculate (*a*) total current, (*b*) over-all power factor, (*c*) total power, (*d*) total reactive kilovolt-amperes.

Solution

(a) $$I_A = \frac{4{,}600}{230 \times 1} = 20 \text{ amp}$$

$$I_B = \frac{11{,}500}{230} = 50 \text{ amp}$$

$$I_C = \frac{5{,}520}{230 \times 0.8} = 30 \text{ amp}$$

$$\Sigma I_h = 20 + (50 \times 0.62) + (30 \times .8) = 75 \text{ amp}$$

$$\Sigma I_v = (-50 \times 0.784) + (30 \times 0.6) = 21.2 \text{ amp}$$

(quadrature component)

$$I_t = \sqrt{(75)^2 + (-21.2)^2} = 77.8 \text{ amp} \quad \text{(lagging current)}$$

(b) $$\text{PF} = \frac{\Sigma I_h}{I_t} = \frac{75}{77.8} = 0.964 \text{ lagging}$$

(c) $$P_t = 4.6 + (11.5 \times 0.62) + 5.52 = 17.25 \text{ kw}$$

Also $$P_t = \frac{230 \times 77.8 \times 0.964}{1{,}000} = 17.25 \text{ kw}$$

(d) $$\text{R-kva} = E\frac{\Sigma I_v}{1{,}000} = \frac{230 \times (-21.2)}{1{,}000} = -4.876 \text{ kvar}$$

It is sometimes necessary to determine the value of a single impedance that will behave in exactly the same way as a combination of parallel loads or impedances. To fulfill the condition of an *equivalent impedance* Z_{eq} such a unit must take the *same current* and *power*, and operate at the *same power factor* as the combination of parallel loads, when it is connected to the *same* source of emf. If the total current and the over-all power factor of the circuit are known, the value of Z_{eq}, and its components R_{eq} and X_{eq}, may be calculated as follows:

$$Z_{eq} = \frac{E}{I_t} \qquad R_{eq} = Z_{eq} \cos \Theta_t \qquad X_{eq} = Z_{eq} \sin \Theta_t$$

EXAMPLE 2. Using the values obtained for the parallel circuit of Example 1, calculate the equivalent impedance, resistance, and reactance of combined circuit.

Solution

$$Z_{eq} = \frac{230}{77.8} = 2.96 \text{ ohms}$$

$$R_{eq} = 2.96 \times 0.964 = 2.85 \text{ ohms}$$

$$X_{eq} = 2.96 \times 0.266 = 0.787 \text{ ohm}$$

Although the foregoing examples are comparatively simple, it should be apparent that their solution involved mathematical procedures that were algebraic, trigonometric, and geometrical. This implies, of course, that, unlike the solution of d-c circuit problems where scalar numbers are used exclusively, a-c circuit problems must deal with vector quantities. Moreover, since trigonometric and geometrical operations are usually inconvenient and often difficult, especially when circuits are complicated or when general resonance studies are made, a mathematical system of *complex algebra* was developed to handle all a-c circuits by algebraic methods entirely. The following sections are concerned with the mechanics of complex algebra and its applications to the analysis and solution of a-c circuits.

Rectangular Coordinates and the j Operator. It is well known that a vector, drawn from some point O, may be specified in general terms by the magnitudes of its projections on x and y axes. However, to do so

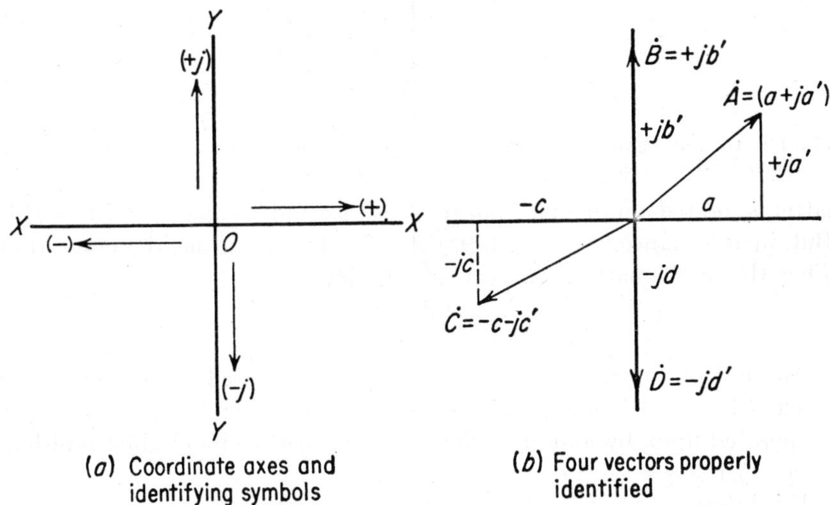

FIG. 139. Diagrams showing system of coordinates and vectors with identifying symbols.

accurately it is necessary (1) to assign arbitrary plus (+) and minus (−) directions to each of two coordinate axes XX and YY, and (2) to distinguish a *y-axis* projection from an *x-axis* projection by an identifying symbol. Figure 139*a* illustrates the system of coordinates in common use, with x-axis projections represented by (+) or (−) quantities, and y-axis projections designated by $(+j)$ or $(-j)$ quantities. Figure 139*b* shows four vectors drawn and identified by this system, with vectors $\dot{A}$ $(= a + ja')$ and $\dot{C}$ $(= -c - jc')$ in the first and third quadrants, respectively, and vectors $\dot{B}$ $(= +jb')$ and $\dot{D}$ $(= -jd')$ along the y axis.

Another important property of the symbol j, in addition to its y-axis significance, is its function as an *operator*, in which respect *it rotates a given vector* 90° *in a counterclockwise direction without changing its magnitude.* Thus, in Fig. 140, when vector A is operated upon, i.e., multiplied, by j it becomes $+jA$. Further, if operator j acts upon vector jA the

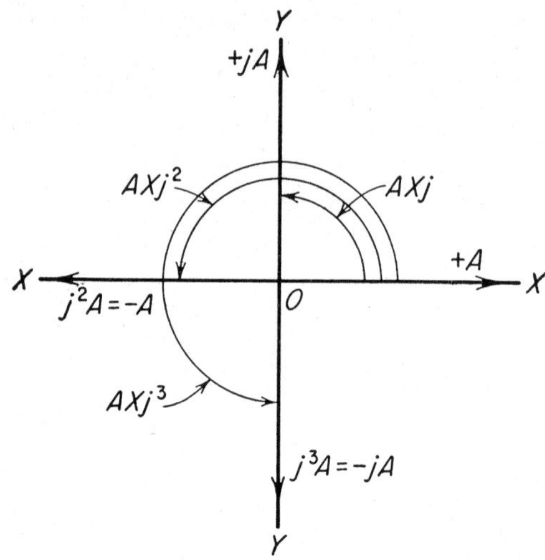

Fig. 140. Diagram showing how the j operator rotates the vector A through successive 90° steps counterclockwise.

latter is rotated another 90° counterclockwise and becomes $j \times jA = j^2A$. But, in accordance with Fig. 139, $j^2A = -A$; this means, therefore, that j has the mathematical value of $\sqrt{-1}$, since

$$j^2 = (\sqrt{-1})(\sqrt{-1}) = -1$$

Another 90° counterclockwise rotation is imposed upon the vector when $j^2A = -A$ is multiplied by j to become $-jA$; finally, when $-jA$ is operated upon by another j the vector returns to its original position, since $-jA \times j = -j^2A = +A$.

It is interesting to note that $j = \sqrt{-1}$ is, *mathematically*, an imaginary number, because the square of a *real* quantity, whether plus or minus, can never result in a negative quantity. This seems to *indicate* that the y axis yields values that are imaginary or unreal, a situation that, *electrically*, does accord with the facts; the mathematical significance of j as an operator does *not* alter the physical reality of quantities that have vertical components.

Vectors that are specified in terms of rectangular coordinates may be manipulated just as readily as any other binomials if proper regard is taken of the x-axis and y-axis components; they may, indeed, be added, subtracted, multiplied, divided, squared, etc., although it will later be shown that another form of representation—the so-called polar form—is more desirable in operations that involve multiplication and division.

Addition and Subtraction. These operations are performed by adding or subtracting the x-axis components and the y-axis components independently. For example, if two currents at the junction in a circuit are

$\dot{I}_1 = a + ja'$ and $\dot{I}_2 = b - jb'$, their sum is $\dot{I}_r = (a + b) + j(a' - b')$. Their difference may, however, be $(\dot{I}_1 - \dot{I}_2) = (a - b) - j(a' + b')$ or $(\dot{I}_2 - \dot{I}_1) = (b - a) + j(-b' - a')$. The absolute value, in each case, will then be $I_r = \sqrt{x^2 + y^2}$ where x and y represent, respectively, the algebraic sums of the horizontal and vertical components. (A dot placed above a symbol indicates that it is a vector.)

EXAMPLE 3. Two currents at a junction in a circuit have the values $\dot{I}_1 = 5 - j8$ and $\dot{I}_2 = 7 + j3$. Determine the absolute values (*a*) of $(\dot{I}_1 + \dot{I}_2)$, (*b*) of $(\dot{I}_1 - \dot{I}_2)$.

Solution

(*a*) $(\dot{I}_1 + \dot{I}_2) = (5 + 7) + j(-8 + 3) = 12 + j(-5) = \sqrt{144 + 25}$
$= 13$ amp

(*b*) $(\dot{I}_1 - \dot{I}_2) = (5 - 7) + j(-8 - 3) = -2 + j(-11) = \sqrt{125}$
$= 11.18$ amp

Since the x and y components of a vector always indicate its direction, it should be clear that the horizontal and vertical components of the resultant vector may be used to determine the angle which it makes with the reference. Thus, in Example 3*a*, the 13-amp vector is represented by a horizontal component of 12 amp and a vertical component of -5 amp; this resultant, therefore, makes a *negative angle*—below the horizontal in the fourth quadrant—with the reference, and its value is $\tan^{-1}(-5)/12 = 22°37'$. In Example 3*b*, the 11.18-amp vector is represented by a horizontal component of -2 amp and a vertical component of -11 amp; this resultant, therefore, makes a *negative angle*—in the third quadrant—with the reference, and its value is $\tan^{-1}(-11)/(-2) = 79°42'$. The complete answers to Example 3 are then $13\underline{/-22°37'}$ amp and $11.18\underline{/180 + 79°42'} = 11.18\underline{/+259°42'}$ amp; the minus sign before the angle means that the vector is rotated clockwise into the fourth quadrant, and the plus sign before the angle indicates that the vector is rotated counterclockwise into the third quadrant. Figure 141 illustrates the vector-diagram solution of Example 3.

Multiplication. In the solution of a-c circuits it is frequently necessary to multiply impedances, currents, voltages, or their combinations. This may be accomplished as with any binomials, with the further understanding that the symbols $+j^2$ and $-j^2$ automatically become -1 and $+1$, respectively. Thus, when vector $\dot{A} = a + ja'$ is multiplied by vector $\dot{B} = b + jb'$, the result is

$$\dot{A} \times \dot{B} = (a + ja')(b + jb') = (ab + j^2a'b') + j(ab' + a'b)$$
$$= (ab - a'b') + j(ab' + a'b)$$

EXAMPLE 4. Find the product of the two vectors $\dot{E} = 96 + j72$ and $\dot{I} = 12 + j5$.

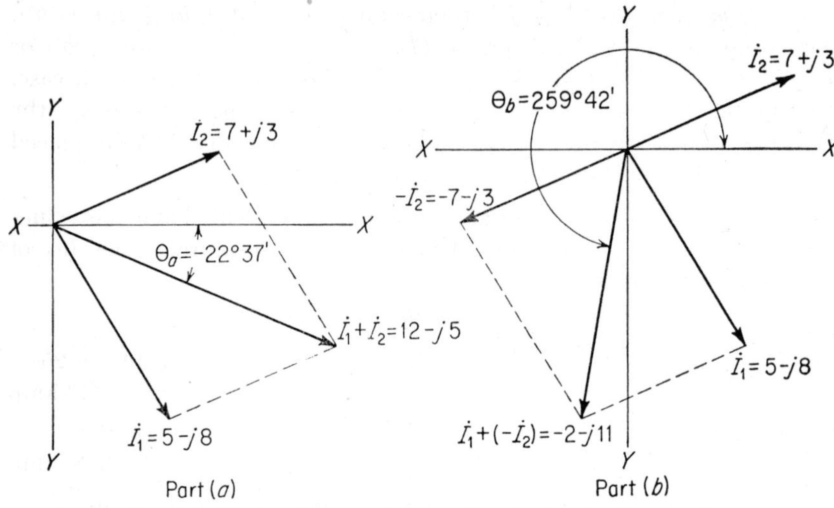

FIG. 141. Vector diagrams showing the solution for Example 3.

Solution

$$\begin{aligned}\dot{E} \times \dot{I} &= (96 + j72)(12 + j5) \\ &= (96 \times 12) - (72 \times 5) + j[(96 \times 5) + (72 \times 12)] \\ &= 792 + j1{,}344 = 1{,}560\underline{/59.5°}\end{aligned}$$

EXAMPLE 5. Find the product of the two vectors $\dot{Z}_1 = 4 + j3$ and $\dot{Z}_2 = 5 - j2$.

Solution

$$\begin{aligned}\dot{Z}_1 \times \dot{Z}_2 = (4 + j3)(5 - j2) = (20 + 6) + j(-8 + 15) &= 26 + j7 \\ &= 26.9\underline{/15.1°}\end{aligned}$$

Division. When two vectors are specified in rectangular coordinates and one of them is to be divided by the other it is first necessary to rationalize the equation, i.e., relieve the denominator of its j term, by multiplying numerator and denominator by the latter's conjugate; when this is done, the denominator becomes a simple number by which the numerator is readily divided. To illustrate, let vector $\dot{A} = a + ja'$ be divided by vector $\dot{B} = b + jb'$. Thus

$$\frac{\dot{A}}{\dot{B}} = \frac{a + ja'}{b + jb'} \times \frac{b - jb'}{b - jb'} = \frac{(ab + a'b') + j(a'b - b'a)}{b^2 + (b')^2}$$

which equation is readily solved.

EXAMPLE 6. Divide the vector voltage $\dot{E} = 75 - j100$ by the impedance expressed as a vector $\dot{Z} = 40 - j30$.

Solution

$$\dot{I} = \frac{\dot{E}}{\dot{Z}} = \frac{75 - j100}{40 - j30} \times \frac{40 + j30}{40 + j30} = \frac{(3{,}000 + 3{,}000) + j(2{,}250 - 4{,}000)}{1{,}600 + 900}$$

$$= \frac{6{,}000 - j1{,}750}{2{,}500} = 2.4 - j0.7 = 2.5\underline{/-16.3°}$$

Vectors Expressed in Polar Notation. The final results given in Examples 4, 5, and 6 are expressed in the *polar form;* these specify the vectors in terms of their *absolute values,* i.e., magnitudes, and the angles they make with the positive horizontal reference. Figure 142 illustrates

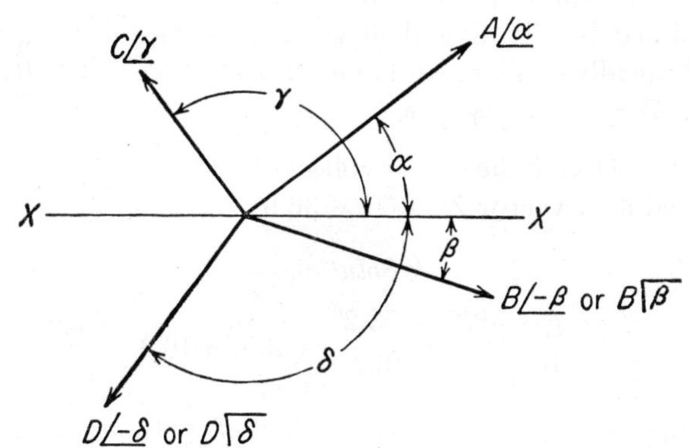

FIG. 142. Diagram illustrating the polar form of vector notation.

four vectors specified in the polar notation. Observe that an angle measured in a counterclockwise direction from the reference is indicated by a symbol as $\underline{/\alpha}$ or $\underline{/\gamma}$, while an angle measured in a clockwise direction from the reference may be represented by such symbols as $\underline{/-\beta}$, $\overline{\backslash\beta}$, $\underline{/-\delta}$, or $\overline{\backslash\delta}$.

The polar form of vector notation is extremely convenient in mathematical operations that involve multiplication, division, reciprocals, and raising quantities to powers; it also lends itself to logarithmic calculations. Vectors in polar form cannot be added or subtracted directly; to obtain their sum or difference they must first be converted to the rectangular form.

Multiplication. The product of two vectors that are given in the polar form is obtained by multiplying their absolute values and adding the angles algebraically. Thus $(A\underline{/\alpha})(B\underline{/\beta}) = A \times B\underline{/\alpha + \beta}$, and $(C\underline{/\gamma})(D\underline{/-\delta}) = C \times D\underline{/\gamma - \delta}$.

EXAMPLE 7. Find the product of the two vectors $\dot{E} = 120\underline{/36.9°}$ and $\dot{I} = 13\underline{/22.6°}$.

Solution

$$\dot{E} \times \dot{I} = (120\underline{/36.9^\circ})(13\underline{/22.6^\circ}) = 1{,}560\underline{/59.5^\circ}$$

EXAMPLE 8. Find the product of the two vectors $\dot{Z}_1 = 5\underline{/36.9^\circ}$ and $\dot{Z}_2 = 5.38\underline{/-21.8^\circ}$.

Solution

$$\dot{Z}_1 \times \dot{Z}_2 = (5\underline{/36.9^\circ})(5.38\underline{/-21.8^\circ}) = 26.9\underline{/15.1^\circ}$$

The foregoing two examples are actually Examples 4 and 5 resolved after the rectangular vectors were converted to the polar form.

Division. The quotient of two vectors that are given in the polar form is obtained by dividing their absolute values and subtracting the angles algebraically. Thus we have $(A\underline{/\alpha})/(B\underline{/\beta}) = (A/B)\underline{/\alpha - \beta}$ and $(C\underline{/\gamma})/(D\underline{/-\delta}) = (C/D)\underline{/\gamma + \delta}$.

EXAMPLE 9. Divide the vector voltage $\dot{E} = 125\underline{/-53.2^\circ}$ by the impedance expressed as a vector $\dot{Z} = 50\underline{/-36.9^\circ}$.

Solution

$$\frac{\dot{E}}{\dot{I}} = \frac{125\underline{/-53.2^\circ}}{50\underline{/-36.9^\circ}} = 2.5\underline{/-16.3^\circ}$$

This example is a solution of Example 6 after the rectangular vectors were converted to the polar form.

Equivalent Impedance of Parallel Circuits. The mathematical principles of vectors, when the latter are expressed in rectangular and polar form, will now be applied to an analysis of various kinds of a-c circuits.

Consider Fig. 137 which shows three basic types of load units Z_A, Z_B, and Z_C connected to a source of emf E; the individual branch currents are therefore I_A, I_B, and I_C, and the resulting total current is I_t. Note that the symbols no longer appear with *dots* as in the previous two sections; this simplification is made for convenience, since it is *always implied* that all quantities are *vectors* and must be treated in accordance with the rules given for rectangular and/or polar notation. Representing the equivalent impedance of the circuit by Z_{eq}, the total current is

$$I_t = \frac{E}{Z_{eq}} = \frac{E}{Z_A} + \frac{E}{Z_B} + \frac{E}{Z_C} = \left(\frac{1}{Z_A} + \frac{1}{Z_B} + \frac{1}{Z_C}\right)$$

from which

$$Z_{eq} = \frac{1}{(1/Z_A) + (1/Z_B) + (1/Z_C)} \tag{105}$$

If only two impedances are connected in parallel (and this is frequently the case),

$$Z_{eq} = \frac{Z_A \times Z_B}{Z_A + Z_B} \tag{106}$$

Note that these equations are similar to those given for resistors in parallel [Eqs. (21) and (22)].

EXAMPLE 10. Calculate the equivalent impedance of a three-branch parallel circuit in which the following individual values are given: $Z_1 = 11.5\underline{/0°}$, $Z_2 = 4.6\underline{/51.7°}$, $Z_3 = 7.67\underline{/-36.9°}$.

Solution

Before starting, it is well to note that Z_1, Z_2, and Z_3 are, respectively, unity-power-factor, lagging-power-factor, and leading-power-factor devices. They are, in fact, the impedances in Examples 1 and 2, the equivalent impedance of which will be checked by the use of Eq. (105).

$$Z_{eq} = \frac{1}{(1/11.5\underline{/0°}) + (1/4.6\underline{/51.7°}) + (1/7.67\underline{/-36.9°})}$$

$$= \frac{1}{0.087 + 0.2174\underline{/-51.7°} + 0.1304\underline{/36.9°}}$$

$$= \frac{1}{(0.087) + (0.1348 - j0.1705) + (0.1043 + j0.0782)}$$

$$= \frac{1}{0.3261 - j0.0923} = \frac{1}{0.338\underline{/-15.4°}} = 2.96\underline{/15.4°}$$

$$\cos \Theta = \cos 15.4° = 0.964$$

EXAMPLE 11. Calculate the equivalent impedance of two parallel-connected units, given that $Z_1 = 20\underline{/30°}$ and $Z_2 = 28.28\underline{/-45°}$.

Solution

$$Z_{eq} = \frac{(20\underline{/30°}) \times (28.28\underline{/-45°})}{(20\underline{/30°}) + (28.28\underline{/-45°})} = \frac{565.6\underline{/-15°}}{(17.3 + j10) + (20 - j20)}$$

$$= \frac{565.6\underline{/-15°}}{37.3 - j10} = \frac{565.6\underline{/-15°}}{38.5\underline{/-15°}} = 14.7\underline{/0°} \quad \text{(a pure resistance)}$$

Power in Parallel Circuits. It was previously shown [Eq. (103)] that the total power in a parallel circuit is equal to the arithmetical sum of the powers in the individual branches. This rule does, in fact, apply to *any* circuit, however complex, if it is interpreted to mean that the total power is equal to the arithmetical sum of the powers in every portion of the circuit. Several methods may be used to calculate the number of watts in any particular section, and the one that is used will generally depend upon the available information. These are (1) by applying the expression $EI \cos \Theta$, where E, I, and $\cos \Theta$ are, respectively, the voltage across, the current in, and the power factor of the section; (2) by applying the expression I^2R, where I is the current in, and R is the resistance of, the section; (3) by applying the expression E_R^2/R, where E_R is the voltage drop across, and R is the resistance of, the resistor.

When the voltage and current are specified in the polar form, it is generally desirable to use the $EI \cos \Theta$ method, prior to which the phase displacement between E and I must be determined. For example, if the voltage and current values are given as $E\underline{/\alpha}$ and $I\underline{/\beta}$, the power-factor angle will be $(\alpha - \beta)$, and the power will be

$$P = EI \cos (\alpha - \beta)$$

A good procedure to follow when the voltage and current are expressed in rectangular coordinates is to multiply the voltage by the *conjugate of the current;* the latter, as previously explained, is merely the current equation with the sign of the j term reversed. The product of E and I then yields an answer in the rectangular form, *the first term* of which *is the power in watts,* while *the second term*—the j term—*gives the reactive volt-amperes in vars.* Thus, if $E = (e + je')$ and $I = (i + ji')$,

$$(e + je')(i - ji') = (ei + e'i') + j(e'i - ei') \qquad \text{va}$$

where $P = (ei + e'i')$ watts and R-va $= (e'i - ei')$ vars. Since it is possible for the last term to be positive *or* negative it is interpreted as follows: a positive answer indicates inductive vars; a negative answer implies capacitive vars.

EXAMPLE 12. A voltage $E = 120\underline{/10°}$ is impressed across a load consisting of two paths in parallel. Branch 1 is an R-L circuit that takes a current $I_1 = 15\underline{/-50°}$, and branch 2 is an R-C circuit whose current is $I_2 = 8\underline{/40°}$. Calculate the power delivered to the load.

Solution

The current in branch 1 *lags behind* the common impressed voltage by $(10 + 50) = 60°$; the current in branch 2 *leads* the common voltage by $(40 - 10) = 30°$. Therefore

$$P_t = (120 \times 15 \times \cos 60°) + (120 \times 8 \times \cos 30°) = 1{,}730 \text{ watts}$$

EXAMPLE 13. The following information is given in connection with a load consisting of two parallel paths connected to a source of emf: $E = 100 - j75$, $I_1 = 9 - j12$, $I_2 = 17.3 + j10$. Calculate the total power and the reactive volt-amperes taken by the circuit.

Solution

Branch 1:

$$(100 - j75)(9 + j12) = (900 + 900) + j(1{,}200 - 675) \text{ va}$$
$$= 1{,}800 + j525$$

Therefore $P_1 = 1{,}800$ watts, and $(\text{R-va})_1 = 525$ vars (inductive).

Branch 2:

$$(100 - j75)(17.3 - j10) = (1{,}730 - 750) + j(-1{,}000 - 1{,}300) \text{ va}$$
$$= 980 - j2{,}300$$

Therefore $P_2 = 980$ watts, and $(\text{R-va})_2 = 2{,}300$ vars (capacitive).

Hence $\quad \text{Total } P_t = 1{,}800 + 980 = 2{,}780$ watts

and

$$\text{Total } (\text{R-va})_t = 525 - 2{,}300 = -1{,}775 \text{ vars (capacitive)}$$

EXAMPLE 14. The impedances of the two parallel paths of a load circuit are $Z_1 = (8 + j2.33)$ and $Z_2 = (2.45 - j5.75)$. If the branch currents I_1 and I_2 are 15 and 20 amp, respectively, calculate the total power and reactive volt-amperes taken by the circuit.

Solution

This is the same circuit as that given in Example 13, but expressed in terms of impedances and currents. The results will be checked by the I^2R method.

Branch 1: $\quad P_1 = (15)^2 \times 8 = 1{,}800$ watts

$(\text{R-va})_1 = (15)^2 \times 2.33 = 525$ vars (inductive)

Branch 2: $\quad P_2 = (20)^2 \times 2.45 = 980$ watts

$(\text{R-va})_2 = (20)^2 \times 5.75 = 2{,}300$ vars (capacitive)

Hence $\quad \text{Total } P_t = 1{,}800 + 980 = 2{,}780$ watts

and

$$\text{Total } (\text{R-va})_t = 525 - 2{,}300 = -1{,}775 \text{ vars (capacitive)}$$

Admittance, Conductance, and Susceptance in Parallel-circuit Problems. Any series circuit containing resistance and reactance may be converted into an *equivalent* parallel circuit in which a resistance is in parallel with a reactance; the fact that the *parallel R-X* circuit is equivalent to the *series R-X* circuit implies that both will take the *same* current at the *same* power factor from the *same* voltage source.

Referring to the upper sketch of Fig. 143*a*, note that it represents a series *R-L* circuit connected to a voltage E; its current I will obviously

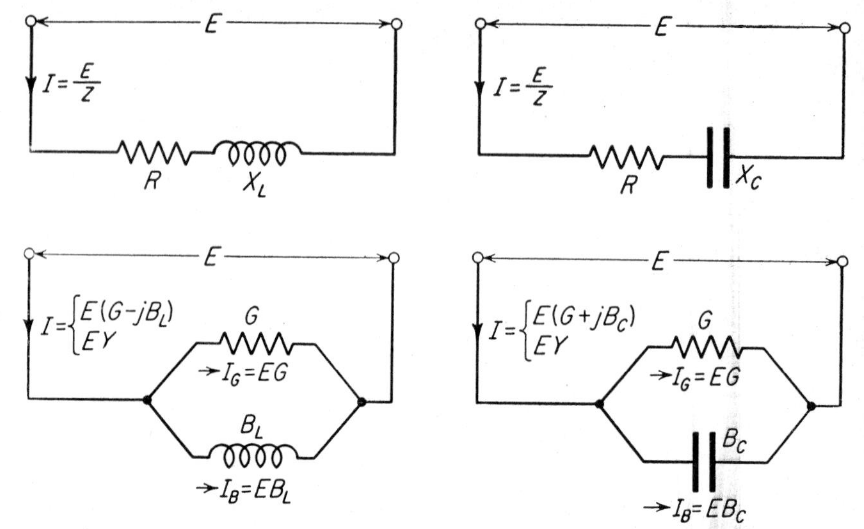

FIG. 143. Diagrams illustrating the conversion from series *R-L* and *R-C* circuits to parallel conductance-susceptance (*G-B*) circuits.

be E/Z. Since $Z = R + jX_L$ and $Z^2 = R^2 + X_L{}^2$, the rationalized current equation becomes

$$I = \frac{E}{R + jX_L} \times \frac{R - jX_L}{R - jX_L} = E\left[\left(\frac{R}{R^2 + X_L{}^2}\right) - j\left(\frac{X_L}{R^2 + X_L{}^2}\right)\right]$$

$$= E\left(\frac{R}{Z^2} - j\frac{X_L}{Z^2}\right)$$

Observe that the current consists of two components that are out of phase with each other by 90°. One of them, $E \times (R/Z^2)$, is in phase with the voltage E, and the other, $E \times (-jX_L/Z^2)$—because of the $-j$ term—*lags behind* the voltage by 90°. Writing the foregoing equation in a simpler form,

$$I = E(G - jB_L) = EY \qquad \text{for an inductive circuit}$$

Bear in mind that

$$\text{Conductance } G = \frac{R}{Z^2} \tag{107}$$

$$\text{Susceptance } B_L = \frac{-X_L}{Z^2} \qquad \text{(inductive circuit)} \tag{108}$$

$$\text{Admittance } Y = (G - jB_L) \qquad \text{(inductive circuit)} \tag{109}$$

The results of this analysis are translated into the lower sketch of Fig. 143*a*.

Referring next to the upper sketch of Fig. 143*b*, note that it represents a series *R-C* circuit connected to a voltage E; its current I, as before, is E/Z. Since $Z = R - jX_C$ and $Z^2 = R^2 + X_C^2$, the rationalized current equation becomes

$$I = \frac{E}{R - jX_C} \times \frac{R + jX_C}{R + jX_C} = E\left[\left(\frac{R}{R^2 + X_C^2}\right) + j\left(\frac{X_C}{R^2 + X_C^2}\right)\right]$$
$$= E\left(\frac{R}{Z^2} + j\frac{X_C}{Z^2}\right)$$

The current again consists of two components that are out of phase with each other by 90°. One of them, $E \times (R/Z^2)$, is in phase with the voltage E, and the other, $E \times (jX_C/Z^2)$—because of the $+j$ term—*leads* the voltage by 90°. Writing the foregoing equation in a simpler form,

$$I = E(G + jB_C) = EY \qquad \text{for a capacitive circuit}$$

In this equation,

$$\text{Conductance } G = \frac{R}{Z^2} \tag{107}$$

$$\text{Susceptance } B_C = +\frac{X_C}{Z^2} \qquad \text{(capacitive circuit)} \tag{110}$$

$$\text{Admittance } Y = (G + jB_C) \qquad \text{(capacitive circuit)} \tag{111}$$

The results of this analysis are translated into the lower sketch of Fig. 143*b*.

The important advantages of this system of notation are often reflected in the simplification that results when complex circuits are analyzed, or in the solution of some types of parallel and related problems.

The circuits of Fig. 143*a* and *b* are combined into the composite parallel circuit of Fig. 144. Note how systematically the change is made from a complex *RL-RC* parallel circuit into one in which a resistor, represented

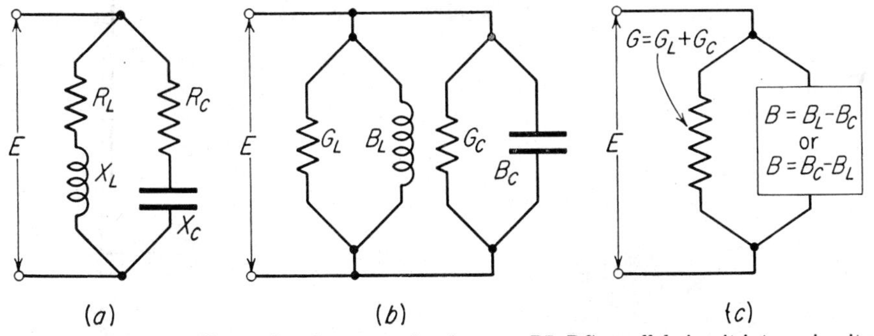

Fig. 144. Diagrams illustrating the conversion from an *RL-RC* parallel circuit into a circuit represented by a parallel conductance-susceptance combination.

by its reciprocal G, is connected in parallel with a reactance, represented by its reciprocal B. An example will now be given to illustrate the procedure in solving a typical problem.

EXAMPLE 15. The following data are given in connection with Fig. 144*a*: $E = 120$ volts, $R_L = 2.4$ ohms, $X_L = 3.2$ ohms, $R_C = 4$ ohms, $X_C = 3$ ohms. Calculate (*a*) the conductance and susceptance of each branch of Fig. 144*b*; (*b*) the total conductance, susceptance, and admittance in Fig. 144*c*; (*c*) the total current.

Solution

(*a*)
$$G_L = \frac{2.4}{(2.4)^2 + (3.2)^2} = 0.15 \text{ mho}$$
$$B_L = \frac{3.2}{16} = 0.2 \text{ mho}$$
$$G_C = \frac{4}{(4)^2 + (3)^2} = 0.16 \text{ mho}$$
$$B_C = \frac{3}{25} = 0.12 \text{ mho}$$

(*b*)
$$G = 0.15 + 0.16 = 0.31 \text{ mho}$$
$$B = 0.2 - 0.12 = 0.08 \text{ mho (inductive)}$$
$$Y = (0.31 - j0.08) \text{ mho}$$

(*c*)
$$I = 120(G - jb)$$
$$I = 120(0.31 - j0.08) = (37.2 - j9.6)$$
$$I = \sqrt{(37.6)^2 + (9.6)^2} = 38.4 \text{ amp}$$

Series-Parallel Circuits. The analysis of a-c circuits and the solution of problems involving combinations of units arranged in series and parallel follow the same principles previously discussed; except for the use of complex quantities they are, in fact, handled in essentially the same way as are simple resistances in d-c circuits.

Consider Fig. 145, which illustrates a typical series-parallel circuit. A suggested procedure in solving such a network is (1) determine the equiva-

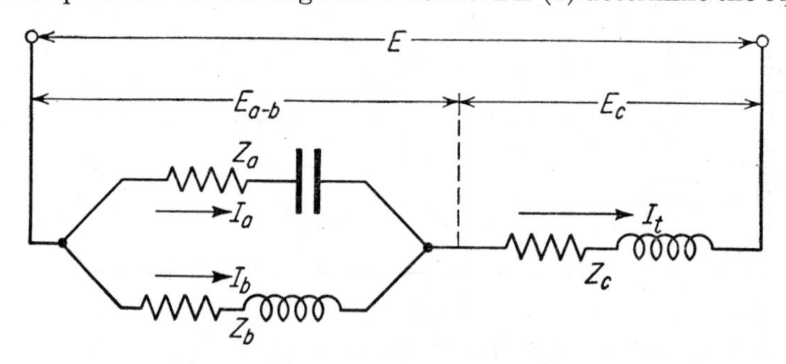

FIG. 145. A typical series-parallel circuit.

lent impedance of the parallel branches Z_a and Z_b; (2) find the total impedance of the circuit by adding the equivalent impedance of the parallel branches to the series branch Z_c; (3) calculate the total-circuit current; (4) find the current in each of the parallel branches; (5) evaluate the power in each part of the circuit, and the total power; (6) determine the circuit power factor. Other values, such as voltage drops, reactive volt-amperes, and individual power factors may also be found if this seems desirable. The foregoing may be stated in equation form as follows:

$$(1) \qquad Z_{ab} = \frac{Z_a \times Z_b}{Z_a + Z_b}$$

$$(2) \qquad Z_{eq} = Z_{ab} + Z_c$$

$$(3) \qquad I_t = \frac{E}{Z_{eq}}$$

$$(4) \qquad I_a = \frac{I_t \times Z_{ab}}{Z_a} \qquad I_b = \frac{I_t \times Z_{ab}}{Z_b}$$

$$(5) \quad P_a = I_a{}^2R_a \qquad P_b = I_b{}^2R_b \qquad P_c = I_t{}^2R_c \qquad P_t = P_a + P_b + P_c$$

$$(6) \qquad \text{PF} = \frac{P_t}{EI_t}$$

EXAMPLE 16. The following information is given in connection with the series-parallel circuit of Fig. 145: $Z_a = (6 - j7.5) = 9.6\underline{/-51.3°}$; $Z_b = (8 + j4) = 8.93\underline{/26.6°}$; $Z_c = (2.8 + j6.1) = 6.7\underline{/65.3°}$; $E = 120\underline{/0°}$. Calculate (*a*) the equivalent impedance of the entire circuit Z_{eq}; (*b*) the total current I_t and currents in the parallel branches I_a and I_b; (*c*) the power taken by each impedance, and the total power; (*d*) the over-all power factor of the circuit; (*e*) the voltage drops across the parallel branch E_{ab} and across the series branch E_c.

Solution

$$(a) \quad Z_{ab} = \frac{(6 - j7.5) \times (8 + j4)}{(6 - j7.5) + (8 + j4)} = \frac{78 - j36}{14 - j3.5} \times \frac{14 + j3.5}{14 + j3.5}$$

$$= \frac{1{,}218 - j231}{208} = 5.86 - j1.1 = 5.96\underline{/-10.6°} \text{ ohms}$$

$$Z_{eq} = (5.86 - j1.1) + (2.8 + j6.1) = 8.66 + j5.0 = 10\underline{/30°} \text{ ohms}$$

$$(b) \quad I_t = \frac{120}{10\underline{/30°}} = 12\underline{/-30°} \text{ amp}$$

$$I_a = \frac{(12\underline{/-30°})(5.96\underline{/-10.6°})}{9.6\underline{/-51.3°}} = 7.45\underline{/10.7°} \text{ amp}$$

$$I_b = \frac{(12\underline{/-30°})(5.96\underline{/-10.6°})}{8.93\underline{/26.6°}} = 8\underline{/-67.2°} \text{ amp}$$

(c) $P_a = (7.45)^2 \times 6 = 333$ watts
$P_b = (8)^2 \times 8 = 512$ watts
$P_c = (12)^2 \times 2.8 = 403$ watts
$P_t = 333 + 512 + 403 = 1{,}248$ watts

(d) $\text{PF} = \dfrac{1{,}248}{120 \times 12} = 0.866$ lagging

Also

$$\text{PF} = \frac{R_{eq}}{Z_{eq}} = \frac{8.66}{10} = 0.866 \text{ lagging}$$

(e) $E_{ab} = I_t Z_{ab} = (12\underline{/-30°})(5.96\underline{/-10.6°}) = 71.5\underline{/-40.6°}$
$E_c = I_t Z_c = (12\underline{/-30°})(6.7\underline{/65.3°}) = 80.4\underline{/35.3°}$

A complete vector diagram for the example is given in Fig. 146.

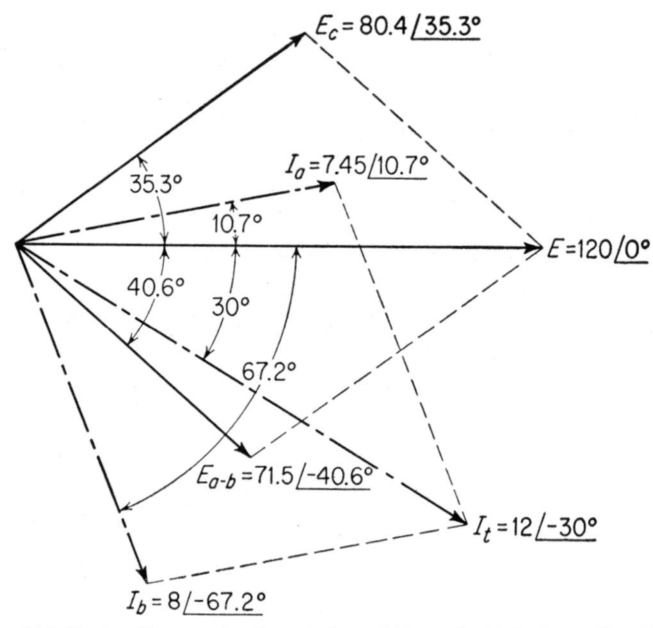

Fig. 146. Vector diagram for the solution of Example 16 (refer to Fig. 145).

Questions

1. What three general types of circuit may be connected in parallel?
2. Upon what factors does the over-all power factor of a parallel circuit depend?
3. Upon what trigonometric function of the power-factor angle does the horizontal component of the current depend? the vertical component of the current?
4. What is the total current in a parallel circuit in terms of the horizontal and vertical components?
5. Explain how the total power is determined in a parallel circuit.

6. Explain how the total reactive volt-amperes is determined in a parallel circuit.
7. How is a vector properly expressed in rectangular coordinates?
8. Using letters to express a vector in general terms and in rectangular coordinates, how should it be written for the first quadrant? the second quadrant? the third quadrant? the fourth quadrant?
9. What is the significance of the j term as an operator? Explain carefully.
10. Explain why the j term has the mathematical value of $\sqrt{-1}$. Why is it an imaginary quantity?
11. Does the j term before a quantity alter the physical significance of that quantity? Explain carefully.
12. How are vectors added and subtracted when expressed in rectangular form? Give several examples to illustrate your answers.
13. What is meant by a *positive angle?* a *negative angle?*
14. How are vectors multiplied when expressed in rectangular form? Give an example to illustrate your answer.
15. When dividing one vector by another, both being expressed in rectangular form, why is it necessary to multiply numerator and denominator by the *conjugate* of the denominator? Give an example to illustrate your answer.
16. Express a vector in general terms and in polar form for the first quadrant, for the second quadrant, for the third quadrant, and for the fourth quadrant.
17. How are vectors multiplied and divided when expressed in polar form? Give examples to illustrate your answers.
18. Explain how the reciprocal of a vector may be determined when it is expressed in rectangular form and in polar form.
19. Explain how to square a vector when it is expressed in polar form.
20. In equation form, what is the equivalent impedance of a number of impedances when they are connected in parallel? What is the equation when *two* impedances are connected in parallel?
21. How does a calculation for the equivalent impedance of a parallel circuit differ from a similar calculation for the equivalent resistance in a d-c circuit?
22. List three methods that may be used to determine the total power in a parallel circuit. Indicate when each should be used.
23. When the power is determined by multiplying the voltage by the conjugate of the current, both in rectangular form, what does a resulting $+j$ term signify? What does a $-j$ term signify?
24. Define *conductance, susceptance, admittance.*
25. What is the sign of the susceptance for an inductive circuit? A capacitive circuit?
26. List the steps, in some logical sequence, that should be followed when solving a series-parallel circuit.

Problems

1. A unity power-factor load of 1,794 watts is connected in parallel with a load of 1,656 watts operating at a lagging power factor of 0.6. If the line voltage is 115, calculate (*a*) the current in each load, (*b*) the total current, (*c*) the total power, (*d*) the over-all power factor, (*e*) the reactive volt-amperes.
2. An additional load of 2,108 watts is connected in parallel with those of Prob. 1. If the over-all power factor of the system is unity, calculate (*a*) the power factor of the added load, (*b*) the total current and power.
3. The following information is given in connection with three loads connected to a 220-volt source: load A = 12 amp at unity power factor; load B is 40 amp at a power factor of 0.5 lagging; load C is 20 amp at a leading power factor of 0.9.

Calculate (*a*) the total current, (*b*) the total power, (*c*) the reactive volt-amperes, (*d*) the over-all power factor.

4. Using the results obtained in Prob. 3, calculate the equivalent impedance, resistance, and reactance of the system of loads.

5. The currents at the junction point in a circuit have the values $I_1 = (16 - j4)$ and $(8 + j22)$. Calculate (*a*) $(I_1 + I_2)$, (*b*) $(I_1 - I_2)$, and (*c*) $(I_2 - I_1)$.

6. Multiply the vectors $(112 + j40)$ and $(9 - j16)$.

7. Divide the quantity $(176 - j132)$ by the vector $(12 + j16)$.

8. Find the reciprocal of $(1.5 + j2.5)$.

9. Convert the quantities in Prob. 6 to the polar form, multiply them, and reconvert the product to the rectangular form.

10. Convert the quantities in Prob. 7 to the polar form, divide the first quantity by the second, and reconvert the quotient to the rectangular form.

11. Square the quantities $15/\underline{25^\circ}$, $8/\underline{-34^\circ}$, $16/\underline{90^\circ}$.

12. Compute $(9/\underline{45^\circ})(26/\underline{-20^\circ})/3/\underline{-52^\circ}$.

13. Calculate the equivalent impedance of a circuit in which a coil of wire having a value of $5/\underline{53.2^\circ}$ ohms is connected parallel with a capacitive reactance of 6.25 ohms.

14. A coil of wire having a value of $(5 + j8)$ ohms is connected in series with a capacitive reactance X_C, and this series combination is then connected in parallel with a resistor R. If the equivalent impedance of the circuit is $4/\underline{0^\circ}$ ohms, calculate the values of X_C and R.

15. Calculate the equivalent impedance of a three-branch parallel network given the following particulars: $Z_1 = 20/\underline{0^\circ}$, $Z_2 = 47/\underline{45^\circ}$, $Z_3 = 25/\underline{-60^\circ}$.

16. Two loads are connected in parallel to a source of emf whose voltage is $(110 + j63.5)$. If the branch currents are $I_1 = (8 - j8)$ and $I_2 = (7.5 + j10)$, calculate the total power and the reactive volt-amperes taken by the circuit.

17. Compute the total power and reactive volt-amperes if the currents in Prob. 16 are $I_1 = (8 + j8)$ and $I_2 = (7.5 - j10)$.

18. Calculate the circuit power factors for Probs. 16 and 17.

19. The following information is given in connection with a load circuit consisting of two parallel branches: $Z_1 = 4.8/\underline{25^\circ}$, $Z_2 = 3.75/\underline{-72^\circ}$, $I_1 = 50$ amp, $I_2 = 64$ amp. Calculate the total power and the reactive volt-amperes taken by the circuit.

20. An impedance equal to $4.4/\underline{60^\circ}$ is connected across a 220-volt source. What should be the value of a second impedance, in parallel with the first, if the total power delivered to the circuit is to be 16.5 kw and the over-all power factor is to be unity?

21. If a pure resistor is connected in parallel with the original impedance of Prob. 20, what should be its ohmic value if the total power delivered to the circuit is to be 16.5 kw? What will be the over-all power factor of the circuit under this condition?

22. Calculate the conductance, susceptance, and admittance of an impedance that is equal to $Z = (3.6 + j4.8)$ ohms.

23. What value of capacitive reactance, connected in parallel with the impedance of Prob. 22, will make the circuit power factor unity?

24. An inductive reactance $Z_L = (11.5 + j10)$ ohms is connected in parallel with a capacitive reactance $Z_C = (8 - j20)$ ohms. Calculate (*a*) the conductance and susceptance of each branch; (*b*) the total conductance, susceptance, and admittance of the circuit; (*c*) the current in each branch, and the total current and power factor, if the impressed emf is 120 volts.

25. The constants in the series-parallel circuit of Fig. 145 have the following values: $Z_a = (20 - j50)$, $Z_b = (10 + j10)$, $Z_c = (9.8 + j5.7)$, $E = 239$. Calculate (*a*) the total impedance of the circuit, (*b*) the total current, (*c*) the over-all power factor and power.

26. An inductive reactance of 8 ohms is connected in parallel with a capacitive reactance of 18 ohms; this combination is then connected in series with a variable resistance. For what value of resistance will the power factor be 0.5, and what current and power will the circuit take if the impressed emf is 118 volts?

CHAPTER 13

RESONANCE IN SERIES AND PARALLEL CIRCUITS

General Aspects of Resonant Circuits. Circuits made up of resistors, inductors, and capacitors are said to be in resonance when the total current is in phase with the impressed voltage; under this condition the resultant reactance will be zero, the circuit will behave like a pure resistance, and the over-all power factor will be unity. Two fundamental properties of inductive reactance X_L and capacitive reactance X_C make possible the existence of resonance; these are (1) the directly opposing actions of X_L and X_C in the sense that they tend to take power-factor currents that are, respectively, zero lagging and zero leading; and (2) the fact that frequency changes affect the values of X_L and X_C in different ways, with the former being directly proportional to f and the latter inversely proportional to f.

Remembering that the average power per cycle delivered to an inductor or a capacitor is zero (see Figs. 128 and 129), it should be understood that equal amounts of energy are interchanged periodically between L and C in a resonant circuit, and that the source of power is responsible only for energy dissipated in the resistance. This unique condition results because a discharging capacitor always gives up energy at exactly the rate required by an inductor, and the energy stored in an inductor is used to charge a capacitor at the proper rate when the electromagnetic field collapses. A circuit in resonance, therefore, stores a constant amount of energy.

Figure 147 shows two simple circuits under conditions of resonance. In the series circuit (Fig. 147*a*) note that $X_L = X_C$, under which condition the voltage drops across the inductor and capacitor, E_L and E_C, are equal; since the circuit behaves like a pure resistance, $E_R = E$ and $I = E/R$. In the parallel circuit (Fig. 147*b*) observe that the vertical components of the current in the R-L and R-C branches, i.e., the *susceptance currents* EB_L and EB_C, are equal and opposite; here again the circuit power factor is unity, which implies that the total current, in phase with the impressed voltage, is the sum of *conductance currents* EG_L and EG_C. Vector diagrams, shown below the two circuit sketches, illustrate these important relationships.

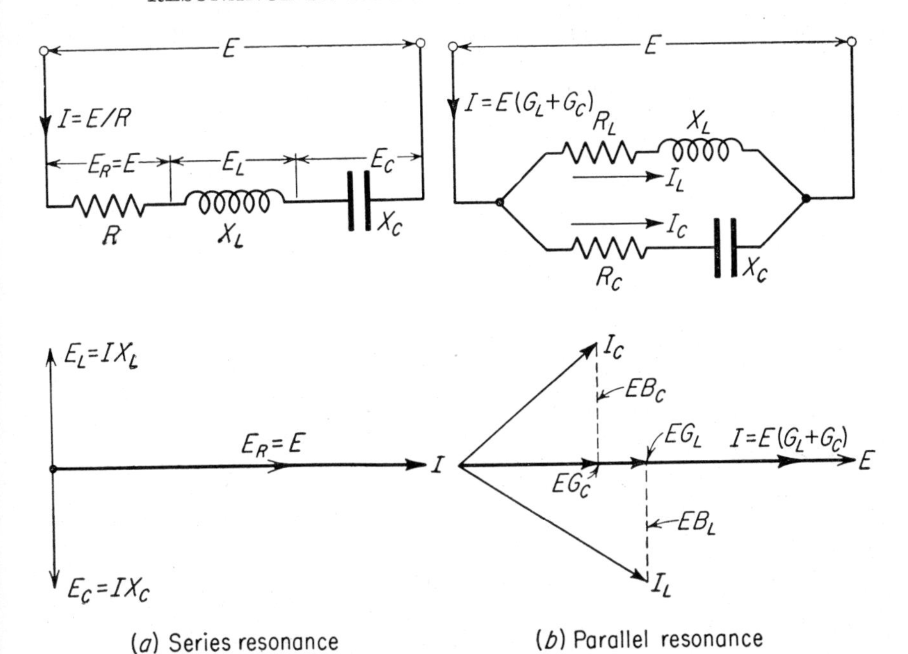

FIG. 147. Diagrams illustrating resonance conditions existing in series- and parallel-resonance circuits.

The Series Resonance Circuit. To attain resonance three basic methods may be used to alter the impedance of a series *R-L-C* circuit; these are (1) changing the frequency, (2) changing the inductance, and (3) changing the capacitance. Moreover, assuming a constant value of resistance, the circuit will be in resonance and the current will be equal to E/R (1) at a particular frequency f if the inductance L and the capacitance C are fixed, (2) at a particular value of L if f and C are fixed, and (3) at a particular value of C if f and L are fixed.

Frequency Variation in Series R-L-C Circuits. Since resonance in a series circuit always implies that the voltage drops across the inductor and capacitor are equal, i.e., $E_L = E_C$, it follows that $IX_L = IX_C$; this means that X_L must equal X_C. Equating the latter in terms of circuit conditions, where $X_L = 2\pi fL$ and $X_C = 10^6/2\pi fC$, the resonant frequency becomes

$$f_r = \frac{10^3}{2\pi\sqrt{LC}} \tag{112}$$

where L and C are expressed in *henrys* and *microfarads*, respectively. The circuit impedance being equal to the resistance R, a minimum value, the current will be a maximum and equal to E/R. Thus, the voltage drop across the resistor will be

$$E_R = \frac{E}{R} \times R = E$$

the voltage drop across the inductor will be

$$E_L = \frac{E}{R} \times 2\pi f_r L = \frac{E}{R} \times 2\pi L \times \frac{10^3}{2\pi \sqrt{LC}} = \frac{E \times 10^3}{R} \sqrt{\frac{L}{C}}$$

and the voltage drop across the capacitor will be

$$E_C = \frac{E}{R} \times \frac{10^6}{2\pi f_r C} = \frac{E \times 10^6}{R \times 2\pi C} \times \frac{2\pi \sqrt{LC}}{10^3} = \frac{E \times 10^3}{R} \sqrt{\frac{L}{C}}$$

A graphical representation of the relationship between the circuit current I and the frequency f is shown in Fig. 148 for constant values of L

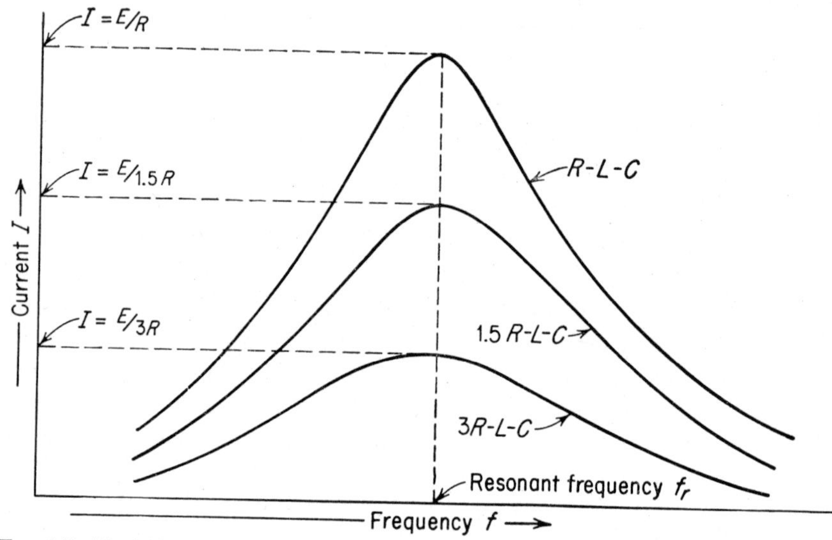

FIG. 148. Typical curves illustrating current vs. frequency relationships in series R-L-C circuits.

and C and different resistances. Note that the current (1) is a maximum at the resonant frequency, (2) changes most rapidly in the region of the resonant frequency, (3) is affected very little by frequency changes that are somewhat removed to either side of the resonant frequency, and (4) varies most sharply for the lowest resistance. In connection with the latter point, a series circuit is said to possess *sharp tuning* characteristics when the resistance is comparatively low and *broad tuning* characteristics when the resistance is comparatively high.

EXAMPLE 1. A series circuit consists of a 30-ohm resistor, a 0.104-henry inductor, and a 40-μf capacitor. If a variable-frequency 120-volt source is connected across its terminals, (*a*) calculate the resonant frequency. For the condition of resonance, determine (*b*) the circuit current and power; (*c*) the voltage drops across the resistor, the inductor, and the capacitor.

Solution

(*a*) $$f_r = \frac{10^3}{2\pi\sqrt{LC}} = \frac{10^3}{2\pi\sqrt{0.104 \times 40}} = \frac{10^3}{2\pi \times 2.04} = 78 \text{ cps}$$

(*b*) $$I = \frac{120}{30} = 4 \text{ amp}$$

$$P = 120 \times 4 = 480 \text{ watts}$$

(*c*) $$E_R = 120 \text{ volts}$$

$$E_L = \frac{E \times 10^3}{R}\sqrt{\frac{L}{C}} = \frac{120 \times 10^3}{30}\sqrt{\frac{0.104}{40}} = 204 \text{ volts}$$

Also

$$E_L = IX_L = 4 \times 2\pi \times 78 \times 0.104 = 204 \text{ volts}$$

and $$E_C = IX_C = 4 \times \frac{10^3}{2\pi \times 78 \times 40} = 204 \text{ volts}$$

An inspection of Eq. (112) indicates that any constant product of L and C will cause a series R-L-C circuit to be resonant at a definite frequency; this means, of course, that a constant-frequency source can be the frequency of resonance for an infinite number of $L \times C$ combinations. Thus, in Example 1 where $L \times C = 0.104 \times 40 = 4.16$, an inductance of 0.052 henry and a capacitance of 80 μf, or an inductance of 0.208 henry and a capacitance of 20 μf, will make the circuit resonant at 78 cps; moreover, the maximum current and power will remain unchanged although the voltage drops E_L and E_C will vary for different combinations of L and C.

EXAMPLE 2. Using values of $L = 0.416$ henry and $C = 10$ μf ($L \times C = 4.16$), recalculate the quantities of Example 1, assuming the resistance and impressed emf to remain unchanged.

Solution

(*a*) $$fr = \frac{10^3}{2\pi\sqrt{0.416 \times 10}} = 78 \text{ cps}$$

(*b*) $$I = \frac{120}{30} = 4 \text{ amp}$$

$$P = 120 \times 4 = 480 \text{ watts}$$

(*c*) $$E_R = 120 \text{ volts}$$

$$E_L = E_C = 4 \times 10^3\sqrt{\frac{0.416}{10}} = 816 \text{ volts}$$

Figure 149 illustrates graphically how the *sharpness of tuning* of a series circuit is affected by different ratios of L to C, the resistance and the products of L and C remaining unchanged. Note particularly that the current varies more abruptly in the region of the resonant frequency as the ratio of L to C increases. This condition results because the values of X_L and X_C are *both* increased as L is raised and C is lowered ($X_L = 2\pi fL$ and $X_C = 10^6/2\pi fC$). Designers of communication equipment take advantage of this special aspect of series R-L-C circuits to provide proper degrees of sharpness of tuning.

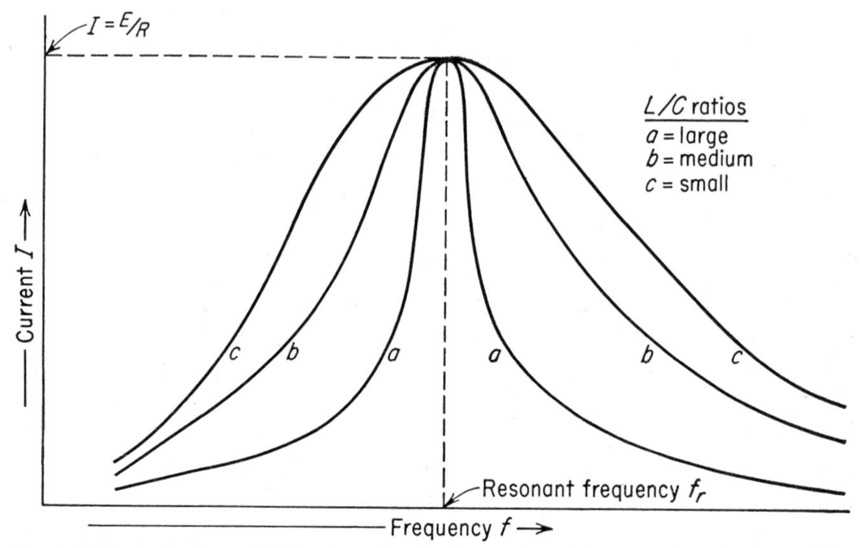

FIG. 149. Typical curves showing how the sharpness of tuning of a series R-L-C circuit is affected by different ratios and constant products of L and C.

Although the voltage drops across the inductor and the capacitor are equal at resonance (see Fig. 147*a*) they do *not* have their *maximum* values at the resonant frequency; as Fig. 150 shows, E_C and E_L do, in fact, reach their maximums, respectively, before and after the current becomes E/R. This *voltage drop* vs. *frequency* response comes about because the current-frequency curve is generally flat in the region of resonance. Thus, just *before* the current reaches its maximum E/R value at f_r it is passing through a constant stage while X_C is steadily diminishing; this means that IX_C will start dropping from its maximum value as soon as the current curve begins to flatten. Conversely, just *after* the current reaches its maximum value at f_r it is still changing very little, while X_L is steadily rising; this means that IX_L will continue to increase until the current starts falling. The extent to which the maximum values of E_C and E_L are separated to either side of the point of resonance will depend upon sharpness of tuning.

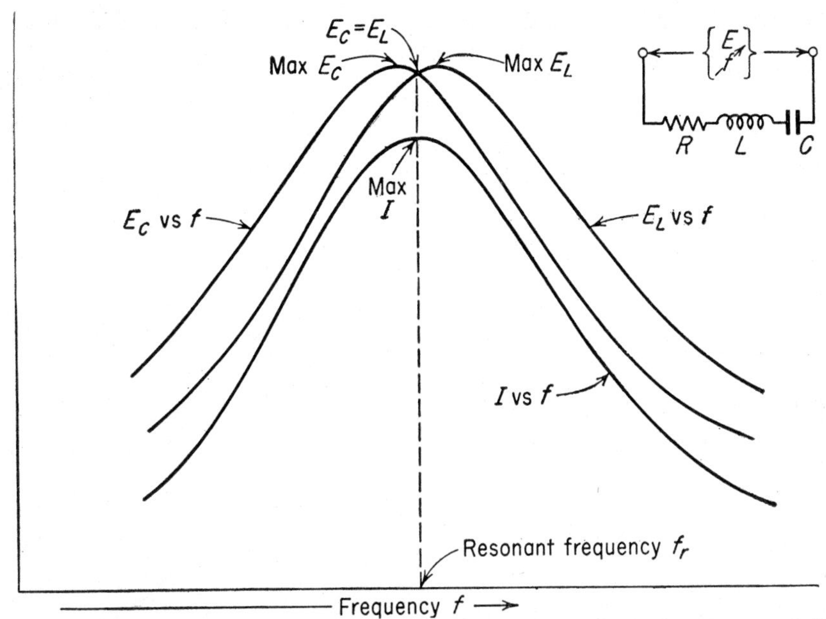

FIG. 150. Curves showing that the maximum values of E_C and E_L do *not* occur at the frequency of resonance.

Inductance Variation in Series R-L-C Circuits. If a constant-voltage constant-frequency source is impressed across a series *R-L-C* circuit in which only the inductance is varied the following conditions will prevail: (1) the capacitive reactance X_C will be constant; (2) the inductive reactance X_L will increase directly with corresponding changes in inductance; (3) the current will be equal to $I = E/Z_C$ when L is zero, will rise to its maximum E/R value at resonance when $X_L = X_C$, and will proceed to fall with further increases in L to become zero as L approaches infinity.

Typical curves showing the relationship between I, E_C, and E_L with respect to L are given in Fig. 151. Note particularly that the maximum voltage drop across the capacitor occurs at resonance, when the current has its maximum E/R value. However, the inductor voltage drop reaches its peak at a point somewhat *beyond* the inductance of resonance; as previously explained, this condition results because the inductive reactance continues to increase while the current, in the flat range, remains substantially constant for a short distance *beyond* the point of resonance. The inductance at which E_L becomes a maximum can be determined in terms of other circuit constants by analyzing the equation for the voltage drop across the inductance; this is

$$E_L = IX_L = \left(\frac{E}{\sqrt{R^2 + (X_L - X_C)^2}}\right) X_L$$

where E, R, and X_C are constants for the circuit under consideration. Since the *slope* of the E_L vs. L curve changes with progressively varying values of inductance, and becomes *zero* when E_L is a maximum (see Fig.

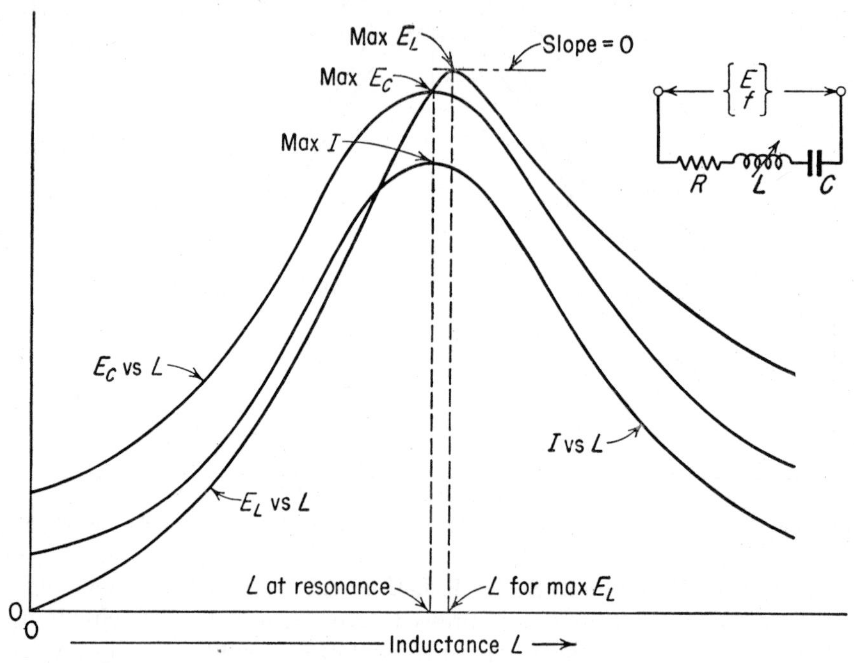

FIG. 151. Curves showing that the maximum value of E_L does *not* occur at the inductance of resonance.

151), the differential calculus indicates that the derivative of the foregoing formula with respect to X_L may be equated to zero to yield the value of L. When this operation is performed,

$$L = C(R^2 + X_C^2)10^{-6} \qquad \text{henry} \qquad (113)^1$$

EXAMPLE 3. A series circuit consisting of a 20-ohm resistor, an 88.3-μf capacitor, and a variable inductor is connected to a 120-volt 60-cycle source. (*a*) Calculate the value of inductance L, the current I, and the voltage drop across the inductor E_L for the condition of resonance; (*b*) determine the value of L, the current I, and the voltage drop across the inductor E_L when the latter has its maximum value.

Solution

(*a*) Since $X_L = X_C$ at resonance, $2\pi \times 60 \times L = 10^6/(2\pi \times 60 \times 88.3)$. Therefore

[1] See Appendix 1Q for derivation.

$$L \text{ (at resonance)} = \frac{10^6}{4\pi^2 \times 3{,}600 \times 88.3} = 0.08 \text{ henry}$$

$$I = \frac{E}{R} = \frac{120}{20} = 6 \text{ amp}$$

$$E_L = IX_L = 6 \times 2\pi \times 60 \times 0.08 = 181 \text{ volts}$$

$$(b)\ L \text{ (for maximum } E_L) = 88.3\left[(20)^2 + \left(\frac{10^6}{2\pi \times 60 \times 88.3}\right)^2\right]10^{-6}$$

$$= 88.3(400 + 900)10^{-6} = 0.115 \text{ henry}$$

$$I = \frac{E}{\sqrt{(R)^2 + (X_L - X_C)^2}}$$

$$= \frac{120}{\sqrt{(20)^2 + (43.3 - 30)^2}} = \frac{120}{24} = 5 \text{ amp}$$

$$E_L = IX_L = 5 \times 43.3 = 216.5 \text{ volts}$$

An important point to be noted in connection with this analysis is that the maximum voltage across the inductor does *not* occur at resonance because the circuit possesses resistance; if it were possible to completely eliminate the circuit resistance, E_L would, in fact, be a maximum and equal E_C at resonance.

Capacitance Variation in Series R-L-C Circuits. Considering next a series R-L-C circuit connected to a constant-voltage constant-frequency source, and in which only the capacitance is varied, the following conditions will prevail: (1) the inductive reactance X_L will be constant; (2) the capacitive reactance X_C will vary inversely with increasing values of capacitance; (3) the current will be zero when C is zero, will rise to its maximum E/R value at resonance when $X_C = X_L$, and will proceed to fall with further increases in C to become $I = E/Z_L$ as C approaches infinity.

Figure 152 illustrates typical curves showing the relationship between I, E_L, and E_C with respect to C. Observe that the maximum voltage drop across the inductor occurs at resonance when the current has its maximum E/R value. However, the capacitor voltage drop reaches its peak at a point somewhat *before* the capacitance of resonance; this is in accordance with previous discussions where it was explained that capacitive reactance continues to decrease while the current, in the flat range, remains substantially constant for a short distance *before* the point of resonance. The capacitance at which E_C becomes a maximum can be determined in terms of other circuit constants by analyzing the equation for the voltage drop across the capacitance; this is

$$E_C = IX_C = \left(\frac{E}{\sqrt{R^2 + (X_C - X_L)^2}}\right)X_C$$

where E, R, and X_L are constants for the circuit under consideration. Since the slope of the E_C vs. C curve changes with progressively varying values of capacitance, and becomes *zero* when E_C is a maximum (see Fig. 152), the derivative of the foregoing equation with respect to X_C may,

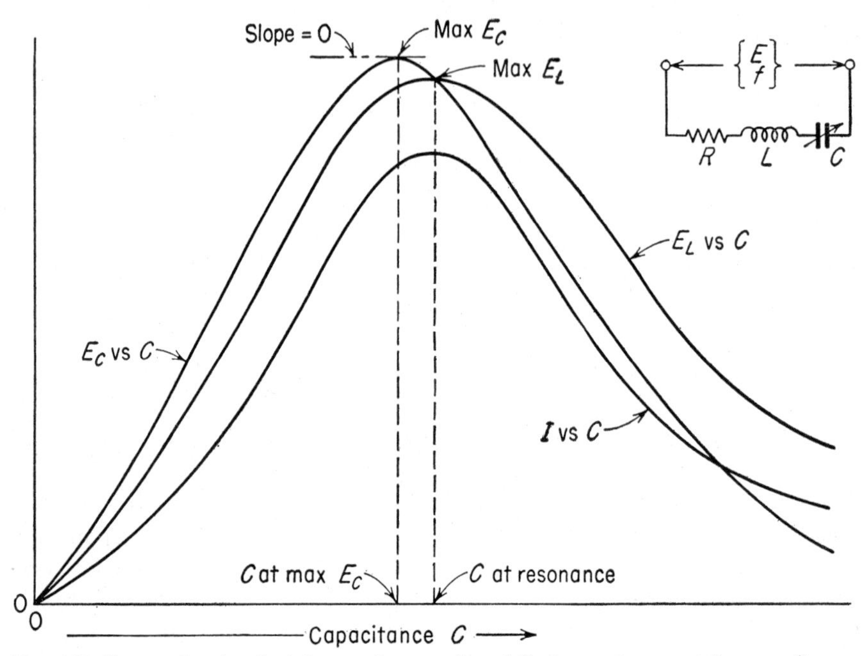

FIG. 152. Curves showing that the maximum value of E_C does *not* occur at the capacitance of resonance.

as before, be equated to zero to yield the value of C. When this operation is performed by the calculus,

$$C = \frac{L \times 10^6}{(R^2 + X_L^2)} \quad \mu\text{f} \tag{114}$$[1]

EXAMPLE 4. A series circuit consisting of a 15-ohm resistor, a 0.06-henry inductor, and a variable capacitor is connected to a 120-volt 60-cycle source. (*a*) Calculate the value of C, the current I, and the voltage drop across the capacitor E_C for the condition of resonance; (*b*) determine the value of C, the current I, and the voltage drop across the capacitor E_C when the latter has its maximum value.

Solution

(*a*) Since $X_C = X_L$ at resonance, $10^6/(2\pi \times 60 \times C) = 2\pi \times 60 \times 0.06$. Therefore

[1] See Appendix 1R for derivation.

$$C \text{ (at resonance)} = \frac{10^6}{4\pi^2 \times 3{,}600 \times 0.06} = 117 \ \mu\text{f}$$

$$I = \frac{E}{R} = \frac{120}{15} = 8 \text{ amp}$$

$$E_C = IX_C = 8 \times \left(\frac{10^6}{2\pi} \times 60 \times 117\right) = 181.5 \text{ volts}$$

(b)
$$C \text{ (for maximum } E_C) = \frac{0.06 \times 10^6}{(15)^2 + (2\pi \times 60 \times 0.06)^2}$$

$$= \frac{0.06 \times 10^6}{737} = 81.5 \ \mu\text{f}$$

$$I = \frac{E}{\sqrt{(R)^2 + (X_C - X_L)^2}}$$

$$= \frac{120}{\sqrt{(15)^2 + (32.5 - 21.6)^2}} = \frac{120}{18.5} = 6.5 \text{ amp}$$

$$E_C = IX_C = 6.5 \times 32.5 = 211 \text{ volts}$$

It is important to understand that the maximum voltage across the capacitor does *not* occur at resonance because the circuit possesses resistance; if it were possible to completely eliminate the circuit resistance, E_C would, in fact, be a maximum and equal E_L at resonance.

Selectivity and the Q of a Series R-L-C Circuit. Since the sharpness of tuning of a series circuit depends upon the *relative* magnitudes of R and L of the impedance coil (see Fig. 148), it seems desirable to have some way of rating the degree of selectivity in terms of R, L, and C. An arbitrary, but convenient, standard of comparison is based upon the symmetry of the *current* vs. *frequency* curve in the region of resonance, and the so-called *half-power* points on such a curve.

Referring to Fig. 153, note that the current at the frequency of resonance f_r is $I_r = E/R$; the equivalent reactance of the circuit is then zero. Because of the curve's symmetry there will be two frequencies, f_1 and f_2, equally spaced to either side of the resonant frequency f_r, at which the equivalent reactance of the circuit is equal to the resistance; under this condition $Z = \sqrt{R^2 + X^2} = \sqrt{R^2 + R^2} = \sqrt{2}\, R$, and $I = E/\sqrt{2}\, R$. Remembering that $P = I^2R$, it is seen that

$$P_1 = P_2 = \left(\frac{E}{\sqrt{2}\, R}\right)^2 R = \frac{E^2}{2R} \qquad \text{and} \qquad P_r = \left(\frac{E}{R}\right)^2 R = \frac{E^2}{R}$$

Obviously, f_1 and f_2 are *half-power* frequencies in terms of power at the resonant frequency.

Since the frequency separation between the half-power points is a good measure of the sharpness of tuning, the values of f_2 and f_1 have been

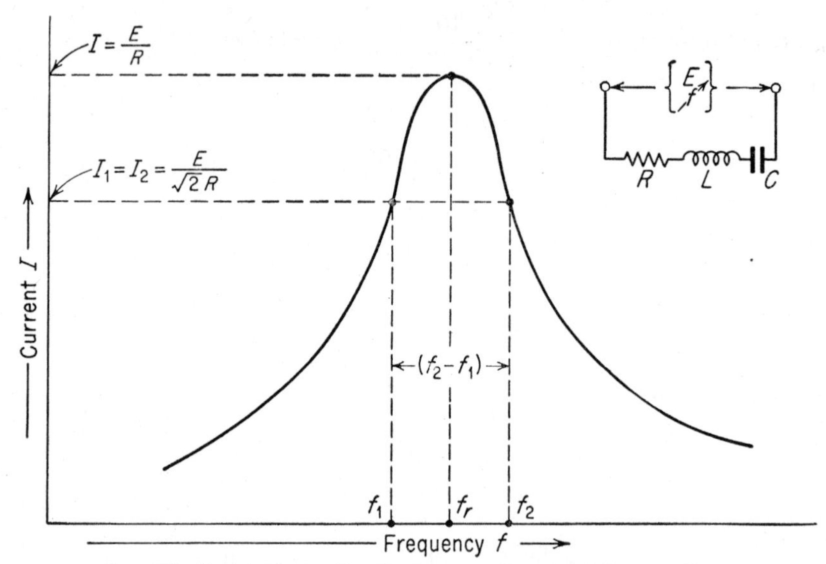

FIG. 153. Sketch illustrating the basis for the selectivity equations.

determined in terms of the resonant frequency and circuit constants; these are

$$f_2 = \left(f_r + \frac{R}{4\pi L}\right) \quad \text{and} \quad f_1 = \left(f_r - \frac{R}{4\pi L}\right)$$

The frequency separation is therefore

$$(f_2 - f_1) = \left(f_r + \frac{R}{4\pi L}\right) - \left(f_r - \frac{R}{4\pi L}\right) = \frac{R}{2\pi L} \qquad (115)^{1}$$

Note that the sharpness of tuning depends upon the ratio of R to L, a small ratio indicating a high degree of selectivity. This, therefore, leads to another way of representing the quality of a circuit, given in terms of the reactance and resistance of the impedance coil that is usually in series with a capacitor. Designating the so-called Q of the coil by $X_L/R = 2\pi f_r L/R$ and relating the frequency separation of Eq. (115) to the frequency of resonance,

$$\frac{(f_2 - f_1)}{f_r} = \frac{R}{2\pi f_r L} = \frac{R}{X_L} = \frac{1}{Q} \qquad (116)$$

Assuming a constant resonant frequency f_r, it should be clear from Eq. (116) that a small value for $(f_2 - f_1)$, i.e., good selectivity, implies a large Q, and this in turn means a coil whose inductive reactance is large with respect to its resistance; this point is extremely important in the design of tuned circuits.

[1] See Appendix 1S for derivation.

It is frequently desirable to specify the Q of a series circuit in terms of R, L, and C. Thus

$$Q = \frac{2\pi f_r L}{R} = \frac{2\pi L}{R} \times \frac{10^3}{2\pi \sqrt{LC}} = \frac{10^3}{R}\sqrt{\frac{L}{C}} \tag{117}$$

EXAMPLE 5. An impedance coil having a resistance of 28.8 ohms and an inductance of 0.024 henry is connected in series with a 0.008-μf capacitor. Calculate (*a*) the Q of the circuit, (*b*) the separation between the half-power frequencies, (*c*) the resonant frequency of the circuit, (*d*) the frequencies f_1 and f_2.

Solution

(*a*) $$Q = \frac{10^3}{R}\sqrt{\frac{L}{C}} = \frac{10^3}{28.8}\sqrt{\frac{0.024}{0.008}} = \frac{1.73 \times 10^3}{28.8} = 60$$

(*b*) $$(f_2 - f_1) = \frac{R}{2\pi L} = \frac{28.8}{2\pi \times 0.024} = 191 \text{ cps}$$

(*c*) $$f_r = Q(f_2 - f_1) = 60 \times 191 = 11{,}460 \text{ cps}$$

(*d*) $$f_2 = 11{,}460 + \frac{191}{2} = 11{,}055.5 \text{ cps}$$

$$f_1 = 11{,}460 - \frac{191}{2} = 11{,}364.5 \text{ cps}$$

$$Q = \frac{2\pi f_r L}{R} = \frac{2\pi \times 11{,}460 \times 0.024}{28.8} = 60 \qquad (Check)$$

Graphical Summary of Series R-L-C Circuits. The foregoing discussions may be summarized graphically to illustrate, rather well, how a series *R-L-C* circuit behaves under conditions of varying frequency, inductance, or capacitance.

Figure 154*a* illustrates how the inductive reactance, capacitive reactance, equivalent reactance, and current change as the frequency is varied, assuming a constant resistance and impressed emf. Note that X_L is arbitrarily plotted above the x axis to distinguish it from an oppositely directed X_C, which is shown below the x axis. The algebraic sum of X_L and X_C is represented by the equivalent reactance line X_{eq}; observe that X_{eq} is zero, and I is a maximum, at the frequency of resonance f_r.

Figure 154*b* illustrates how the same quantities are affected by variations of inductance L, assuming constant values of E, f, R, and C. In this diagram the current is $I = E/X_C$ when L is zero, and reaches a maximum of $I = E/R$ when X_{eq} is zero.

Figure 154*c* illustrates how the circuit conditions are affected by variations of capacitance C, assuming constant values of E, f, R, and L. In this diagram the current again reaches a maximum of $I = E/R$ when X_{eq} is zero.

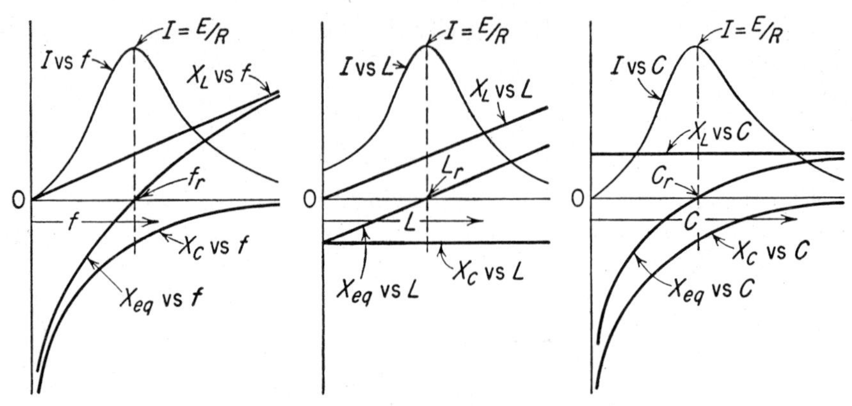

FIG. 154. Graphs illustrating the behavior of series *R-L-C* circuits with varying values of frequency, inductance, and capacitance.

General Aspects of Parallel Resonance Circuits. When a circuit consisting of two or more branches in parallel is in resonance, the over-all power factor, like that in a series circuit, is unity. Unlike a series circuit, however, the total current "feeding" all branches is a *minimum* because *the algebraic sum of the quadrature components of current is zero;* this implies, of course, that the total current is in phase with the voltage, as it should be when the power factor is unity. The term *antiresonance* is sometimes used for unity-power-factor parallel circuits to distinguish it from a similar condition in series circuits.

A parallel circuit can exhibit resonance properties only when one or more branches contain an excess of inductive reactance with respect to other branches that possess an excess of capacitive reactance. In the simple case, however, like that illustrated by Fig. 155*a*, two branches are

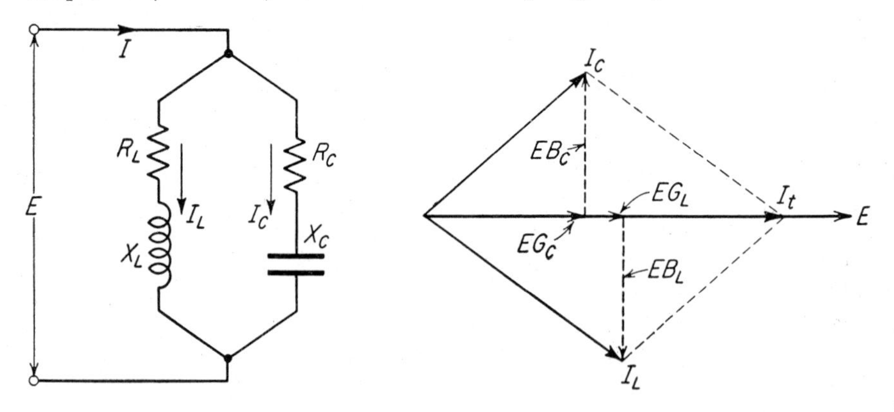

FIG. 155. Diagrams illustrating a simple two-branch parallel-resonant circuit.

connected in parallel, one path being a series R-L circuit and the other a series R-C circuit; the vector diagram of Fig. 155*b* indicates the condition of resonance when the circuit power factor is unity.

Although all series circuits may be adjusted to resonance by varying the frequency, inductance, or capacitance, this is not always possible in parallel circuits; the latter may, on the other hand, be made resonant under certain conditions by altering the *resistance* in one or more of its branches, an adjustment that has no such effect in a series circuit.

Frequency Variation in Two-branch Parallel Circuits. When the two-branch parallel circuit of Fig. 155 is in resonance the quadrature components of the currents I_C and I_L are equal; therefore, $EB_L = EB_C$, and unity power factor will result when $B_L = B_C$. Substituting their equivalents in terms of circuit constants,

$$\frac{2\pi f_r L}{R_L^2 + (2\pi f_r L)^2} = \frac{10^6/2\pi f_r C}{R_C^2 + (10^6/2\pi f_r C)^2}$$

which reduces to

$$4\pi^2 f_r^2 LC^2 R_C^2 + 10^{12}L = 10^6 R_L^2 C + 10^6(4\pi^2 f_r^2 L^2 C)$$

and
$$4\pi^2 f_r^2 LC(R_C^2 C - 10^6 L) = 10^6 R_L^2 C - 10^{12}L$$

from which
$$f_r = \frac{10^3}{2\pi\sqrt{LC}}\sqrt{\frac{R_L^2 C - 10^6 L}{R_C^2 C - 10^6 L}} \tag{118}$$

It is interesting to note that Eq. (118) reduces to $f_r = 10^3/2\pi\sqrt{LC}$ when the resistance in the inductive branch R_L is equal to the resistance in the capacitive branch R_C; the formula is then exactly similar to the one derived for resonance in a series circuit, i.e., Eq. (112).

Further analysis of Eq. (118) indicates that resonance is *not* possible for combinations of parameters that will make the quantity under the radical negative. For example, if $10^6 L$ is less than $R_L^2 C$ but greater than $R_C^2 C$ the radical yields an imaginary number; the same is true if $10^6 L$ is greater than $R_L^2 C$ but less than $R_C^2 C$. The behavior of parallel circuits is, in this respect, unlike that of all series combinations of R, L, and C for which there is, theoretically, some resonant frequency.

In some special circuits it is customary to eliminate the capacitor-branch resistor R_C. When this is done and R_L is made extremely small the quantity under the radical becomes unity, and the resonant frequency is again $f_r = 10^3/2\pi\sqrt{LC}$.

EXAMPLE 6. The following information is given in connection with a two-branch parallel circuit such as Fig. 155*a*: $R_L = 10$, $R_C = 20$, $X_C = 40$, $E = 120$, $f = 60$. For the condition of resonance, calculate (*a*) the two values of L, (*b*) the two values of line current.

Solution

(*a*) For resonance, $B_L = B_C$

$$\frac{X_L}{R_L^2 + X_L^2} = \frac{X_C}{R_C^2 + X_C^2}$$

$$\frac{X_L}{100 + X_L^2} = \frac{40}{400 + 1{,}600}$$

$$\frac{X_L}{100 + X_L^2} = \frac{1}{50}$$

$$X_L^2 - 50X_L + 100 = 0$$

$$X_L = \frac{50 \pm \sqrt{2{,}500 - 400}}{2} = 47.8 \text{ or } 2.2$$

Therefore $$L = \frac{47.8}{2\pi \times 60} = 0.1265 \text{ henry}$$

and $$L = \frac{2.2}{377} = 0.00583 \text{ henry}$$

(*b*) For resonance, $I_t = E(G_L + G_C)$

$$I_t = 120\left[\frac{10}{100 + 2{,}280} + \frac{20}{400 + 1{,}600}\right] = 120(0.0042 + 0.01)$$
$$= 1.704 \text{ amp}$$

or

$$I_t = 120\left[\frac{10}{100 + 4.84} + 0.01\right] = 120(0.0955 + 0.01) = 12.66 \text{ amp}$$

EXAMPLE 7. Calculate the resonant frequency of a two-branch parallel circuit, given the following particulars: $R_L = 40$, $R_C = 20$, $L = 0.254$ henry, $C = 40\ \mu$f.

Solution

$$f_r = \frac{10^3}{2\pi \sqrt{0.254 \times 40}} \sqrt{\frac{1{,}600 \times 40 - 10^6 \times 0.254}{400 \times 40 - 10^6 \times 0.254}} = 50 \sqrt{\frac{-190{,}000}{-238{,}000}}$$
$$= 44.5 \text{ cps}$$

EXAMPLE 8. At what frequency will the circuit of Example 7 be in resonance if $R_L = R_C$? Assume L and C to remain unchanged.

Solution

$$f_r = \frac{10^3}{2\pi \sqrt{0.254 \times 40}} = 50 \text{ cps}$$

EXAMPLE 9. At what frequency will the circuit of Example 7 be in resonance if $R_L = 20$ and $R_C = 40$? Assume L and C to remain unchanged.

Solution

$$f_r = 50\sqrt{\frac{400 \times 40 - 10^6 \times 0.254}{1{,}600 \times 40 - 10^6 \times 0.254}} = 50\sqrt{\frac{-238{,}000}{-190{,}000}} = 55.8 \text{ cps}$$

Resistance Variations in Two-branch Parallel Circuits. In contrast to a series *R-L-C* circuit it is often possible to adjust a two-branch parallel combination like Fig. 155 to resonance by varying R_L or R_C; this possibility exists because the resistors control, in part, the quadrature components of the currents in the two paths.

Considering a constant-frequency constant-voltage source, a two-branch parallel circuit will be in resonance when $B_L = B_C$. Using ωL for $2\pi fL$, and ωC for $2\pi fC$,

$$\frac{\omega L}{R_L^2 + \omega^2 L^2} = \frac{10^6/\omega C}{R_C^2 + 10^{12}/\omega^2 C^2} = \frac{10^6 \omega C}{\omega^2 C^2 R_C^2 + 10^{12}}$$

This becomes

$$\omega^2 C^2 L R_C^2 + 10^{12} L = 10^6 C R_L^2 + 10^6 \omega^2 L^2 C$$

But $\qquad \omega^2 C^2 = \dfrac{10^{12}}{X_C^2} \qquad$ and $\qquad \omega^2 L^2 C = \dfrac{10^6 X_L}{X_C}$

Making the proper substitutions and dividing through by L, the equation reduces to

$$\frac{10^{12} R_C^2}{X_C^2} + 10^{12} = \frac{10^6 C R_L^2}{L} + \frac{10^{12} X_L}{X_C}$$

A further simplification may be made by dividing through by 10^{12} and substituting $10^6/X_L X_C$ for C/L. Thus

$$\frac{R_C^2}{X_C^2} + 1 = \frac{R_L^2}{X_L X_C} + \frac{X_L}{X_C}$$

Solving for the capacitance- and inductance-branch resistances,

$$R_C = \sqrt{\frac{X_C}{X_L} R_L^2 + X_C X_L - X_C^2} \qquad (119)$$

and

$$R_L = \sqrt{\frac{X_L}{X_C} R_C^2 + X_L X_C - X_L^2} \qquad (120)$$

EXAMPLE 10. The following data are given for a two-branch parallel circuit: $E = 125$, $X_L = 15$, $X_C = 25$, $R_C = 15$. For what value of R_L will the circuit be in resonance, and what will be the total current and power under this condition?

Solution

$$R_L = \sqrt{\left(\frac{15}{25}\right) 225 + (15)(25) - 225} = \sqrt{285} = 16.85 \text{ ohms}$$

$$I_t = 125 \left[\frac{16.85}{(16.85)^2 + (15)^2} + \frac{15}{(15)^2 + (25)^2} \right] = 125(0.033 + 0.0177)$$
$$= 6.35 \text{ amp}$$

$$P_t = 125 \times 6.35 = 795 \text{ watts}$$

EXAMPLE 11. A 30,000-cycle source is connected to an impedance coil having a resistance of 60 ohms and an inductance of 0.425 mh. For what value of resistance, in series with a 0.106-μf capacitor, will the circuit be in resonance if the two branches are paralleled? Neglecting both resistances, calculate the resonant frequency.

Solution

$$X_L = 2\pi \times 30,000 \times 0.000425 = 80$$

$$X_C = \frac{10^6}{2\pi} \times 30,000 \times 0.106 = 50$$

$$R_C = \sqrt{\left(\frac{50}{80}\right) 3,600 + (80)(50) - 2,500} = 61.2 \text{ ohms}$$

$$f_r = \frac{10^3}{2\pi \sqrt{LC}} = \frac{10^3}{2\pi \sqrt{0.000425 \times 0.106}} = \frac{10^6}{2\pi \sqrt{45}} = 23,800 \text{ cps}$$

Resonance in Combinations of Series and Parallel Circuits. Special types of communication circuits are frequently designed to act selectively to one (or more) frequency and to reject another (or others); this implies, of course, that the impedance of the circuit will be low (or zero) to the *passed* frequency and high (infinite) to the *blocked* frequency. Such networks, consisting of inductances and capacitances, are generally referred to as *filters*. Figure 156 shows several combinations of L and C in which all resistances are neglected, for convenience, in this discussion.

The proper functioning of a filter is based upon the principles (1) that a series circuit is in resonance when the impedance is low, so that the current, at a given frequency, is high; and (2) that a parallel circuit is tuned to resonance when the impedance is high, so that the current, at a given frequency, is low. This means that the networks of Fig. 156 must be regarded (1) as series circuits, in whole or part, when tuned to the frequency it is desired to pass; and (2) as parallel circuits, in whole or part, when tuned to the frequency it is desired to block.

Assume that it is required to pass frequency f_p and to block frequency f_b. To do this: (1) in Fig. 156*a*, L and C_s must be tuned to frequency f_p, and L, C_s, and C_p must be tuned to frequency f_b; (2) in Fig. 156*b*, L_s and

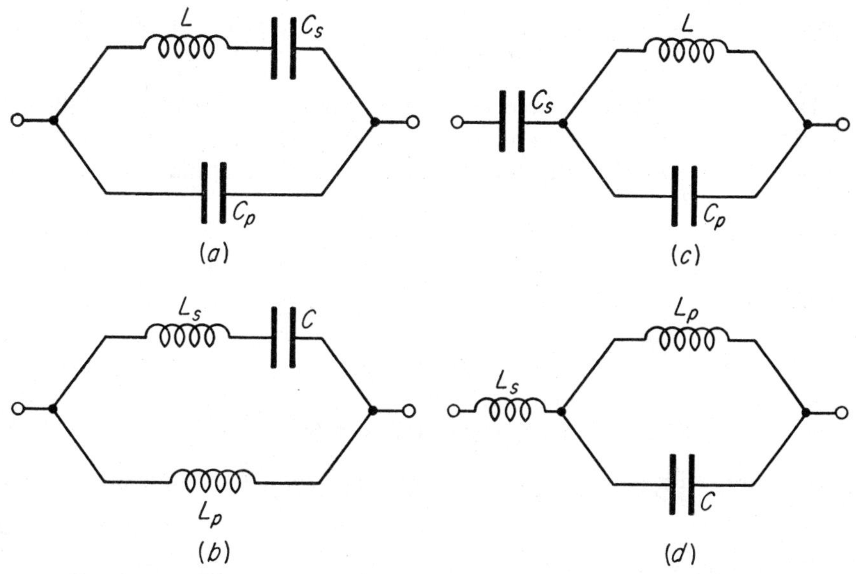

FIG. 156. Inductance-capacitance circuits arranged for tuning purposes.

C must be tuned to f_p and L_s, C, and L_p must be tuned to f_b; (3) in Fig. 156c, L and C_p must be tuned to f_b, and C_s, L, and C_p must be tuned to f_p; (4) in Fig. 156d, L_p and C must be tuned to f_b, and L_s, L_p, and C must be tuned to f_p. Examples will now be given to illustrate the foregoing analysis.

EXAMPLE 12. A filter like that of Fig. 156a is to be designed to pass a 3,000-cycle wave and block a 4,000-cycle wave. If the capacitance of C_s is 0.4 μf, determine the inductance of L and the capacitance of C_p.

Solution

The series circuit consisting of L and C_s will be made resonant to 3,000 cps.

$$3{,}000 = \frac{10^3}{2\pi \sqrt{L \times 0.4}}$$

$$L = \frac{1}{4\pi^2 \times 0.4 \times 9} = 0.00705 \text{ henry, or } 7.05 \text{ mh}$$

The entire parallel-series circuit will be made resonant to 4,000 cps.

The reactance of the series branch is

$$X_{\text{ser}} = (2\pi \times 4{,}000 \times 0.00705) - \frac{10^6}{2\pi \times 4{,}000 \times 0.4}$$
$$= 77 \text{ ohms } (\textit{inductive})$$

Therefore $$C_p = \frac{10^6}{2\pi \times 4{,}000 \times 77} = 0.517 \ \mu f$$

EXAMPLE 13. It is desired to design a filter like that of Fig. 156*d* to block a 20,000-cycle wave and pass a 30,000-cycle wave. If the inductance of L_p is 0.00317 henry, determine the values of C and L_s.

Solution

The parallel circuit consisting of L_p and C will be made resonant to 20,000 cps.

$$20{,}000 = \frac{10^3}{2\pi \sqrt{0.00317 \times C}}$$

$$C = \frac{1}{4\pi^2 \times 0.00317 \times 400} = 0.02 \ \mu f$$

The entire series-parallel circuit will be made resonant to 30,000 cps.

$$X_{L_p} = 2\pi \times 30{,}000 \times 0.00317 = 597\underline{/90^\circ}$$

$$X_C = \frac{10^6}{2\pi \times 30{,}000 \times 0.02} = 266\underline{/-90^\circ}$$

$$X_{eq} \text{ (for parallel branches)} = \frac{(597\underline{/90^\circ})(266\underline{/-90^\circ})}{(597\underline{/90^\circ}) + (266\underline{/-90^\circ})} = \frac{(597)(266)}{331\underline{/90^\circ}}$$
$$= 480\underline{/-90^\circ} \ (\textit{capacitive})$$

Therefore $$X_{L_s} = 480 = 2\pi \times 30{,}000L$$

and $$L = \frac{480}{2\pi \times 30{,}000} = 0.00255 \text{ henry}$$

Parallel Resonance at All Frequencies. It was previously shown that given values of L and C will make a two-branch parallel circuit resonant at the same frequency as a series circuit when $R_L = R_C$. If, in addition to the latter equality, the resistance is made equal to $10^3 \sqrt{L/C}$, the parallel circuit displays the interesting property of being resonant at *all* frequencies. This may be demonstrated by the following analysis.

Since $B_L = B_C$ in a two-branch parallel circuit,

$$\frac{\omega L}{R_L^2 + \omega^2 L^2} = \frac{10^6/\omega C}{R_C^2 + 10^{12}/\omega^2 C^2} = \frac{10^6 \omega C}{\omega^2 C^2 R_C^2 + 10^{12}}$$

This becomes

$$\omega^2 C^2 L R_C^2 + 10^{12} L = 10^6 \omega^2 L^2 C + 10^6 C R_L^2$$

Dividing through by LC, the equation reduces to

$$\omega^2 C R_C^2 + \frac{10^{12}}{C} = 10^6 \omega^2 L + \frac{10^6 R_L^2}{L}$$

Note that the left side of the equation, containing C terms, applies to the capacitance branch, while the right side of the equation, containing L terms, applies to the inductive branch. If $R_L^2 = R_C^2 = 10^6 L/C$,

$$\omega^2 C \left(\frac{10^6 L}{C}\right) + \frac{10^{12}}{C} = 10^6 \omega^2 L + \left(\frac{10^6}{L}\right)\left(\frac{10^6 L}{C}\right)$$

which becomes

$$\underset{\text{(inductive branch)}}{10^6 \omega^2 L + \frac{10^{12}}{C}} = \underset{\text{(capacitive branch)}}{10^6 \omega^2 L + \frac{10^{12}}{C}}$$

Note that the quantities on *both* sides of the equal sign are identical so that each branch is affected identically by a change in ω, or frequency.

EXAMPLE 14. The following data are given in connection with a two-branch parallel circuit: $R_L = R_C = 80$, $L = 0.32$ henry, $C = 50$ μf. Show that $B_L = B_C$ at 30 cycles, at 60 cycles, and at 100 cycles.

Solution

f	$X_L = 2\pi f L$	X_L^2	$X_C = 10^6/2\pi f C$	X_C^2
30	60.2	3,620	106	11,240
60	120.4	14,480	53	2,810
100	201	40,400	31.8	1,010

For 30 cps:

$$B_L = \frac{60.2}{6{,}400 + 3{,}620} = 0.006 \text{ mho}$$

$$B_C = \frac{106}{6{,}400 + 11{,}240} = 0.006 \text{ mho}$$

For 60 cps:

$$B_L = \frac{120.4}{6{,}400 + 14{,}480} = 0.00575 \text{ mho}$$

$$B_C = \frac{53}{6{,}400 + 2{,}810} = 0.00575 \text{ mho}$$

For 100 cps:

$$B_L = \frac{201}{6{,}400 + 40{,}400} = 0.0043 \text{ mho}$$

$$B_C = \frac{31.8}{6{,}400 + 1{,}010} = 0.0043 \text{ mho}$$

EXAMPLE 15. An impedance coil has a resistance of 50 ohms and an inductance of 0.2 henry. What series combination of R_C and C, connected in parallel with the coil, will make the circuit resonant at all frequencies?

Solution

$$R_C = 50 \text{ ohms}$$

$$C = \frac{10^6 L}{R_C^2} = \frac{10^6 \times 0.2}{2,500} = 80 \ \mu\text{f}$$

Questions

1. What is meant by the term *resonance?*
2. How does a circuit behave when it is in resonance?
3. What fundamental properties of inductive reactance and capacitive reactance make resonance possible?
4. Explain why a resonant circuit stores a constant amount of energy.
5. What energy is expended in a circuit that is in resonance? Explain carefully.
6. Why is the voltage drop across the resistor in a series *R-L-C* circuit equal to the impressed emf under the condition of resonance?
7. Why is the line current in phase with the impressed emf when a parallel circuit is in resonance?
8. Give three basic methods that may be used to alter the impedance and attain resonance in a series *R-L-C* circuit.
9. At what frequency, in terms of L and C, will a series *R-L-C* circuit be in resonance?
10. Why is the circuit current a maximum when a series *R-L-C* is in resonance?
11. What is meant by *sharp* tuning? For what relative values of R does it exist in a series *R-L-C* circuit?
12. What is meant by *broad* tuning? For what relative values of R does it exist in a series *R-L-C* circuit?
13. For what relative values of L/C does sharp tuning exist in a series *R-L-C* circuit? Answer the same question for broad tuning.
14. Explain why the maximum voltage drops across the inductor and capacitor do *not* occur at resonance in a series *R-L-C* circuit when f is the variable.
15. Explain why the maximum voltage drop across the inductor does *not* occur at resonance in a series *R-L-C* circuit when L is the variable.
16. Explain why the maximum voltage drop across the capacitor does *not* occur at resonance in a series *R-L-C* circuit when C is variable.
17. Why is X_L equal to X_C under all conditions of series resonance?
18. Explain why the voltage drops across the inductor and/or the capacitor may be larger than the impressed emf when a series circuit is in resonance.
19. What is meant by the *half-power* points on the *current* vs. *frequency* curve of a series *R-L-C* circuit? What use is made of these points in connection with circuit selectivity? Explain carefully.
20. What is meant by *frequency separation,* referring to circuit selectivity?
21. What is meant by the Q of an impedance coil? Why is a high Q generally desirable?
22. How must an impedance coil be constructed if its Q is to be high?
23. In a series *R-L-C* circuit why does a low value of C yield a high value of Q when the constants of the impedance coil are fixed?
24. Why must the algebraic sum of the quadrature components in a parallel circuit be zero at resonance?
25. List four possible ways to adjust a two-branch parallel circuit to resonance.
26. Explain why a parallel circuit may be tuned to resonance by adjusting resistances in the inductive and capacitive branches. In contrast, why is it not possible to tune a series circuit to resonance by adjusting the resistance?

27. Under what conditions is it not possible to tune a parallel circuit to resonance? Give examples to illustrate your answer.
28. For given values of L and C when will a two-branch parallel circuit be in resonance at the same frequency as a series R-L-C circuit?
29. What is meant by a *filter network?* What function does it serve?
30. What important principles are responsible for the ability of a filter to pass one frequency and block another?
31. Neglecting resistances, illustrate by sketches how a filter may be constructed to pass one frequency and block another.
32. Under what conditions is it possible for a two-branch parallel circuit to be resonant at all frequencies?

Problems

1. A series circuit consists of an impedance coil having a resistance of 55 ohms and an inductance of 0.281 henry, and a 25-μf capacitor. (*a*) Calculate the resonant frequency. For the condition of resonance, and an impressed emf of 110 volts, determine (*b*) the total current and power; (*c*) the voltage drops across the impedance coil, the capacitor, and the resistor.
2. A series R-L-C circuit is to be made resonant when connected to a 208-volt 400-cycle source. If the inductance is 0.0396 henry, determine the capacitance of the capacitor and the minimum ohmic value of the resistor if the voltage drop across the capacitor is to be limited to 600 volts.
3. Calculate the circuit current in Prob. 2 (*a*) if the frequency is reduced to 350 cps, (*b*) if the frequency is raised to 450 cps.
4. A series circuit consisting of a 16-ohm resistor, a 79.5-μf capacitor, and a variable inductor is connected to a 116-volt 50-cycle source. (*a*) For the condition of resonance calculate the inductance, current, and voltage drop across the inductor; (*b*) determine the inductance, current, and voltage drop across the inductor when the voltage drop across the latter is a maximum.
5. An impedance coil takes 144 watts at a lagging power factor of 0.6. What values of capacitance and resistance should be connected in series with the coil if the power input to the latter is to remain unchanged and the over-all circuit power factor is to be unity?
6. (*a*) Determine the resonant frequency and the impedance of a series circuit consisting of a 5-ohm resistor, a 250×10^{-6}-μf capacitor, and a 127.5×10^{-6}-henry inductor. (*b*) What will be the resonant frequency and impedance if the values are changed to 7.2 ohms, 125×10^{-6} μf, and 255×10^{-6} henry?
7. A series circuit consisting of a 16-ohm resistor, a 0.1275-henry inductor, and a variable capacitor is connected to a 116-volt 50-cycle source. (*a*) For the condition of resonance calculate the capacitance, current, and voltage drop across the capacitor; (*b*) determine the capacitance, current, and voltage drop across the capacitor when the voltage drop across the latter is a maximum.
8. Calculate the resonant frequency and the Q of a series circuit consisting of a 2.5-ohm resistor, a 0.02-henry inductor, and a 2-μf capacitor.
9. For the circuit of Prob. 8, determine the half-power frequencies f_1 and f_2.
10. A series R-L-C circuit has a Q of 75 and a pass band between half-power frequencies of 160 cps. Calculate the frequency of resonance and upper and lower frequencies of the pass band.
11. A variable capacitance C is connected in parallel with an impedance coil having a resistance of R ohms and an inductance of L henrys. For the condition of resonance, derive an expression for C in microfarads in terms f_r, R, and L.

12. A variable inductive reactance X_L is connected in parallel with a series combination of resistance R and a capacitive reactance X_C. For the condition of resonance derive an expression for X_L in terms of R and X_C.

13. An impedance coil having a resistance of 30 ohms and a 50-cycle inductive reactance of 33.3 ohms is connected to a 125-volt 60-cycle source. A series circuit consisting of a 20-ohm resistor and a variable capacitor is then connected in parallel with the coil. (*a*) For what values of capacitance will the circuit be in resonance? (*b*) Calculate the two values of line current for the condition of resonance.

14. Calculate the resonant frequency of a two-branch parallel circuit given the following particulars: $R_L = 30$ ohms, $R_C = 30$ ohms, $L = 0.106$ henry, $C = 48$ μf.

15. Calculate the resonant frequency of the two-branch parallel circuit given the following particulars: $R_L = 20$ ohms, $R_C = 20$ ohms, $L = 1.106$ henry, $C = 365$ μf.

16. An impedance coil having a resistance of 20 ohms and an inductance of 4 mh is connected in parallel with a 0.4-μf capacitor. Calculate the resonant frequency (*a*) taking the resistance into account, (*b*) neglecting the resistance.

17. The following data are given for a two-branch parallel circuit: $E = 120$, $R_L = 30$, $X_L = 25$, $X_C = 40$. Calculate the value of R_C that will make the circuit resonant, and determine the total current and power under this condition.

18. A 20,000-cycle source is connected to a series circuit consisting of a 50-ohm resistor and a 0.266-μf capacitor. An impedance coil, whose resistance and inductance are 25 ohms and 0.191 mh, respectively, is then connected in series with a variable resistor, after which the combination is paralleled with the *R-C* circuit. For what value of the variable resistor will the entire circuit be in resonance?

19. A parallel-series filter like that of Fig. 156*b* is to be designed to pass a wave having a frequency of 3,500 cps and block a 2,500-cps wave. The series inductor has a value of 0.0023 henry. Calculate the capacitance of the series capacitor and the parallel inductor.

20. It is desired to design a series-parallel type of filter like that shown in Fig. 156*c* to pass a 20,000-cycle wave and block a 30,000-cycle wave. If the capacitance of the parallel capacitor C_p is 0.015 μf, determine the values of L and C_s.

21. An impedance coil has a resistance of 60 ohms and an inductance of 0.144 henry. What series combination of R and C should be connected in parallel with the coil to make the circuit resonant at all frequencies?

22. An impedance coil whose resistance and inductance are 18 ohms and 3.82 mh, respectively, is connected in parallel with a series combination of a 5.3-μf capacitor and a variable resistor. For what value of resistance will the circuit be in resonance at 1,000 cps?

CHAPTER 14

CIRCUIT ANALYSIS BY VECTOR LOCI

General Aspects of Circuits with Varying Parameters. It is often necessary to analyze circuits—series, parallel, or combinations thereof—to determine how they behave when one or more parameters are varied. Since a-c circuits may contain resistors, inductors, and capacitors in numerous combinations, a progressive change in one of them may or may not result in (1) current and/or power-factor variations when the voltage is kept constant, or (2) voltage and/or power-factor variations when the current is maintained constant.

It will presently be shown that simple basic circuits consisting of combinations of resistance, inductive reactance, and capacitive reactance display definite patterns of change when a uniform increase or decrease is made in one of the elements. Such patterns, when plotted vectorially to account for variations that are continuous, are called *vector loci;* they generally take the form of circles or straight lines. Analysis of these loci will then yield such important information as maximum and minimum values of current, voltage, and power factor and, as in the case of certain parallel circuits, will indicate whether or not a condition of resonance is possible. Vector loci are therefore extremely helpful to a general interpretation of the operating characteristics of a-c circuits.

The Series R-X_L Circuit. When a constant voltage is applied to a series R-L circuit, the current and power factor may be varied over a considerable range (1) by rheostatic adjustment of the resistance or (2) by changing the inductive reactance, using a variable inductor or an adjustable-frequency source. Moreover, if each change is made to take place uniformly between zero and extremely large, i.e., infinite, ohmic values, the vector loci will be semicircles.

The Variable-resistance Constant-reactance Circuit. Figure 157*a* illustrates a series R-X_L circuit which is connected to a constant-voltage constant-frequency source and in which the resistance is assumed to vary over wide limits. The current will obviously be E/X_L when $R = 0$, and drop toward zero as the resistance is increased progressively to infinity; moreover, the power factor will be zero lagging when the current is a maximum and will approach unity with increasing values of resistance.

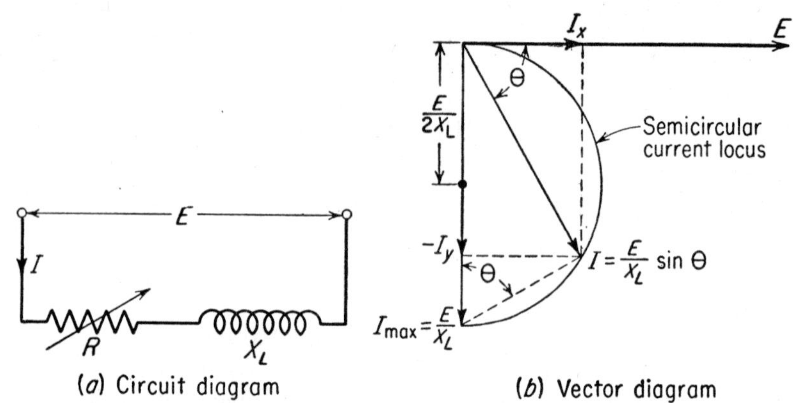

(a) Circuit diagram (b) Vector diagram

FIG. 157. Diagrams illustrating a variable-resistance constant-inductive-reactance circuit.

The general expression for the current is

$$I = \frac{E}{\sqrt{R^2 + X_L^2}} = \frac{E}{Z}$$

Multiplying numerator and denominator by X_L gives

$$\boldsymbol{I} = \left(\frac{E}{Z}\right)\left(\frac{X_L}{X_L}\right) = \frac{E}{X_L} \sin \Theta$$

where X_L/Z is the sine of the power-factor angle. This equation for a circle is in the polar form, and the ratio of the *constant terms*, E/X_L, is both the maximum current and the diameter of the circle. Figure 157*b* shows these relationships, and indicates, by its *semicircular vector locus*, how the current and power factor vary.

Analyzing this circuit through Fig. 157*b* in another way, using the complex notation, and assuming the voltage E to be in the reference vector,

$$E = \dot{I}\dot{Z} = (I_x - jI_y)(R + jX_L) = (I_xR + I_yX_L) + j(-I_yR + I_xX_L)$$

Note that this expression for voltage is represented by two components which may be separated and equated as follows:

Horizontal component:

$$E = I_xR + I_yX_L$$

Vertical component:

$$0 = -I_yR + I_xX_L$$

These simultaneous equations may be solved for the current I by eliminating the variable term R; thus, multiplying the first one by I_y and the second one by I_x,

$$EI_y = I_xI_yR + I_y^2X_L$$
$$0 = I_xI_yR + I_xX_L$$

When the second equation is subtracted from the first and the result is rearranged,

$$I_x^2 + I_y^2 - \frac{E}{X_L} I_y = 0$$

The next step is to complete the squares; this is done by adding $E^2/4X_L^2$ to both sides. Thus

$$I_x^2 + \left(I_y^2 - \frac{E}{X_L} I_y + \frac{E}{4X_L^2}\right) = \frac{E^2}{4X_L^2}$$

which becomes

$$I_x^2 + \left(I_y - \frac{E}{2X_L}\right)^2 = \left(\frac{E}{2X_L}\right)^2$$

This is also an equation of a circle, and indicates further (1) that the radius is $E/2X_L$ and (2) that the center of the circle is displaced *downward* by $E/2X_L$.

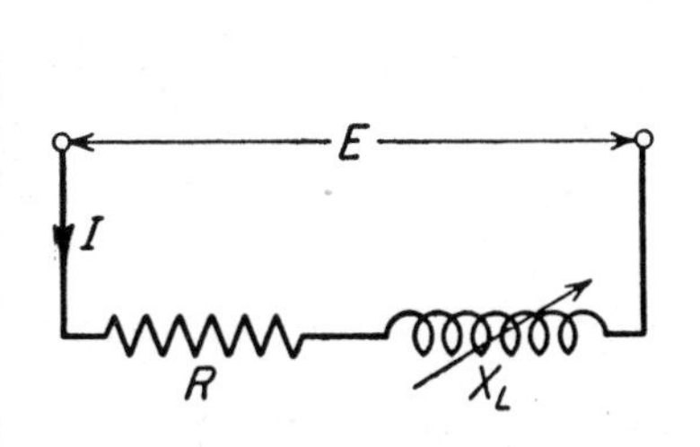

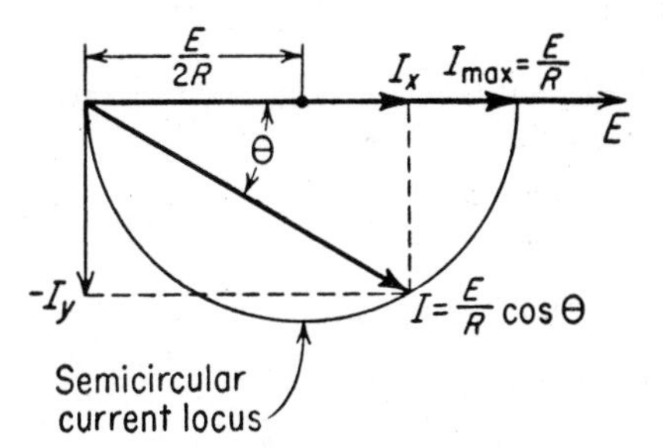

(*a*) Circuit diagram (*b*) Vector diagram

FIG. 158. Diagrams illustrating a variable-inductive-reactance constant-resistance circuit.

The Variable-reactance Constant-resistance Circuit. Figure 158*a* illustrates a series R-X_L circuit which is connected to a constant-voltage constant-frequency source, and in which the inductive reactance is assumed to vary widely. The current will obviously be E/R when $X_L = 0$, and drop toward zero as the inductive reactance is increased progressively to infinity; moreover, the power factor will be unity when the current is a maximum and will approach zero with increasing values of inductive reactance. As before, the general expression for the current is $I = E/Z$, and, when numerator and denominator are multiplied by R, it becomes

$$I = \left(\frac{E}{Z}\right)\left(\frac{R}{R}\right) = \frac{E}{R}\cos\Theta$$

where R/Z is the power factor of the circuit. This equation for a circle is in the polar form, and the ratio of the *constant terms* E/R is both the maximum current and the diameter of the circle. Figure 158*b* shows these relationships, and indicates, by its *semicircular vector* locus, how the current and power factor vary.

Analyzing this circuit through Fig. 158*b* by using the complex notation, and assuming the voltage E to be the reference vector,

$$E = \dot{I}\dot{Z} = (I_x - jI_y)(R + jX_L) = (I_xR + I_yX_L) + j(-I_yR + I_xX_L)$$

Separating the horizontal and vertical components as before,

$$E = I_xR + I_yX_L$$

and

$$0 = -I_yR + I_xX_L$$

Solving for the current by eliminating the variable X_L, the first one will be multiplied by I_x and the second one by I_y; thus

$$EI_x = I_x^2R + I_xI_yX_L$$

and

$$0 = -I_y^2R + I_xI_yX_L$$

Next, subtracting the second equation from the first, and rearranging terms,

$$I_x^2 + I_y^2 - \frac{E}{R}I_y = 0$$

Completing the squares in the latter expression by adding $E^2/4R^2$ to both sides gives

$$I_x^2 + I_y^2 - \frac{E}{R} + \frac{E}{4R^2} = \frac{E}{4R^2}$$

which reduces to

$$I_x^2 + \left(I_y - \frac{E}{2R}\right)^2 = \left(\frac{E}{2R}\right)^2$$

This is again an equation of a circle, and indicates further (1) that the radius is $E/2R$ and (2) that the center of the circle is displaced *to the right* by $E/2R$.

EXAMPLE 1. A 120-volt source is connected to a series circuit consisting of a 24-ohm inductive reactance and a resistor which is variable between the limits of 7 and 55 ohms. Draw a vector locus showing the current range, and indicate thereon the circle diameter, maximum and minimum currents, and the angles between the reference voltage vector and the maximum and minimum currents.

Solution

$$\text{Circle diameter} = I_{\text{diam}} = \frac{E}{X_L} = \frac{120}{24} = 5 \text{ amp}$$

$$\text{Maximum current} = I_{\text{max}} = \frac{E}{Z_{\text{min}}} = \frac{120}{\sqrt{(7)^2 + (24)^2}} = 4.8 \text{ amp}$$

$$\text{Minimum current} = I_{\text{min}} = \frac{E}{Z_{\text{max}}} = \frac{120}{\sqrt{(55)^2 + (24)^2}} = 2 \text{ amp}$$

$$\text{Angle for maximum current} = \sin^{-1}\frac{4.8}{5} = 73.7°$$

$$\text{Angle for minimum current} = \sin^{-1}\frac{2}{5} = 23.6°$$

The vector locus is shown in Fig. 159.

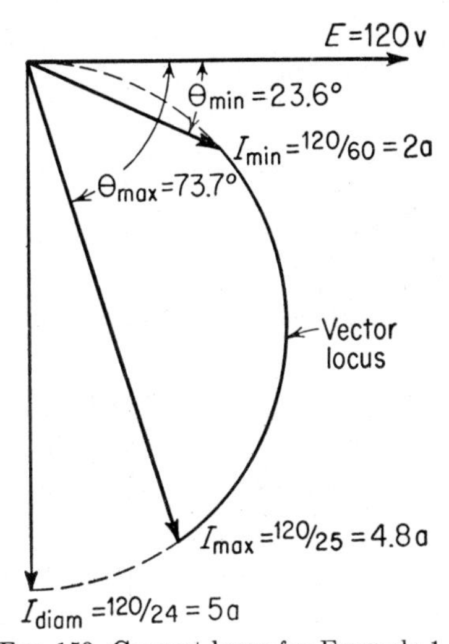

FIG. 159. Current locus for Example 1.

EXAMPLE 2. A 110-volt 60-cycle source is connected to a series circuit consisting of a 20-ohm resistor and an inductor which is variable between the limits of 0.0243 and 0.136 henry. Draw a vector locus showing the current range, and indicate thereon the circle diameter, maximum and minimum currents, and the angles between the reference voltage vector and the maximum and minimum currents.

Solution

$$\text{Circle diameter} = \frac{E}{R} = \frac{110}{20} = 5.5 \text{ amp}$$

$$\text{Maximum current} = I_{\max} = \frac{110}{\sqrt{(20)^2 + (377 \times 0.0243)^2}} = 5 \text{ amp}$$

$$\text{Minimum current} = I_{\min} = \frac{110}{\sqrt{(20)^2 + (377 \times 0.136)^2}} = 2 \text{ amp}$$

$$\text{Angle for maximum current} = \cos^{-1} \frac{5}{5.5} = 24.6°$$

$$\text{Angle for minimum current} = \cos^{-1} \frac{2}{5.5} = 68.7°$$

The vector locus is shown in Fig. 160.

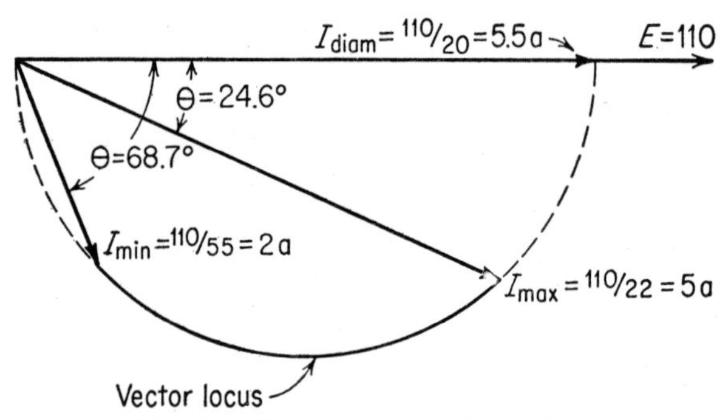

FIG. 160. Current locus for Example 2.

The Series R-X$_C$ Circuit. The analysis of series R-X_C circuits, when carried out in the same way as in the foregoing section for inductive circuits, will also show that the current loci are circular under conditions of varying resistance or varying capacitive reactance. However, since capacitor currents always lead their respective impressed emfs, the circles will occupy positions *above* the horizontal reference voltage vector. The general expression for the current in a circuit with constant X_C and variable R is

$$I_x^2 + \left(I_y + \frac{E}{2X_C}\right)^2 = \left(\frac{E}{2X_C}\right)^2$$

Referring to Fig. 161, note that the radius of the circle is $E/2X_C$, and that the center is displaced by $E/2X_C$ *above* the x axis. A similar equa-

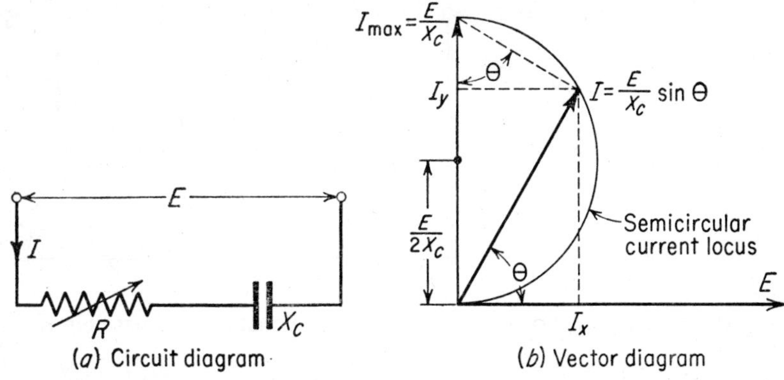

FIG. 161. Diagrams illustrating a variable-resistance constant-capacitive-reactance circuit.

tion involving a circuit with a constant R and a variable X_C is

$$I_x^2 + \left(I_y + \frac{E}{2R}\right)^2 = \left(\frac{E}{2R}\right)^2$$

Referring to Fig. 162, note that the radius of the circle is $E/2R$ and that the center of the circle is displaced to the *right* of the origin by $E/2R$.

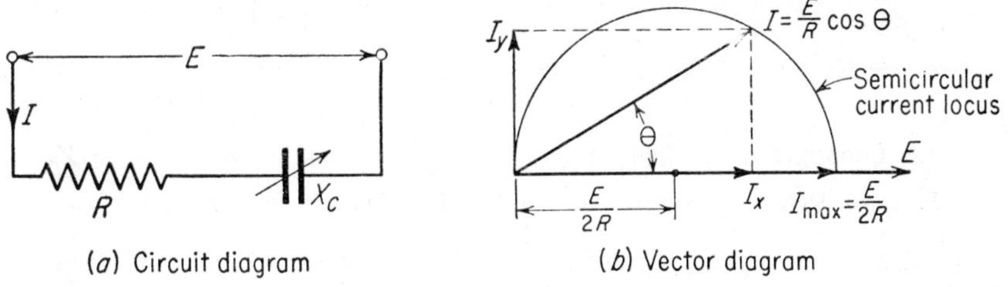

FIG. 162. Diagrams illustrating a variable-capacitive-reactance constant-resistance circuit.

Impedance Loci for Series R-X_L and R-X_C Circuits. It is sometimes helpful to know how the total impedance of a circuit varies as one of the parameters is changed over wide limits. Remembering that R and X are related to each other as the sides of a right triangle, a progressive change in one of them, with the other constant, will yield a *straight-line* impedance locus that is (1) parallel to the x axis if R is varied and (2) parallel to the y axis if X is varied. Sketches showing the behavior of each of the basic types of series R-X circuit are shown in Fig. 163. Note that resistance and reactance have, respectively, been assigned to horizontal and vertical axes in conformity with an arbitrary reference-current vector; moreover, X_L is shown above the X axis and X_C below the x axis to indicate that their respective voltage drops lead and lag the circuit currents.

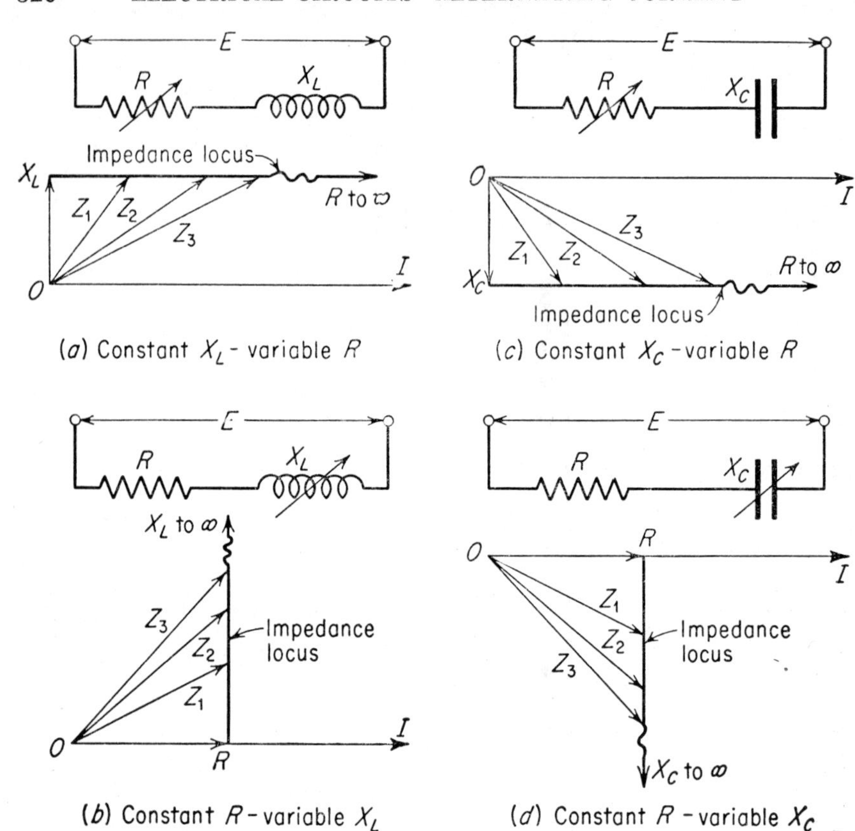

FIG. 163. Diagrams showing vector loci for impedance in series R-X circuits.

The Series R-X_L-X_C Circuit. The behavior of a constant-potential series circuit consisting of resistance, inductive reactance, and capacitive reactance, and in which R, X_L, X_C, or the frequency is varied, is concisely illustrated by current and impedance loci; the latter do, in fact, clearly indicate how lagging and leading currents, maximum and minimum currents, and resonance conditions are affected by such changes.

When this type of circuit is studied from the standpoint of a variable resistance it may be regarded as an R-X_L combination *or* one containing R and X_C; this simplification is permissible because inductive reactance and capacitive reactance oppose one another in a series circuit, as a result of which the magnitude and *kind* of equivalent reactance are determined, in effect, by the values of X_L and X_C. Thus, for example, if X_L is greater than X_C the current and impedance loci are properly represented by Figs. 157 and 163*a*; on the other hand, a value of X_C that is larger than X_L means that the loci of Figs. 161 and 163*c* are applicable.

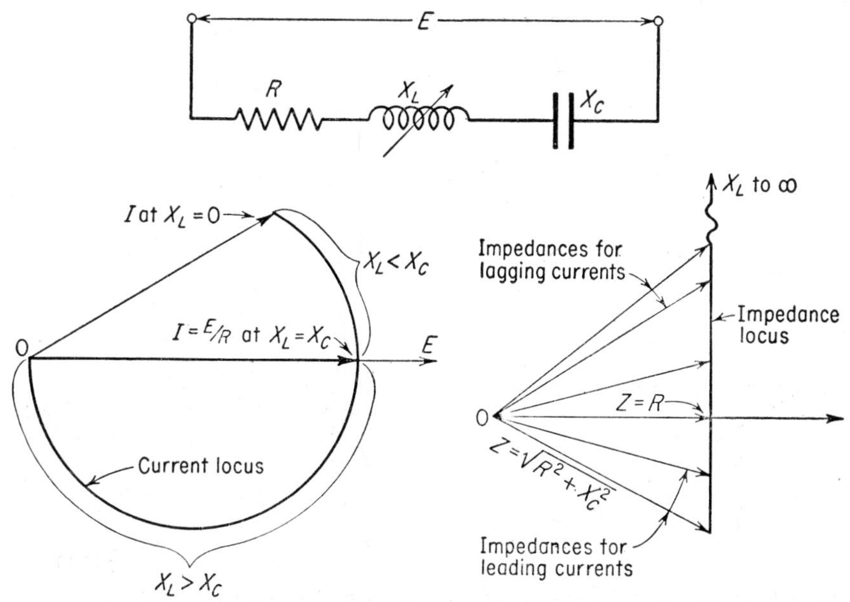

FIG. 164. Current and impedance loci for a series R-L-C circuit in which X_L is varied.

Circuit with Variable X_L. The circular-current locus of Fig. 164 illustrates the relationships existing under conditions of varying X_L. Note particularly that the current (1) leads the voltage when X_L is less than X_C; (2) passes through resonance, and has its maximum value of E/R, when $X_L = X_C$; and (3) lags behind the voltage for all values of X_L that are greater than X_C. Especially significant in the impedance locus of Fig. 164 is the fact that minimum impedance occurs at resonance when $Z = R$; this indicates, of course, that the current will be a maximum then because the effective circuit reactance is zero.

Circuit with Variable X_C. The circular current locus of Fig. 165 illustrates the relationships existing under conditions of varying X_C. Observe that the current (1) lags behind the voltage when X_C is less than X_L; (2) passes through resonance, and has its maximum value of E/R, when $X_C = X_L$; and (3) leads the voltage for all values of X_C that are greater than X_L. Note also in the impedance locus of Fig. 165 that minimum impedance occurs at resonance when $Z = R$; this again verifies the fact that the current will be a maximum then because the effective circuit reactance is zero.

Circuit with Variable Frequency. The behavior of the constant-potential series R-L-C circuit is interesting under conditions of variable frequency for the reason that inductive reactance and capacitive reactance

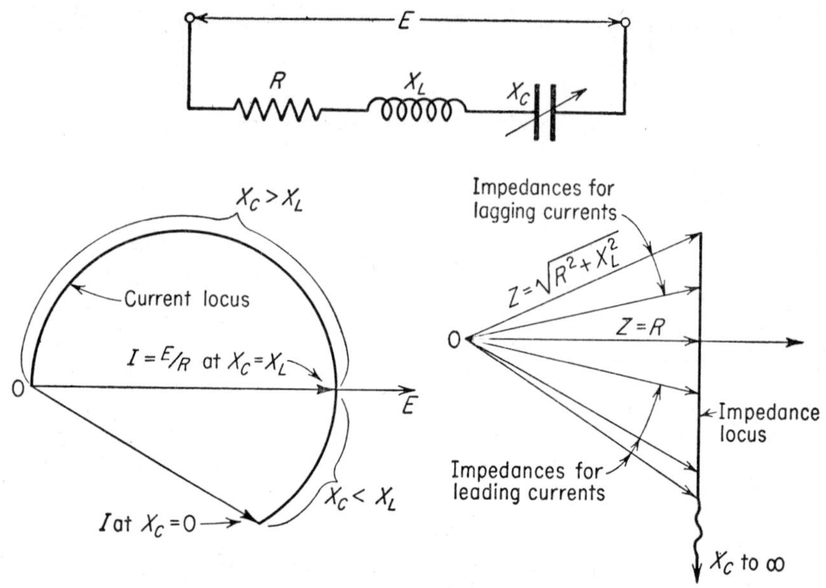

FIG. 165. Current and impedance loci for a series *R-L-C* circuit in which X_C is varied.

are affected in different ways by changes in f. Recalling that X_L is *directly* proportional to f, i.e., $X_L = 2\pi fL$, and that X_C is *inversely* proportional to f, i.e., $X_C = 10^6/2\pi fC$, it should be clear that, in this type of circuit, the current may be made to pass through a complete range of power factors—from lagging, through unity, to leading, and vice versa—by frequency adjustment; moreover, the current locus will be a circle with its diameter resting on the x axis and equal to E/R. The semicircle above the x axis, indicating leading currents, means that X_C is greater than X_L, a situation that implies a frequency that is less than the resonant frequency; the semicircle below the x axis, on the other hand, means that the currents lag behind the voltage because the frequency, now larger than the resonant frequency, makes X_L greater than X_C.

Figure 166 illustrates the foregoing analysis graphically. Note especially that the current and power factor approach zero for comparatively low or high frequencies, with zero-leading power factors at low frequencies and zero-lagging power factors at high frequencies.

EXAMPLE 3. A series circuit consisting of a resistance of 60 ohms, an inductance of 0.4 henry, and a capacitance of 17.6 μf is connected to a variable-frequency source, the potential of which is maintained constant at 120 volts. If the frequency is varied through a range of 40 to 80 cps, calculate (*a*) the resonant frequency, (*b*) the current and power factor at 40 cps, and (*c*) the current and power factor at 80 cps. (*d*) Draw the complete current locus for the problem.

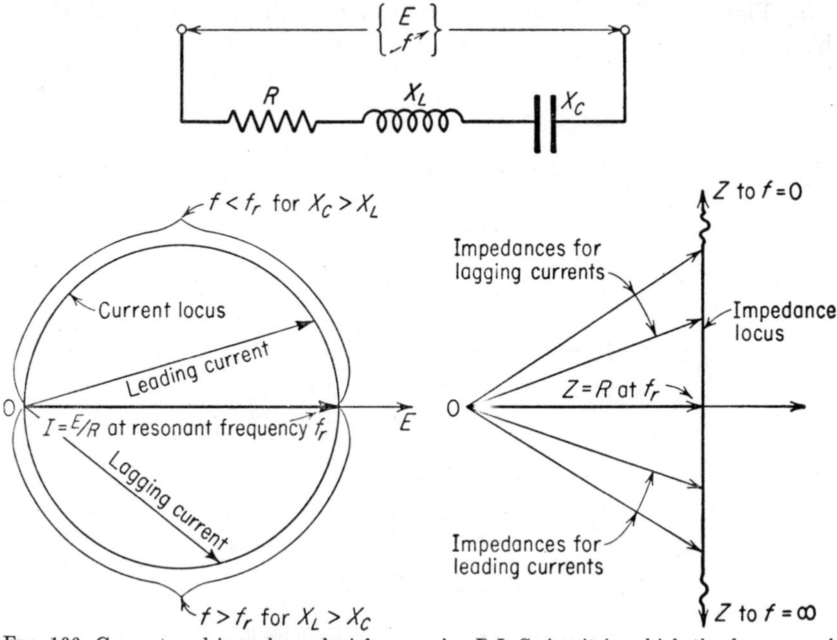

FIG. 166. Current and impedance loci for a series *R-L-C* circuit in which the frequency is varied.

Solution

(a) $$f_r = \frac{10^3}{2\pi\sqrt{0.4 \times 17.6}} = 60 \text{ cps}$$

(b) $$X_{eq} \text{ (at 40 cps)} = \frac{10^6}{2\pi \times 40 \times 17.6} - (2\pi \times 40 \times 0.4) = 226 - 100 = 126 \text{ ohms } (\textit{capacitive})$$

$$I = \frac{120}{\sqrt{(60)^2 + (126)^2}} = 0.86 \text{ amp}$$

$$\cos\Theta = \frac{R}{Z} = \frac{60}{\sqrt{(60)^2 + (126)^2}} = 0.43 \text{ leading}$$

$$\text{PF angle} = \cos^{-1} 0.43 = 64.5° \text{ leading}$$

(c) $$X_{eq} \text{ (at 80 cps)} = (2\pi \times 80 \times 0.4) - \frac{10^6}{2\pi \times 80 \times 17.6} = 200 - 113 = 87 \text{ ohms } (\textit{inductive})$$

$$I = \frac{120}{\sqrt{(60)^2 + (87)^2}} = 1.14 \text{ amp}$$

$$\cos\Theta = \frac{60}{\sqrt{(60)^2 + (87)^2}} = 0.57 \text{ lagging}$$

$$\text{PF angle} = \cos^{-1} 0.57 = 55.2° \text{ lagging}$$

(*d*) Figure 167 shows the current locus and all identifying values for this example.

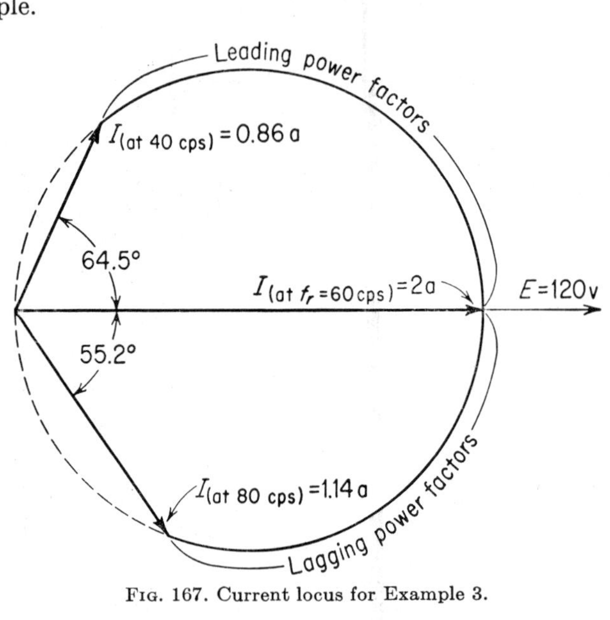

FIG. 167. Current locus for Example 3.

Current Loci for Parallel Circuits. The principles discussed in the foregoing articles may be applied to the plotting of total-current loci in parallel circuits; the latter, when properly interpreted, can then yield information often difficult to obtain by analytical methods. The current locus will, for example, indicate at a glance whether or not a parallel circuit *can* be made resonant, *if* there is more than one value of current at which resonance will occur, *how much* current and *what* power factor may be expected, and *what values* of maximum and minimum current and power factor are possible.

Assuming that the impressed voltage is constant, and that the current varies in only one branch of a parallel circuit, it is generally a simple matter to draw the total-current locus by adding the variable-current locus to the constant-current vector. This is accomplished by superimposing the variable-current locus upon the constant-current vector in such a way that progressively increasing values of changing current are added vectorially to the properly plotted constant-current vector. A number of illustrations and appropriate discussions follow.

Straight-line Current Loci. Figure 168 shows several two-branch parallel circuits in which the current is varied in the *single-element path.* In each case the total-current locus, a straight line, starts from the tip of the constant-current vector and proceeds to lengthen in the proper direction with diminishing values of R, X_L, or X_C. The total-current locus is obvi-

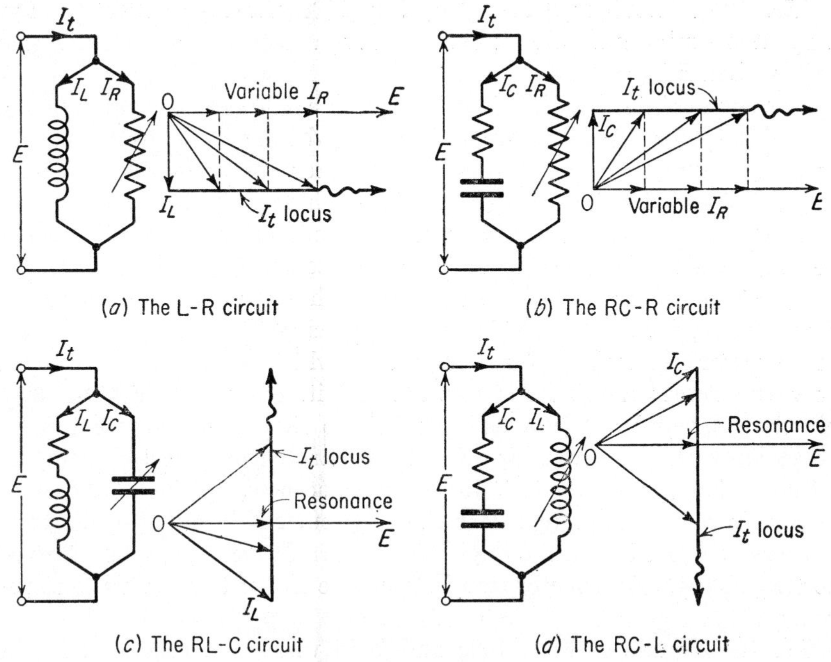

FIG. 168. Two-branch parallel circuits yielding straight-line current loci.

ously the sum of a constant-current vector and a variable-current locus, since any value of total current, measured from the origin to the horizontal or vertical straight line, is the vector sum of the currents in the two branches.

Figure 168*a*, drawn in accordance with the foregoing procedure, is for an *L-R* parallel circuit in which the resistance is varied. Note that the current is a minimum, and lags behind the voltage by 90°, when the resistance is infinite, and proceeds to increase, with accompanying higher values of power factor, as the resistance is decreased. As expected, a circuit like this cannot be tuned to resonance and tends to approach a condition of unity power factor at very low values of resistance.

The *RC-R* circuit of Fig. 168*b* shows how the variable current in a resistance branch adds to the constant current in an *R-C* branch. Here again the total-current locus is a straight line parallel to the x axis, indicating that resonance is not possible.

Figure 168*c* illustrates an *RL-C* circuit in which the current in the capacitance branch is varied. As previously shown analytically (Chap. 13), an arrangement such as this will be in resonance when the quadrature components in the two branches are equal; moreover, as the total-current locus indicates, I_t is a minimum at unity power factor.

The *RC-L* circuit represented by Fig. 168*d* also shows that the total current is a minimum when it passes through resonance, a condition that exists when $EB_C = EB_L$.

Current Loci for RL-RC Parallel Branches. Much of what was discussed in Chaps. 12 and 13 becomes clearer when analyzed by the vector-locus procedure. This is especially true for the two-branch *RL-RC* parallel circuit, illustrated by Fig. 169, in which there are four elements that may be varied. Assuming a constant-potential constant-frequency source, each total-current locus is constructed as follows: (1) draw the constant-current vector to the proper length and at the correct power-factor angle, for the branch in which no change is made; (2) draw the semicircular current locus for the branch in which one element is assumed to vary between the limits of zero and infinite ohms; (3) shift the semicircular current locus to a new position so that its zero-current point coincides with the arrow tip of the constant-current vector, doing so without changing its relative direction. The new position of the semicircular locus will now represent the total-current locus; also, the total current, measured from the origin to the current locus, may be expected to vary as the radius vector sweeps from one end of the semicircle to the other.

For the circuits of Figs. 169*a* and *b*, in which the resistance in the inductive branch R_L *or* the capacitive branch R_C is varied, observe that the total current (1) may be adjusted over a range of leading and lagging power factors, (2) may be adjusted to unity power factor, and (3) has its maximum value for the radius vector that passes through the center of shifted semicircle.

For the circuits of Figs. 169*c* and *d*, in which the inductive reactance X_L *or* the capacitive reactance X_C is varied, observe that the total current (1) may be adjusted over a range of leading and lagging power factors; (2) may have *two* unity-power-factor values; (3) has its minimum value for the radius vector that, extended beyond current locus, passes through the center of the shifted circle.

Although the diagrams of Fig. 169 were drawn for general two-branch parallel circuits it should *not* be inferred that current and power-factor variations and resonance conditions will follow similar patterns for all resistance and reactance combinations. The extent to which these variations will take place will, indeed, depend upon the relative magnitudes of R and X.

EXAMPLE 4. A parallel circuit consists of a 15-ohm capacitive reactance in one branch and a resistance of 15 ohms in series with a variable reactor in another branch. If the circuit voltage is 120 and the inductive reactance is assumed to vary from zero to infinity, draw the total-current

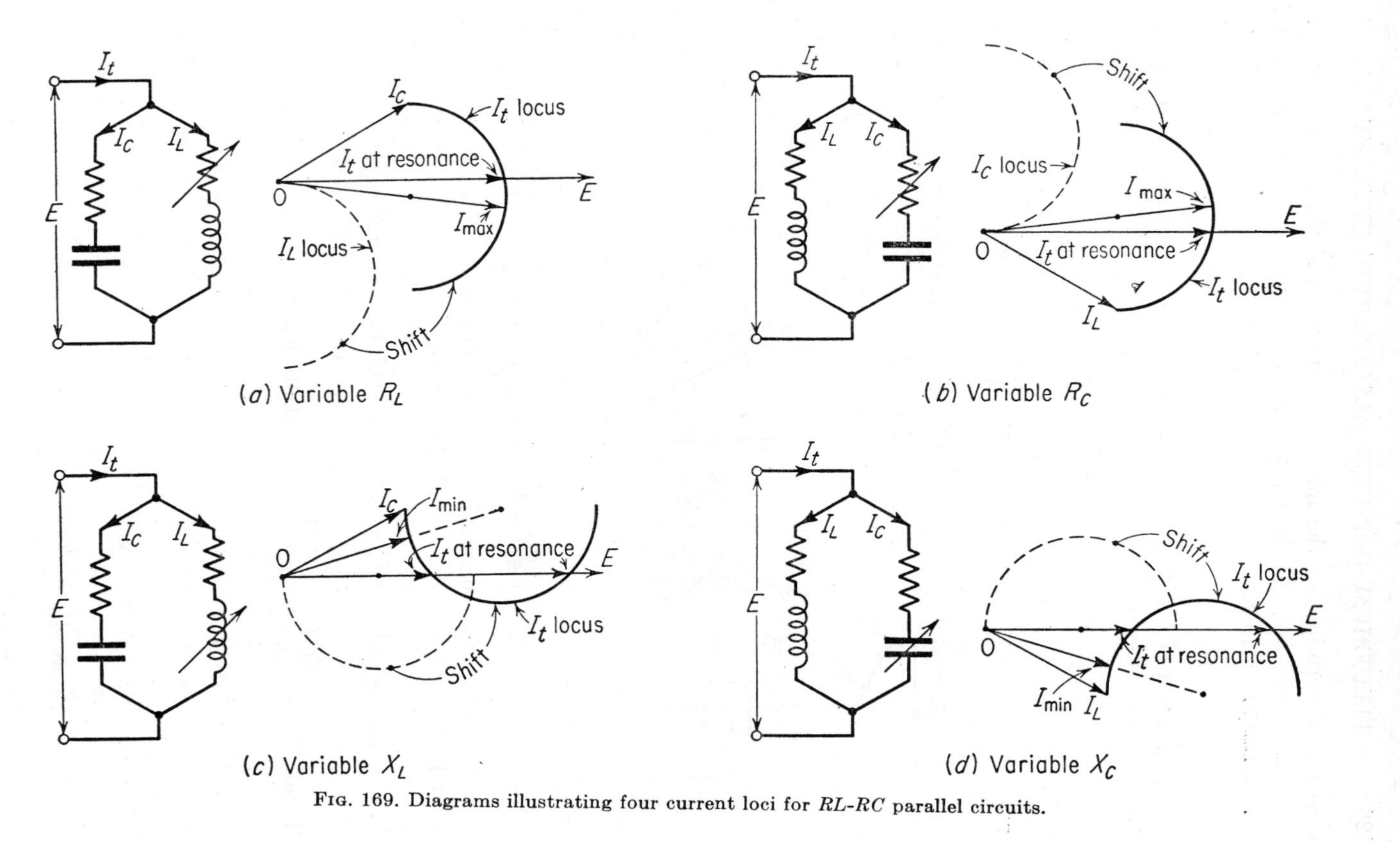

FIG. 169. Diagrams illustrating four current loci for *RL-RC* parallel circuits.

locus and determine (*a*) the minimum current and the power factor at which it occurs, and (*b*) the current at maximum power factor and the maximum power factor.

Solution

The diagram of Fig. 170 was drawn after the capacitance current and the circle diameter were calculated; these are

$$I_C = \frac{120}{15} = 8 \text{ amp}$$

and

$$\text{Circle diameter} = \frac{120}{15} = 8 \text{ amp}$$

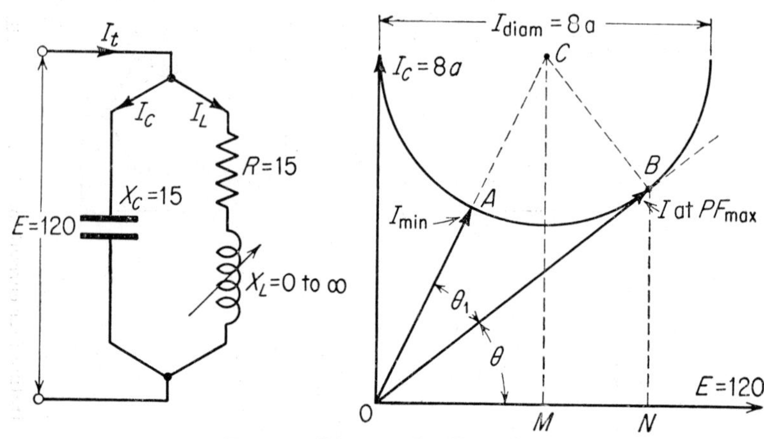

FIG. 170. Diagrams for Example 4.

(*a*) The minimum current is the vector OA, since its extension passes through the center of the semicircle. Thus

$$I_{\text{min}} = OA = OC - AC = \sqrt{(OM)^2 + (CM)^2} - AC$$
$$= \sqrt{(4)^2 + (8)^2} - 4 = 4.95 \text{ amp}$$

$$\text{PF (at } I_{\text{min}}) = \frac{OM}{OC} = \frac{4}{(4 + 4.95)} = 0.447 \text{ leading}$$

(*b*) The current at maximum power factor is vector OB, since the tangent line makes the *smallest* angle with the reference voltage vector.

$$I \text{ (at max PF)} = OB = \sqrt{(OC)^2 - (CB)^2} = \sqrt{(4.95 + 4)^2 - (4)^2}$$
$$= 8 \text{ amp}$$

$$\theta_1 = \sin^{-1} \frac{4}{8.95} = 26.6°$$
$$2\theta_1 = 53.2°$$
$$\theta = 90° - 53.2° = 36.8°$$

Therefore $\qquad PF_{max} = \cos 36.8° = 0.8$ leading

EXAMPLE 5. A parallel circuit consists of 25-ohm inductive reactance in one branch and a resistance of 6.25 ohms in series with a variable capacitor in another branch. If the circuit voltage is 125 and the capacitive reactance is assumed to vary from zero to infinity, draw the total-current locus and determine (*a*) the minimum current and the power factor at which it occurs, (*b*) the maximum current and the power factor at which it occurs, and (*c*) the two values of unity-power-factor current.

Solution

The diagram of Fig. 171 was drawn after the inductance current and the circle diameter were calculated; these are

$$I_L = \frac{125}{25} = 5 \text{ amp}$$

and

$$\text{Circle diameter} = \frac{125}{6.25} = 20 \text{ amp}$$

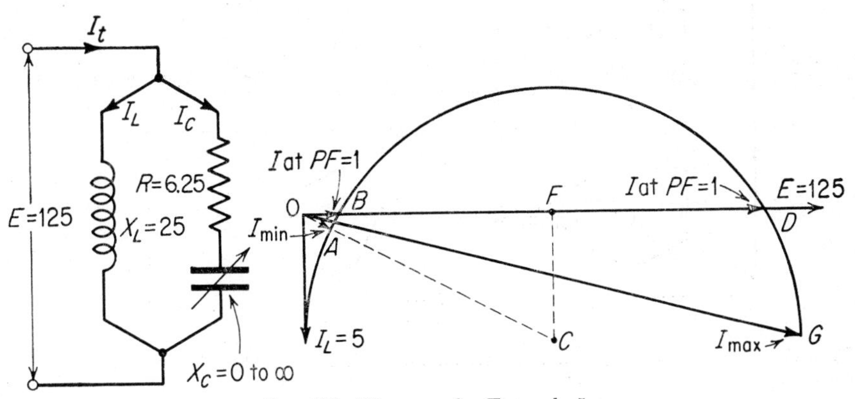

FIG. 171. Diagrams for Example 5.

(*a*) The minimum current is the vector OA, since its extension passes through the center of the semicircle. Thus

$$I_{min} = OA = \sqrt{(OF)^2 + (FC)^2} - AC = \sqrt{(10)^2 + (5)^2} - 10 = 1.18 \text{ amp}$$

$$\text{PF (at } I_{min}) = \frac{OF}{OC} = \frac{10}{11.18} = 0.895 \text{ lagging}$$

(*b*) $$I_{max} = OG = \sqrt{(20)^2 + (5)^2} = 20.6 \text{ amp}$$

$$\text{PF (at } I_{max}) = \frac{20}{20.6} = 0.97 \text{ lagging}$$

(c) $BF = FD = \sqrt{(BC)^2 - (FC)^2} = \sqrt{(10)^2 - (5)^2} = 8.65$

I (at PF = 1) $= OB = OF - BF = 10 - 8.65 = 1.35$ amp

Also

$$I \text{ (at PF} = 1) = OD = OB + BF + FD$$
$$= 1.35 + 8.65 + 8.65 = 18.65 \text{ amp}$$

The Constant-current Parallel Circuit. When it is necessary to set up circuits that are characterized by special requirements, it is often found that their design is facilitated by the use of vector-loci principles. One such problem, for example, concerns a circuit in which the power factor must be varied between very wide limits, say between zero lagging and zero leading, but whose current must remain substantially constant throughout the entire power-factor range. This is readily accomplished by employing a two-branch parallel circuit similar to that of Fig. 172,

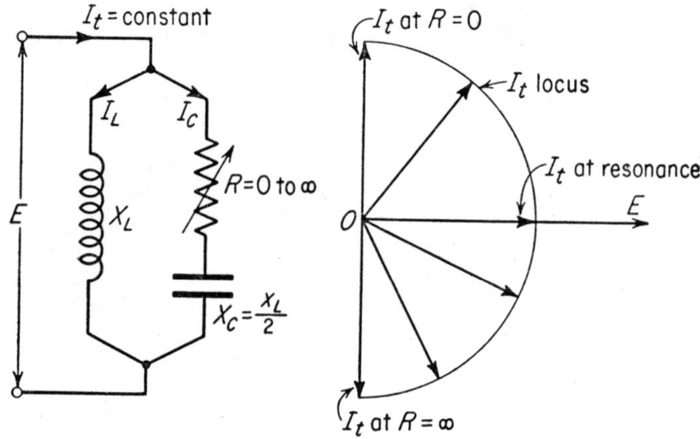

FIG. 172. A two-branch parallel circuit and current locus illustrating constant-current variable-power-factor operation.

and in which the ohmic value of X_C is one-half X_L. Looking at the circuit from the point of view of the two limits of R, i.e., infinity and zero, when $R = \infty$, $I = E/X_L$, and the power factor is zero lagging: when $R = 0$, $I = (E/X_C) - (E/X_L) = (2E/X_L) - (E/X_L) = E/X_L$, and the power factor is zero leading.

Referring to Fig. 172, note that the semicircular current locus has a diameter that is *twice* the constant-current vector represented by I_L. This means, of course, that the center of the semicircle is at the origin, and any change in resistance will merely rotate the total-current vector. At $R = \infty$ the current vector is directed straight down, and at $R = 0$

it is vertically up. Resonance occurs when the quadrature currents in the two branches are equal.

Vector Locus Applied to Induction-motor Performance. One of the most useful applications of the vector locus is in connection with the analysis of induction-motor performance. Such use is possible because this type of motor may be represented by a two-branch parallel circuit in which a variable resistor can be made equivalent to the machine's mechanical load and replace it, while all other elements are constant. Figure 173 illustrates a typical circle diagram for such a motor plotted, as

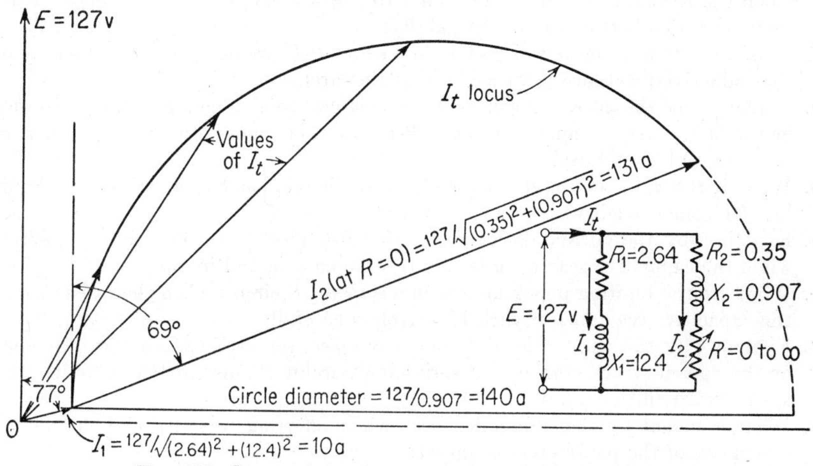

FIG. 173. Current locus for a typical a-c induction motor.

is customary, with the constant voltage vector as a *vertical* reference. Actual resistance and inductive reactance values, taken from a 10-hp-motor design, are shown on the connections diagram, and calculated results for the total-current locus are given on the latter.

When the motor is operating without mechanical load the variable resistance R is infinite and the only current is I_1, which is 10 amp. As load is applied to the motor the value of R, which replaces and is equivalent to the load, diminishes; I_2 therefore increases, and with it the total current I_t. The vector current, represented by distances from the origin O to the total-current locus, thus progresses from the arrow tip of I_1 to the extreme end of the arc. In this example the current can vary between values of 10 and 131 amp, with approximately 26 amp being a normal full-load figure. In practice a circle diagram as indicated will yield such important information as current values for different loads, efficiencies, power factors, torques, maximum values of torque, horsepower output, and power factor, and other quantities.

Questions

1. Define *vector locus.*
2. Under what conditions is a uniform current change produced in a circuit? Give examples to illustrate your answer.
3. What general information is it possible to obtain from vector loci?
4. What is the shape of the current locus in a series *R-L* circuit when the resistance is varied uniformly? when the inductive reactance is varied uniformly?
5. What is the value of the diameter of the semicircle locus in a series *R-L* circuit in which the resistance is varied? in which the inductive reactance is varied?
6. Explain why the current locus in a series *R-L* circuit is a complete semicircle when the resistance is varied between zero and infinity; when the inductive reactance is varied between zero and infinity.
7. What are the limiting power factors in a series *R-L* circuit when the resistance or the inductive reactance is varied? Explain carefully.
8. Explain why the current locus is not a *complete* semicircle when the resistance or the inductive reactance in a series *R-L* circuit changes between limits that are not zero and/or infinity.
9. What is the value of the diameter of the semicircle locus in a series *R-C* circuit in which the capacitive reactance is varied?
10. Explain why the current locus in a series *R-C* circuit is a complete semicircle when the capacitive reactance is varied between zero and infinity.
11. What are the limiting power factors in a series *R-C* circuit when the resistance or the capacitive reactance is varied? Explain carefully.
12. Explain why the current locus is not a *complete* semicircle when the resistance or the capacitive reactance in a series *R-C* circuit changes between limits that are not zero and/or infinity.
13. What is meant by the *impedance locus* when referring to series *R-X* circuits in which one of the parameters is varied?
14. What is the shape of the impedance locus of a series *R-X* circuit in which one of the parameters is varied? Indicate how these loci are related to the x and y axes.
15. How should a series R-X_L-X_C circuit be regarded when the resistance is varied? Explain for the conditions in which X_L is greater than X_C, and X_C is greater than X_L.
16. Why is it possible for the power factor to be lagging *and* leading in a series circuit in which X_L or X_C is varied? Explain carefully.
17. When is the power factor unity in a series R-X_L-X_C circuit under conditions of varying X_L? under conditions of varying X_C?
18. What is the diameter of the circular locus in a series R-X_L-X_C circuit when X_L is varied? when X_C is varied?
19. What is the shape of the current locus in a series *R-L-C* circuit in which the frequency is varied over wide limits?
20. What is the diameter of the circular locus in a series *R-L-C* circuit in which the frequency is varied? What is the position of the diameter? Why does the diameter represent the condition of resonance?
21. List some of the important information that may be obtained from the total-current locus of a parallel circuit.
22. What general procedure should be followed for the construction of the total-current locus of a two-branch parallel circuit? Explain carefully.
23. What is the shape of the total-current locus of a two-branch parallel circuit in which the parameter in a *single-unit* branch is varied? Make sketches showing

the position of such loci for variations of resistance, inductive reactance, and capacitive reactance.

24. Describe the procedure for constructing the total-current locus of a two-branch *RL-RC* parallel circuit.

25. Explain why only *one* current of resonance is possible when a resistor is varied in a two-branch *RL-RC* parallel circuit.

26. Explain why *two* currents of resonance are possible when an inductive reactance or a capacitive reactance is varied in a two-branch *RL-RC* parallel circuit.

27. Under what conditions is it *not* possible to tune a two-branch *RL-RC* circuit to resonance? Explain carefully, using the current-locus diagram to illustrate your answer.

28. Illustrate, by drawing a total-current locus for a two-branch parallel circuit, how the power factor can be lagging only; how the power factor can be leading only.

29. Using a total-current locus for a two-branch parallel circuit to illustrate your answer, explain how to determine (*a*) the minimum current, (*b*) the maximum current, (*c*) the maximum power factor, (*d*) the minimum power factor.

30. Make sketches to illustrate how a constant-current variable-power-factor circuit may be constructed, and explain its operation.

31. Make a sketch showing how the vector locus is applied to the analysis of an induction motor. Carefully explain its usefulness for the determination of such data as minimum and maximum current, and minimum and maximum power factor.

Problems

1. An impedance coil having a resistance of 5 ohms and an inductive reactance of 12 ohms is connected in series with a variable resistance which is adjustable from 0 to 30 ohms. Assuming a constant impressed emf of 156 volts, draw the current locus for the circuit indicating thereon (*a*) the circle diameter, (*b*) maximum and minimum values of current, (*c*) the power-factor angles for maximum and minimum currents.

2. An impedance coil having a resistance of 4 ohms and an inductive reactance of 2 ohms is connected in series with a reactor that is variable between 1 and 11.4 ohms. Assuming a constant applied emf of 120 volts, draw the current locus for the circuit indicating thereon (*a*) the circle diameter, (*b*) the maximum and minimum values of current, (*c*) the power-factor angles for maximum and minimum currents.

3. In the circuit of Prob. 2 the current is to be maintained constant at 9 amp by adjusting the impressed emf as the inductive reactance is varied between 1 and 11.4 ohms. Using the current as a horizontal reference vector sketch the voltage locus, indicating thereon (*a*) the circle diameter of the voltage locus, (*b*) the minimum and maximum values of voltage, (*c*) the power-factor angles for minimum and maximum voltages.

4. A series circuit, consisting of a 5-ohm resistor, a 106-μf capacitor, and a resistor that may be varied between 0 and 50 ohms, is connected to a 125-volt 60-cycle source. Draw the current locus for the circuit, indicating thereon (*a*) the circle diameter, (*b*) the maximum and minimum values of current, (*c*) the power-factor angles for maximum and minimum current.

5. A series circuit consisting of a 20-ohm resistor, a 50-μf capacitor, and a 0.244-henry inductor is connected to a 120-volt variable-frequency source. (*a*) At what frequency will the circuit be in resonance, and what will be the current under this condition? (*b*) What will be the current and power-factor angle when the frequency is 30 cps? (*c*) What will be the current and power-factor angle when the frequency is 70 cps? Using the calculated data draw the current locus.

6. A 15-ohm capacitive reactance is connected in parallel with a series combination consisting of a 15-ohm resistor and an inductive reactance that is variable between zero and infinite ohms. Draw the total-current locus, assuming a constant applied emf of 120 volts, and calculate (*a*) the minimum current and the power factor under this condition, (*b*) the maximum power factor and the value of the current under this condition.

7. A 15-ohm inductive reactance is connected in parallel with a series combination consisting of a 7.5-ohm resistor and a capacitive reactance that is variable between zero and infinite ohms. Draw a total-current locus, assuming a constant applied emf of 120 volts, and calculate (*a*) the unity-power-factor current, (*b*) the minimum current and the power factor under this condition, (*c*) the maximum current and the power factor under this condition.

8. A 12-ohm resistor is connected in parallel with a series combination consisting of a 12-ohm inductive reactance and a resistor that is variable between zero and infinite ohms. Draw a total-current locus, assuming a constant applied emf of 120 volts, and calculate (*a*) the unity-power-factor current, (*b*) the maximum current and the power factor under this condition, (*c*) the minimum power factor and the current under this condition.

9. The following information is given in connection with a two-branch parallel circuit: $E = 120$, $R_C = 7.5$ ohms, $X_C = 7.5$ ohms, $X_L = 10$ ohms, $R_L = 0$ to ∞. Draw the total-current locus and calculate (*a*) the unity-power-factor current, (*b*) the minimum power factor and the corresponding current, (*c*) the maximum current and the corresponding power factor, (*d*) the minimum lagging power factor and the corresponding current.

10. A series combination consisting of a 16-ohm resistor and an inductive reactance of 12 ohms is connected in parallel with a capacitive reactance that is variable between 12 ohms and infinity. Draw the total-current locus, assuming an impressed emf of 120 volts, and calculate (*a*) the unity-power-factor current, (*b*) the minimum lagging power factor and the corresponding current, (*c*) the minimum leading power factor and the corresponding current.

11. A 25-ohm capacitive reactance is connected in parallel with a series combination consisting of a 12.5-ohm inductive reactance and a resistance that is variable between zero and infinite ohms. Draw the total-current locus, assuming a constant applied emf of 125 volts, and calculate the unity-power-factor current, and the minimum power factors and their corresponding currents.

12. A capacitive reactance of 40 ohms is connected in parallel with a series combination consisting of a 10-ohm resistor and an inductive reactance that is variable between zero and infinite ohms. Draw a total-current locus, assuming a constant impressed emf of 120 volts, and calculate (*a*) the minimum current and the corresponding power factor, (*b*) the maximum current and the corresponding power factor, (*c*) the two unity-power-factor currents, (*d*) the minimum lagging power factor and the corresponding current.

13. For what value of resistance in the series branch of Prob. 12 will the circuit be resonant at only one value of inductive reactance? Draw the total-current locus under this condition and determine the unity-power-factor current.

14. A 48-ohm capacitive reactance is connected in parallel with a series combination consisting of a 24-ohm resistor and a capacitive reactance that is variable between zero and infinite ohms. Draw a total-current locus, assuming a constant impressed emf of 120 volts, and calculate (*a*) the maximum current and the corresponding power factor, (*b*) the maximum power factor and the corresponding current.

15. The following particulars are given in connection with the so-called equivalent circuit of an induction motor: $R_1 = 4.4$ ohms and $X_1 = 20.8$ ohms for the constant-impedance branch; $R_2 = 0.74$ ohm, $X_2 = 1.64$ ohms, and $R = 0$ to ∞ for the variable-impedance branch; $E = 254$ volts. Draw a total-current locus similar to that of Fig. 173, indicating thereon (*a*) the circle diameter, (*b*) the current and power-factor angle for the constant-impedance branch, (*c*) the maximum current and its corresponding power-factor angle for the variable-impedance branch.

CHAPTER 15

NETWORK LAWS, THEOREMS, AND PRINCIPLES

General Aspects of Complex-circuit Analysis. The solution of a-c circuit problems involving complex arrangements of resistors, inductors, and capacitors, often with two or more sources of emf, becomes exceedingly difficult by the straightforward methods previously discussed. This is apparent when it is remembered that the parameters and voltages in a-c systems, unlike those in d-c circuits where all quantities are scalars, must be treated as vectors, which, in turn, must employ complex-algebra techniques. To simplify such solutions several helpful "tools," in the form of laws, theorems, and principles, have been developed; when properly used they will reduce the amount of calculation considerably.

Much of the subject matter of Chap. 4, Kirchhoff's Laws and Basic Theorems, is applicable to a-c networks, provided that the circuit elements, voltages, and currents are regarded as complex quantities. Thus, for example, *Kirchhoff's laws* and *Thévenin's theorem* may be reworded to account for *impedances*, and *vector* sums of voltages and currents, instead of resistances, and algebraic sums of voltages and currents; similar restatements of the *superposition theorem*, the Δ-Y and Y-Δ transformations, and the *maximum-power-transfer theorem* are also permissible. In addition, several other theorems and principles have been developed to further facilitate the analysis of complex a-c circuits.

Kirchhoff's Laws. The two laws, originally expressed by Kirchhoff to apply to d-c circuits, are suitable for a-c networks when restated as follows:

1. *The current law: the vector sum of the currents at any junction of an electric circuit is zero.*

2. *The voltage law: the vector sum of the emfs and the impedance voltages in any continuous path of an electric circuit is zero.*

These laws may be used only under conditions that are represented by *linear-bilateral* circuit elements as contrasted with *nonlinear-unilateral* devices. The terms merely indicate whether or not the current is proportional to the voltage, and if the circuit behaves similarly or not for positive and negative voltages. Common resistors, air-core inductors, and capacitors are, in this respect, linear, whereas vacuum and gas-filled tubes, and iron-core inductors are nonlinear. All types of rectifiers, and these include selenium and copper-oxide units as well as vacuum and gas-filled tubes, are unilateral, whereas resistors, inductors, and capacitors are bilateral.

Current and voltage equations are set up in essentially the same way as was done for d-c circuits. However, when there are two or more sources of voltage it will be necessary to take the added precaution to specify them so that they correspond to properly labeled minus (−) and plus (+) symbols on the circuit diagrams; this is essential for the purpose of maintaining the current vector relations. To illustrate, consider Fig. 174, which shows two generators delivering current to a load impedance through a pair of line impedances. Note particularly the polarity

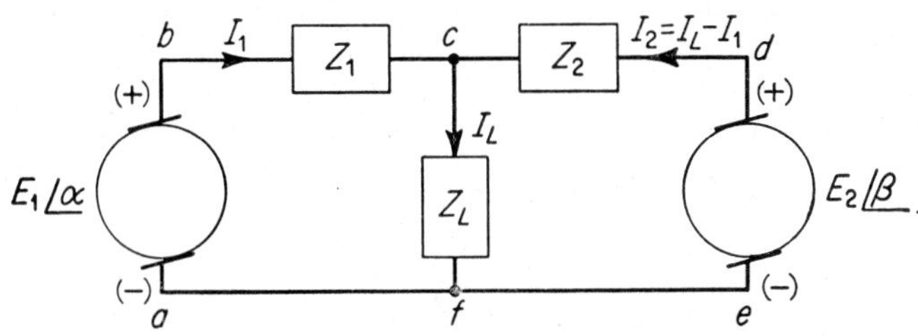

FIG. 174. Circuit diagram showing a load impedance connected to two generators through two line impedances.

markings on the generators since they relate to the angles attached to the polar form of the voltages. Specifically $E_1\underline{/\alpha}$ refers to a voltage rise *through* the generator from a to b, i.e., from *minus to plus;* also $E_2\underline{/\beta}$ refers to a voltage rise through the generator from e to d, i.e., from minus to plus. If, for example, $E_1\underline{/\alpha} = 100\underline{/30°}$ volts, its corresponding rectangular form will be $(86.6 + j50)$ volts. Conversely, $-(E_1\underline{/\alpha})$ represents a voltage through the generator from b to a, i.e., from *plus to minus,* so that $-(100\underline{/30°})$ volts is, in the rectangular form, $(-86.6 - j50)$ volts.

Referring to Fig. 174, assume that it is desired to determine the *vector* currents I_1, I_2, and I_L, the indicated arrow directions of which are chosen arbitrarily. Since I_L is the vector sum of I_1 and I_2 two voltage equations may be written as follows:

$$E_1\underline{/\alpha} - I_1Z_1 - I_LZ_L = 0$$

and

$$E_2\underline{/\beta} - (I_L - I_1)Z_2 - I_LZ_L = 0$$

When the polar forms of the voltages and impedances are replaced by their equivalent rectangular coordinates the two expressions may be solved simultaneously to yield the three currents.

EXAMPLE 1. The following information is given in connection with Fig. 174: $E_1 = 120\underline{/0°}$, $E_2 = 120\underline{/36.9°}$, $Z_1 = Z_2 = 12\underline{/0°}$, $Z_L = 12\underline{/90°}$. Calculate the values of I_L, I_1, and I_2.

Solution

Using the rectangular coordinates for the various quantities,

$$E_1 = 120$$
$$E_2 = 96 + j72$$
$$Z_1 = 12$$
$$Z_2 = 12$$
$$Z_L = j12$$

The two voltage equations are

$$120 - 12I_1 - j12I_L = 0$$

or

$$I_1 = 10 - jI_L$$

and

$$96 + j72 - 12(I_L - I_1) - j12I_L = 0$$

or

$$I_1 - I_L - jI_L = -8 - j6$$

Substituting the value of I_1 from the first equation into the second.

$$10 - jI_L - I_L - jI_L = -8 - j6$$

or

$$I_L(1 + j2) = 18 + j6$$

from which

$$I_L = \frac{18 + j6}{1 + j2} = \frac{18.98/18.5^\circ}{2.24/63.5^\circ} = 8.48/-45^\circ \text{ amp}$$

Also

$$I_1 = 10 - jI_L = 10 - (j8.48/-45^\circ) = 10 - 8.48/45^\circ$$
$$= 10 - (6 + j6) = 4 - j6 = 7.2/56.2^\circ \text{ amp}$$

and

$$I_2 = I_L - I_1 = 6 - j6 - 4 + j6 = 2/0^\circ \text{ amp}$$

The Superposition Theorem. When a bilateral-linear a-c network is complicated by the presence of two or more sources of emf it may be treated as though each voltage energizes the circuit from its position independently of all other voltages, in each case assuming the latter to be replaced by their internal impedances; the composite current at any point in the circuit then becomes the vector sum of the independent currents acting simultaneously. This important principle is extremely helpful in network analysis because it eliminates the necessity of setting up and solving several simultaneous equations, each one often involving complex quantities. Called the *superposition theorem*, it may be stated as follows:

In a network of impedances that is energized by two or more sources of emf, (a) the current in any impedance or (b) the voltage across any impedance is equal (a) to the vector sum of the separate currents in the impedance or (b) to the voltages across the impedance, assuming that each source of emf, acting independently of the others, is applied separately in turn while the others are replaced by their respective internal values of impedance.

A typical problem, similar to that of Example 1, will now be solved to illustrate the application of the superposition theorem.

EXAMPLE 2. The circuit diagram of Fig. 175*a* shows two generators delivering current to an inductive-load impedance through a pair of line impedances. For the values indicated calculate the load current I_L, the load voltage E_L, and the load power P_L.

Solution

The problem will be divided into the following three parts: (1) the determination of I_{L_1} assuming generator 2 to be replaced by a short circuit as in Fig. 175*b*; (2) the determination of I_{L_2} assuming generator 1 to be replaced by a short circuit as in Fig. 175*c*; (3) the determination of the actual load current I_L, the load voltage E_L, and the load power P_L.

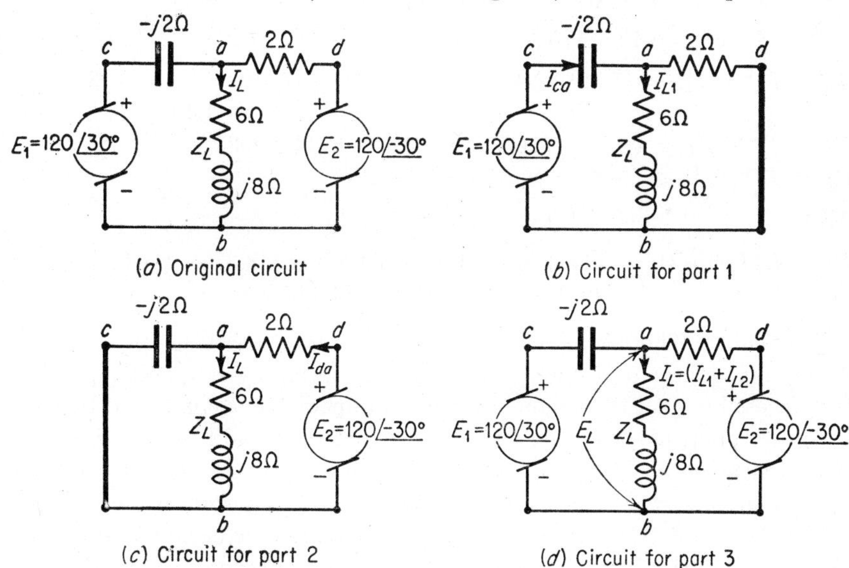

FIG. 175. Circuit diagram for Example 2 illustrating the superposition theorem.

Part 1 (refer to Fig. 175*b*):

$$Z_{ab} = \frac{(6 + j8)(2)}{(6 + j8) + (2)} = \frac{12 + j16}{8 + j8} \times \frac{8 - j8}{8 - j8} = 1.75 + j0.25$$

$$Z_{cb} = -j2 + 1.75 + j0.25 = 1.75 - j1.75 = 2.47\underline{/-45^\circ}$$

$$I_{ca} = \frac{120\underline{/30^\circ}}{2.47\underline{/-45^\circ}} = 48.6\underline{/75^\circ}$$

$$I_{L_1} = \frac{E_1 - (I_{ca}Z_{ca})}{Z_L} = \frac{(104 + j60) - [(48.6\underline{/75^\circ})(2\underline{/-90^\circ})]}{6 + j8}$$

$$= \frac{(104 + j60) - (94 - j25.2)}{6 + j8} = \frac{10 + j85.2}{6 + j8} \times \frac{6 - j8}{6 - j8} = \frac{742 + j431}{100}$$

$$= 7.42 + j4.31$$

Part 2 (refer to Fig. 175*c*):

$$Z_{ab} = \frac{(6 + j8)(-j2)}{(6 + j8) + (-j2)} = \frac{16 - j12}{6 + j6} \times \frac{6 - j6}{6 - j6} = 0.333 - j2.333$$

$$Z_{db} = 2 + 0.333 - j2.333 = 2.333 - j2.333 = 3.3\underline{/-45^\circ}$$

$$I_{da} = \frac{120\underline{/-30^\circ}}{3.3\underline{/-45^\circ}} = 36.4\underline{/15^\circ}$$

$$I_{L_2} = \frac{E_2 - (I_{da}Z_{da})}{Z_L} = \frac{(104 - j60) - [(36.4\underline{/15^\circ})(2)]}{6 + j8}$$

$$= \frac{(104 - j60) - (70.3 + j18.8)}{6 + j8} = \frac{33.7 - j78.8}{6 + j8} \times \frac{6 - j8}{6 - j8}$$

$$= \frac{-428 - j742}{100} = -4.28 - j7.42$$

Part 3 (refer to Fig. 175*d*):

$$I_L = I_{L_1} + I_{L_2} = (7.42 + j4.31) + (-4.28 - j7.42) = 3.14 - j3.11$$
$$= 4.42\underline{/-44.8^\circ} \text{ amp}$$

$$E_L = I_L \times Z_L = (4.42\underline{/-44.8^\circ})(10\underline{/53.1^\circ}) = 44.2\underline{/8.3^\circ} \text{ volts}$$

$$P_L = I_L^2 \times R_L = (4.42)^2 \times 6 = 117 \text{ watts}$$

Also

$$P_L = E_L I_L \cos \Theta_L = (44.2\underline{/8.3^\circ})(4.42\underline{/-44.8^\circ}) \cos [8.3^\circ - (-44.8^\circ)]$$
$$= 44.2 \times 4.42 \cos 53.1^\circ = 117 \text{ watts}$$

Thévenin's Theorem. Complex a-c circuits consisting of bilateral-linear impedances and one or more sources of supply frequently present two accessible load terminals. When an impedance is connected to such a two-terminal network the load current may be readily determined by the application of *Thévenin's theorem*, which may be stated as follows:

In any two-terminal network of bilateral-linear impedances and sources of emf, the current in a load impedance connected to the output terminals is equal to the current that would exist in the same impedance if it were connected in series with (a) a simple emf whose voltage is measured at the open-circuited network terminals and (b) a simple impedance whose magnitude is that of the network looking back from the two terminals into the network with all the sources of emf replaced by their internal impedances.

The physical significance of this extremely useful theorem is illustrated by Fig. 176, which represents the network *before* and *after* the impedance Z_L is connected to the load terminals. The schematic of Fig. 176*a* indicates the condition in an open circuit, in which the voltage E_o has, presumably, been determined by measurement or calculation; Fig. 176*b* shows a known impedance Z_L connected to the load terminals, in which the internal impedance of the network Z_i, looking back into the network with all the sources of emf replaced by their internal imped-

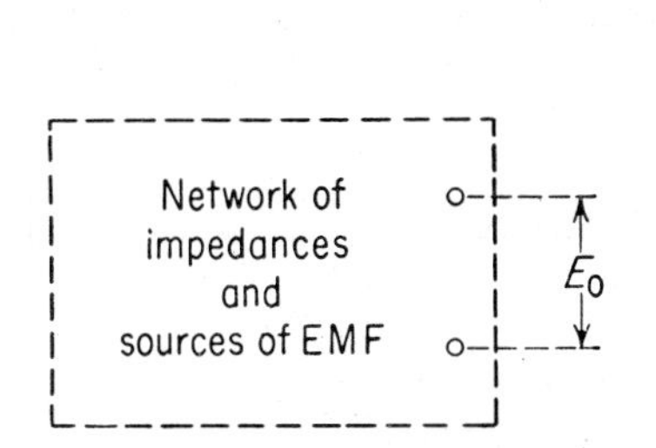

(a) Schematic of original network

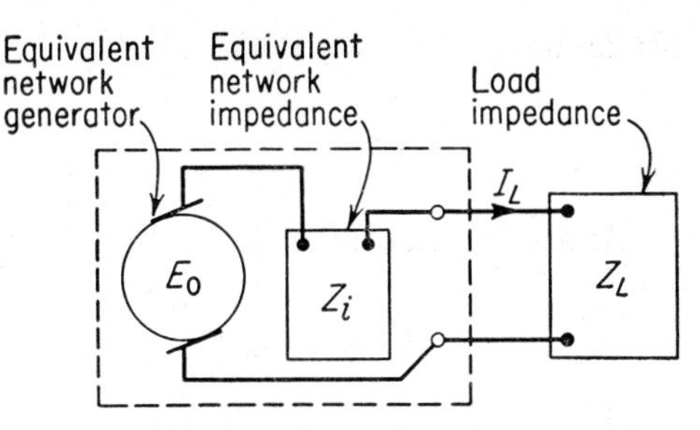

(b) Equivalent circuit by Thevenin's theorem

FIG. 176. Sketches illustrating how a network is converted to an equivalent Thévenin's-theorem circuit.

ances, has been determined. In accordance with Thévenin's theorem the load current is

$$I_L = \frac{E_o}{Z_i + Z_L} \tag{121}$$

This equation may be verified mathematically by considering the so-called *T-network*, an arrangement of impedances that is basic to a-c

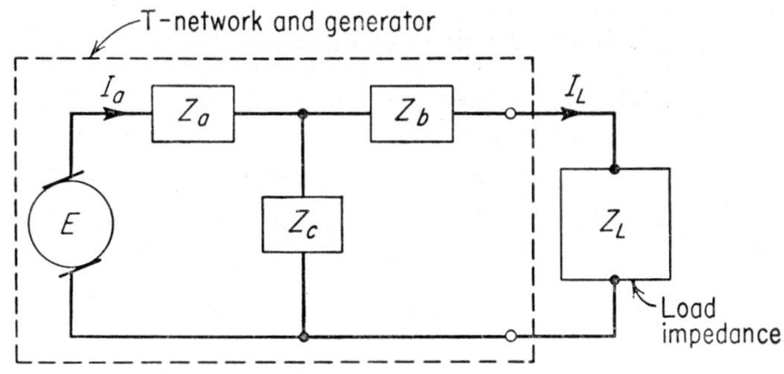

FIG. 177. Circuit diagram showing a load impedance connected to a source of emf through a T-network.

circuit theory. Referring to Fig. 177, which represents such a network, the total current delivered by the generator is

$$\begin{aligned} I_a &= \frac{E}{Z_a[Z_c(Z_b + Z_L)/(Z_b + Z_c + Z_L)]} \\ &= \frac{E(Z_b + Z_c + Z_L)}{Z_aZ_b + Z_cZ_a + Z_aZ_L + Z_bZ_c + Z_cZ_L} \\ &= \frac{E(Z_b + Z_c + Z_L)}{Z_aZ_b + Z_bZ_c + Z_cZ_a + Z_L(Z_a + Z_c)} \end{aligned}$$

But the load current is equal to

$$I_L = I_a \frac{Z_c}{Z_b + Z_c + Z_L}$$

It follows, therefore, that

$$I_L = \frac{EZ_c}{Z_aZ_b + Z_bZ_c + Z_cZ_a + Z_L(Z_a + Z_c)}$$

Analyzing the same circuit by Thévenin's theorem,

$$E_0 = E \times \frac{Z_c}{Z_a + Z_c}$$

and

$$Z_i = Z_b + \frac{Z_cZ_a}{Z_a + Z_c} = \frac{Z_aZ_b + Z_bZ_c + Z_cZ_a}{Z_a + Z_c}$$

By Eq. (121),

$$I_L = \frac{E \times [Z_c/(Z_a + Z_c)]}{[(Z_aZ_b + Z_bZ_c + Z_cZ_a)/(Z_a + Z_c)] + Z_L}$$

which reduces to

$$I_L = \frac{EZ_c}{Z_aZ_b + Z_bZ_c + Z_cZ_a + Z_L(Z_a + Z_c)}$$

Note that the equations for the load current I_L are exactly the same by both methods of analysis.

Two examples will now be given to illustrate Thévenin's theorem.

EXAMPLE 3. The following data are given in connection with the T-network and load of Fig. 177: $E = 120\underline{/0^\circ}$, $Z_a = Z_b = -j30$ ohms (capacitive reactance), $Z_c = 30$ ohms (resistance), $Z_L = 45$ ohms (resistance). Using Thévenin's theorem, calculate the load current, voltage, and power.

Solution

$$E_0 = 120 \times \frac{30}{30 - j30} = 120 \times \frac{30}{30\sqrt{2}\underline{/-45^\circ}} = 85\underline{/45^\circ}$$

$$Z_i = -j30 + \frac{30 \times 30\underline{/-90}}{30 - j30} = -j30 + \frac{900\underline{/-90}}{30\sqrt{2}\underline{/-45}} = 15 - j45$$

$$I_L = \frac{E_o}{Z_i + Z_L} = \frac{85\underline{/45^\circ}}{(15 - j45) + 45} = \frac{85\underline{/45^\circ}}{75\underline{/-36.9^\circ}} = 1.133\underline{/81.9^\circ} \text{ amp}$$

$$E_L = (1.133\underline{/81.9^\circ})(45) = 51\underline{/81.9^\circ}$$

$$P_L = I_L^2R = (1.133)^2 \times 45 = 57.8 \text{ watts}$$

EXAMPLE 4. Referring to Fig. 177, assume the following values for the various quantities: $E = 120\underline{/0^\circ}$, $Z_a = 40$ ohms (resistance), $Z_b = 15.6 + j19.2$ ohms (resistance-inductive reactance), $Z_c = -j30$ ohms (capacitive reactance), $Z_L = -j40$ ohms (capacitive reactance). Applying Thévenin's theorem, calculate the load current, voltage, and power.

Solution

$$E_0 = 120 \times \frac{30\underline{/-90^\circ}}{40 - j30} = 120 \times \frac{30\underline{/-90^\circ}}{50\underline{/-36.9^\circ}} = 72\underline{/-53.1^\circ}$$

$$Z_i = (15.6 + j19.2) + \frac{40 \times 30\underline{/-90}}{50\underline{/-36.9^\circ}} = (15.6 + j19.2) + 24\underline{/-53.1^\circ}$$

$$= 15.6 + j19.2 + 14.4 - j19.2 = 30 \text{ ohms}$$

$$I_L = \frac{E_0}{Z_i + Z_L} = \frac{72\underline{/-53.1^\circ}}{30 - j40} = \frac{72\underline{/-53.1^\circ}}{50\underline{/-53.1^\circ}} = 1.44\underline{/0^\circ} \text{ amp}$$

$$E_L = (1.44\underline{/0^\circ})(40\underline{/-90^\circ}) = 57.6\underline{/-90^\circ} \text{ volts}$$

$$P_L = 0 \qquad \text{(for a capacitive reactance)}$$

When it is found necessary to apply Thévenin's theorem to practical problems that involve complex circuits of impedances and voltages, it is sometimes difficult to determine the impedance of a network Z_i as previously defined. In such cases it may be more convenient to calculate, or measure experimentally, the so-called *short-circuit current* I_{sc} which, divided into the open-circuit voltage E_0, yields the value of Z_i. This is a particularly useful modification of Thévenin's theorem, schematic

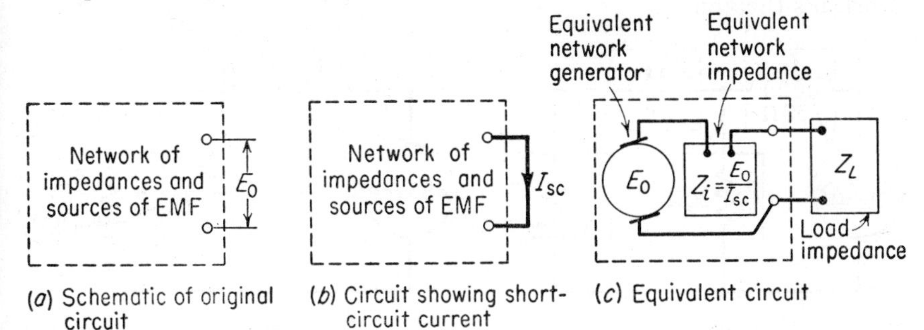

(*a*) Schematic of original circuit (*b*) Circuit showing short-circuit current (*c*) Equivalent circuit

FIG. 178. Sketches illustrating how a network is converted to an equivalent Thévenin's theorem circuit.

diagrams for which are illustrated by Fig. 178. Starting with sketch *a* note that the open-circuit voltage E_0 is determined as before; sketch *b* then indicates the significance of the short-circuit current I_{sc}, i.e., a current that would exist in a short circuit if the output terminals are joined by a zero-resistance conductor; finally, sketch *c* shows the equivalent circuit of the entire network and load. Written in equation form, the load current therefore becomes,

$$I_L = \frac{E_0}{(E_0/I_{sc}) + Z_L} \tag{121a}$$

EXAMPLE 5. The following information is given for the circuit of Fig. 177: $E = 120\underline{/0^\circ}$, $Z_a = j30$ ohms (inductive reactance), $Z_b = -j30$ ohms (capacitive reactance), $Z_c = 30$ ohms (resistance), $Z_L = (15 - j15)$ ohms (resistance-capacitive reactance). Using Norton's theorem, calculate the load current I_L.

Solution

$$E_0 = 120 \times \frac{30}{30 + j30} = 120 \times \frac{30}{30\sqrt{2}\,/45^\circ} = 85/-45^\circ$$

$$Z_{sc} = j30 + \frac{30 \times 30/-90^\circ}{30\sqrt{2}\,/-45^\circ} = j30 + 21.2/-45^\circ = 15 + j15 = 21.2/45^\circ$$

$$I_{sc} = \frac{E}{Z_{sc}} \times \frac{Z_c}{(Z_b + Z_c)} = \frac{120}{21.2/45^\circ} \times \frac{30}{30\sqrt{2}\,/-45^\circ} = 4/0^\circ$$

$$I_L = \frac{E_0}{(E_0/I_{sc}) + Z_L} = \frac{85/-45^\circ}{\dfrac{85/-45^\circ}{4/0^\circ} + (15 - j15)}$$

$$= \frac{85/-45^\circ}{(15 - j15) + (15 - j15)} = \frac{85/-45^\circ}{30\sqrt{2}\,/-45^\circ} = 2/0^\circ \text{ amp}$$

Figure 179 illustrates the original circuit and its equivalent in terms of Norton's theorem.

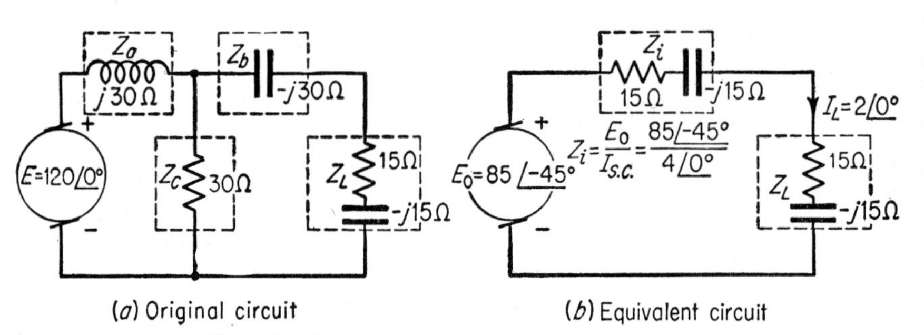

FIG. 179. Circuit diagrams illustrating Example 5.

Reciprocity Theorem. An interesting principle concerns the behavior of the network when a source of voltage is shifted from one point in a circuit to another. When this is done the current that will appear at the point first occupied by the voltage will be the same as the current that appeared originally at the point to which the voltage is shifted. This is illustrated by Fig. 180, where sketches *a* and *b* show that current I and voltage E occupy interchanged positions. This principle has become quite useful in circuit analysis and, as such, has been given the status of a theorem. Called the *reciprocity theorem*, it may be stated as follows:

In any network of bilateral-linear impedances, a shift of a source of voltage E from one point in a circuit to a second is accompanied by a corresponding shift of current I from the second point to the first.

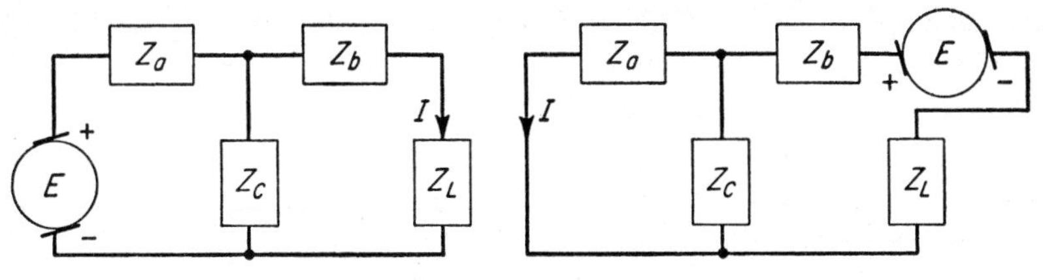

(a) Original circuit (b) Circuit showing shifted generator

FIG. 180. Diagrams illustrating the reciprocity theorem.

Referring to Fig. 180a, the equivalent impedance of the network, looking from the generator into the circuit, is

$$Z_{eq} = Z_a + \frac{Z_c(Z_b + Z_L)}{Z_b + Z_c + Z_L} = \frac{Z_aZ_b + Z_bZ_c + Z_cZ_a + Z_L(Z_a + Z_c)}{Z_b + Z_c + Z_L}$$

and the current is

$$I = \frac{E}{Z_{eq}} \times \frac{Z_c}{Z_b + Z_c + Z_L} = \frac{EZ_c}{Z_aZ_b + Z_bZ_c + Z_cZ_a + Z_L(Z_a + Z_c)}$$

Referring to Fig. 180b, the equivalent impedance of the network, looking from the generator into the circuit, is

$$Z_{eq} = Z_b + Z_L + \frac{Z_cZ_a}{Z_a + Z_c} = \frac{Z_aZ_b + Z_bZ_c + Z_cZ_a + Z_L(Z_a + Z_c)}{Z_a + Z_c}$$

and the current is

$$I = \frac{E}{Z_{eq}} \times \frac{Z_c}{Z_a + Z_c} = \frac{EZ_c}{Z_aZ_b + Z_bZ_c + Z_cZ_a + Z_L(Z_a + Z_c)}$$

Note that the validity of the theorem is proved by the identity of the two values of current in Figs. 180a and b.

The reciprocity theorem may be extended to take into account changes in current in a given part of a circuit when a known voltage is introduced or removed from another part. This will be illustrated by an example that follows.

EXAMPLE 6. Referring to Fig. 180a, assume that the generator voltage $E = 120\underline{/10°}$ and the current $I = 6.6\underline{/-40°}$. What will be the current I in Fig. 180b (a) if $E = 100\underline{/30°}$, (b) if $E = 140\underline{/-30°}$?

Solution

(a) $$I = 6.6\underline{/-40} \times \frac{100\underline{/30°}}{120\underline{/10°}} = 5.5\underline{/-20°} \text{ amp}$$

(b) $$I = 6.6\underline{/-40°} \times \frac{140\underline{/-30°}}{120\underline{/10°}} = 7.7\underline{/-80°} \text{ amp}$$

EXAMPLE 7. When switch S_2 is open and switch S_1 is closed in Fig. 181, the currents are $I_1 = (6 - j8)$ and $I_2 = (5.2 + j3)$. Calculate the current I_1 when switch S_1 is open, and (a) switch S_2 is closed to the left, and (b) switch S_2 is closed to the right.

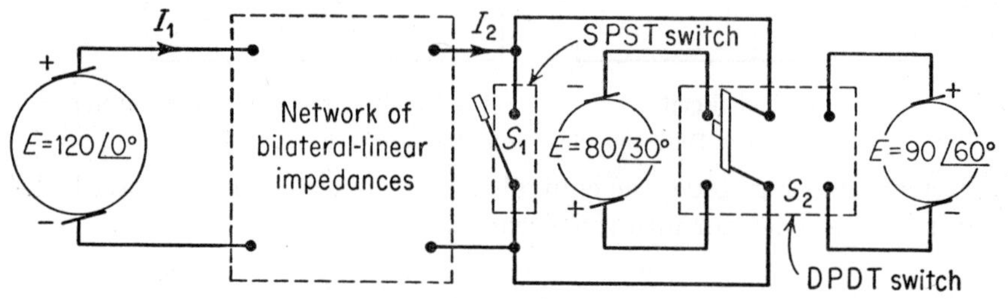

FIG. 181. Circuit diagram for Example 7.

Solution

$$(a)\ I_1 = (6 - j8) + \frac{80/30^\circ}{120/0^\circ} \times (5.2 + j3) = (6 - j8) + \frac{80/30^\circ}{120/0^\circ} \times 6/30^\circ$$

$$= (6 - j8) + (2 + j3.47) = (8 - j4.53) \text{ amp}$$

$$(b)\ I_1 = (6 - j8) - \frac{90/60^\circ}{120/0^\circ} \times 6/30^\circ = (6 - j8) - (j4.5)$$

$$= (6 - j12.5) \text{ amp}$$

Principle of Maximum Power Transfer. Large electrical systems are never designed for maximum power transfer from generator to load because, under this condition, the transmission efficiency is low and the operating costs, which involve fixed charges and power losses, are high. On the other hand, this is not generally true of small battery circuits and communication networks for the reason that these systems usually handle comparatively little power and must be made to serve loads that are often intermittent in character; maximum utilization of such equipment is often more important than other considerations. The following analysis, concerned as it is with the problems of maximum power transfer, therefore has limited practical application.

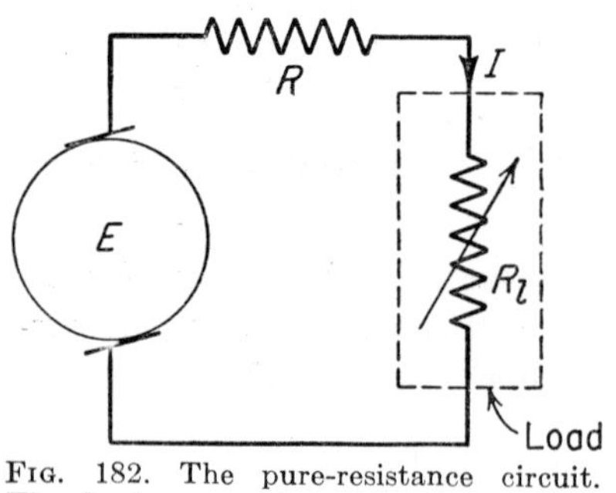

FIG. 182. The pure-resistance circuit. The load power is a maximum when $R = R_l$.

The Pure-resistance Circuit. Consider first the simple circuit of Fig. 182 which illustrates a constant-voltage generator, whose internal resistance is considered part of the line resistance R, delivering power to a variable resistor R_l. For some value of the latter, the circuit current will be $I = E/(R + R_l)$, and the load power becomes

$$P_l = I^2R_l = \frac{E^2R_l}{(R + R_l)^2}$$

If numerical values are substituted in this expression, assuming R_l to vary between 0 and ∞, calculations will prove that maximum load power will be delivered when $R_l = R$; this is shown in the table given in Chap. 4 on page 80. Also, a graphical plot of power P_l as ordinate vs. resistance R_l as abscissa will indicate that maximum load power occurs when $R_l = R$, under which condition the slope of the graph is zero. The latter point is significant because the slope of a curve is, mathematically, the so-called derivative of its equation; also, since the derivative is zero for maximum load power, the calculus will show that $R_l = R$ for this point on the curve. Substituting the value of R for R_l, the maximum load power in a pure resistance circuit is

$$P_{l_{max}} = \frac{E^2R}{(R + R)^2} = \frac{E^2}{4R} \qquad (122)^1$$

EXAMPLE 8. A 240-volt constant-potential generator, whose internal resistance is 0.4 ohm, is connected to a variable-load resistor through a line resistor of 1.1 ohms. For what value of load resistance will load power be a maximum, and what will be the load current and power under this condition?

Solution

$$R_l = R = 0.4 + 1.1 = 1.5 \text{ ohms}$$

$$I = \frac{240}{1.5 + 1.5} = 80 \text{ amp}$$

$$P_l = \frac{(240)^2}{4 \times 1.5} = 9{,}600 \text{ watts}$$

Also $\quad P_l = (80)^2 \times 1.5 = 9{,}600$ watts

The R-X Line- and Load-impedance Circuit. When the line and load are both impedances, each one containing resistance and reactance, the current will be

$$I = \frac{E}{\sqrt{(R + R_1)^2 + (X + X_1)^2}}$$

The current will obviously be a maximum when the equivalent-circuit reactance is zero, a condition that is fulfilled when (1) *a line inductive reactance* X_L = *a load capacitive reactance* X_{l_C} or (2) *a line capacitive reactance* X_C = *a load inductive reactance* X_{l_L}. The line and load imped-

[1] See Appendix 1T for derivation.

ances are then said to be *conjugates* of each other, since $Z = Z_l$ and (1) $Z_l = R_l - jX_l$ when $Z = R + jX$ or (2) $Z_l = R_l + jX_l$ when $Z = R - jX$. Moreover, the maximum load power will be given by Eq. (122), because the entire circuit behaves like a pure resistance (see Fig. 183).

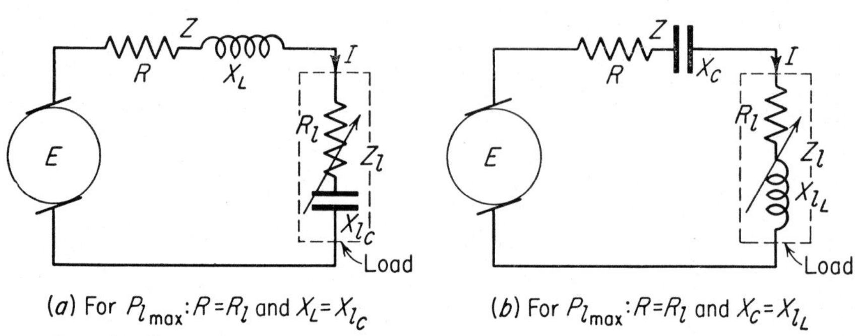

FIG. 183. Circuit diagrams illustrating two conditions for maximum load power.

EXAMPLE 9. A 120-volt constant-potential generator delivers load to an impedance whose values of R_l and X_l are readily adjustable. If the line impedance (this includes the internal impedance of the generator) is $(3 + j4)$ ohms, calculate, for maximum load power, (*a*) the load impedance, (*b*) the load current, (*c*) the load power.

Solution

(*a*)
$$Z_l = 3 - j4$$

(*b*)
$$I = \frac{120}{(3 + 3) + j(4 - 4)} = 20 \text{ amp}$$

$$P_l = \frac{(120)^2}{4 \times 3} = 1{,}200 \text{ watts}$$

The R-X Circuit, with Variable-impedance and Constant-power-factor Load. When the line contains both resistance and reactance (either inductive or capacitive), and the load impedance, although variable in magnitude, can be adjusted so that it will have a constant ratio of R_l to Z_l, i.e., constant-load power factor, the circuit current will be

$$I = \frac{E}{\sqrt{(R + Z_l \cos \Theta_l)^2 + (X + Z_l \sin \Theta_l)^2}}$$

where $Z_l \cos \Theta_l$ and $Z_l \sin \Theta_l$ are the load resistance and the load reactance, respectively; also, since the power factor is assumed to be constant in this analysis, $\cos \Theta_l$ and $\sin \Theta_l$ are both constants. The load power, being equal to $I^2R_l = I^2Z_l \cos \Theta_l$, therefore becomes

$$R_1 = \frac{EZ_l \cos \Theta_l}{(R + Z_l \cos \Theta_l)^2 + (X + Z_l \sin \Theta_l)^2}$$

This equation may be treated in essentially the same way as the one for the pure resistance circuit; i.e., its derivative, by the calculus, may be set equal to zero to determine the condition for maximum load power; when this is done it is found that

$$Z_l = \sqrt{R^2 + X^2} = Z \qquad (123)^1$$

This implies, therefore, that this type of circuit will yield maximum load power when the absolute value of the load impedance is equal to the absolute value of the line impedance. In a special case, where the load impedance is a pure resistor, i.e., a constant unity-power-factor load, $R = Z$ for maximum load power.

EXAMPLE 10. A 120-volt constant-potential generator delivers load to a variable impedance whose ratio of R_l to Z_l is kept constant at 0.866 lagging. If the line impedance (this includes the internal impedance of the generator) is $(1.2 + j0.5)$ ohms, calculate, for maximum load power, (*a*) the load impedance, (*b*) the load current, (*c*) the load power.

Solution

(*a*) $$Z_l = Z = \sqrt{(1.2)^2 + (0.5)^2} = 1.3 \text{ ohms}$$

(*b*) $$R_l = Z \cos \Theta = 1.3 \times 0.866 = 1.126$$

$$X_l = Z \sin \Theta = 1.3 \times 0.5 = 0.65$$

$$Z_{eq} = \sqrt{(1.2 + 1.126)^2 + (0.5 + 0.65)^2} = 2.59 \text{ ohms}$$

$$I = \frac{120}{2.59} = 46.3 \text{ amp}$$

(*c*) $$P_{l_{max}} = I^2 R_l = (46.3)^2 \times 1.126 = 2{,}410 \text{ watts}$$

EXAMPLE 11. Calculate the maximum load power in Example 10, if the load is a variable resistor.

Solution

$$R_l = Z = \sqrt{(1.2)^2 + (0.5)^2} = 1.3 \text{ ohms}$$

$$Z_{eq} = \sqrt{(1.2 + 1.3)^2 + (0.5)^2} = 2.55 \text{ ohms}$$

$$P_{l_{max}} = \left(\frac{E}{Z_{eq}}\right)^2 R_l = \left(\frac{120}{2.55}\right)^2 \times 1.3 = 2{,}880 \text{ watts}$$

Δ-Y and Y-Δ Transformations. Alternating-current circuits are sometimes composed of complex arrangements of impedances; the latter may, in fact, be interconnected to form networks that are extremely difficult to handle by the rules, laws, and theorems previously discussed. Under such conditions it is generally necessary to transform all or parts of the complex circuits into their simpler electrical equivalents before a solution is attempted. Two basic arrangements of impedances within

[1] See Appendix 1U for derivation.

and parts of larger networks which are frequently responsible for the difficulties indicated are Δ-connected impedances and Y-connected impedances; they are shown in Fig. 184. Often, a transformation of a delta (Δ) into an equivalent star (Y), or a star (Y) into an equivalent delta (Δ), will convert a troublesome circuit into a comparatively simple one.

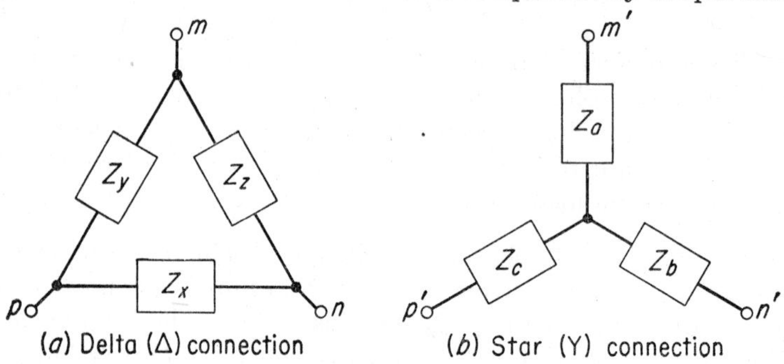

FIG. 184. Two basic interconnections of impedances.

The two types of interconnection are said to be equivalent when the impedance between *any pair* of terminals in a star (Y) is exactly equal in magnitude and phase angle to the impedance between a *corresponding pair* of terminals in a delta (Δ). Thus, in Fig. 184, the two circuits will be equivalent when the three delta (Δ) impedances between terminals *mn*, *np*, and *pm* are *respectively* equal to the three star (Y) impedances between *similarly labeled* terminals $m'n'$, $n'p'$, and $p'n'$.

The equations derived in Chap. 4, pages 73–74, for resistors apply equally well for impedances in a-c circuits if the elements are properly treated as complex numbers; they will therefore be restated here in symbols corresponding to those indicated on Fig. 184. Thus

To transform a delta (Δ) *into an equivalent star* (Y):

$$Z_a = \frac{Z_y Z_z}{Z_x + Z_y + Z_z}$$
$$Z_b = \frac{Z_x Z_z}{Z_x + Z_y + Z_z} \qquad (124)$$
$$Z_c = \frac{Z_x Z_y}{Z_x + Z_y + Z_z}$$

To transform a star (Y) *into an equivalent delta* (Δ):

$$Z_x = \frac{Z_a Z_b + Z_b Z_c + Z_c Z_a}{Z_a}$$
$$Z_y = \frac{Z_a Z_b + Z_b Z_c + Z_c Z_a}{Z_b} \qquad (125)$$
$$Z_z = \frac{Z_a Z_b + Z_b Z_c + Z_c Z_a}{Z_c}$$

EXAMPLE 12. Figure 185*a* illustrates a Wheatstone-bridge circuit upon which have been indicated the values of the various impedances. Calculate the total current I.

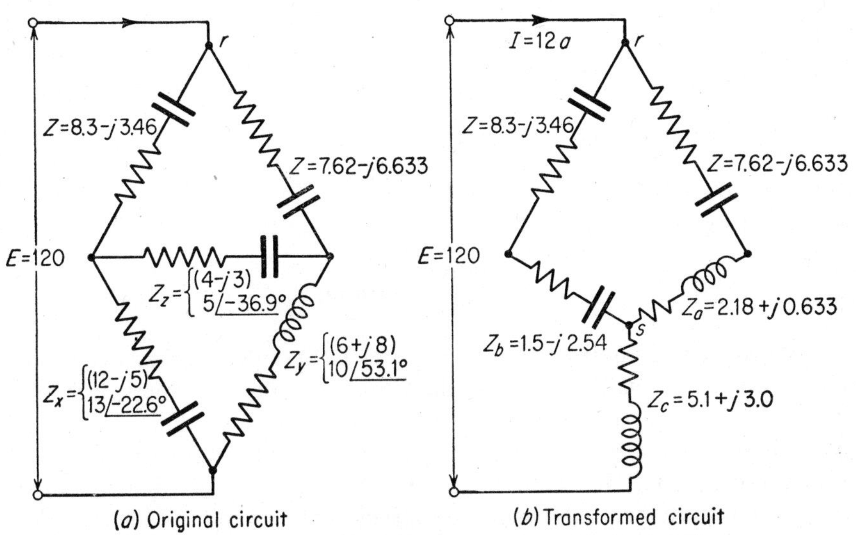

FIG. 185. Circuit diagrams for Example 12.

Solution

Before this network is solved it will be desirable to transform the delta-connected impedances represented by Z_x, Z_y, and Z_z into their star-connected equivalents Z_a, Z_b, and Z_c. To do this the three parts of Eq. (124) will be used. Since the denominator of each of the latter contains a common vector sum, its value will first be determined. Thus

$$(Z_x + Z_y + Z_z) = (12 - j5) + (6 + j8) + (4 - j3) = 22 \text{ ohms}$$

The equivalent star impedances are

$$Z_a = \frac{(10\underline{/53.1^\circ})(5\underline{/-36.9})}{22} = 2.27\underline{/16.2^\circ} = 2.18 + j0.633$$

$$Z_b = \frac{(13\underline{/-22.6^\circ})(5\underline{/-36.9^\circ})}{22} = 2.95\underline{/-59.5^\circ} = 1.5 - j2.54$$

$$Z_c = \frac{(13\underline{/-22.6^\circ})(10\underline{/53.1^\circ})}{22} = 5.90\underline{/30.5^\circ} = 5.1 + j3.0$$

Referring next to Fig. 185*b*, note that the impedance between points r and s is made up of two parallel paths, one of which has the value

$$(7.62 - j6.633) + (2.18 + j0.633) = 9.8 - j6$$

and the other has the value

$$(8.3 - j3.46) + (1.5 - j2.54) = 9.8 - j6$$

Since they are both equal to each other,

$$Z_{rs} = \frac{(9.8 - j6)}{2} = 4.9 - j3$$

Hence, the equivalent impedance of the entire circuit is

$$Z_{eq} = (4.9 - j3) + (5.1 + j3) = 10 \text{ ohms}$$

and the total current becomes

$$I = \frac{120}{10} = 12 \text{ amp}$$

Components of Equivalent π (Delta) and T (Star) Networks. In power circuits, and especially those energized by three-phase systems, it is customary to refer to a *three-terminal network* of impedances as a *delta* or a *star;* these terms are used because they are generally drawn to resemble the Δ and the Y. In communication circuits, however, their counterparts are usually arranged as *four-terminal networks* and, as such, appear respectively like the Greek letter π or the T. Figure 186 illustrates the

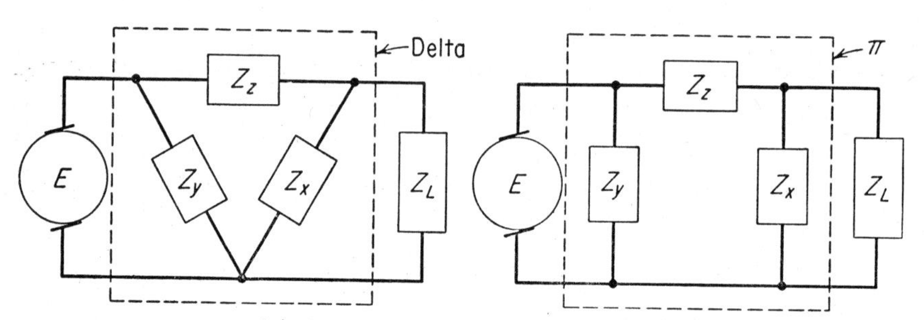

(a) Equivalent Delta and π networks

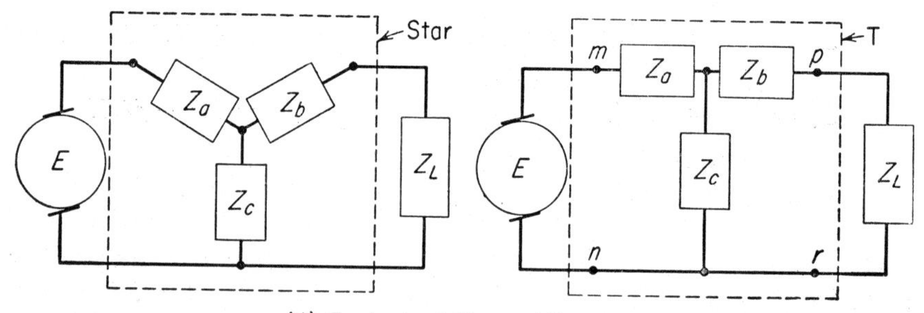

(b) Equivalent Star and T networks

FIG. 186. Diagrams illustrating the equivalence of three-impedance networks.

similarity between the π and the Δ on the one hand, and the Y and the T on the other; it also indicates how the three-terminal network becomes one having four terminals, one pair of which is connected to the source and the other pair to the load.

After a group of impedances are interconnected to form a π or a T, it is sometimes necessary to determine the individual values of Z_x, Z_y, and Z_z, or Z_a, Z_b, and Z_c without disconnecting them to measure each one independently. This is best accomplished by performing (1) two simple open-circuit tests, one from each of the two pairs of terminals, and (2) a short-circuit test from the input side. The following analysis will show how the test data may be used to evaluate the impedances in a T-network; it will not be necessary to do so for a π-network because, as the foregoing section proved, any T (star) may be transformed into an equivalent π (delta) by applying Eq. (125).

Referring to the T-network of Fig. 186*b*, assume that the load Z_L and the generator are disconnected. The *open-circuit impedance* "looking in" at terminals *mn* is

$$Z_{oc_a} = Z_a + Z_c$$

and the *open-circuit impedance* "looking in" at terminals *pn* is

$$Z_{oc_b} = Z_b + Z_c$$

If terminals *pr* are linked together, the *short-circuit impedance* "looking in" at terminals *mn* is

$$Z_{sc} = Z_a + \frac{Z_b Z_c}{Z_b + Z_c} = \frac{(Z_a Z_b + Z_b Z_c + Z_c Z_a)}{Z_b + Z_c}$$

Multiplying Z_{oc_a} by Z_{oc_b} it is found that

$$Z_{oc_a} \times Z_{oc_b} = (Z_a Z_b + Z_b Z_c + Z_c Z_a) + Z_c^2$$

from which

$$(Z_a Z_b + Z_b Z_c + Z_c Z_a) = (Z_{oc_a} Z_{oc_b}) - Z_c^2$$

Substituting the latter expression in the one for the short-circuit impedance, rearranging terms, and simplifying,

$$Z_c = \sqrt{Z_{oc_a} Z_{oc_b} - Z_{oc_b} Z_{sc}} \tag{126}$$

The equations for Z_b and Z_a are then readily found by substituting Eq. (126) in those for Z_{oc_b} and Z_{oc_a} given above; these are

$$Z_b = Z_{oc_b} - Z_c \tag{127}$$
$$Z_a = Z_{oc_a} - Z_c \tag{128}$$

Example 13. The three units in a T-network (Fig. 186*b*) are pure resistances, and the results from two open-circuit tests and a short-circuit test are $Z_{oc_a} = 20$, $Z_{oc_b} = 36$, $Z_{sc} = 16$. (*a*) Calculate the values of Z_c, Z_b, and Z_a, and (*b*) determine their π equivalents.

Solution

(*a*)
$$Z_c = \sqrt{(20 \times 36) - (36 \times 16)} = 12 \text{ ohms}$$
$$Z_b = 36 - 12 = 24 \text{ ohms}$$
$$Z_a = 20 - 12 = 8 \text{ ohms}$$

(*b*)
$$Z_x = \frac{(8 \times 24) + (24 \times 12) + (12 \times 8)}{8} = \frac{576}{8} = 72 \text{ ohms}$$
$$Z_y = \frac{576}{24} = 24 \text{ ohms}$$
$$Z_z = \frac{576}{12} = 48 \text{ ohms}$$

EXAMPLE 14. The following information is given in connection with a T-network like Fig. 186*b*: $Z_{oc_a} = 4/\underline{-90°}$, $Z_{oc_b} = 4/\underline{90°}$, $Z_{sc} = 40/\underline{-90°}$. Determine the values of Z_c, Z_b, and Z_a.

Solution

$$Z_c = \sqrt{(4/\underline{-90°})(4/\underline{90°}) - (4/\underline{90°})(40/\underline{-90°})}$$
$$= \sqrt{16 - 160} = \sqrt{-144} = 12/\underline{90°} \text{ ohms}$$
$$Z_b = (4/\underline{90°}) - (12/\underline{90°}) = -8/\underline{90°} = 8/\underline{-90°} \text{ ohms}$$
$$Z_a = (4/\underline{-90°}) - (12/\underline{90°}) = (4/\underline{-90°}) + (12/\underline{-90°}) = 16/\underline{-91°} \text{ ohms}$$

Questions

1. Under what conditions are Kirchhoff's laws and Thévenin's theorem, discussed in Chap. 4 under d-c circuits, applicable to a-c circuits? Can the same statement be made for the superposition theorem, Δ-Y and Y-Δ transformations, and the maximum-power-transfer theorem? Explain.
2. State *Kirchhoff's voltage and current laws* as applied to a-c circuits.
3. What is meant by a linear-bilateral circuit? How does it differ from a nonlinear-bilateral circuit?
4. List several linear devices; nonlinear devices.
5. List several bilateral devices; unilateral devices.
6. What is meant by the *conjugate* of a complex quantity? Give several pairs of examples relating to voltages, currents, and impedances.
7. State the *superposition theorem* as applied to a-c circuits.
8. In what way is the superposition theorem helpful when a network contains two or more sources of emf?
9. State *Thévenin's theorem* as applied to a-c circuits.
10. What is meant by the expression "looking back into a network with all the sources of emf replaced by their internal impedances"?
11. In what way does *Norton's theorem* differ from *Thévenin's theorem?* In what respect are they similar?
12. How is the "looking-back" impedance Z_i determined for use in *Norton's theorem?*
13. State the *reciprocity theorem* as applied to a-c circuits.

14. Draw a complex circuit diagram and, using symbols, show in a second diagram how the reciprocity theorem is used.
15. Explain how the *reciprocity theorem* may be extended to take account of a current change in one part of a circuit when a known voltage is introduced or removed from another part.
16. Under what conditions is the maximum power transferred to a load when the circuit parameters are resistive?
17. Under what conditions is the maximum power transferred to a *completely* variable load when (*a*) the line contains both resistance and inductive reactance, (*b*) the line contains both resistance and capacitive reactance?
18. Under what conditions is the maximum power transferred to a variable load, the power factor of which is maintained constant, when the line contains (*a*) resistance only, (*b*) resistance and inductive reactance, (*c*) resistance and capacitive reactance?
19. In what way do the Δ-Y, Y-Δ transformation equations for a-c circuits differ from those applicable to d-c circuits?
20. Make diagrams showing the equivalence of (*a*) a π and a Δ; (*b*) a T and a Y.
21. Distinguish between a *three-terminal* network and a *four-terminal* network as applied to Δ-π and Y-T arrangements of impedances.
22. Make a sketch showing a T-network, use symbols to indicate their values, and write (*a*) the open-circuit equations from each end, (*b*) the short-circuit equations from each end.

Problems

1. Referring to Fig. 174, set up a voltage equation for the circuit *abcdefa*.
2. The following information is given in connection with Fig. 174: $E_1 = 100\underline{/0°}$, $E_2 = 100\underline{/53.1°}$, $Z_1 = Z_2 = 20\underline{/0°}$, $Z_L = 20\underline{/-90°}$. Calculate the values of I_L, I_1, and I_2.
3. Solve Prob. 2 assuming that $E_1 = E_2 = 100\underline{/0°}$.
4. Referring to Fig. 174, the following data are given for the two voltages and the three impedances: $E_1 = 120\underline{/30°}$, $E_2 = 120\underline{/-30°}$, $Z_1 = 2$ ohms (resistance), $Z_2 = 2\underline{/90°}$ ohms (inductive reactance), $Z_L = 10\underline{/-53.1°}$. Calculate the value of the load current I_L and the voltage across the load, using the superposition theorem.
5. The following particulars are given for the T-network of Fig. 177: $E = 120\underline{/0°}$, $Z_a = 40$ ohms (resistance), $Z_c = (15.6 + j19.2)$ ohms (resistance-inductive reactance), $Z_c = -j30$ ohms (capacitive reactance), $Z_L = -j40$ ohms (capacitive reactance). Using Thévenin's theorem calculate the current through, and the voltage across, the load impedance Z_L.
6. Using Thévenin's theorem calculate the load current and voltage, given the following data: $E = 120\underline{/0°}$, $Z_a = Z_b = j9$, $Z_c = 12$, $Z_L = (3.68 - j8.76)$.
7. Using the data of Prob. 6, calculate the short-circuit current I_{sc}, as illustrated in Fig. 178, for use in Eq. (121*a*), p. 343; after evaluating this check the load current as determined by Thévenin's theorem in Prob. 6.
8. The following information is given in connection with Fig. 177: $E = 120\underline{/0°}$, $Z_a = 12\underline{/-90°}$, $Z_b = 12\underline{/90°}$, $Z_c = 12$, $Z_L = 8.5\underline{/45°}$. Calculate the load current I_L and the load voltage E_L.
9. The current $I = 15\underline{/-30°}$ when $E = 120\underline{/10°}$ in Fig. 180*a*. What will be the current I in Fig. 180*b* if $E = 110\underline{/40°}$?
10. In Fig. 180*a* the current $I = 4.33 - j2.5$ when $E = 110\underline{/0°}$. For what voltage in Fig. 180*b* will the current I be $6\underline{/30°}$?

11. When switch S_2 is open and switch S_1 is closed in Fig. 181, the currents are $I_1 = (8 + j5)$ and $I_2 = (4 - j3)$. Calculate the current I_1 when switch S_1 is open and (*a*) switch S_2 is closed to the right, and (*b*) switch S_2 is closed to the left.

12. A 48-volt battery has an internal resistance of 0.22 ohm and is connected to a variable-resistance load through a line resistance of 1.28 ohms. For what value of load resistance will the load power be a maximum, and what will be the load current, load power, and power loss under this condition?

13. A 228-volt constant-potential generator delivers load to a variable impedance whose values of R and X are readily adjustable. Assuming a "looking-back" impedance of $(6 + j4.5)$ ohms, calculate, for maximum load power, (*a*) the load impedance, (*b*) the current, (*c*) the load power and power factor.

14. If the load in Prob. 13 is a variable resistor calculate, for maximum load power, the load resistance and power.

15. If the load in Prob. 13 contains a constant inductive reactance of 3.5 ohms and a variable resistance, calculate, for maximum load power, (*a*) the load resistance and impedance, (*b*) the load current and power.

16. If the load in Prob. 13 contains a constant resistance of 4.8 ohms and a variable inductive reactance, calculate, for maximum load power, (*a*) the load reactance and impedance, (*b*) the load current and power.

17. Referring to Fig. 185*a*, transform the *upper delta* into an equivalent star and determine the total current I as in Example 12.

18. Referring to Fig. 185*a*, transform the star that is made up of Z_x, Z_z, and $Z = (8.3 - j3.46)$ into an equivalent delta. Proceed then to determine the total current I.

19. The following data are given for the star connection of Fig. 184*b*: $Z_a = 6\underline{/90°}$, $Z_b = 6\underline{/0°}$, $Z_c = 6\underline{/-90°}$. Calculate the values of Z_x, Z_y, and Z_z of an equivalent delta as shown in Fig. 184*a*.

20. Referring to Fig. 186*b*, the following data are given in connection with the T-network: $Z_{oca} = (8 + j6)$, $Z_{ocb} = (8 - j6)$, $Z_{sc} = (2.88 + j2.16)$. Calculate the values of Z_c, Z_b, and Z_a.

CHAPTER 16

COUPLED CIRCUITS AND MUTUAL INDUCTION

General Aspects of Magnetically Coupled Circuits. When two electric circuits are so disposed with respect to one another that any part of the flux established in one of them links with the other, they are said to be coupled. Furthermore, if the voltage impressed on the first circuit, called the primary, is alternating, the current in it will also be alternating, and the flux linking with the second circuit, the secondary, will vary in magnitude and direction. Since, as Faraday showed, an emf is always induced in a circuit when there is a change in its flux linkages, a voltage will be developed in the secondary, which, in turn, may be made to serve as an electrical source for that circuit. This means, of course, that energy may be transferred electromagnetically from one circuit to another even though there is no metallic connection between them. This important phenomenon, called transformer action, is responsible for the practical operation of many kinds of devices and machines in a-c systems.

The extent to which two circuits are magnetically coupled will depend upon such factors as their proximity, the magnetic permeability of the substance that links them, and, when there is no common magnetic substance to couple them, the geometrical arrangement of the circuits. The *coefficient of coupling* is a term that is both an indication and a measure of the closeness of the magnetic link between circuits. As defined in Chap. 8, it is the fractional part of the flux in one circuit or winding that links with the other. Expressed as a decimal it can have numerical values between zero and unity, a high value implying "tight" coupling and a low value indicating "loose" coupling. Represented by the symbol K it is therefore the ratio of the secondary flux Φ_S to the primary flux Φ_P; i.e., $K = \Phi_S/\Phi_P$.

Since the induced emf in the secondary of a pair of coupled circuits is a voltage of *mutual induction,* its value will depend upon both the rate at which the current changes in the primary and the so-called *mutual inductance* between the circuits. The latter, symbolized by the letter M and expressed in *henry* units, is defined as the ratio of the *average* induced secondary voltage to the rate of change of primary current. Stated another way, the mutual inductance between two circuits is one henry when a change of one ampere per second in the primary results in an average induced emf of one volt in the secondary; this means, of course, that the higher the induced emf per unit current change, the higher the mutual inductance.

When a pair of circuits is magnetically coupled, each one possesses the property of self-inductance. This obviously implies that there is a connection between the self-inductances of the two circuits L_P and L_S, the mutual inductance between the circuits M, and the coefficient of coupling K, because L_P, L_S, and M are *together* responsible for the magnitude of K; as was proved mathematically in Chap. 8, the relationship is given by the important expression $K = M/\sqrt{L_P L_S}$; i.e., the coefficient of coupling is the ratio of the mutual inductance to the geometric mean of the individual self-inductances.

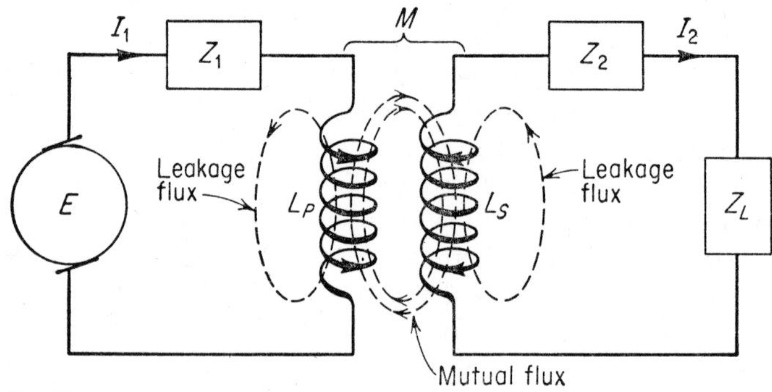

FIG. 187. Diagram illustrating a circuit in which two coils are magnetically coupled.

The foregoing discussion is illustrated, with several simplifications, by Fig. 187. Assuming that the total impedances of the primary and secondary are respectively indicated by lumped values Z_1 and Z_2, note that the two circuits are shown coupled together by a pair of coils, the self-inductances and the mutual inductance of which are L_P, L_S, and M. Observe also the two components of flux produced by the primary, namely, the mutual flux Φ_M that is responsible for the secondary induced voltage, and the leakage flux Φ_l that fails to link primary and secondary. With the primary energized by a sinusoidal wave of voltage E, a current I_1 will exist in the primary and a current I_2 will be delivered to the load impedance Z_L.

EXAMPLE 1. A 60-cycle sinusoidal wave of voltage is impressed across the primary of a pair of coils that are inductively coupled. If the *effective* open-circuit emf induced in the secondary is 50 volts and the primary current is 3 amp, calculate the mutual inductance between the coils.

Solution

The average secondary voltage per half cycle $E_{av} = (2/\pi)E_m = (2/\pi)(\sqrt{2}\,E) = (2\sqrt{2}/\pi) \times 50 = 45$ volts. The average rate of current change in the primary between zero and maximum is

$$\frac{I_m}{(1/4f)} = 4fI_m = 4 \times 60 \times (\sqrt{2} \times 3) = 1{,}020 \text{ amp per sec}$$

Therefore

$$M = \frac{45}{1{,}020} = 0.044 \text{ henry}$$

EXAMPLE 2. Calculate the coefficient of coupling between the coils in Example 1 if the self-inductances of the primary and secondary are respectively, 0.08 and 0.045 henry.

Solution

$$K = \frac{0.044}{\sqrt{0.08 \times 0.045}} = 0.733$$

Mutual Reactance. When two circuits or coils are magnetically coupled and *both* carry currents (see Fig. 187), the mutual inductance between them is responsible for *two* reactive voltages, one in the primary and the other in the secondary. These voltages, resulting from current changes in the two circuits, are similar to emfs of self-induction, although, unlike the latter, each one is developed because of a current change in the *other*, not in its own, circuit. Stated mathematically, the emfs of self-induction are

$$e_{L_1} = L_P \frac{di_1}{dt} \qquad \text{and} \qquad e_{L_2} = L_S \frac{di_2}{dt}$$

whereas the emfs of mutual induction are

$$e_{M_1} = M \frac{di_2}{dt} \qquad \text{and} \qquad e_{M_2} = M \frac{di_1}{dt}$$

where the di/dt terms indicate rates of current change expressed in differential form. Note particularly that a voltage of mutual induction is developed in a circuit only when it is coupled to another *current-carrying* circuit. Under certain conditions it is possible for a circuit to be linked to several others, in which event a number of emfs will be induced in it by mutual induction.

Assuming a sine wave of voltage to be impressed across the primary of Fig. 187, the current I_1 will also vary sinusoidally. Since the *average* value of the sine wave of voltage that is induced in the secondary is proportional to both the mutual inductance M and the rate of current change in the primary,

$$E_{av} = M \frac{I_m}{(1/4f)} = 4fMI_m$$

where $1/4f$ is the time, in seconds (one-quarter of a cycle) it takes for the current to change by I_m amp. But $E_{av} = (2/\pi)E_m$, and E and I are respectively equal to $E_m/\sqrt{2}$ and $I_m/\sqrt{2}$; therefore

$$\frac{2}{\pi} \times \frac{E_m}{\sqrt{2}} = 4fM \times \frac{I_m}{\sqrt{2}}$$

from which

$$\frac{2}{\pi} E = 4fMI$$

and

$$E = (2\pi fM)I$$

Since volts E is always equal to the product of ohms and amperes, it follows that the bracketed term has *ohm* units; designating the latter as *mutual reactance* it is equated to the symbolized quantity

$$X_M = 2\pi fM \tag{129}$$

EXAMPLE 3. The mutual inductance between two coupled circuits is 0.0715 henry, and the 60-cycle currents in the primary and secondary are 6.2 and 3.8 amp, respectively. Calculate the mutual reactance, and the primary and secondary induced emfs due to mutual inductance.

Solution

$$X_M = 2\pi \times 60 \times 0.0715 = 27 \text{ ohms}$$
$$E_{M_P} = 27 \times 3.8 = 102.8 \text{ volts}$$
$$E_{M_S} = 27 \times 6.2 = 167.4 \text{ volts}$$

Air-core-transformer Analysis. In an arrangement such as Fig. 187, where electrical energy is transferred from an energized circuit (the primary) to a load circuit (the secondary), the currents I_1 and I_2 may be assumed to have any arbitrary directions for the purposes of circuit analysis. It is then possible, by using the right-hand rule, to determine whether the primary- and secondary-coil fluxes are in the same direction, to aid, or in opposite directions, to buck. If, as in Fig. 188*a*, the current and coil-winding directions indicate *additive* fluxes, the mutual inductance is represented by a $+M$; on the other hand, when the primary and secondary fluxes are *subtractive* and tend to cancel, as in Fig. 188*b*, the mutual inductance is designated by a $-M$. For a single-generator circuit (Fig. 187) either sign may be assumed to yield exactly the same result. However, in systems in which there are two or more sources of supply it is imperative that current and coil-winding directions be taken

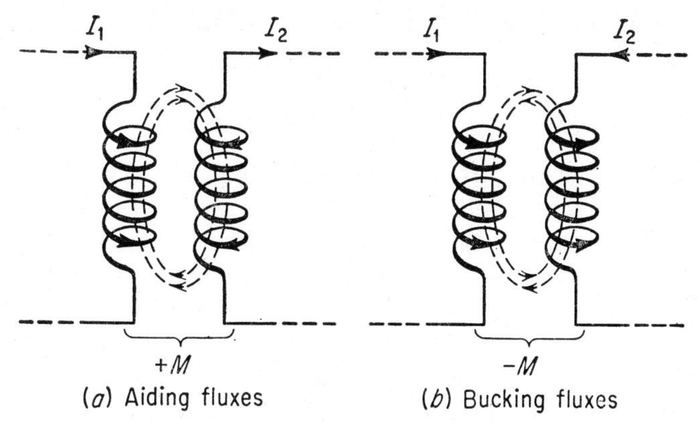

FIG. 188. Sketches illustrating how the signs of the mutual inductance between coupled circuits are determined.

into account, because the reactance voltages due to self-inductance and mutual inductance may act additively or subtractively; arbitrary assumptions are therefore not permissible under such conditions if a correct solution is to be obtained.

The following analysis of a simple transformer circuit, in which a single source of emf is applied to the primary, is based upon sinusoidal quantities of E and I, and constant values of impedances Z and mutual reactance X_M. Referring to Fig. 187, assume that Z_1 is the total impedance of the *entire* primary circuit, Z_2 is the total impedance of the *entire* secondary circuit exclusive of the load impedance Z_L, and M is arbitrarily given a + sign to make X_M positive. Writing Kirchhoff's voltage equation for the primary,

$$E = I_1Z_1 + I_2X_M$$

A similar equation for the secondary is

$$0 = I_2(Z_2 + Z_L) + I_1X_M$$

Substituting the value of $I_2 = (-I_1X_M)/(Z_2 + Z_L)$ from the second expression into the first,

$$E = I_1Z_1 - I_1\left(\frac{X_M^2}{Z_2 + Z_L}\right)$$

Solving for the primary and secondary currents,

$$I_1 = \frac{E(Z_2 + Z_L)}{Z_1(Z_2 + Z_L) - X_M^2} \tag{130}$$

and

$$I_2 = \frac{EX_M}{Z_1(Z_2 + Z_L) - X_M^2} \tag{131}$$

If the numerator and denominator of Eq. (130) are divided by $(Z_2 + Z_L)$,

$$I_1 = \frac{E}{Z_1 - X_M^2/(Z_2 + Z_L)}$$

The denominator of the latter expression is obviously an *equivalent impedance* that presents itself to the generator voltage E to cause current I_1 to flow in the primary; it is therefore *the* equivalent impedance of the complete circuit as it appears to the generator. Sometimes called the *input impedance* or *driving-point impedance*, it is

$$Z_{eq} = Z_1 - \frac{X_M^2}{(Z_2 + Z_L)} \tag{132}$$

Finally, dividing Eq. (130) for I_1 by Eq. (131) for I_2, and rearranging terms, a value of I_2 may be obtained in terms of I_1, usually evaluated first, and other known quantities. Thus

$$I_2 = I_1\left(\frac{X_M}{Z_2 + Z_L}\right) \tag{133}$$

EXAMPLE 4. The following information is given in connection with Fig. 187: $E = 120\underline{/0°}$, $Z_1 = (4.75 + j10.16)$, $Z_2 = (3 + j12.66)$, $Z_L = (2 - j4)$, $X_M = 5\underline{/90°}$. Calculate (*a*) the equivalent (driving-point) impedance of the entire circuit, (*b*) the primary current I_1, (*c*) the secondary current I_2. (The values of Z_1 and Z_2 are, respectively, the total impedances of primary and secondary.)

Solution

$$(a)\ Z_{eq} = (4.75 + j10.16) - \frac{(5\underline{/90°})^2}{(3 + j12.66) + (2 - j4)}$$

$$= (4.75 + j10.16 - \frac{25\underline{/180°}}{(5 + j8.66)} = (4.75 + j10.16) + \frac{25}{10\underline{/60°}}$$

$$= (4.75 + j10.16) + (1.25 - j2.16) = (6 + j8) = 10\underline{/53.1°}$$

$$(b)\ I_1 = \frac{120\underline{/0°}}{10\underline{/53.1°}} = 12\underline{/-53.1°}$$

$$(c)\ I_2 = (12\underline{/-53.1})\left(\frac{5\underline{/90°}}{10\underline{/60°}}\right) = 6\underline{/-23.1°}$$

Equivalent T-network of Coupled Circuits. It is frequently helpful, particularly when dealing with communication systems, to convert circuits that are inductively coupled into equivalent networks in which the impedances are interconnected *directly* with one another. Such networks, of which the T and the π are examples, are said to be *conductively coupled* and are, for the most part, somewhat easier to handle. Obviously, inductively and conductively coupled circuits are equivalent only when they present exactly the same impedance to, and take exactly the same currents from, a given source of emf.

Since the T-network was treated in some detail in Chap. 15, and is therefore familiar to the student, it will be desirable to consider it as an

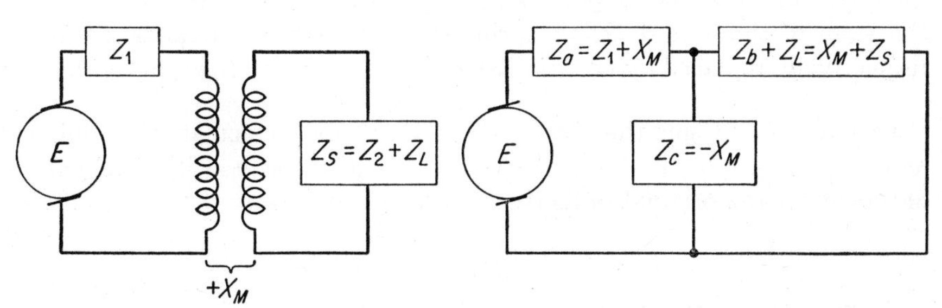

FIG. 189. Diagrams illustrating the equivalence of inductively coupled and conductively coupled circuits.

equivalent for the inductively coupled circuits. Referring to Fig. 189*a*, and replacing the quantity $(Z_2 + Z_L)$ in Eq. (132) by Z_S for convenience,

$$Z_{eq} = Z_1 + \frac{-X_M{}^2}{Z_S}$$

This expression may be modified by adding X_M to Z_1 and subtracting X_M from $(-X_M{}^2/Z_S)$; thus

$$Z_{eq} = (Z_1 + X_M) + \left(\frac{-X_M{}^2}{Z_S} - X_M\right)$$

or

$$Z_{eq} = (Z_1 + X_M) + \frac{(-X_M{}^2 - X_M Z_S)}{Z_S}$$

$$= (Z_1 + X_M) + \left[\frac{-X_M(X_M + Z_S)}{Z_S}\right]$$

Since the numerator of the last term is the *product* of two quantities, its denominator will be made the *sum* of the *same* two quantities by adding $-X_M$ and $+X_M$ to Z_S. When this is done,

$$Z_{eq} = (Z_1 + X_M) + \left[\frac{(-X_M)(X_M + Z_S)}{(-X_M) + (X_M + Z_S)}\right]$$

This equation, the equivalent of Eq. (132), may be represented by a simple *series-parallel conductively coupled circuit* like Fig. 189*b*, in which, referring to the original T-network of Fig. 186*b*,

$$Z_a = Z_1 + X_M$$
$$(Z_b + Z_L) = X_M + Z_S$$
and
$$Z_c = -X_M$$

A comparison of the two sketches of Fig. 189 indicates that the T-network is a rather striking modification of the coupled circuits. Note particularly that (1) the coupling reactance $+X_M$ is replaced by $-X_M$ in the stem of the T and (2) the primary and secondary impedances are, respectively, replaced by $(Z_1 + X_M)$ and $(X_M + Z_S)$ in the arms of the T.

Example 5. Using the given data of Example 4, calculate the equivalent impedance of a T-network, checking the result with the value obtained for the original inductively coupled circuits.

Solution

$$Z_a = Z_1 + X_M = (4.75 + j10.16) + j5 = (4.75 + j15.16)$$
$$Z_b + Z_L = X_M + Z_S = j5 + (3 + j12.66) + (2 - j4) = (5 + j13.66)$$
$$Z_c = -j5$$
$$Z_{eq} = (4.75 + j15.16) + \frac{(-j5)(5 + j13.66)}{-j5 - (5 + j13.66)}$$
$$= (4.75 + j15.66) + \frac{72.5\underline{/-20.2^\circ}}{10\underline{/60^\circ}}$$
$$= (4.75 + j15.16) + (1.25 - j7.16) = (6 + j8) \qquad (Check)$$

Ratios of Transformation of Inductively Coupled Circuits. One of the most important practical applications of electromagnetic coupling in power and communication systems concerns the transfer of electrical energy from one circuit to another. This is accomplished in the well-known transformer without a change in frequency, although it may or may not be accompanied by a change in voltage and current. A further use of electromagnetic induction, particularly in communication circuits, is the transfer of *maximum* power from a low-energy source to a useful load; the latter, involving a special transformer that is capable of matching a given load impedance to the so-called "looking-back" circuit impedance, is generally referred to as *impedance matching*. (This was discussed in Chap. 15, page 346, under the heading, Principle of Maximum Power Transfer, in which it was shown that maximum power is transferred when the load impedance is equal to, or is the conjugate of, the line impedance.)

Considering a transformer in which the primary and secondary coils are perfectly coupled, i.e., with the coefficient of coupling unity, an equal voltage will be induced in *each turn* of both windings because the latter are linked by the same varying mutual flux. Expressing this statement in equation form $E_P/N_P = E_S/N_S$, from which

$$\frac{E_P}{E_S} = \frac{N_P}{N_S} = a \qquad (134)$$

where E_P, N_P, E_S, and N_S are the respective primary and secondary *induced emfs* and *turns*, and a is the so-called *ratio of transformation.* Since the primary resistance and exciting current are both generally low, the voltage drop in the input winding will be negligible when the secondary is open-circuited; under this condition the primary induced and impressed voltages may be assumed to be equal, and the ratio of transformation given by Eq. (134) may be regarded as a ratio of *terminal* emfs when there is no current in the secondary winding.

When load current is delivered by the secondary winding of a transformer, the number of ampere-turns in the latter is accompanied by an equal increase in the number of primary ampere-turns. This is true because the secondary ampere-turns would, by Lenz's law, tend to nullify the original exciting ampere-turns, to destroy the magnetic coupling, unless the primary were reinforced by an equivalent increase in ampere-turns; moreover, since transformer action is sustained under load, the volt-ampere input must be at least equal to, and in the ideal transformer *is* equal to, the volt-ampere output. Expressing these statements in equation form for the ideal transformer,

$$N_P I_P = N_S I_S \qquad \text{and} \qquad E_P I_P = E_S I_S$$

from which

$$\frac{E_P}{E_S} = \frac{I_S}{I_P} = a \qquad (135)$$

The foregoing may be summarized as follows:

1. The primary voltage may be lowered, i.e., stepped down, by employing fewer secondary than primary turns.
2. The primary voltage may be raised, i.e., stepped up, by employing more secondary than primary turns.
3. In a step-down transformer the secondary current is a times as much as the primary current.
4. In a step-up transformer the primary current is a times as much as the secondary current.

As previously pointed out, transformers are frequently used in communication circuits to match a given load impedance to a known primary impedance; this practice makes it possible for a low-power source to deliver maximum output although it is accomplished at the expense of low efficiency. To understand why the ratio of transformation of the transformer is the criterion in impedance matching it is important to recognize the fact that a certain voltage drop across a secondary load impedance must "appear" to the primary as though it were equal to the definite voltage drop in the primary impedance. Under such operating conditions the source, therefore "appears" to be delivering current to two equal impedances in series, in which event maximum load power is delivered; see Eq. (123). Assuming a *step-down* transformer for illustration, a primary voltage drop $I_P Z_P$ would have to be a times as much as an existing secondary voltage drop $I_S Z_S$ if the two drops are to be equivalent in the sense that they are equal percentages of their respective winding emfs. However, since the primary current is $1/a$ times as much as the secondary current, it follows that a primary impedance must be a^2 as great as a secondary impedance if they are to be equivalent. Conversely, a *step-up* transformer makes a certain secondary impedance "appear" to the primary as if it were a^2 times smaller so that, for maximum power transfer, Z_S must be $a^2 Z_P$. Several examples will now be given to illustrate the foregoing discussion.

EXAMPLE 6. A power transformer having a step-down ratio of 10 to 1 has its primary winding connected to a 2,300-volt source. If the secondary load current is 40 amp, calculate (*a*) the primary current, (*b*) the secondary load impedance, (*c*) the equivalent primary impedance of the load.

Solution

(*a*) $$I_P = \frac{40}{10} = 4 \text{ amp}$$

(*b*) $$Z_S = \frac{2{,}300/10}{40} = 5.75 \text{ ohms}$$

(*c*) $$Z_S \text{ (in primary terms)} = a^2 Z_S = 100 \times 5.75 = 575 \text{ ohms}$$

$$I_P = \frac{2{,}300}{575} = 4 \text{ amp} \qquad (\textit{Check})$$

EXAMPLE 7. A step-up transformer has 400 primary turns and 2,400 secondary turns. Its primary is connected through a 6-ohm capacitive reactance to a 21.6-volt a-c source whose internal resistance is 2.5 ohms. Assuming ideal transformer operation, calculate (*a*) the resistance of a secondary load that will receive maximum power, and (*b*) the load power under this condition.

Solution

(*a*) $$R_S = \left(\frac{2{,}400}{400}\right)^2 \times \sqrt{(2.5)^2 + (6)^2} = 234 \text{ ohms}$$

(*b*) $$Z_{\text{eq}} = (2.5 - j6) + \frac{234}{(6)^2} = 9 - j6 = 10.8 \text{ ohms}$$

$$I_P = \frac{21.6}{10.8} = 2 \text{ amp}$$

$$I_S = \frac{I_P}{a} = \frac{2}{6} = 0.333 \text{ amp}$$

$$P_S = (0.333)^2 \times 234 = 26 \text{ watts}$$

EXAMPLE 8. A transformer is to be used to match a secondary load impedance of 800 ohms to a generator-line impedance of 128 ohms. What should be the ratio of transformation of the transformer for maximum power transfer?

Solution

A step-up transformer will be required to couple an 800-ohm secondary to a 128-ohm primary; thus

$$a^2 \times 128 = 800$$

and

$$a = \sqrt{800/128} = \sqrt{6.25} = 2.5$$

Inductive Coupling in Series Circuits. When two or more parts of a series circuit are coupled magnetically the over-all impedance will be determined by the magnitudes and polarities of the mutual reactances as well as the individual impedances. In the simplest case, where one pair of coils are linked together, the mutual inductance acts equally to reinforce or nullify the two self-inductances, aiding the latter when the individual mutual fluxes are additive, and opposing them when the fluxes are subtractive.

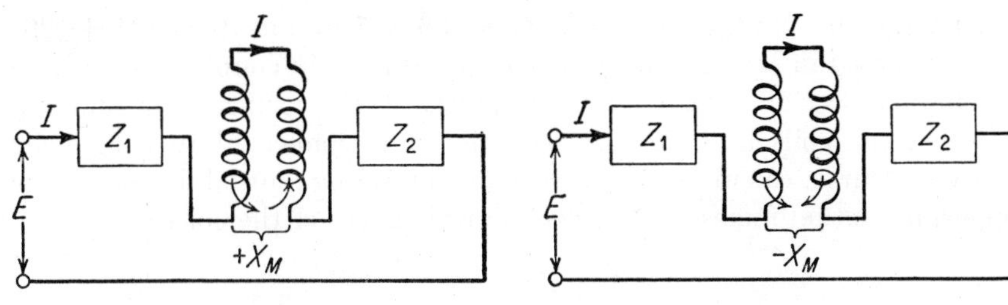

FIG. 190. Series circuits representing mutual reactance that aids and opposes self-reactances.

Figure 190 illustrates the two kinds of coupling for series circuits, diagrams *a* and *b* representing the conditions of mutual reactance that are respectively aiding and opposing. Since there is one circuit current, the voltage equations may be written as follows:

For *additive* mutual reactance, i.e., $+X_M$:

$$E = (IZ_1 + IX_M) + (IZ_2 + IX_M) = I(Z_1 + Z_2 + 2X_M)$$

For *subtractive* mutual reactance, i.e., $-X_M$:

$$E = (IZ_1 - IX_M) + (IZ_2 - IX_M) = I(Z_1 + Z_2 - 2X_M)$$

It is interesting to note that, when two similar coils are subtractively interconnected in series and are perfectly coupled ($K = 1$), the two equal self-inductances are nullified by the double action of the mutual induction; under this condition the circuit impedance is made up of units entirely outside the coupled coils.

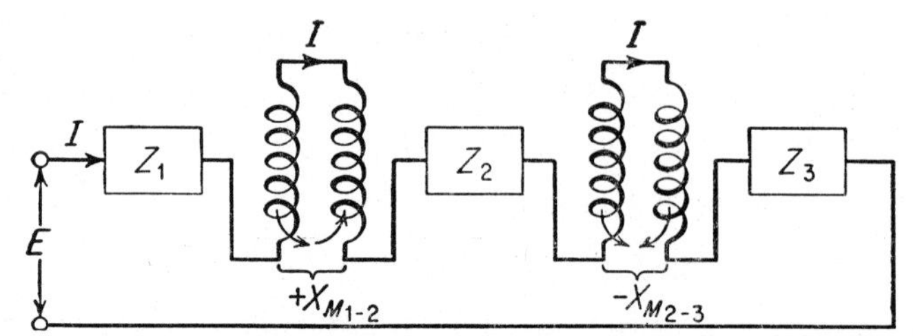

FIG. 191. A series circuit illustrating two pairs of magnetically coupled coils.

Additive and subtractive coupling are shown in the three-part series circuit of Fig. 191. In this arrangement of three impedances and two sets of coupled coils the voltage equation is

$$E = I(Z_1 + Z_2 + 2X_{M_{1-2}} - 2X_{M_{2-3}})$$

EXAMPLE 9. Two impedances $Z_1 = (36 - j16)$ and $Z_2 = (44 + j20)$ are connected in series through a pair of inductively coupled coils whose self-inductances are 0.025 and 0.081 henry. If the coefficient of coupling between the coils is 0.472, and the circuit is connected to a 60-cycle 115-volt source, calculate the current (*a*) for aiding mutual fluxes, (*b*) for opposing mutual fluxes. (Neglect the resistances of the coils.)

Solution

(*a*)
$$M = K\sqrt{L_1 \times L_2} = 0.472\sqrt{0.025 \times 0.081} = 0.0212 \text{ henry}$$
$$X_M = 2\pi \times 60 \times 0.0212 = 8 \text{ ohms}$$
$$(X_{L_1} + X_{L_2}) = 2\pi \times 60(0.025 + 0.081) = 40 \text{ ohms}$$
$$Z_{eq} = Z_1 + Z_2 + (X_{L_1} + X_{L_2}) + 2X_M$$
$$= (36 - j16) + (44 + j20) + j40 + j16 = (80 + j60)$$
$$I = \frac{115}{80 + j60} = \frac{115}{100/36.9^\circ} = 1.15/-36.9^\circ \text{ amp}$$

(*b*)
$$Z = (36 - j16) + (44 + j20) + j40 - j16$$
$$= 80 + j28 = 84.7/19.3^\circ$$
$$I = \frac{115}{84.7/19.3^\circ} = 1.36/-19.3^\circ$$

Inductive Coupling in Parallel Circuits. When a source of emf is impressed across two or more circuits that are both in parallel and inductively coupled, the current in each branch will be determined by the magnitudes and directions of the mutual reactances between it and other circuits as well as its own impedance. In the simplest case, where one pair of coils are linked together, the current in each circuit acts with the mutual reactance to increase or decrease the self-reactance of the other circuit, aiding the latter when the individual mutual fluxes are additive, and opposing them when the fluxes are subtractive.

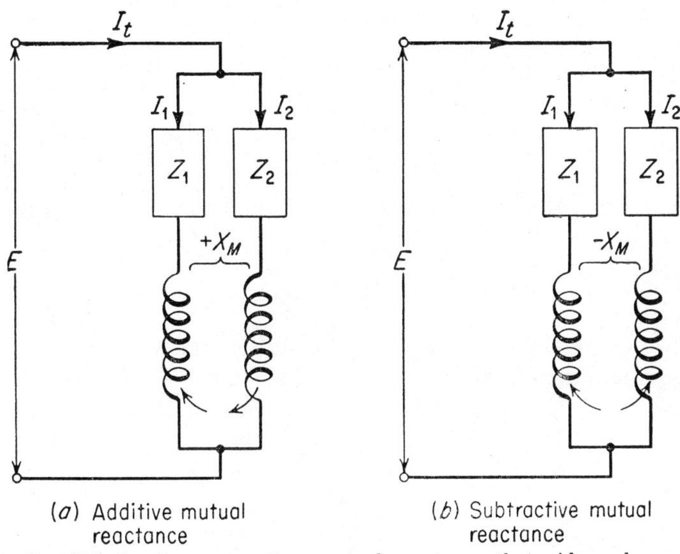

FIG. 192. Parallel circuits representing mutual reactance that aids and opposes self-reactances.

Figure 192 illustrates the two kinds of coupling for parallel circuits, diagrams a and b representing the conditions of mutual reactance that are respectively aiding and opposing. With the same voltage impressed across both branches two sets of current equations are possible, one set for the additive action of the mutual reactance, and the other for the subtractive action.

Writing two voltage equations for the condition of $+X_M$ (Fig. 192a),

$$E = I_1Z_1 + I_2X_M$$

and

$$E = I_2Z_2 + I_1X_M$$

These two expressions may be solved simultaneously for I_1 by multiplying the first one by Z_2 and the second one by X_M. Thus

$$EZ_2 = I_1Z_1Z_2 + I_2X_MZ_2$$

and

$$EX_M = I_1X_M^2 + I_2X_MZ_2$$

Subtracting the second equation from the first and rearranging terms,

$$I_1 = \frac{E(Z_2 - X_M)}{Z_1Z_2 - X_M{}^2}$$

The original two expressions may also be solved simultaneously for I_2 by multiplying the first one by X_M and the second one by Z_1. Thus

$$EX_M = I_1Z_1X_M + I_2X_M{}^2$$

and

$$EZ_1 = I_1Z_1X_M + I_2Z_1Z_2$$

Subtracting the first equation from the second and rearranging terms,

$$I_2 = \frac{E(Z_1 - X_M)}{Z_1Z_2 - X_M{}^2}$$

Writing two voltage equations for the condition of $-X_M$ (Fig. 192*b*),

$$E = I_1Z_1 - I_2X_M$$

and

$$E = I_2Z_2 - I_1X_M$$

These two expressions may be solved simultaneously for I_1 and I_2, as in the foregoing derivations for $+X_M$. When this is done,

$$I_1 = \frac{E(Z_2 + Z_M)}{Z_1Z_2 - X_M{}^2}$$

and

$$I_2 = \frac{E(Z_1 + Z_M)}{Z_1Z_2 - X_M{}^2}$$

The total current for each of the two conditions is

For *additive* mutual reactance, i.e., $+X_M$:

$$I_t = I_1 + I_2 = \frac{E(Z_1 + Z_2 - 2X_M)}{Z_1Z_2 - X_M{}^2}$$

For *subtractive* mutual reactance, i.e., $-X_M$:

$$I_t = I_1 + I_2 = \frac{E(Z_1 + Z_2 + 2X_M)}{Z_1Z_2 - X_M{}^2}$$

EXAMPLE 10. Two impedances $Z_1 = (6 - j21.8)$ and $Z_2 = (6 - j3.2)$ are connected in parallel to a 120-volt 60-cycle source, and are inductively coupled by a pair of coils whose inductive reactances are respectively $j9$ and $j16$ ohms. If the coefficient of coupling between the coils is 0.4, and the mutual fluxes are additive, calculate the individual branch currents and the total current. (Consider the values of Z_1 and Z_2 to include the respective resistances of the coupled coils.)

Solution

This problem will be solved by first evaluating the various quantities to be used in the expressions for I_1, I_2, and I_t.

$$X_M = K\sqrt{X_1X_2} = 0.4\sqrt{j9 \times j16} = j4.8$$

$$(Z_2 - X_M) = [(6 - j3.2 + j16) - j4.8] = (6 + j8) = 10\underline{/53.1^\circ}$$

$$Z_1Z_2 = (6 - j21.8 + j9)(6 - j3.2 + j16)$$

$$= (14.1\underline{/-64.9^\circ})(14.1\underline{/+64.9^\circ}) = 200\underline{/0^\circ}$$

$$X_M^2 = (j4.8)^2 = -23$$

$$(Z_1 - X_M) = [(6 - j21.8 + j9) - j4.8] = (6 - j17.6)$$
$$= 18.6\underline{/-71.2^\circ}$$

$$(Z_1 + Z_2 - 2X_M) = (6 - j12.8) + (6 + j12.8) - (j9.6) = (12 - j9.6)$$
$$= 15.35\underline{/-38.7^\circ}$$

$$I_1 = \frac{E(Z_2 - X_M)}{Z_1Z_2 - X_M^2} = \frac{(120)(10\underline{/53.1^\circ})}{200 + 23} = 5.37\underline{/53.1^\circ} \text{ amp}$$

$$I_2 = \frac{E(Z_1 - X_M)}{Z_1Z_2 - X_M^2} = \frac{(120)(18.6\underline{/-71.2^\circ})}{223} = 10\underline{/-71.2^\circ} \text{ amp}$$

$$I_t = \frac{E(Z_1 + Z_2 - 2X_M)}{Z_1Z_2 - X_M^2} = \frac{(120)(15.35\underline{/-38.7})}{223} = 8.25\underline{/-38.7^\circ} \text{ amp}$$

Multiple Coupling of Circuits. It is sometimes necessary to couple several circuits inductively so that one or more of them reacts with two others. Such multiple coupling involves two emfs of mutual induction in each of the circuits that is doubly linked; moreover, either or both of the latter voltages may oppose the emf of self-induction. For the purpose of determining the currents in the various portions of the complex network it is therefore imperative that voltage equations be set up with extreme care, particularly with regard to the polarities of the emfs of mutual reactance.

Assuming that only one of the circuits is connected to a sinusoidal source of voltage it is always true that the mutual reactances between each of the coupled circuits and the one that is energized will be negative, and should therefore be designated by $-X_M$ terms. The mutual reactances between circuits in which voltages are *induced*, not impressed, may be positive ($+X_M$) or negative ($-X_M$) depending upon the directions of the windings with respect to one another.

The foregoing discussion will be illustrated by the three-part network of Fig. 193. Before setting up the three voltage equations it will be helpful to point out the following relations: (1) The mutual reactances

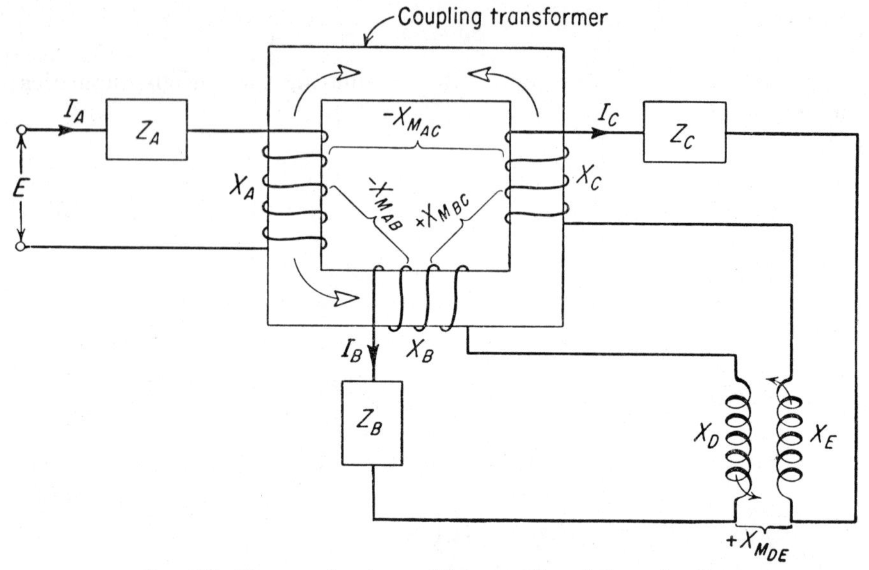

FIG. 193. Diagram showing multiple coupling of three circuits.

between the energized circuit A and the two circuits B and C to which it is coupled are represented by $-X_{M_{AB}}$ and $-X_{M_{AC}}$. (2) The mutual reactance between circuits B and C, neither of which is connected to a source of emf, is represented by a $+X_{M_{BC}}$ because their fluxes aid. (3) The mutual reactance between coils D and E is represented by a $+X_{M_{DE}}$ because their fluxes aid. (4) The self-reactances of the various coils are represented by the symbols X_A, X_B, X_C, X_D, and X_E, each one indicating that it is a reactance part of the impedance of the circuit indicated by the subscript.

Referring to Fig. 193, and bearing in mind the statements previously made, the three voltage equations are

For circuit A:

$$E = I_A(Z_A + X_A) - I_B X_{M_{AB}} - I_C X_{M_{AC}}$$

For circuit B:

$$0 = I_B(Z_B + X_B + X_D) - I_A X_{M_{AB}} + I_C(X_{M_{BC}} + X_{M_{DE}})$$

For circuit C:

$$0 = I_C(Z_C + X_C + X_E) - I_A X_{M_{AC}} + I_B(X_{M_{BC}} + X_{M_{DE}})$$

Other Types of Coupling. It was shown in a previous section (see Fig. 189) that a pair of inductively coupled circuits may be represented by an equivalent T-network, equivalent, that is, in the sense that the input and load currents are the same in both. The stem of the T, being common to both, serves as the coupling impedance; moreover, any impedance variation in one portion of the network affects the flow of current in the other. This, in general, being the essential property of coupled circuits, means that various parameter arrangements may be employed to permit the transfer of energy from one circuit to another and, in some combinations, to act selectively with regard to certain frequencies.

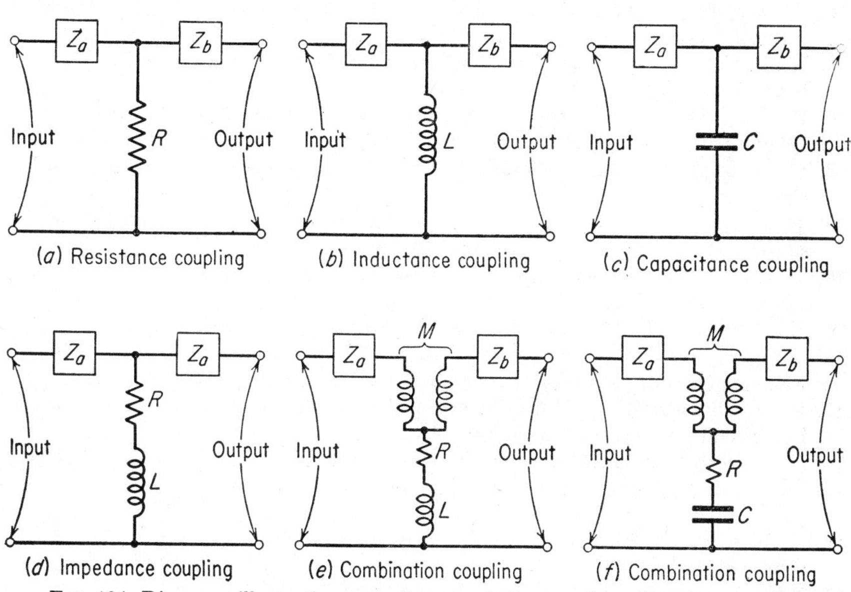

FIG. 194. Diagrams illustrating several types of direct and combination coupling.

The diagrams of Fig. 194 illustrate several types of coupled circuits frequently found in communication systems; they are called *directly coupled* or *combination coupled* as distinguished from *inductively coupled* circuits, because there is a direct metallic connection between input and output. Furthermore, the specific designation of each one indicates the kind of unit that is used for the stem of the T. The following points may be made for each of the sketches:

Sketch a. This is called *resistance coupling*, because input and output are connected through a common resistor.

Sketch b. This is called *inductance coupling*, because, neglecting the resistance of the coil, the input and output are connected through a common inductor.

Sketch c. This is called *capacitance coupling*, because input and output are connected through a common capacitor.

Sketch d. This is called *impedance coupling*, because input and output are connected through a common impedance (R-L) coil.

Sketches e and f. When input and output are linked inductively *and* directly, this is called *combination coupling.* The direct coupling may be an R-L, an R-C, or an R, L, or C unit.

Questions

1. Under what conditions can it be said that electric circuits are coupled?
2. What happens in a circuit when it is coupled to another that is energized?
3. Which of two coupled circuits is called the primary? the secondary?
4. What is meant by *transformer action?* Name several devices and machines that function by transformer action.
5. Define the term *coefficient of coupling* as applied to the magnetic coupling between two coils.
6. Upon what factors does the coefficient of coupling depend?
7. Define *mutual inductance* in general terms.
8. Under what conditions does unit mutual inductance exist between two coupled circuits?
9. What is the relation between mutual inductance, coefficient of coupling, and the self-inductances of the coupled circuits?
10. Make a sketch showing a pair of coupled coils and, with one of them energized, illustrate the paths of the mutual and leakage fluxes.
11. What is meant by *mutual reactance* and how does it manifest itself?
12. Assuming two circuits to be coupled magnetically, with current in both of them, write expressions for voltages of self-induction and mutual induction.
13. Under what condition is it possible to develop several voltages of mutual induction in a circuit? Illustrate your answer by a sketch.
14. How are the mutual reactance and the mutual inductance related to each other?
15. Distinguish between an air-core and a magnetic-core transformer from the standpoint of coupling and permeability.
16. Under what conditions are coils said to be coupled *additively? subtractively?* What sign is given to the mutual inductance M for each?
17. What is meant by the term *input impedance? driving-point impedance?*
18. Distinguish between *inductively coupled* and *conductively coupled* circuits. When are the two said to be equivalent to each other?
19. In replacing inductively coupled circuits with a T-network what is the value of the stem of the T? of each of the two arms of the T?
20. Define the term *impedance matching.* What significance does it have in communication systems?
21. Under what condition is a load impedance matched to the "looking-back" impedance?
22. Define *ratio of transformation* of a transformer.
23. How is it possible to determine the ratio of transformation of a transformer experimentally? Give reasons for your answer.
24. What is a *step-up* transformer? a *step-down* transformer?
25. Explain why a voltage is stepped up; stepped down.
26. Assuming a perfect transformer that delivers a secondary load, what relation does the secondary current bear to the primary current? the secondary kilovolt-amperes to the primary kilovolt-amperes?
27. What is the equivalent impedance of the secondary circuit in terms of the primary in a step-down transformer? a step-up transformer?
28. When two impedances are connected in series through a coupling transformer, how is the total impedance of the circuit affected by an additive mutual reactance? a subtractive mutual reactance?

29. Under what condition will the mutual reactance between two inductively coupled coils that are connected in series nullify the self-reactances of the coils? Explain carefully.

30. Upon what does the current in each of two parallel-connected circuits depend when they are coupled inductively? Explain.

31. Make a sketch showing how a coil may be inductively coupled to two others.

32. If three coils A, B, and C are inductively coupled and coil B is energized by an a-c source, what is the polarity of the mutual reactance between B and A? B and C? A and C?

33. What is meant by *direct coupling* as distinguished from inductive coupling?

34. List several types of directly coupled circuits. Illustrate each one by a sketch.

35. What is meant by *combination coupling?* Illustrate by a sketch.

Problems

1. Calculate the mutual inductance between two coils that are inductively coupled, if 112 volts is induced in the secondary when the 60-cycle primary current is 2.8 amp.

2. A coil has a resistance of 10 ohms, a self-inductance of 0.0265 henry, and a mutual inductance of 0.02 henry with respect to a neighboring coil. If a sinusoidal 115-volt 60-cycle source is applied to the first coil, determine the induced voltage in the second coil.

3. The coefficient of coupling between a pair of similar coils is 0.268. When connected in series aiding the total inductance is 0.142 henry, and when connected is series opposing the total inductance is 0.082 henry. Calculate (*a*) the mutual inductance between the coils, and (*b*) the self-inductance of each coil.

4. A 500-turn coil having a self-inductance of 0.09 henry is magnetically linked to a 1,500-turn coil. If the coefficient of coupling between them is 0.6, calculate the mutual inductance between the coils. (Self-inductance is proportional to the *square* of the number of turns.)

5. Calculate the 60-cycle mutual reactance for the coils of Prob. 3.

6. The mutual inductance between two coupled circuits is 0.0167 henry, and the 478-cycle primary and secondary currents are respectively 0.25 and 0.18 amp. Calculate the emfs induced in the two circuits because of mutual inductance.

7. Two inductively coupled coils are connected in series bucking and to a variable-voltage 796-cycle source. If the coefficient of coupling between them is 0.4, and their respective resistances and self-inductances are 32 and 56 ohms, and 0.0054 and 0.015 henry, calculate the impressed emf for a circuit current of 0.25 amp.

8. Solve Prob. 7 for the aiding connection of the coils.

9. Referring to the circuit diagram of Fig. 187, the following information is given: $E = 120\underline{/0°}$, $Z_1 = (6.615 + j5.2)$, $Z_2 = (3.5 + j5)$, $Z_L = (5.16 - j10)$, $X_M = j4$. Calculate (*a*) the driving-point impedance, (*b*) the primary current I_1, (*c*) the secondary current I_2.

10. Using the given data of Prob. 9, calculate the impedances of the equivalent T-network (Fig. 189*b*) and check the input and load currents.

11. A 5-ohm resistance is inductively coupled to a 4-ohm resistance through a mutual reactance of 2 ohms. What voltage should be impressed across the primary if the current in that circuit is to be 2 amp?

12. A primary inductive reactance of 5 ohms is coupled to a 4-ohm capacitive reactance of 4 ohms through a mutual reactance of 2 ohms. If the primary is connected to a 12-volt source what will be the input and load currents?

13. A power transformer has a rating of 5 kva, 2,400 to 240 volts, step-down. Calculate the ratio of transformation, and the primary and secondary currents when rated load is being delivered. (Neglect the primary exciting current.)

14. Determine the secondary load impedance, and its equivalent primary impedance, in Prob. 13.

15. A small transformer has a step-up ratio of 5 to 1. If the primary exciting current is $(0.135 - j1.05)$ amp, and the secondary load current is $0.5/\underline{-30^\circ}$ amp, calculate the primary current under load.

16. A transformer has a step-up ratio of 2.5 to 1 and is assumed to be ideal. If the primary is connected through a 5.2-ohm reactor to a 50-volt source whose internal resistance is 3 ohms, calculate the value of a load resistor for maximum power transfer. Also determine the power delivered to the load.

17. A transformer is to be used to match a secondary load impedance of 150 ohms to a generator-line impedance of 216 ohms. What should be the ratio of transformation of the transformer for maximum power transfer?

18. The primary of a step-up transformer having a ratio of transformation of 3.5 to 1 is connected to a 126-volt 60-cycle source through an impedance of $(2 + j8)$ ohms. The secondary is then connected to a load consisting of a resistor and capacitor in series, both of which are completely variable. For what values of R and C will maximum power be delivered to the load, and what will be the power under this condition?

19. Solve Prob. 18 by replacing the variable capacitor with a variable inductor.

20. Two impedances $Z_1 = (50 + j39.3)$ and $Z_2 = (36.6 - j31.2)$ are connected in series through a pair of inductively coupled coils whose self-inductances are 0.049 and 0.025 henry. If the coefficient of coupling between the coils is 0.531, and the circuit is energized by a 125-volt 60-cycle source, calculate the circuit current and power (*a*) for additive mutual fluxes, (*b*) for subtractive mutual fluxes.

21. Two impedances Z_1 and Z_2 are connected in series through a pair of inductively coupled coils each of which has a self-reactance of X_L. If the coefficient of coupling between the coils is unity, what is the equivalent circuit impedance (*a*) if the mutual fluxes are additive? (*b*) if the mutual fluxes are subtractive?

22. The following information is given in connection with the series circuit of Fig. 191: $E = 113$, $Z_1 = (8 - j3)$, $Z_2 = (7 + j9)$, $Z_3 = (5 + j10)$, $X_{M_{1-2}} = +j5$, $-X_{M_{2-3}} = -j3$. Calculate the circuit current.

23. The following data are given for the parallel circuit of Fig. 192*a*: $E = 123$, $Z_1 = (8 - j3)$, $Z_2 = (8 + j3)$, $X_M = j3$. Calculate the currents I_1, I_2, and I_t.

24. Solve Prob. 23 for the circuit of Fig. 192*b*.

25. Refer to Fig. 193 and change the polarity of $+X_{M_{DE}}$ to $-X_{M_{DE}}$. Write equations for circuits B and C.

CHAPTER 17

ALTERNATING-CURRENT INSTRUMENTS AND MEASUREMENTS

General Types and Uses of Alternating-current Instruments. The sensitivity of a-c instruments for the measurement of such quantities as volts, amperes, and watts is generally less than that of d-c instruments measuring similar quantities. This is because the magnetic field, usually provided by a pair of strong permanent magnets in the d-c instrument, the D'Arsonval type, must be produced by the very current that is responsible for the deflecting torque. Moreover, since iron cannot be used in a-c instruments to amplify the effect of the exciting ampere-turns—hysteresis and eddy-current effects would then be objectionable, except where a good degree of accuracy is not important—comparatively high values of current must pass through the coil to compensate for existing weak magnetic fields. In addition, alternating currents give rise to induced emfs in neighboring coils or metal parts which, together with frequency variations and harmonic current components, produce instrument errors not present in d-c measurements.

Four general types of a-c instrument are usually found in practice; these employ the *electrodynamometer* movement, the *concentric-vane* mechanism, the *radial-vane* mechanism, and the *thermocouple*. Each one has its special characteristics, subject, of course, to certain limitations as to accuracy, sensitivity, and cost, as well as fields of application. The electrodynamometer type may be designed for voltage measurements but is used most frequently to indicate power; because of the difficulty in conducting high values of current to a moving coil they are not suitable as ammeters. The concentric-vane type, used as a voltmeter or ammeter, has the advantage of being simple in construction and fairly low in cost; moreover, by properly shaping the vanes it may be designed for special applications, particularly where the scale must be widened to give accurate readings in a limited range. The radial-vane type, used as a voltmeter or ammeter, is quite sensitive and has a scale that is more linear than those previously mentioned; it does, however, require better design and better magnetic vanes for precise measurements. Thermocouple instruments are generally employed in high-frequency circuits, and have been designed to give excellent performance at frequencies up to 100 megacycles. All will be discussed in some detail in subsequent sections.

The Electrodynamometer Instrument. Most fundamental of all indicating devices is the electrodynamometer mechanism illustrated by a simplified sketch in Fig. 195. Since it contains no magnetic materials such as iron, indications are of true effective (rms) values. Known as a current-sensitive instrument because deflections result from current in fixed and moving coils, it is extremely versatile in its ability to measure current, voltage, or power, both d-c and a-c; moreover, when specially constructed with crossed coil movements it can be used to indicate power factor, phase angle, frequency, and capacity.

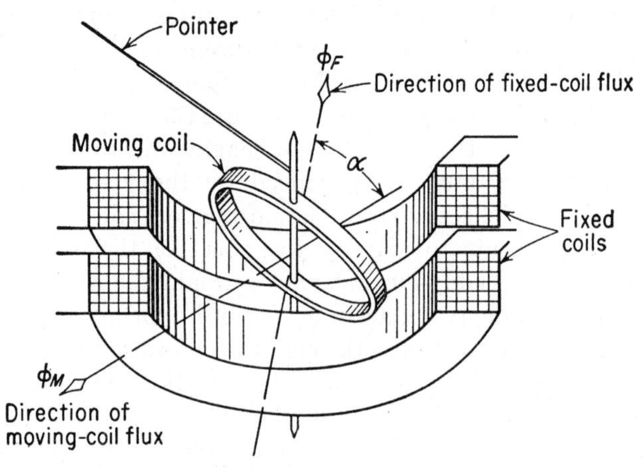

FIG. 195. Simplified sketch showing the electrodynamometer movement and the directions of the two reacting fields.

As usually constructed it consists of a pair of fixed coils that are connected in series aiding and separated to permit a vertical spindle to pass through for bearing support above and below the coils. Fastened to the spindle is a centrally mounted moving coil to which current is "fed" through a pair of flat spiral springs (see Fig. 82), the latter serving also to provide the countertorque against which the movement is calibrated. When the zero setting is made both springs are given initial deflections so that they act against each other. Since the moving coil must be extremely sensitive to small current variations it is light and accurately balanced, and is, moreover, wound with fine wire because it is energized through low-current-carrying springs.

Referring to Fig. 195, assume that current passes through the fixed coils in a counterclockwise direction and through the moving coil in a clockwise direction. Under this condition two magnetic fields will be set up as shown, and, since both sets of fluxes tend to conform to a collinear axis (see Chap. 5 for the second law of magnetism) the moving coil, free to turn, rotates clockwise to give the pointer an upscale position; the moving coil comes to rest when the electromagnetic turning moment is equal to the increased countertorque resulting from the wound-up springs. When the current reverses in an a-c circuit, both field directions are affected simultaneously, and this means that the clockwise direction of the torque will be unaffected; the instrument may therefore be used in a-c as well as d-c circuits. Effective damping is provided by mounting an aluminum vane on the pointer and having it rotate in a close-fitting chamber.

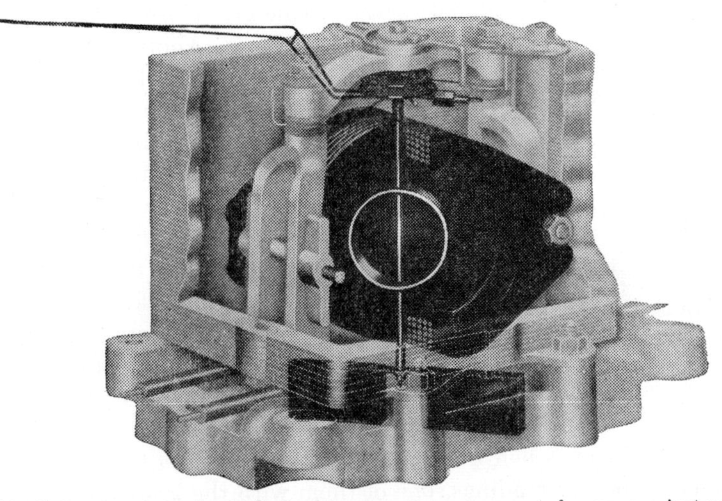

FIG. 196. Cutaway view of an electrodynamometer movement for an a-c instrument. (*Weston Electrical Instrument Corp.*)

The magnitude of the torque, being proportional to the individual fluxes and the sine of the angle between them, will depend upon the currents in the fixed and moving coils (Φ is directly proportional to I when no iron is present) and the relative positions of the latter with respect to each other. Thus, in Fig. 195, $T = kI_F I_M \sin \alpha$, where I_F and I_M are, respectively, the fixed- and moving-coil currents, and k is a factor of proportionality. Since the angle α changes for varying values of current, the calibrated scale in this type of instrument will not be uniform; it will, in fact, be open, i.e., spread out, in the middle range of values, and closely divided at the upper and lower ends.

A cutaway view of an electrodynamometer movement for a Model 432 Weston instrument is shown in Fig. 196.

The Electrodynamometer Voltmeter. When the fixed coils are wound with many turns of fine wire and are connected in series with a high resistance and the fine-wire moving coil, it may be used as a voltmeter. Such an instrument is not particularly sensitive because, unlike a d-c voltmeter that is provided with a pair of strong permanent magnets, the deflecting torque results from two reacting weak fields each of which is produced by an extremely low exciting current; even so, the a-c instrument takes about five times as much current as one designed for d-c service. Moreover, the calibrated scale is far from uniform since deflections are practically proportional to the square of the voltage; this means that the lower end of the scale, where the divisions are closely spaced, is quite inaccurate, although the middle and upper portions of the scale give reasonably precise indications. Another disadvantage of the electro-dynamometer voltmeter, a sketch of which is shown in Fig. 197, is that it is susceptible to error from stray magnetic fields; this is because extraneous fluxes are particularly effective when acting upon a useful field that is essentially weak.

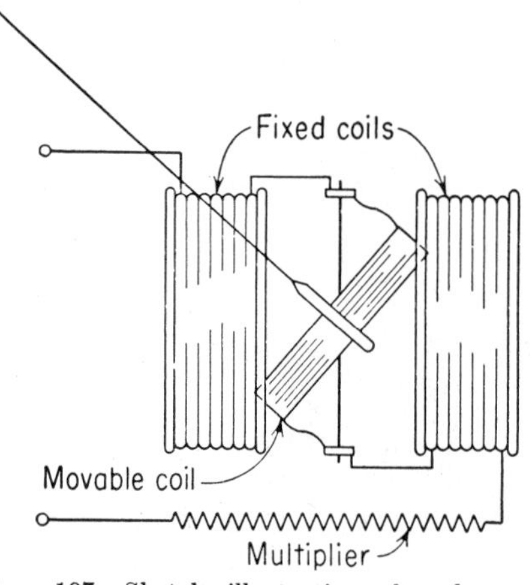

Fig. 197. Sketch illustrating the electrodynamometer type of voltmeter.

Since the average and effective values of a d-c voltage are equal, this type of instrument can be used with equal accuracy in d-c circuits; however, when doing so, it is generally a good practice to use the average of two readings, one of them with the leads interchanged, to offset the effect of stray fields and the earth's magnetism.

A unique modification of the usual construction of the electrodynamometer voltmeter illustrated by Figs. 195 and 196, where the vertical spindle passes directly through two diametrically opposite points on the moving coil, is to put a brace across the coil and have the spindle pass through its center so that the spindle fastens to the brace at a considerable angle. This arrangement causes the magnetic axis of the moving coil to be tilted from the horizontal when the pointer registers zero. With connections made as previously described, the moving coil tends to align itself along the fixed-coil axis when current passes through it. This is called an *inclined-coil* voltmeter; its scale may be lengthened somewhat and made more uniform because the coil can turn through a larger angle before its magnetic axis is coincident with the fixed-coil axis.

The Electrodynamometer Wattmeter. For the measurement of power in an a-c circuit the fixed coils of the electrodynamometer instrument are designed to carry the line current while the moving coil, with its series multiplier resistance, is used as a potential indicator. With this arrangement the deflecting torque is, at every instant of time, determined by the values of the currents in both the fixed and moving coils. Since the currents in the two elements change in magnitude and direction periodically, it should be clear that an upscale deflection will result only when the two sets of fluxes, as shown in Fig. 195, are properly directed with respect to one another. Assuming the coils to be connected so that instantaneous torques always produce upscale deflections at *unity power factor*, the *average torque* becomes a measure of the *average power*, which, by Eq. (90), is the product of the effective values of E and I; the pointer, fastened to a comparatively high-inertia moving-coil system, therefore swings up to an average torque position to indicate the average power in the circuit. At zero power factor, on the other hand, the average torque per cycle will be zero because, as shown in Fig. 128, the current

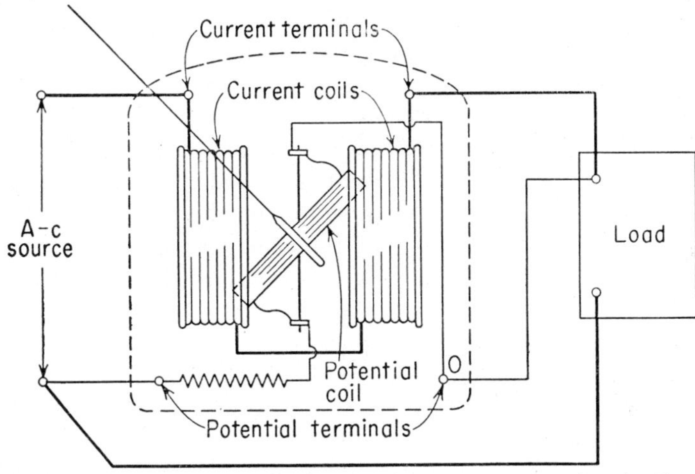

FIG. 198. Sketch illustrating internal and external wattmeter connections for the measurement of power.

and voltage are directed to give equal upscale and downscale deflections during successive quarter cycles; the pointer, under this condition, therefore gives a zero indication. At power factors other than unity the moving system will experience both upscale and downscale deflections, but, as shown in Figs. 131 and 133, the former will always exceed the latter the average torque will therefore be a measure of the average positive power in accordance with Eq. (97a).

Figure 198 illustrates how the wattmeter connections should be made for the measurement of power. Note that the instrument may be regarded as a combination voltmeter-ammeter, with a rather low current led into the moving coil through spiral springs, and a relatively large current—the load current—made to pass through a pair of fixed coils containing few turns of heavy wire. Since the average developed torque for a given set of EI and $\cos \Theta$ values will be a function of the angle α (Fig. 195) between the fixed and moving coils, the deflection per unit of power will not be uniform over the entire scale; the calibration of the wattmeter will, in fact, make it necessary to have closely spaced divisions at the lower and upper ends of the scale and widely spaced divisions in the middle region.

The fact that a wattmeter can be connected to give a downscale deflection means that it is necessary to label the current and potential terminals in some way if the instrument is to indicate properly. This is generally done by having engraved $\pm$ markings at appropriate terminals to indicate how the connections should be made for upscale readings. Another point that should be borne in mind is that the end of the potential (moving) coil that is *not* connected to the multiplier (marked O in Fig. 198) should be fastened to the line in which the current (fixed) coils are inserted; this precautionary measure is necessary if the voltage and current coils are to be at the same—a safe—potential.

The Concentric-vane Instrument. An extremely simple and rugged type of instrument, and one that has the added advantage that no current is carried by the moving element, operates on the principle that a force of repulsion exists between two pieces of soft iron placed in a magnetic field. Called a *concentric-vane mechanism,* it consists of three basic parts; these are (1) a solenoid of copper wire wound to create a vertically directed magnetic field, (2) a strip of soft iron that is somewhat tongue-shaped and fitted concentrically near the inside surface of the coil, and (3) a cylindrically shaped strip of soft iron with a slightly smaller radius than the fixed piece which, fitted with a pointer, is fastened to a spindle that is free to turn in a pair of support bearings. Figure 199 illustrates the construction of the instrument and clearly shows the fixed tongue-shaped (darkened) strip surrounding the cylindrical vane that is fastened to the spindle-pointer-spring assembly, both being centered on the inside of the surrounding solenoid. For operation as a voltmeter the exciting coil has many turns of fine wire and is connected in series with a resistance multiplier; when designed for use as an ammeter excitation

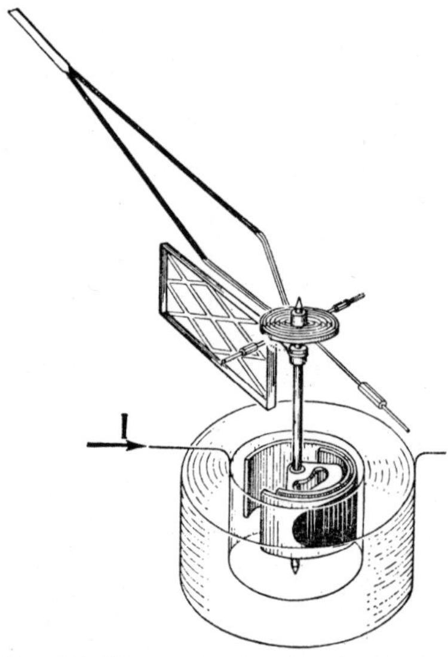

FIG. 199. Illustration showing the details of construction of a concentric-vane type of instrument. (*Weston Electrical Instrument Corp.*)

is provided by the normal line current through a comparatively few turns of heavy wire.

When current passes through the actuating coil, the upper and lower cylindrically shaped edges of both iron vanes are similarly magnetized. The upper edges will be *north* and the lower edges will be *south* for a counterclockwise coil current (looking down on top); conversely, the upper and lower edges will be, respectively, *south* and *north* for a clockwise current. This means, of course, that both cylindrical vanes will be similarly polarized for *either* current direction, and a force of repulsion (*like poles repel*) will always exist between the iron strips. Since the moving vane is attached to a pivoted shaft, the torque that is developed

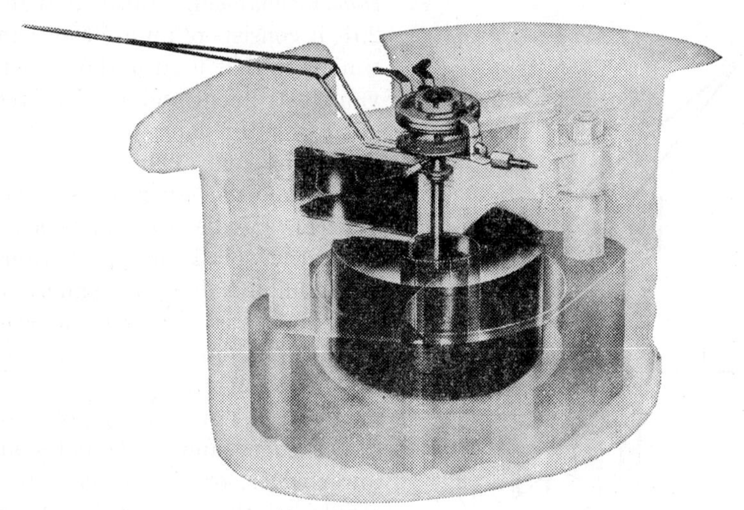

FIG. 200. Phantom view of an actual concentric-vane type of instrument. (*Weston Electrical Instrument Corp.*)

by the force of repulsion rotates the attached pointer against a counter-torque exerted by a spiral spring. The final position of the pointer on a calibrated scale will obviously be determined by the magnitude of the effective current.

An important detail of construction in this type of instrument is the *damping vane* attached to the pointer. Clearly seen in Fig. 199, it is a light aluminum frame, strengthened by flanges on all sides, that rotates with small clearance in a closed chamber. Used in a-c circuits, as is generally the case, the instrument develops a *pulsating* torque, and this in turn tends to cause the pointer tip to vibrate; however, effective damping as indicated, together with a pointer that is rigidly trussed, eliminates such vibration over a wide frequency range and serves to prevent possible bending on heavy overloads.

Since the upscale deflecting torque in this type of instrument is independent of the current direction it will operate on direct as well as alternating current. However, being subject to the effect of hysteresis it cannot be accurately calibrated with direct current; moreover, when calibrated with a-c it has a precision of about 1 to 2 per cent in d-c measurements. An interesting feature of the mechanism is that it is possible to shape the vanes to secure special scale characteristics.

A phantom view of an actual concentric-vane instrument, depicting all important details of construction, is shown in Fig. 200.

The Radial-vane Instrument. Another type of instrument that operates on the principle described in the foregoing section employs a *radial-vane* mechanism. Illustrated in Fig. 201, it consists of an exciting winding similar to that used in the concentric-vane instrument and a pair of rectangular soft-iron vanes placed in the center of the coil. One of the vanes is fixed while the other is fastened to a vertical spindle to which are also attached a spiral spring, a pointer, and an aluminum damping vane. When current passes through the exciting coil, whether direct or alternating current, the soft-iron vanes are similarly magnetized, with *north* poles at the upper edges and *south* poles at the lower edges, or vice versa; a force of repulsion is therefore produced. Since one of the vanes is fastened rigidly and the other is free to turn, a deflecting torque is developed that rotates the moving element against a countertorque exerted by the spiral spring. The final position of the pointer will, of course, depend upon the winding current because the rotational force is a function of the excitation. The aluminum damping vane, attached to the shaft just below the pointer, rotates in a close-fitting chamber to bring the moving element to rest quickly.

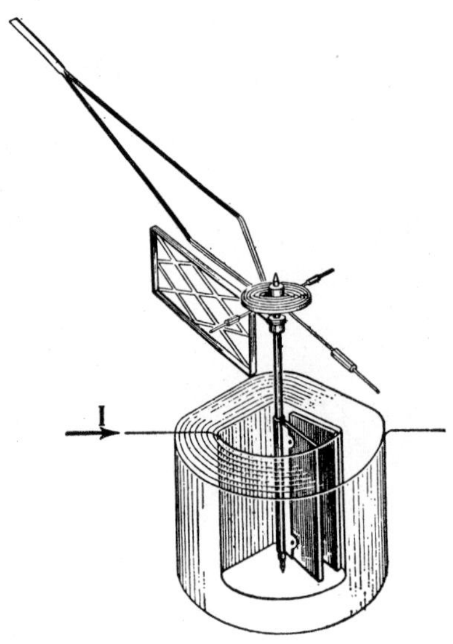

Fig. 201. Illustration showing the details of construction of a radial-vane type of instrument. (*Weston Electrical Instrument Corp.*)

This radial-vane instrument is used as an ammeter or voltmeter and, when carefully designed, is extremely sensitive; also, it has a scale that is more linear than the types previously discussed.

The Thermocouple Instrument. When it is necessary to make measurements at comparatively high frequencies, and especially in the audio- and radio-frequency ranges, it is generally desirable to use an arrangement in which the instrument deflection depends upon the heating value of the current. To this end it is customary to place the junction of a thermocouple in contact with a resistor alloy that is heated by the current to be measured; the emf that results at the cold ends of the thermocouple is impressed across a d-c D'Arsonval type of instrument (see Chap. 3, page 38, under the heading, Electrical Effects and Energy Transformations). Since the heating effect in the resistor is independent of the *direction* of the current and the thermal emf is practically proportional to the temperature difference between the junction and ends of the thermocouple, a millivoltmeter may be made to indicate indirectly an effective current of any frequency or wave form.

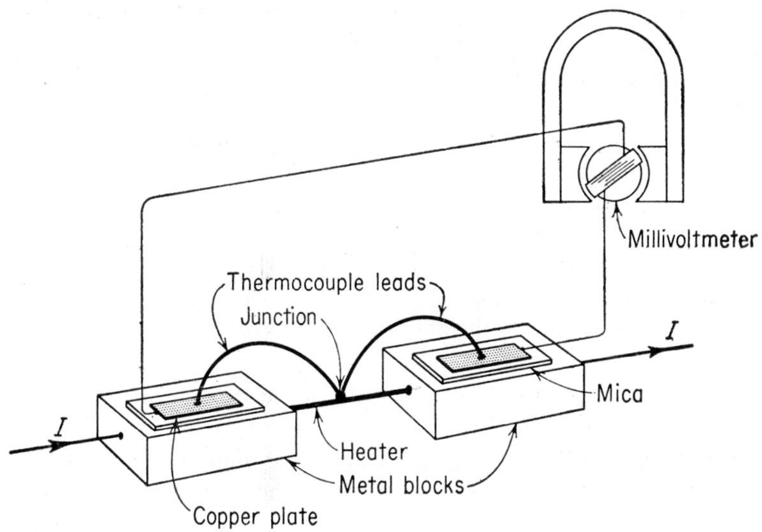

FIG. 202. Sketch illustrating a thermocouple instrument.

The diagram of Fig. 202 illustrates how the thermocouple principle is applied to the measurement of current. The wire of resistor alloy that has a negligible temperature coefficient of resistance is connected between a pair of extremely heavy metal blocks, the purpose being to maintain the latter at a reasonably constant temperature when the current to be measured passes from block to block through the heater. The junction of the thermocouple is then placed in contact with the heater and the free ends of the dissimilar conductors are fastened to thin copper plates each of which is separated from its block by a sheet of mica. Connections are finally made from the copper plates to the d-c millivoltmeter. Since this construction provides compensation for ambient temperature changes, it is referred to as *cold-junction compensation.*

Remembering that the heating is a function of the square of the current in the heater wire, the scale of the indicating instrument can be calibrated with evenly spaced divisions in terms of I^2 or with a square-law arrangement of divisions—closely spaced at the low end and widely spaced at the high end—in terms of the effective current I. Another scheme employs a special design of millivoltmeter which provides a current scale I with uniformly spaced divisions. This is accomplished by having an instrument with a variable air gap between moving coil and permanent magnets; the air gap increases and the flux density decreases as the coil rotates toward the upscale position, in consequence of which the sensitivity is reduced where the divisions would normally be widely spaced. Another point that should be mentioned is that thermocouple millivoltmeters are generally more delicate than shunted instruments used for general d-c measurements; this is because their full-scale deflection occurs at about 15 mv, the maximum thermocouple output, in contrast with ordinary 50-mv movements.

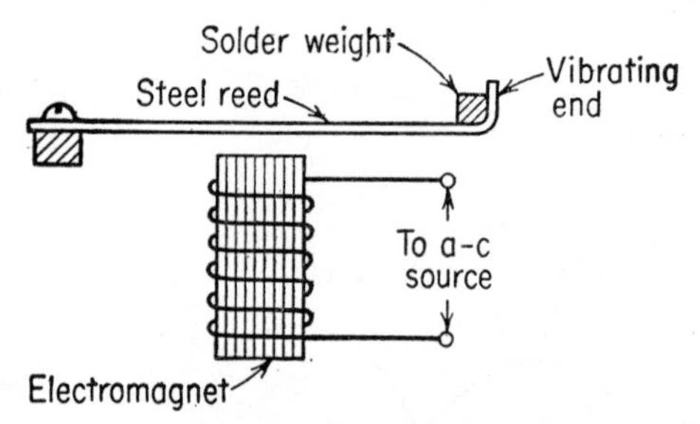

Fig. 203. Sketch illustrating one of the tuned steel reeds and the exciting electromagnet in a vibrating-reed frequency indicator.

Frequency Indicators. Although these instruments have very limited application, several principles are used in their construction. In one type, the so-called *vibrating-reed* frequency indicator, a large number of steel reeds are lined up in front of an electromagnet, being rigidly clamped at one end and free to vibrate at the other. The reeds, all of which are bent up and painted white at the visible (front) end, are mechanically tuned to vibrate at different frequencies, usually in steps of one half-cycle. When current of a given frequency passes through the coil, the reed that has the same natural period of vibration as the line frequency will swing up and down with the greatest amplitude; several others on either side of the tuned reed will also vibrate slightly, though none of the others will respond. Since it is necessary to keep the reeds polarized so that the mechanically tuned elements will vibrate in unison with the changing a-c polarities, a permanent magnet is mounted near the bank. A sketch illustrating one of the tuned (weighted) steel reeds and the position of the electromagnet is given in Fig. 203.

To overcome the objection of stepped-frequency measurements characteristic of vibrating-reed indicators, instruments have been developed to move a pointer over a calibrated scale. In one such type, illustrated by Fig. 204, a pair of fixed coils A and B are mounted 90° apart, and a simple soft-iron core M, fastened to a spindle and carrying a pointer, is free to rotate. Coil A is connected in series with an inductive reactance X_A and coil B is in series with a resistance R_B. A second inductive reactance X is in parallel with coil B and R_B, while another resistance R is connected across coil A and X_A. With this arrangement the soft-iron core takes up a position that is determined by the *resultant* magnetic field created by the combined actions of coils A and B. When the frequency increases, the current decreases in the X_A*-coil* A–X circuit and increases in the R*-coil* B–R_B circuit; under this condition the direction of the resultant magnetic field shifts to change the position of the soft-iron core and move the pointer upscale. The opposite effect takes place when the frequency is decreased. The series inductive reactance X_l serves merely to damp the higher harmonic components that may be present in a voltage wave that is distorted.

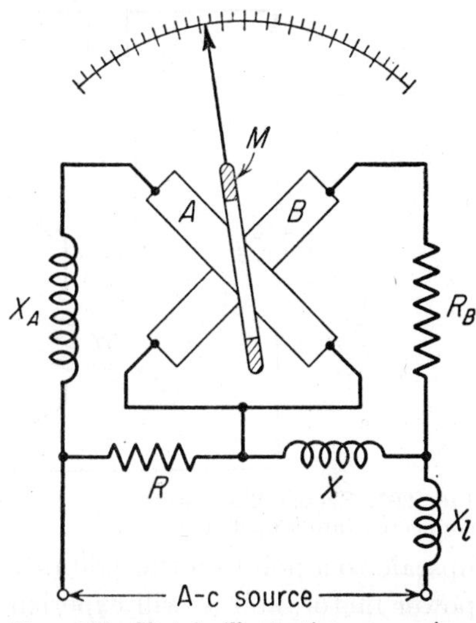

FIG. 204. Sketch illustrating a moving-pointer type of frequency instrument.

Other types of frequency indicators involve special bridge circuits that produce shifting magnetic fields and reed devices that are entirely mechanical in operation.

Power-factor Indicators. There are two general types of power-factor instrument, one of them similar in construction to the electrodynamometer wattmeter, and the other involving the induction principle. The mechanism of the first class (Fig. 205) consists of a pair of stationary series-connected coils A and B that carry the line current, and two coils M and N, placed 90° with respect to each other, that are rigidly mounted on a spindle so that the assembly is free to rotate. Coil M is connected in series with a resistance R and coil N is in series with an inductive reactance X, the two series combinations being joined in parallel and placed across the load terminals. With this arrangement the current in coil M will be out of phase with the current in coil N by about 90 elec deg; moreover, coils M and N are displaced in space by 90°. At unity power factor, for example, the field produced by the fixed coils A and B will exert maximum torque on movable coil M (the one with the series resistor); this will cause the pointer fixed to the moving system to deflect

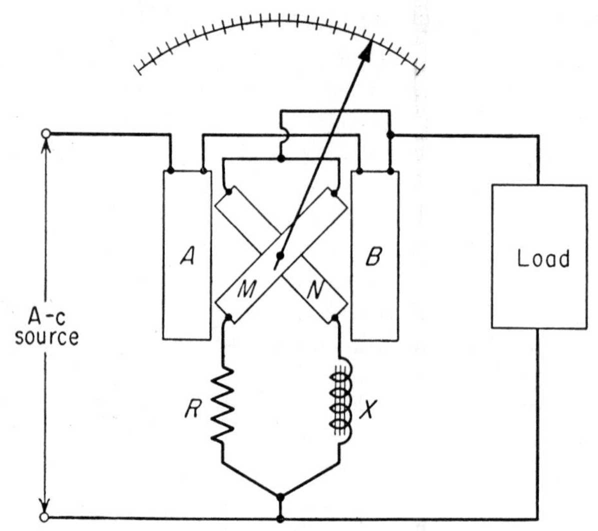

FIG. 205. Sketch illustrating an electrodynamometer type of power-factor instrument connected into a load circuit.

upscale to a point on the calibrated scale marked 100. Similarly, at zero power factor, coil N will experience maximum torque, in which case the moving system will rotate the pointer downscale to a zero mark on the scale. Obviously, for power factors other than unity and zero the pointer will receive corresponding deflections on the calibrated scale. Since the indications are affected by frequency variations because the current in the inductive branch of the moving-coil system is a function of f, the instrument must be used in constant-frequency circuits and particularly in those for which the calibration is made; however, by proper design of the reactor, the effect of moderate variations in frequency can be kept small.

Watthour Meters. For the measurement of electrical energy it is necessary to use a *watthour meter;* this is an *integrating* device, in contrast with an instrument such as an ammeter, a voltmeter, or a wattmeter, which *indicates* the quantity being measured. It is, for a-c service, a small *shaded-pole motor*[1] in which a flat aluminum disk rotates to operate a registering mechanism through a system of accurately made gears. Since the speed of the disk is directly proportional to the power in the circuit, the meter registers *energy,* and specifically *kilowatthours.* The dials are generally read monthly by properly trained men, and the energy cost is calculated from the meter readings taken on successive months.

The watthour meter must be an extremely well designed, very precise piece of equipment because it does, in fact, represent the "cash register"

[1] C. S. Siskind, "Electrical Machines, Direct and Alternating Current," Chap. 10, McGraw-Hill Book Company, Inc., New York, 1950.

of the electrical public-service industry. Figure 206 is a photograph of a typical meter for outdoor mounting, with the cover removed. To secure a very high degree of precision its calibration must include adjustments for light load, full load, low lagging power factor, and temperature. Moreover, the meter must be accurate under all kinds of weather conditions and must, in addition, be capable of withstanding overloads that are as much as 500 per cent.

Fig. 206. Typical watthour meter for outdoor service, with the cover removed. (*Duncan Electric Mfg. Co.*)

To calibrate the meter, it is connected with a standard wattmeter, voltmeter, and ammeter in a *constant-load* circuit as shown in Fig. 207, and the number of disk revolutions is counted for a definite period with the aid of a stop watch. With the number of *watthours per disk revolution* known—this figure is always given on the face of the meter and is symbolized by k_h—the energy consumption can be readily computed by the equation

$$\text{Watthours} = k_h \times \text{rph} \tag{136}$$

where rph is the number of disk revolutions per hour (generally determined by counting revolutions for a short interval such as one minute and multiplying by the number of time intervals per hour). With the power maintained constant during the testing period, watthours *per hour* as given by Eq. (136) is also equal to the circuit power.

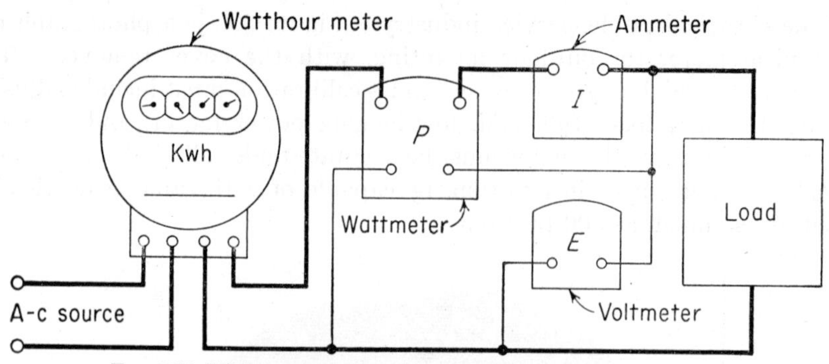

FIG. 207. Wiring connections for calibrating a watthour meter.

Complete meter calibration generally involves tests and adjustments for full load, light load, and overload, with the power factor set for unity and then at 0.5 lagging.

EXAMPLE 1. A watthour meter having a disk constant $k_h = 3.6$ (see Fig. 206) is tested with a unity power-factor load. If 20 disk revolutions are counted in a period of exactly 2 min and the line voltage is 120, calculate the circuit power and current.

Solution

$$\text{rph} = 20 \times 30 = 600$$

$$P = 3.6 \times 600 = 2{,}160 \text{ watts}$$

$$I = \frac{2{,}160}{120} = 18 \text{ amp}$$

Cost of Electrical Service. Residential and small farm, office, and store consumers are generally charged monthly by electrical public-service companies on the basis of a sliding-rate scale, the rate per kilowatthour decreasing in steps as the amount of energy used is increased. In most cases where the energy consumption is extremely low, or where special electrical installations are made for the convenience of those who are not in the direct load center, fixed minimum charges are made. For large consumers, on the other hand, it is customary to have a sliding scale of rates lower than "residential" rates for *energy* and, in addition, other charges that take into account such load conditions as maximum power demand and low power factor, as well as the fluctuating cost of power-plant fuel. In shops and factories where the power and power-factor demands generally swing between very wide limits, the public-service company must install extra overhead transmission and transformer equipment capable of taking care of maximum as well as normal requirements. And since this adds to the fixed charges for electrical service without increasing the energy income in proportion to the cost of such equipment, it has generally been agreed that maximum demand and low power-factor charges should be made.

It must be understood, of course, that the primary basis for the cost of electrical service is *energy*, measured in kilowatthours. For the measurement of such energy all installations are equipped with watthour meters previously described, usually at a point in the line where the wires enter the building. They are designed for many kinds of service such as two- and three-wire single-phase, and polyphase circuits, and for a number of voltage, current, and frequency ranges.

A typical residential rate schedule might be the following: 5 cents per kilowatthour for the first 35 kwhr; 4 cents per kilowatthour for the next 35 kwhr; 2½ cents for the next 130 kwhr; and 2 cents per kilowatthour for any additional energy consumption. For example, a customer who used 264 kwhr of energy for a month would pay

Step 1:	35×0.05	= \$1.75
Step 2:	35×0.04	= 1.40
Step 3:	130×0.025	= 3.25
Step 4:	64×0.02	= 1.28
	Total cost	= \$7.68

Where high-capacity good-load-factor units—such as electric water heaters—are installed, public-service companies frequently give attractively low rates for energy consumption in the upper brackets. In one such case, a charge of 1.3 cents per kilowatthour is made for energy in excess of 200 kwhr.

Rate schedules for industrial power and light service, generally three-phase alternating current, vary somewhat on the basis of connected load, maximum demand, and energy consumption. In addition to the basic charge for energy (kilowatthours) there are at least three other items of cost, representing property investment and operating expense, that must be included in the bill for service. The latter come under the headings of (1) maximum load and load factor,[1] (2) adjustment for power factor, and (3) adjustment for the cost of powerhouse fuel.

One such schedule for power and light service, available to customers having a billing maximum load of 25 kw or more, is the following:

Maximum-load Charge

\$1.50 per month per kilowatt of billing maximum load in the month, where the maximum load is adjusted, for billing purposes, to a basic power factor of 0.80 lagging. For power factors *less* than 0.80 lagging, as determined from installed reactive kilovolt-ampere-hour meters, the

[1] The maximum load shall be measured by suitable indicating or recording instruments, and in any month the maximum load shall be the average number of kilowatts in the thirty-minute interval during which the energy metered is greater than in any other thirty-minute interval in such month.

maximum load is *increased proportionately*, whereas for power factors *greater* than 0.80 lagging the maximum load is *decreased proportionately*.

Energy Charge

2.25 cents per kilowatthour for the first 3,000 kwhr used in any month

1.8 cents per kilowatthour for the next 7,000 kwhr used in the same month

1.2 cents per kilowatthour for the next 10,000 kwhr used in the same month

1.0 cent per kilowatthour for the next 80,000 kwhr used in the same month

0.8 cent per kilowatthour for the next 100,000 kwhr used in the same month

0.7 cent per kilowatthour for all over 200,000 kwhr used in the same month

An actual bill taken from the files of the Public Service Company of Indiana, Inc., for electric service rendered a Lafayette, Ind., manufacturer is given to illustrate how the monthly bill is calculated on the above schedule.

EXAMPLE 2. The following information, taken from meter readings and preliminary calculations, is given in connection with one month's electric service: total energy = 138,000 kwhr; maximum load = 475 kw; average power factor = 0.672 lagging; fuel-clause adjustment = 0.1141 cent per kilowatthour based on applicable average fuel cost of \$0.1973 per million Btu. Determine the cost of the service to the customer.

Solution

Maximum-load Charge

$$\text{Billing maximum load (adjusted to power factor)} = 475 \times \frac{0.80}{0.672} = 565.5 \text{ kw}$$

$$\text{Maximum-load charge} = 565.5 \times \$1.50 = \$848.25$$

Fuel-clause Charge

$$138{,}000 \times \$0.001141 = \$157.46$$

Energy Charge

3,000 kwhr at 0.0225	=	\$ 67.50
7,000 kwhr at 0.018	=	126.00
10,000 kwhr at 0.012	=	120.00
80,000 kwhr at 0.010	=	800.00
38,000 kwhr at 0.008	=	304.00
138,000 kwhr total	=	\$1,417.50

$$\text{Total monthly bill} = \$848.25 + \$157.46 + \$1{,}417.50 = \$2{,}423.21$$

Wattmeter Connections. When a wattmeter is to be connected into a circuit to measure power it is desirable to regard it as a combination ammeter-voltmeter; the two sets of ammeter and voltmeter terminals are connected in much the same way as are independent instruments. There are, however, two ways to do this, each of which involves a reading *error* which must be corrected. Moreover, most standard portable wattmeters provide for two current and two voltage ranges, which means that, for each set of selected terminals, a proper *scale factor* must be applied to the deflection to determine the correct value of power.

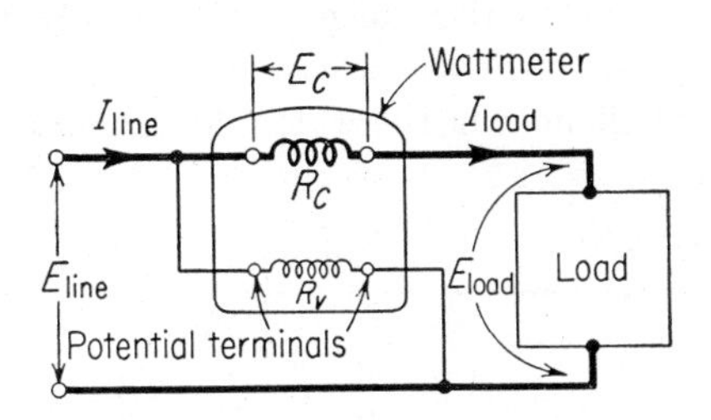

(*a*) Wattmeter connected with current coil in load circuit and potential coil across line terminals

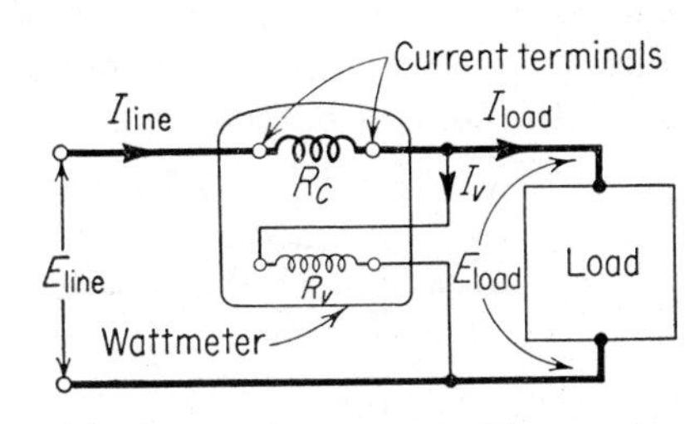

(*b*) Wattmeter connected with current coil in line circuit and potential coil across load terminals

FIG. 208. Diagrams showing wattmeter connected in two ways.

The *true* power taken by a load is, obviously, a function of the *load current and the load voltage.* Two diagrams are shown in Fig. 208 to illustrate that it is *not* possible to connect the wattmeter in a circuit to fulfill both current and voltage conditions simultaneously. In Fig. 208*a* load current passes through the current element of the wattmeter as it should, but the potential element is connected to the *line* terminals, *not* the *load* terminals; conversely, Fig. 208*b* shows the potential element of the wattmeter connected to the *load* terminals, but the current element carries *line, not load,* current. This implies, therefore, that the wattmeter always gives a larger deflection than the true load power (1) by an amount equal to the power loss in the current element of Fig. 208*a*, or (2) by an amount equal to the power loss in the potential element of Fig. 208*b*.

Considered another way, note in Fig. 208*a* that the potential element of the wattmeter is connected to register the sum of two voltages, namely, E_{load} *plus* E_c; the true *load* power is therefore

$$P_{load} = P_{rec} - (I_{load}^2 \times R_c)$$

where P_{rec} is the recorded wattmeter reading and R_c is the resistance of the current element of the wattmeter. In Fig. 208*b*, the current element of the wattmeter is connected to register the sum of two currents, namely,

I_{load} *plus* I_v; the true power is therefore

$$P_{load} = P_{rec} - \left(\frac{E_{load}^2}{R_v}\right)$$

where R_v is the resistance of the potential element of the wattmeter. The foregoing two equations are given on the supposition that a power measurement with a wattmeter is accompanied by voltage and current measurements with a voltmeter and an ammeter. Figure 209 illustrates the usual connections in a circuit in which watts, volts, and amperes are measured; in this arrangement of instruments the voltmeter should be disconnected (releasing the contact button) while the wattmeter is being read, the contact button in the potential element of the wattmeter should

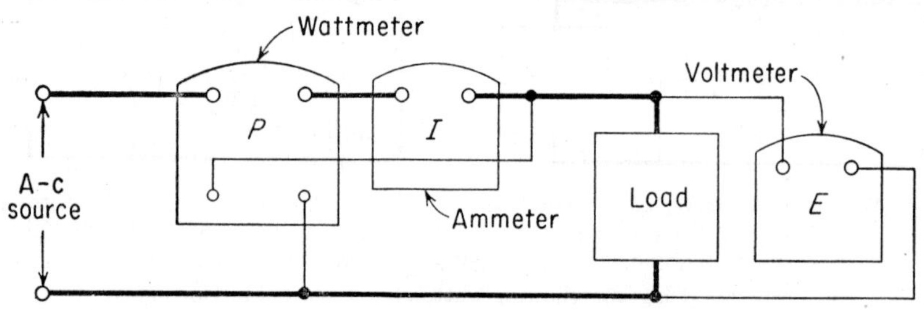

FIG. 209. Circuit diagram showing connections for the measurement of watts, amperes, and volts.

be released when the ammeter is being read, and the wattmeter includes the power loss in the resistance R_v of the potential circuit.

EXAMPLE 3. A wattmeter having a potential-element resistance of 3,600 ohms is connected with an ammeter and a voltmeter like the diagram of Fig. 209. If $P_{rec} = 820$ watts, $I_{load} = 8$ amp, and $E_{load} = 120$ volts, calculate the load power and power factor.

Solution

$$P_{load} = P_{rec} - \left(\frac{E_{load}^2}{R_v}\right) = 820 - \left[\frac{(120)^2}{3{,}600}\right] = 816 \text{ watts}$$

$$\text{PF} = \frac{P_{load}}{E_{load} \times I_{load}} = \frac{816}{120 \times 8} = 0.85$$

Multirange Wattmeters. As with d-c instruments (Chap. 7) it is desirable to extend the operating range of a wattmeter to two or more standard-voltage circuits, e.g., 115 and 230 volts. Thus the current may have either of two maximum values, one of them twice the other. Terminal connections are then made on such *multirange wattmeters* to fulfill existing voltage and current *circuit conditions*, and this generally means that a so-called *scale factor*—a multiplying factor—must be applied to the deflections on a given calibrated scale.

Since the wattmeter contains a potential (voltmeter) and a current (ammeter) circuit the instrument range may be extended to either or both, though usually the latter; the operating potential of the instrument is increased by connecting a resistance, a *multiplier*, in series with the potential circuit, whereas two current ranges, one twice the other, are provided by a series- or parallel-connection arrangement of two current coils. (Current coils in a-c instruments cannot be shunted by resistances because of the presence of inductance.)

The two current coils (shown in Fig. 198) may be connected in series or parallel by using a simple terminal-link arrangement as illustrated by

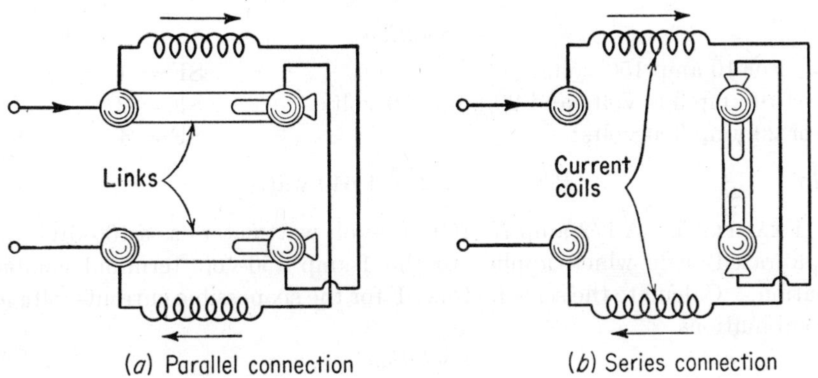

FIG. 210. Sketches illustrating how the two current coils in a wattmeter are connected in parallel or series by a terminal-link arrangement.

Fig. 210. Two links with pronged openings at one end and slotted openings near the other may be connected to the surface-mounted terminals in either of two ways. When the links are tightly clamped as in Fig. 210*a* the two coils are in parallel for the larger of the two permissible maximum values of line current; when both links are slipped into the position shown by Fig. 210*b* the two coils are in series for the smaller of the two permissible values of line current. For both connections the maximum *coil* current is the same. Standard wattmeters are available for current combinations such as 1/2 amp, 2.5/5 amp, 5/10 amp, 10/20 amp, 20/40 amp, 30/60 amp, and others.

The multiplier resistors for the potential coils are usually internally connected as in d-c instruments (see Figs. 79 and 80) and are available in many two- and three-voltage ranges that include such potentials as 75, 150, 300 volts, and others. In some cases, where a desired voltage range is not provided by a given instrument, an external multiplier resistance can be used; when this is done, the wattmeter deflection, for this addition, must be multiplied by a factor determined, as with d-c voltmeters, by Eq. (52).

Several examples will now be given to illustrate the application of multirange wattmeters.

EXAMPLE 4. A multirange wattmeter is designed for a current combination of 10 and 20 amp, and a voltage combination of 150 and 300 volts. (These are maximum permissible values.) Divisions on the calibrated scale are 0 to 1,000 watts, and this applies to the use of the 10-amp 150-volt terminal combination. (*a*) What are the scale factors SF of the wattmeter for the four possible current-voltage combinations? (*b*) When the 20-amp 150-volt terminals are used what circuit power is measured when the deflection is 820 watts? (Neglect the wattmeter error.)

Solution

(*a*) For 10 amp 150 volts: SF = 1
For 10 amp 300 volts and 20 amp 150 volts: SF = 2
For 20 amp 300 volts: SF = 4

(*b*)
$$P = 820 \times 2 = 1{,}640 \text{ watts}$$

EXAMPLE 5. A 1/2-amp 75/150/300-volt wattmeter has a 100-division calibrated scale which applies to the 1-amp 150-volt terminal combination. Calculate the scale factors SF for the six possible current-voltage combinations.

Solution

For 1 amp 75 volts: SF = 0.5
For 1 amp 150 volts and 2 amp 75 volts: SF = 1
For 1 amp 300 volts and 2 amp 150 volts: SF = 2
For 2 amp 300 volts: SF = 4

EXAMPLE 6. The resistances of the potential circuits of Example 5 are: for 75 volts, 2,219 ohms; for 150 volts, 4438 ohms; for 300 volts, 8,876 ohms. Make power calculations for the following, assuming that the connections are as shown in Fig. 209: (*a*) with $E = 119$ volts and using the 1 amp 150 volts combination the deflection is 82.5 watts; (*b*) with $E = 231$ volts and using the 2 amp 300 volts combination the deflection is 76 watts; (*c*) with $E = 66.5$ volts and using the 2 amp 75 volts combination the deflection is 63.5 watts.

Solution

(*a*)
$$P = (1 \times 82.5) - \frac{(119)^2}{4{,}438} = 79.3 \text{ watts}$$

(*b*)
$$P = (4 \times 76) - \frac{(231)^2}{8{,}876} = 298 \text{ watts}$$

(*c*)
$$P = (1 \times 63.5) - \frac{(66.5)^2}{2{,}219} = 61.5 \text{ watts}$$

Example 7. What is the load power factor for all the ampere-voltage combinations of Example 5 when the wattmeter registers full-scale deflection under conditions of maximum permissible current and voltage?

Solution

$$\text{PF (for the 1-amp 150-volt combination)} = \frac{100}{1 \times 150} = 0.667$$

$$\text{PF (for the 2-amp 300-volt combination)} = \frac{400}{2 \times 300} = 0.667$$

The same result will obtain for any of the other combinations.

Questions

1. Why is the sensitivity of a-c instruments generally less than that of d-c instruments?
2. Why is it not possible to use iron in a-c instruments if precise measurements are important? Explain, pointing out the effects of hysteresis, eddy currents, and induced emfs.
3. List the four general types of a-c instrument. Indicate some of the advantages of each type, and their fields of application.
4. Describe the construction of the electrodynamometer instrument.
5. For what kinds of service can the electrodynamometer instrument be used?
6. Explain how an electrodynamometer voltmeter operates on alternating current. Can it be used in d-c circuits?
7. Describe the damping mechanism in an electrodynamometer type of instrument.
8. On the electrodynamometer type of wattmeter, how are the fixed and moving coils energized? Why?
9. Indicate the factors which determine the torque developed by an electrodynamometer type of instrument.
10. Why is the scale of an electrodynamometer instrument *not* uniformly divided?
11. Describe the construction of the *inclined-coil* voltmeter. What special advantages does it have?
12. Explain why an electrodynamometer type of wattmeter indicates average power. How does the deflecting torque take the circuit power factor into account?
13. Why is it desirable to regard a wattmeter as a combination voltmeter-ammeter when it is connected into a circuit?
14. Is it possible to connect a wattmeter to give a downscale deflection? Explain carefully.
15. Why is it necessary to label the wattmeter terminals with symbols such as $\pm$?
16. Explain the significance of the terminal marked *O* in Fig. 198.
17. Describe the construction of the *concentric-vane* type of instrument.
18. Explain the principle of operation of the concentric-vane instrument. For what kinds of measurement is it commonly constructed?
19. Explain how the *damping* vane operates in the concentric-vane instrument. Why is this an important element of the mechanism?
20. Will a concentric-vane instrument operate in a d-c circuit? Can it be calibrated with direct current? Explain carefully.
21. Describe the construction of the *radial-vane* type of instrument.
22. Explain the principle of operation of the radial-vane instrument. For what kinds of measurement is it commonly constructed?

23. Upon what fundamental principle is the *thermocouple* type of instrument based?
24. Describe the construction of the thermocouple instrument indicating the purpose of each part.
25. For what types of measurement is the thermocouple instrument adapted?
26. What kinds of scale divisions is it possible to have on the instrument that accompanies the thermocouple? Explain carefully.
27. What kind of an emf, d-c or a-c, is developed by the thermocouple?
28. Is it possible to use the thermocouple type of instrument for d-c measurements?
29. Is a thermocouple voltmeter possible? Give reasons for your answer.
30. What maximum voltage can be expected from a thermocouple?
31. Explain why the measuring instrument that accompanies a thermocouple is more delicate than a similar type of d-c instrument.
32. Describe the construction of the *vibrating-reed* type of frequency meter.
33. Explain the principle of operation of the vibrating-reed frequency meter.
34. Describe the construction of a frequency meter in which a pointer moves over a calibrated scale. Also explain its principle of operation.
35. List other types of frequency meter, explaining how they are constructed and their principles of operation.
36. Give two general types of power-factor meter.
37. Describe the construction of the electrodynamometer type of power-factor meter and explain its principle of operation.
38. Why is the power-factor meter of the electrodynamometer type suitable only for the frequency for which it is designed?
39. Distinguish between an indicating instrument and a recording meter.
40. What is the principle of operation of a watthour meter? What kind of electrical quantity does it measure?
41. Why must a watthour meter be extremely well designed to measure kilowatthours accurately?
42. What kinds of adjustments are necessary on a watthour meter to make it accurate?
43. What is meant by the *disk constant* of a watthour meter?
44. Explain how a watthour meter is calibrated.
45. What general plan underlies the rate schedule for residential consumers?
46. Explain how a public-service company determines the cost of energy used by residential consumers.
47. List the factors that must be taken into account in organizing a rate schedule for power consumers.
48. Why are demand, power factor, and fuel charges justifiable in power-consumer rate schedules?
49. Explain why a wattmeter reading is always in error when a power measurement is made. In what two ways can the current coils be connected? the potential coil?
50. When the current coils of a wattmeter are connected in the line circuit, where is the potential coil connected?
51. When the current coils of a wattmeter are connected in the load circuit, where is the potential coil connected?
52. Indicate how the errors are corrected for Questions 50 and 51.
53. What is meant by a multirange wattmeter? What advantages do such instruments have?
54. What determines the terminal connections to a multirange wattmeter?
55. What is meant by the *scale factor* of a wattmeter?
56. How is the voltage range of a wattmeter extended?
57. Why is it *not* possible to use a shunt across the current coils of a wattmeter to extend the current range?

58. What method is used to obtain two current ranges in a wattmeter?
59. What can be done to increase the voltage range of a given wattmeter? Explain.
60. List several voltage and current combinations of standard wattmeters.

Problems

1. A 15-amp 120/240-volt watthour meter has a disk constant of 2. When tested on a unity power-factor load 24 disk revolutions are counted in a period of 3 min. If the line voltage is adjusted to 120, calculate the circuit power and current.
2. How many disk revolutions would be counted per minute in Prob. 1 if the power factor were changed to 0.5 lagging, assuming the line current and voltage to remain the same?
3. Calculate the number of revolutions made by the disk of a wattmeter similar to that of Prob. 1 for an energy consumption of 52 kwhr.
4. Calculate the disk constant of a watthour meter that makes 40 revolutions in 6 min when it is measuring a constant load of 1,000 watts.
5. How much energy is measured by a watthour meter having a disk constant of 3.6 for 18,000 revolutions of the disk?
6. Using the rate schedule given on page 391, calculate the monthly bill for a residential consumption of 158 kwhr.
7. Using the rate schedule for power consumers given on page 391, calculate the monthly bill on the basis of a consumption of 61,000 kwhr and a maximum load of 182 kw, a lagging power factor of 0.693, and fuel-clause adjustment of 0.126 cent per kilowatthour.
8. Solve Prob. 7 assuming a power factor of 0.921.
9. A 5-amp 150-volt wattmeter has a potential-circuit resistance of 3,320 ohms. What true power is taken by a 115-volt load if the deflection is 425 watts and the potential terminals are connected as shown in Fig. 208*b*?
10. A 2-amp 300-volt wattmeter has a current-coil resistance of 0.162 ohm. What true power is taken by a 1.57-amp load if the deflection is 280 watts and the potential terminals are connected as shown in Fig. 208*a*?
11. Calculate the power factor of a load that takes 16 amp at 118 volts if the wattmeter, connected with its potential terminals across the load, registers 1,600 watts. The potential-circuit resistance is 2,320 ohms.
12. A 5/10-amp 75/150/300-volt wattmeter is designed with a 250-division scale which applies, for full-scale deflection, to the 5 amp 75-volt combination of terminals. Calculate the scale factors for the various current-voltage combinations.
13. The resistances of the potential circuits of Prob. 12 are: for 75 volts, 1,812 ohms; for 150 volts, 3,624 ohms; for 300 volts, 7,248 ohms. Make power calculations for the following, assuming the potential circuit to be connected directly across the load in each case: (*a*) with $E = 60.2$ volts and using the 5-amp 75-volt terminals the deflection is 212 watts; (*b*) with $E = 120$ volts and using the 10-amp 150-volt terminals the deflection is 206 watts; (*c*) with $E = 225$ volts and using the 10-amp 300-volt terminals the deflection is 156 watts.
14. A 20-amp 150-volt wattmeter deflects full scale when the circuit power is 2,250 watts. Calculate the load power factor under conditions of maximum permissible current and voltage.

CHAPTER 18

POLYPHASE CIRCUITS

General Comparisons between Single-phase and Polyphase Systems and Equipment. A polyphase system generally consists of an arrangement of two or more similar single-phase systems in which the maximum values of the independent voltage waves do not occur at the same instants of time. The most common combination is the three-phase system, an interconnection of three single-phase systems, whose voltage waves, though similar in amplitude and frequency, are displaced by 120 elec deg from one another; in the two-phase system two voltage waves are displaced by 90 elec deg from each other. For special installations such as rotary converters, electrolytic service, and others, it is sometimes found desirable to have systems of 6, 12, and more phases; these involve voltage waves that are displaced by 60, 30, etc., elec deg.

The equipment used in polyphase systems has many advantages over those employed for single-phase service. Generators are larger, more economical per kilowatt, and operate at higher efficiencies; this means that large polyphase generating stations, for the most part three-phase, can be constructed to provide wide-scale low-cost service. Also, power-transmission lines are, comparatively, less expensive, the weight of the copper for three-phase, for example, being three-fourths of equivalent single-phase lines. Polyphase motors and associated equipment such as switchgear, transformers, and control units can likewise be larger and much more powerful when designed for polyphase service; these are extremely important considerations in industrial-plant operation.

A serious objection to the use of single-phase for power applications is its pulsating nature; this is particularly noticeable in motor operation where the power is not only zero four times per cycle on lagging power-factor loads (see Fig. 131) but becomes negative for two periods of time in each cycle; this generally results in a nonuniform application of load torque and a noticeable change in speed from instant to instant. Polyphase motors, on the other hand, operate smoothly and take power at constant rates and with no reversals; they are, moreover, more economical and efficient, and less subject to service interruptions than their single-phase counterparts.

Single-phase power can be, and more often than not is, obtained from a polyphase service; this is readily done by connecting to a proper pair of the multiple-wire system. In such cases the voltage may or may not be correct; when not it is a simple matter to employ a transformer having the proper ratio of transformation to modify the existing voltage.

Generation of Three- and Two-phase Voltages. Practically all modern a-c generators are constructed for three-phase service; some of the older machines still in operation, and an occasional generator built for special service are two-phase. When 6, 12, or any other number of phases are required for applications like rotary converters, mercury-arc rectifiers, and others, it is customary to use transformers to change from standard three-phase (or two-phase) to the desired multiphase system. In a three-phase generator, there are three interconnected windings in which three emf waves are developed that are displaced *in time* by 120 elec deg; in a two-phase generator, there are two independent or interconnected windings in which two emf waves are developed that are displaced *in time* by 90 elec deg. To produce the time displacements indicated the windings are mounted on a laminated, slotted, ring-type structure—the so-called *stator*—so that they are displaced *in space* by the same number of electrical degrees their voltage waves must differ in time, the voltages being generated by the action of a single d-c field structure that rotates concentrically within the stator. Figure 211 illustrates schematically how the independent windings are arranged *in space* for three- and two-phase service; the simplified two-pole diagrams clearly show that the three windings of the three-phase machine are displaced

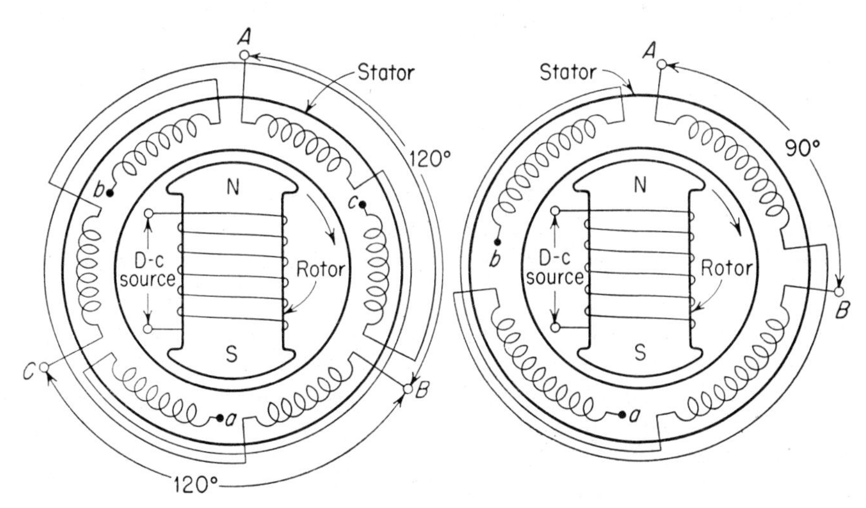

FIG. 211. Schematic diagrams illustrating polyphase winding arrangements.

120° with respect to one another, while the two windings of the two-phase machine are 90° apart.

Since the independent windings of three- or two-phase machines are similar their voltage waves will be identical, although displaced by the proper number of degrees along the time axis. This means that the zero and maximum values of the various phases will occur, respectively, at

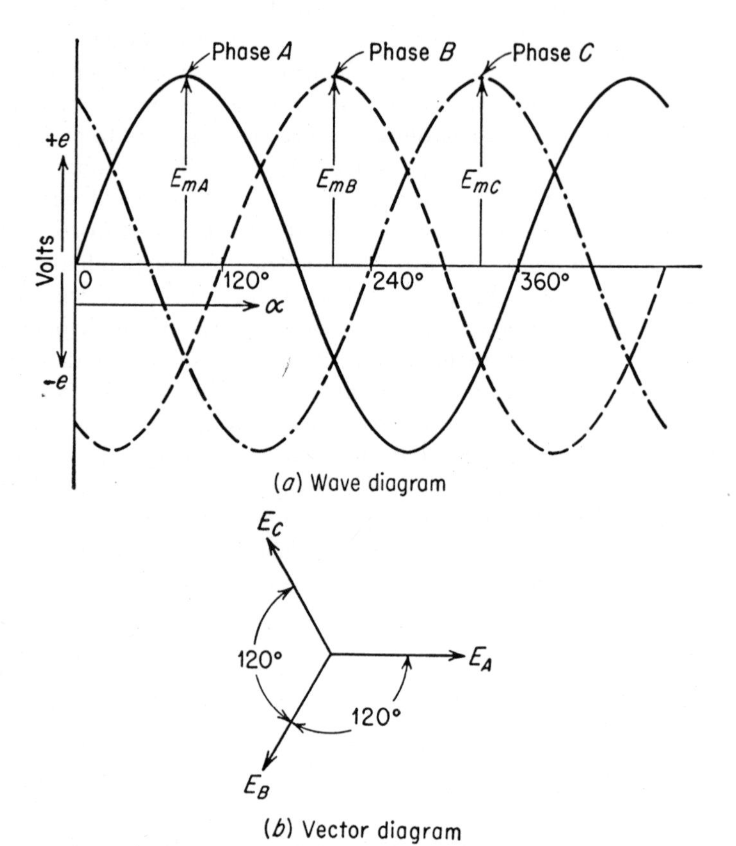

(a) Wave diagram

(b) Vector diagram

FIG. 212. Voltage diagrams for a three-phase system with a phase sequence of *A-B-C*.

120 elec deg intervals in three-phase generators, and at 90 elec deg intervals in two-phase machines. The diagram of Fig. 212*a* shows how the waves are related in a three-phase system, with phase *B* lagging behind phase *A* by 120 elec deg, and phase *C* lagging behind phase *B* by 120 elec deg; note also the vector diagram of Fig. 212*b* which shows the relationship between the effective voltages. Similar diagrams are given in Fig. 213 for a two-phase system; these show that phase *B* lags behind phase *A* by 90 elec deg.

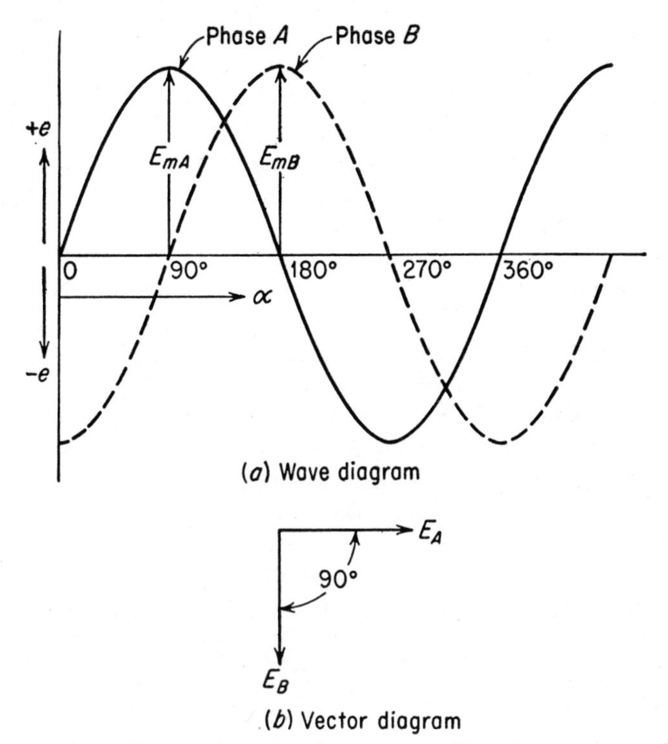

FIG. 213. Voltage diagrams for a two-phase system with a phase sequence of *A-B*.

Assuming sinusoidal voltage variations, and using the emf of phase A as a reference, the following equations may be written for the voltages in a three-phase system:

$$e_A = E_m \sin \alpha$$
$$e_B = E_m \sin (\alpha - 120°)$$
$$e_C = E_m \sin (\alpha - 240°)$$

Also, the equations for the voltages in a two-phase system are

$$e_A = E_m \sin \alpha$$
$$e_B = E_m \sin (\alpha - 90°)$$

Comparing these equations with their respective wave diagrams it should be understood that the order of the phases—the *phase sequence*—is ABC for the three-phase system and AB for the two-phase system. This is so because of the order or sequence in which the emfs come to their corresponding maximum values; in the three-phase system it is E_{mA}, E_{mB}, and E_{mC}; in the two-phase system it is E_{mA} and E_{mB}. The phase sequences can readily be changed by reversing the direction of rotation of the field structure in Fig. 211; under this condition they would be ACB for three-phase and BA for two-phase. Once the phase sequence of the generator is established, the order in which the line wires are connected to the load will determine how the latter will behave. For one set of connections a three-phase induction motor will, for example, rotate in one direction, and for an interchange of one pair of wires the motor will reverse its direction of rotation. When the loads are stationary and unbalanced, consisting of various combinations of R, L, and C, two completely different sets of calculated values will be obtained for the two phase sequences.

Vector Notation in Polyphase Circuits. Although the effective voltages developed in the different phases of an a-c generator (usually called an *alternator*) are numerically equal, their vector positions are determined by the manner in which the windings are arranged in the machine. This implies that, with symmetrical placement of windings, vector directions are properly specified only when the symbols indicate how the winding circuits must be *traced* to yield the correct phase displacement. Thus, for example, the voltage of phase A in Fig. 211 is ahead of the voltage in phase B by 120 elec deg when phase A is traced from a to A and

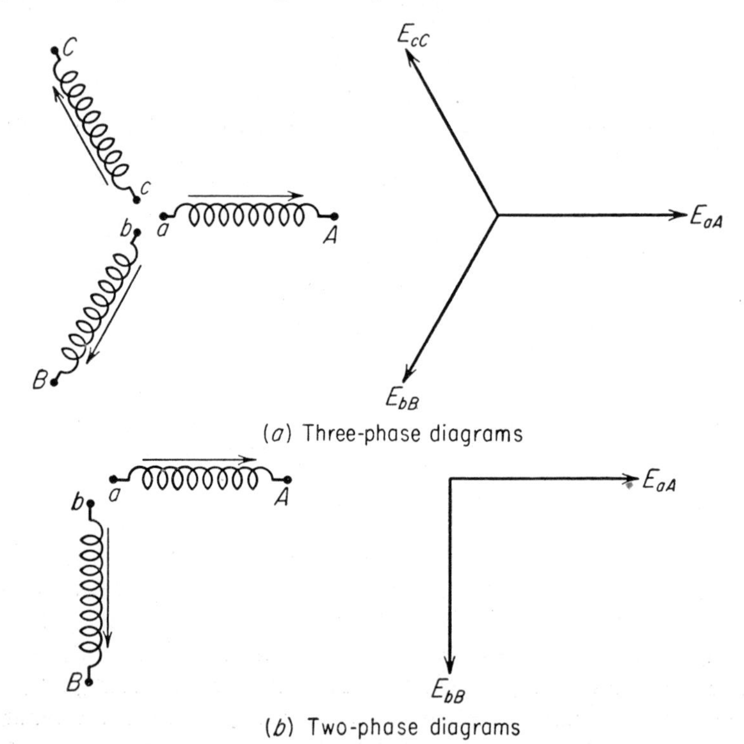

(*a*) Three-phase diagrams

(*b*) Two-phase diagrams

FIG. 214. Winding and vector diagrams illustrating the double-subscript notation.

phase B is traced from b to B; similarly the voltage of phase C lags behind the voltage of phase B by 120 elec deg when phase C is traced from c to C *and* phase B is traced from b to B. Understanding this, it therefore seems logical to represent vector quantities by a double-subscript notation, with the order of the latter indicating how the circuit is traced. Figure 214 illustrates this convenient scheme of notation for three- and two-phase alternator windings and their voltages.

When polyphase windings are interconnected, resultant voltages must be determined, and this frequently makes it necessary to trace a winding in a direction opposite to that originally shown. Under such conditions the vectors are merely reversed and the opposite subscript notations are applied to the quantities. This is illustrated in Fig. 215 in which the

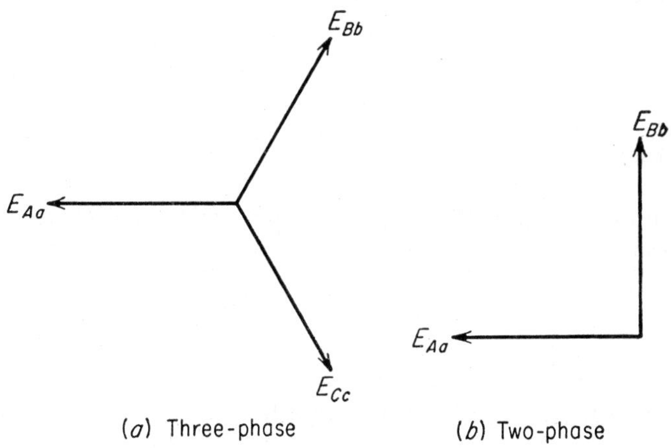

FIG. 215. Vector diagrams illustrating a reversed-subscript notation in comparison with Fig. 214.

three- and two-phase vector diagrams are represented by voltages that are the reverse of those in Fig. 214.

The foregoing scheme of notation will now be applied to several winding interconnections to determine the magnitude and direction of resultant voltages. Referring to Fig. 214a, assume that points a and b are connected together. To determine the voltage E_{BA} it is necessary to trace the winding from B to A, and this means that E_{BA} is the vector sum of E_{Bb} and E_{aA}, i.e., $\dot{E}_{BA} = \dot{E}_{Bb} + \dot{E}_{aA}$; this is shown in Fig. 216a and indicates that E_{BA} is $\sqrt{3}$ times as much as either of the equal coil voltages and 30° ahead of E_{aA}. Figure 216b illustrates a connection between C and A, as a result of which E_{ac} becomes equal to $\dot{E}_{aA} + \dot{E}_{Cc}$; in this case E_{ac} is again equal to $\sqrt{3}$ times as much as either coil voltage but lags behind E_{aA} by 30°. Finally, Fig. 216c illustrates a connection between C and b, and this results in a voltage E_{cB} that is equal to the

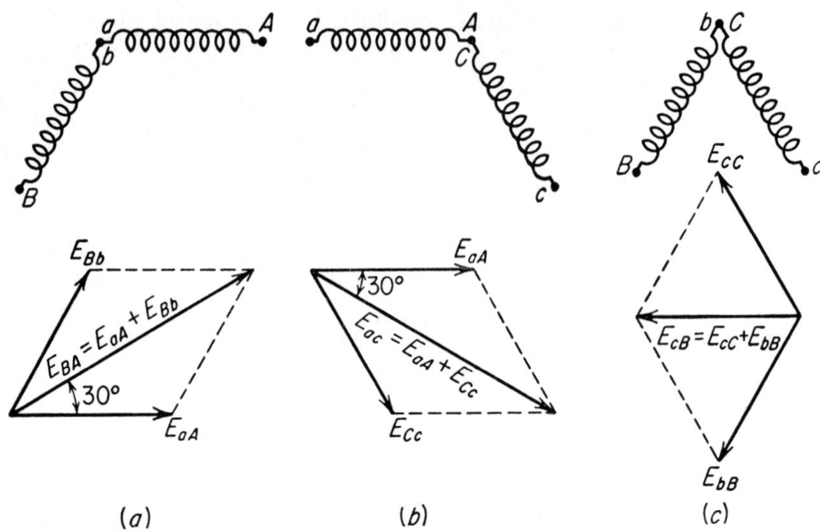

FIG. 216. Illustrations showing interconnected alternator coils and how the resultant terminal voltages are determined.

vector sum of E_{cC} and E_{bB}; this connection makes the resultant voltage equal to either coil voltage with an angular displacement of 180° with respect to E_{aA}.

Applying the same procedure to interconnections of the coils in the two-phase diagram of Fig. 214*b* will yield resultant terminal voltages that are $\sqrt{2}$ times as much as either of the equal coil voltages; the displacement of the resultant voltage will, however, depend upon the way in which coils are interconnected.

The Three-phase Star or Y Connection. Although each of the three phases of Fig. 214*a* can act independently, in which case it would be a six-wire three-phase system, it is the general practice to interconnect the windings (or loads) to form either a three-wire or a four-wire three-phase system. A possible arrangement is shown in Fig. 217*a* in which three identical coil ends such as *a*, *b*, and *c* are joined to become a common or *neutral* point. Since the individual *phase voltages* are equal and displaced 120 elec deg from one another, the three terminal or *line voltages* will also be equal and displaced by 120 elec deg. Expressing the voltage from *line to neutral* by the term *neutral voltage* and representing it by the symbol E_N it is easily shown that the three equal line voltages are $E_L = \sqrt{3}\,E_N$. This follows from the discussion in the foregoing section, and is illustrated further by the vector diagram of Fig. 217*b* which shows that E_L bisects the 60° angle of the rhombus formed by the voltages E_N; it should also be noted that the three line voltages labeled E_{BA}, E_{CB}, and E_{AC} are 30 elec deg ahead of the respective neutral voltages labeled E_{NA},

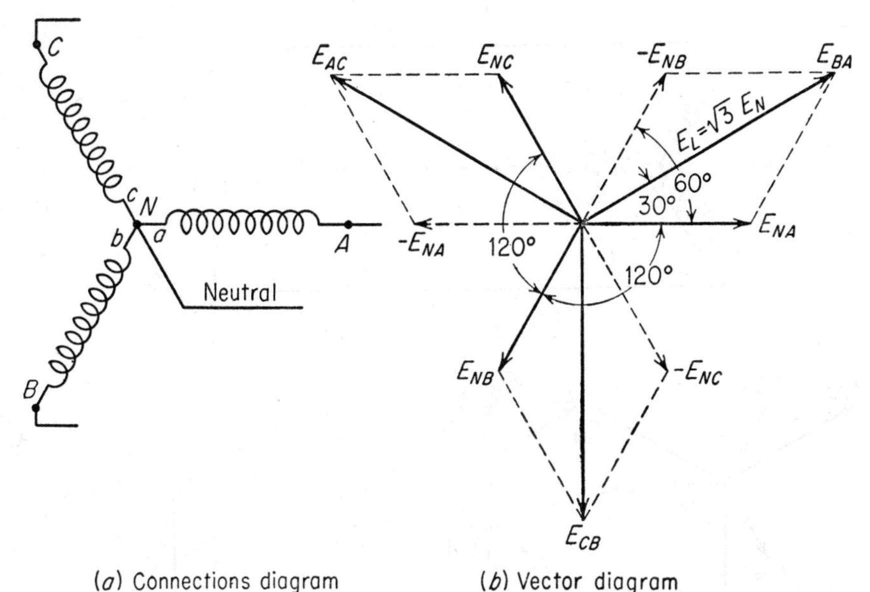

FIG. 217. Diagrams illustrating the three-phase star system.

E_{NB}, and E_{NC}. If the neutral is brought out and used with the three line wires it is called a *four-wire three-phase system;* in such cases an alternator, or its equivalent transformer equipment, can supply three independent single-phase loads such as lighting service as well as three-phase power loads. If, on the other hand, the neutral is not used but is left intact, usually by grounding, it is called a *three-wire three-phase system;* it is characterized by its general application to three-phase loads only.

When a star-connected system operates under conditions of *balanced loading* the three line currents I_L are equal in magnitude and, as with the voltages, differ in time phase by 120 elec deg; their positions *with respect to the neutral voltages* are, moreover, determined by the load power factor. This is clearly illustrated in the circuit diagram of Fig. 218*a* and the three accompanying vector diagrams which represent the unity, lagging, and leading power-factor conditions of balanced loading. Note particularly that the three line currents I_A, I_B, and I_C are (1) in phase with the respective neutral voltages E_{NA}, E_{NB}, and E_{NC} (Fig. 218*b*) for unity power factor; (2) behind the respective *neutral* voltages (Fig. 218*c*) for lagging power factor; and (3) ahead of the respective *neutral* voltages (Fig. 218*d*) for leading power factor. It should also be pointed out that the arrow directions given to the current symbols in Fig. 218*a* are intended to imply the direction of *energy flow* from source to load; they have no significance as current, which obviously changes during successive alternations.

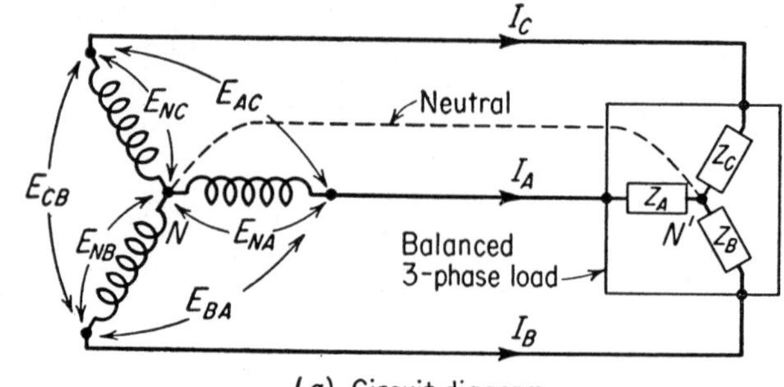

(a) Circuit diagram

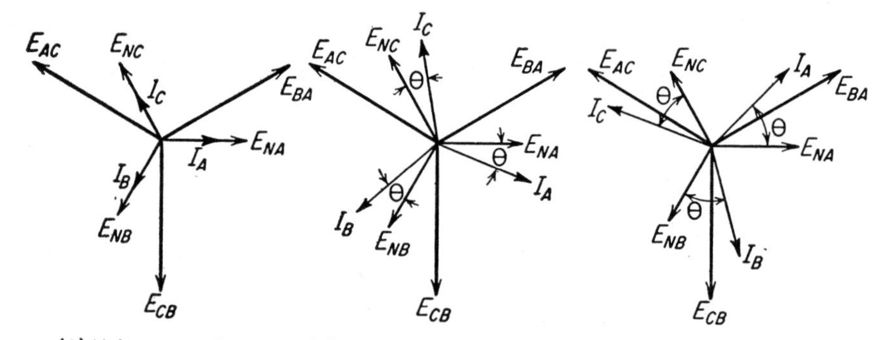

(b) Unity power factor (c) Lagging power factor (d) Leading power factor

FIG. 218. Circuit diagram and vector diagrams illustrating a star-connected source delivering balanced loads at unity, lagging, and leading power factors.

When the load is connected in star, it is possible to have a wire join its neutral with that of the neutral of the source. This is shown in Fig. 218*a*, where the neutral wire, a broken line, joins N and N'. Assuming that the three identical loads are serviced by independent single-phase sources through respective line wires and a common neutral return wire NN', it should be clear that the current in NN' is the vector sum of I_A, I_B, and I_C. However, such a sum is always equal to *zero* when the load is balanced, because the currents, being equal and differing in phase by 120°, have horizontal and vertical components that sum up to zero. It follows, therefore, that a neutral wire, since it carries no current, may be omitted from the wiring.

The Three-phase Delta or Mesh Connection. If the three similar single-phase windings of a three-phase alternator (Fig. 211*a*) are connected as shown in Fig. 219*a*, i.e., with A joined to c, and C joined to b, the voltage between the open-ended terminals E_{aB} will be zero; this is clarified by the vector diagram of Fig. 219*b*, which, in accordance with previously discussed principles, shows that $\dot{E}_{aA} + \dot{E}_{cC} + \dot{E}_{bB} = 0$. This means, therefore, that no current will flow in the *mesh* if points B and a are joined because these terminals are always at exactly the same poten-

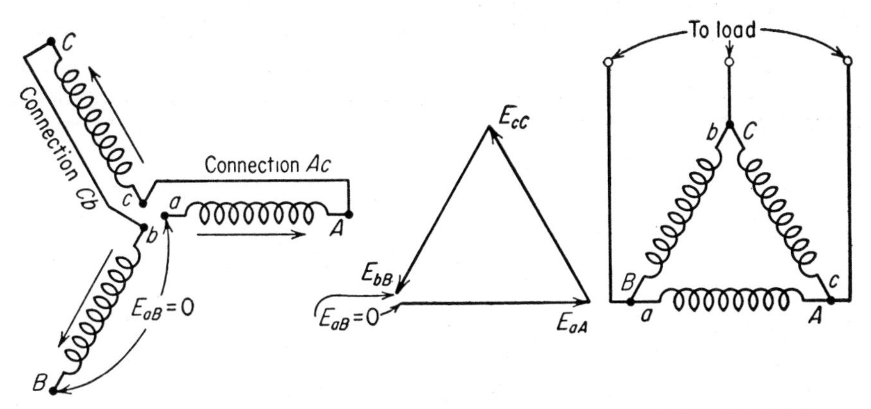

FIG. 219. Diagrams showing the development of the delta connection.

tial. Figure 219*c* illustrates the completed diagram, which, from its appearance, is called a *delta* connection. The *corners* of the delta may now serve as the terminals of a three-phase source whose voltages, *equal to the phase voltages*, are displaced 120 elec deg with respect to one another.

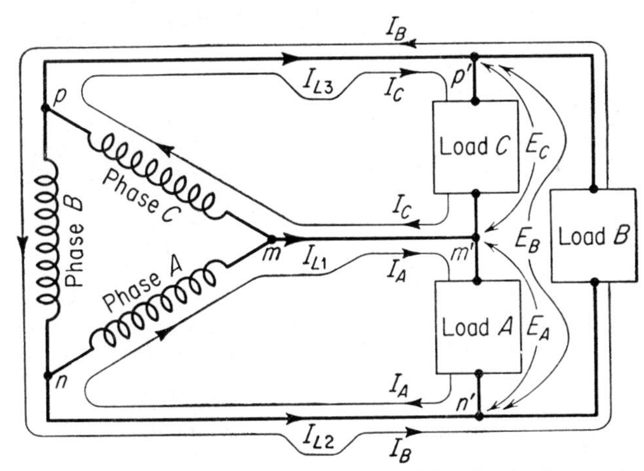

FIG. 220. Diagram showing a delta-connected source delivering load currents indicated by I_A, I_B, and I_C. Note that the three line currents I_{L1}, I_{L2}, and I_{L3} are vector differences of indicated load currents.

Figure 220 illustrates a delta-connected source delivering three loads A, B, and C. If the latter are identical the load currents I_A, I_B, and I_C will be equal and will bear the same power-factor angle to the respective phase voltages E_A, E_B, and E_C; under such conditions the system is said to be balanced and, as indicated by the arrow directions of I_A, I_B, and

I_C, each phase-load combination may be regarded as an independent part of the composite system. Moreover, as the diagram also shows, each of the three line currents is a *vector difference* of two corresponding phase currents. Thus, in Fig. 220,

$$\begin{aligned} \text{Current in } mm' &= \dot{I}_{L1} = \dot{I}_A - \dot{I}_C \\ \text{Current in } nn' &= \dot{I}_{L2} = \dot{I}_B - \dot{I}_A \\ \text{Current in } pp' &= \dot{I}_{L3} = \dot{I}_C - \dot{I}_B \end{aligned} \tag{137}$$

An important point to be noted in connection with the foregoing three current equations is that *the vector sum of the three line currents is zero;* that is,

$$\dot{I}_{L1} + \dot{I}_{L2} + \dot{I}_{L3} = 0$$

Two complete vector diagrams illustrating a delta-connected source delivering balanced lagging and leading power-factor loads are given in

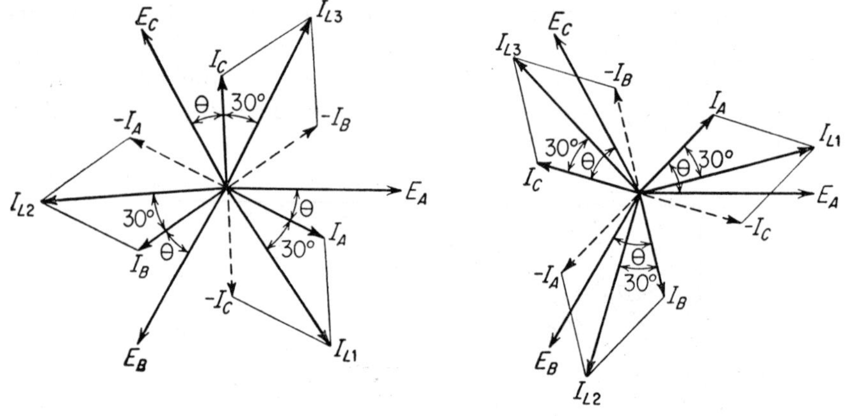

FIG. 221. Vector diagrams representing a delta-connected source delivering balanced loads at lagging and leading power factors.

Fig. 221. Note particularly that (1) there are three line or phase voltages E_A, E_B, and E_C; (2) the three phase currents I_A, I_B, and I_C bear the proper power-factor angles with respect to the respective line voltages E_A, E_B, and E_C; (3) the line currents I_{L1}, I_{L2}, and I_{L3} are determined by applying Eq. (137). For the condition of balanced loading the three line currents will obviously be equal and, like the phase currents, are displaced by 120 elec deg. Expressing the phase current by the symbol I_{PH} it is easily seen that the three equal line currents are $I_L = \sqrt{3}\, I_{PH}$; note, in the vector diagrams of Fig. 221, that I_L bisects the 60° angle of the rhombus formed by the currents I_{PH}; the line currents therefore lag behind the phase currents by 30 elec deg.

Power in Three-phase Balanced Systems. The total power P_t in a three-phase *balanced* system, whether star- or delta-connected, is *three times the power per phase.* Thus

For a Y-connected system:

$$P_t = 3 \times E_N I_L \cos \Theta$$

For a Δ-connected system:

$$P_t = 3 \times E_L I_{PH} \cos \Theta$$

Since it is desirable to express the power equation in terms of line voltage E_L and line current I_L, substitutions, in accordance with the foregoing sections, will be made for the neutral voltage E_N and the phase current I_{PH}. For the star connection $E_N = E_L/\sqrt{3}$, and for the delta connection $I_{PH} = I_L/\sqrt{3}$. It follows therefore that

In a Y-connected system:

$$P_t = 3 \times \left(\frac{E_L}{\sqrt{3}}\right) I_L \cos \Theta$$

In a Δ-connected system:

$$P_t = 3 \times E_L \left(\frac{I_L}{\sqrt{3}}\right) \cos \Theta$$

from which, for *any* balanced system,

$$P_t = \sqrt{3}\, E_L I_L \cos \Theta \qquad (138)$$

where Θ is the load power-factor angle that is always represented by the angle between the *phase voltage and the phase current.*

EXAMPLE 1. A star-connected source, the voltage across each phase of which is 120, delivers a balanced load of 40 kw at a power factor of 0.855 lagging. Calculate the line current.

Solution

$$E_L = \sqrt{3}\, E_N = \sqrt{3} \times 120 = 208 \text{ volts}$$

$$I_L = \frac{P_t}{\sqrt{3}\, E_L \cos \Theta} = \frac{40 \times 1{,}000}{\sqrt{3} \times 208 \times 0.855} = 130 \text{ amp}$$

EXAMPLE 2. A 230-volt delta-connected source delivers a balanced load of 45 kw. If the line current under this condition is 138 amp, calculate (*a*) the load power factor, (*b*) the current in each phase of the delta, and (*c*) the power delivered by each phase.

Solution

(*a*) $$\text{PF} = \cos \Theta = \frac{P_t}{\sqrt{3}\, E_L I_L} = \frac{45 \times 1{,}000}{\sqrt{3} \times 230 \times 138} = 0.82$$

(*b*) $$I_{PH} = \frac{I_L}{\sqrt{3}} = \frac{138}{\sqrt{3}} = 79.6 \text{ amp}$$

(*c*) $$P_{PH} = \frac{45{,}000}{3} = 15{,}000 \text{ watts}$$

Also

$$P_{PH} = E_{PH} \times I_{PH} \times \text{PF} = 230 \times 79.6 \times 0.82 = 15{,}000 \text{ watts}$$

EXAMPLE 3. What line current is delivered to a 50-hp 440-volt three-phase motor that operates at a power factor of 0.86 and an efficiency of 0.878?

Solution

$$\text{Power input to motor} = P_t = \frac{\text{hp} \times 746}{\text{eff}} = \frac{50 \times 746}{0.878} = 42{,}500 \text{ watts}$$

$$I_L = \frac{P_t}{\sqrt{3}\, E_L \cos \Theta} = \frac{42{,}500}{\sqrt{3} \times 440 \times 0.86} = 65 \text{ amp}$$

Two-phase Systems. Many of the first polyphase systems were two-phase or four-phase, with the latter frequently referred to as quarter-phase. Although these have been almost completely superseded by three-phase systems there are still some two-phase in use, especially where the original equipment is serviceable or where two-phase machines are found to have certain advantages.

As Figs. 211*b* and 213 show, a two-phase system is characterized by a 90-elec-deg displacement between voltages; the latter are developed in the alternator by two independent windings that are separated in space by the same number of degrees as the time displacement of emfs. Several winding arrangements have been used, in the simplest of which the two phases are completely insulated from each other, while in the others the phases are interconnected to develop certain desirable voltage combinations. Figure 222 illustrates four possible two- or four-phase systems and their accompanying vector diagrams.

When the windings are insulated from each other as in Fig. 222*a*, it is called a four-wire two-phase system; each phase then acts independently of the other and no common load can be supplied by both. Figure 222*b* illustrates a general type of three-wire two-phase system; note that a so-called neutral wire is obtained by connecting two ends, one from each of the windings, and that two different voltages are obtained. Another

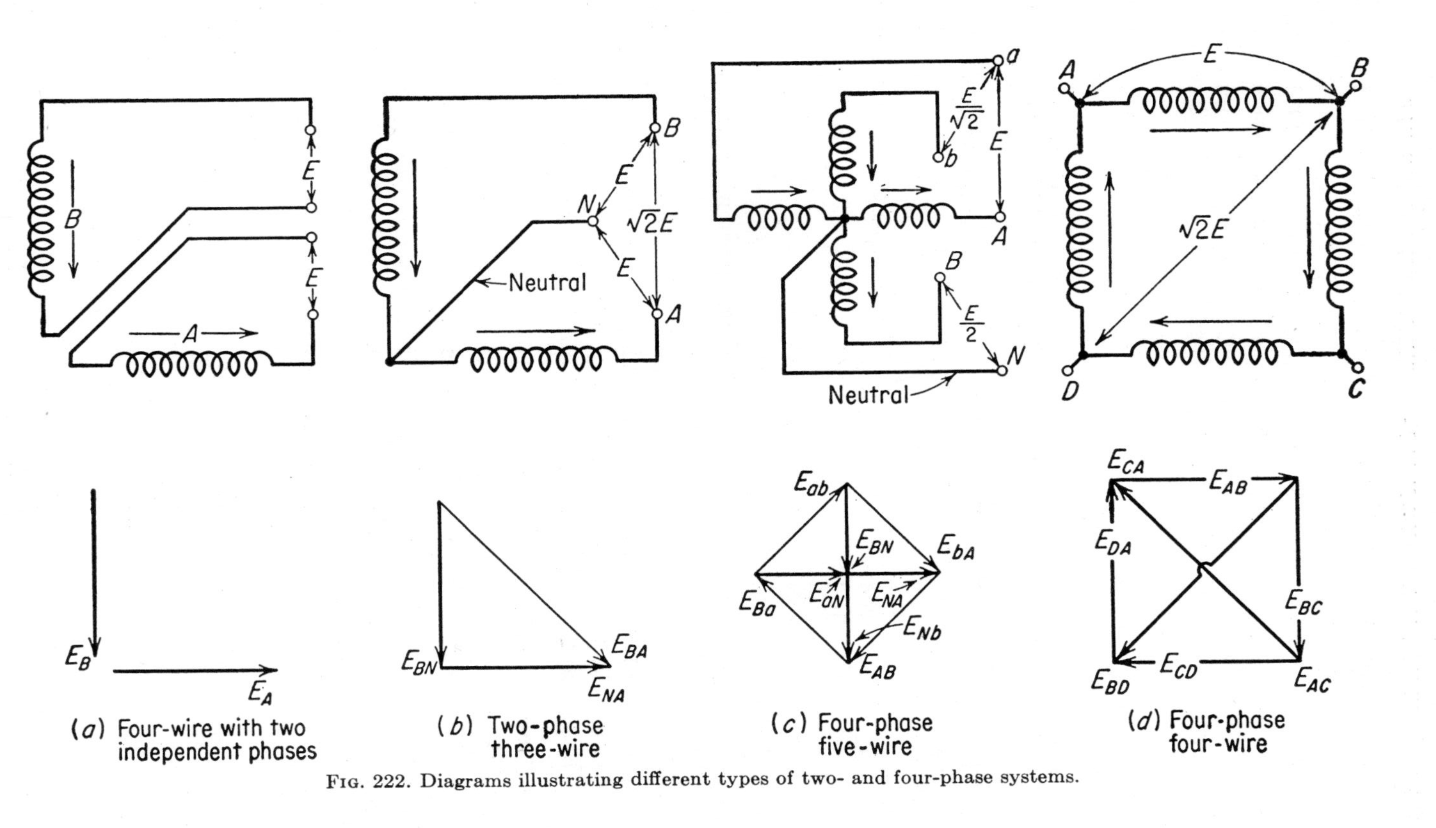

FIG. 222. Diagrams illustrating different types of two- and four-phase systems.

system, complicated by the fact that five wires result from the interconnection, is represented in Fig. 222*c*; in this arrangement the midpoints of the two phases are joined to supply the neutral, and this results in two- and four-phase sets of voltages. The mesh connection of Fig. 222*d* is formed by properly interconnecting the halves of the two phases; although no neutral is obtained with this scheme it does yield two- and four-phase sets of voltages.

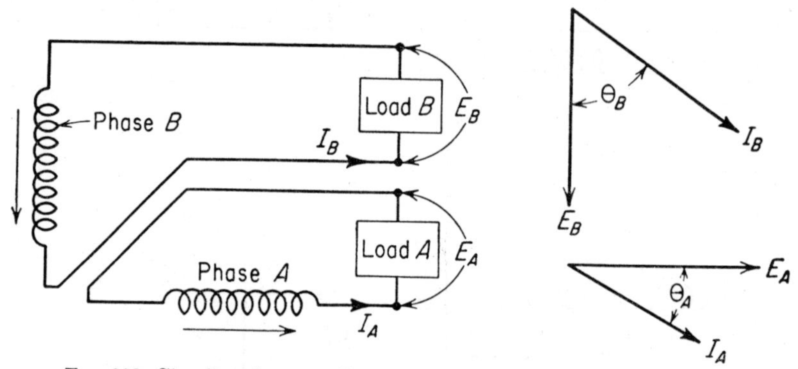

FIG. 223. Circuit and vector diagrams for a two-phase four-wire system.

The Two-phase Four-wire System. A diagram showing a two-phase four-wire source delivering independent loads A and B is given in Fig. 223. Note that there is no interconnection, and this makes it possible to regard each phase as an independent single-phase system. Since the two voltages are usually equal, i.e., $E_A = E_B = E$, the currents are $I_A = E/Z_A$ and $I_B = E/Z_B$. The total circuit power is therefore

$$P_t = P_A + P_B = E_A I_A \cos \Theta_A + E_B I_B \cos \Theta_B = E(I_A \cos \Theta_A + I_B \cos \Theta_B)$$

The total power in such a system can be measured by using two wattmeters, inserting one in each of the phases as shown in Fig. 208.

EXAMPLE 4. Referring to the four-wire two-phase diagram of Fig. 223, loads A and B are impedances of $Z_A = (3.6 + j4.8)$ and $Z_B = (11.25 - j6.5)$. If the phase voltages $E_A = E_B = 117$ volts, calculate (*a*) the individual load currents, (*b*) the power taken by each load, (*c*) the total circuit power.

Solution

(*a*)
$$I_A = \frac{117}{(3.6 + j4.8)} = 19.5\underline{/-53.1°} \text{ amp}$$

$$I_B = \frac{117}{(11.25 - j6.5)} = 9\underline{/30°} \text{ amp}$$

(*b*)
$$P_A = 117 \times 19.5 \times 0.6 = 1{,}369 \text{ watts}$$
$$P_B = 117 \times 9 \times 0.5 = 526.5 \text{ watts}$$

(*c*)
$$P_t = 1{,}369 + 526.5 = 1{,}895.5 \text{ watts}$$

The Two-phase Three-wire System. When a junction is made between any two ends, one from each of the two phases, a two-phase three-wire system is formed. This is illustrated in Fig. 224 by the source that delivers two single-phase loads between each of the outside lines and the neutral, and a third single-phase load between the two outside lines. Since the phase voltages $E_{NA} = E_{NB} = E$, and the latter are 90 elec deg out of phase, the load between the outside lines will be subjected to a voltage of $E_{BA} = \sqrt{2}\, E$. It is important to note that this system differs from the four-wire system in the following respects: (1) the neutral wire carries the *difference* between the currents in the two *phase* loads BN and NA, and thereby lowers the cost and improves the efficiency of operation;

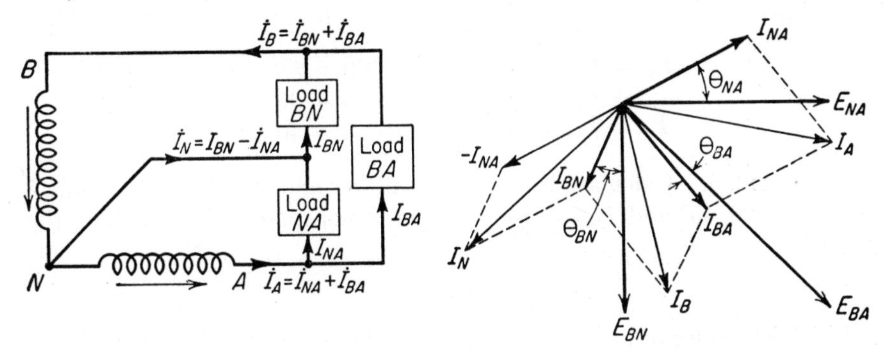

Fig. 224. Circuit and vector diagrams for a two-phase three-wire system.

(2) a higher voltage load BA can be delivered by combining the two phases and using the outside two lines (the neutral wire has no function for this load). The individual load currents I_{NA}, I_{BN}, and I_{BA} are determined in the usual way, considering line-to-neutral phases and the line-to-line phase separately. The total power is obtained by adding the individual powers, i.e.,

$$P_t = E(I_{NA} \cos \Theta_{NA} + I_{BN} \cos \Theta_{BN}) + \sqrt{2}\, EI_{BA} \cos \Theta_{BA}$$

The vector diagram of Fig. 224 shows how the neutral current I_N and the line currents I_A and I_B are determined. Note that

$$\dot{I}_N = \dot{I}_{BN} - \dot{I}_{NA}$$
$$\dot{I}_A = \dot{I}_{NA} + \dot{I}_{BA}$$
$$\dot{I}_B = \dot{I}_{BN} + \dot{I}_{BA}$$

The total power in such a system can be measured by using three wattmeters, inserting each one in a separate load circuit; this must, of course, be done by connecting the current and potential coils of the wattmeters to register the proper currents and voltages.

Example 5. The following information is given in connection with the two-phase three-wire circuit diagram of Fig. 224: $E_{NA} = E_{BN} = 120$,

$I_{NA} = 20\underline{/-45°}$, $I_{BN} = 25\underline{/45°}$, $I_{BA} = 15\underline{/0°}$. Calculate (*a*) the power taken by each load and the total power, (*b*) the currents in the line wires I_A and I_B and in the neutral wire I_N.

Solution

(*a*)

$$P_{NA} = 120 \times 20 \times 0.707 = 1{,}697 \text{ watts}$$
$$P_{BN} = 120 \times 25 \times 0.707 = 2{,}121 \text{ watts}$$
$$P_{BA} = \sqrt{2} \times 120 \times 15 \times 1.0 = 2{,}546 \text{ watts}$$
$$P_t = 1{,}697 + 2{,}121 + 2{,}546 = 6{,}364 \text{ watts}$$

(*b*) The three currents were intentionally selected so that their vector positions, for simplicity, would all fall on the E_{BA} voltage vector. Thus

$$\dot{I}_N = \dot{I}_{BN} - \dot{I}_{NA} = 25 - 20 = 5 \text{ amp}$$
$$\dot{I}_A = \dot{I}_{NA} + \dot{I}_{BA} = 20 + 15 = 35 \text{ amp}$$
$$\dot{I}_B = \dot{I}_{BN} + \dot{I}_{BA} = 25 + 15 = 40 \text{ amp}$$

EXAMPLE 6. Calculate the values of power and current in Example 5 if $I_{NA} = 20\underline{/45°}$ and $I_{BN} = 25\underline{/-45°}$, all other quantities remaining the same.

Solution

(*a*) The values of power will be exactly the same as those calculated in Example 5; i.e., $P_{NA} = 1{,}697$ watts, $P_{BN} = 2{,}121$ watts, $P_{BA} = 2{,}546$ watts, and $P_t = 6{,}364$ watts.

(*b*) Now, I_{NA} will be advanced 45° into the first quadrant, and I_{BN} will be retarded 45° into the third quadrant. Thus, I_{NA} and I_{BN} will be directly opposite, vectorially, and both will be displaced 90° with respect to I_{BA}. Therefore

$$I_N = 25 + 20 = 45 \text{ amp}$$
$$I_A = \sqrt{(20)^2 + (15)^2} = 25 \text{ amp}$$
$$I_B = \sqrt{(25)^2 + (15)^2} = 29.15 \text{ amp}$$

The Four-phase Five-wire System. The circuit diagram of Fig. 225 illustrates a four-phase five-wire system delivering three loads; these are (1) the load *NB* between one line and neutral, (2) the load between two adjacent line wires, and (3) a balanced two-phase load. To determine the several currents in such a system it is extremely important that all directions and power-factor angles be considered carefully. Note particularly the current directions on the diagram, and the values of I_b, I_A, and I_B, each of which represents vector sums of two currents that can be traced to loads. It should also be pointed out that a balanced two-phase load implies that phases *aA* and *bB* divide the total load equally.

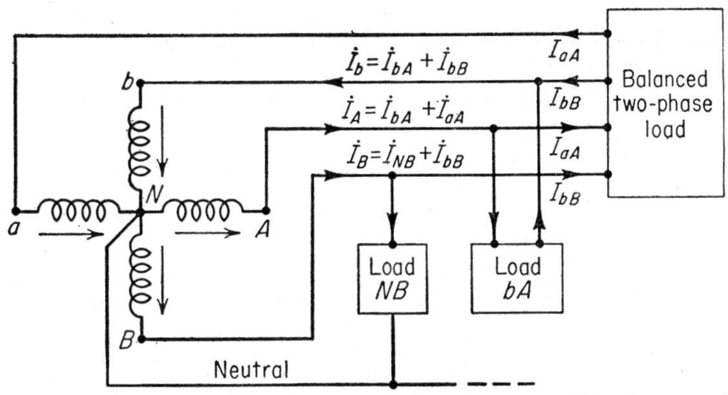

FIG. 225. Circuit diagram showing a four-phase five-wire source delivering several loads.

EXAMPLE 7. The following information is given in connection with Fig. 225: $E_{aA} = E_{bB} = 230$ volts; load $NB = 2{,}300$ watts at unity power factor; load $bA = 3{,}450$ watts at a power factor of 0.707 leading; the two-phase balanced load is 11,500 watts at unity power factor. Calculate (a) the currents I_{NB}, I_{bA}, I_{aA}, and I_{bB}; (b) the currents I_B, I_A, and I_b; (c) the total kilowatt load on the system.

Solution

(a)
$$I_{NB} = \frac{2{,}300}{115 \times 1} = 20 \text{ amp}$$
$$I_{bA} = \frac{3{,}450}{115\sqrt{2} \times 0.707} = 30 \text{ amp}$$
$$I_{aA} = I_{bB} = \frac{11{,}500/2}{230 \times 1} = 25 \text{ amp}$$
(b)
$$\dot{I}_B = \dot{I}_{NB} + \dot{I}_{bB} = 20 + 25 = 45 \text{ amp}$$
$$\dot{I}_A = \dot{I}_{bA} + \dot{I}_{aA} = 30 + 25 = 55 \text{ amp}$$
$$\dot{I}_b = \dot{I}_{bA} + \dot{I}_{bB} = \sqrt{(30)^2 + (25)^2} = 39 \text{ amp}$$
(c)
$$P_t = 2{,}300 + 3{,}450 + 11{,}500 = 17{,}250 \text{ watts}$$

The Four-phase Four-wire System. In the circuit diagram of Fig. 226 a four-phase four-wire mesh-connected source is shown delivering a balanced load; the latter may consist of any combination of resistors, inductors, and capacitors, each of which will take the same current I that passes through the windings of the source. The system obviously operates at a disadvantage since the four equal line currents are $\sqrt{2}\,I$, about 41 per cent more than the winding and load currents. It does offer the possibility, however, that a two-phase load can be delivered from diametrically opposite corners of the mesh at a voltage of $\sqrt{2}\,E$, about 41 per cent more than the winding voltage.

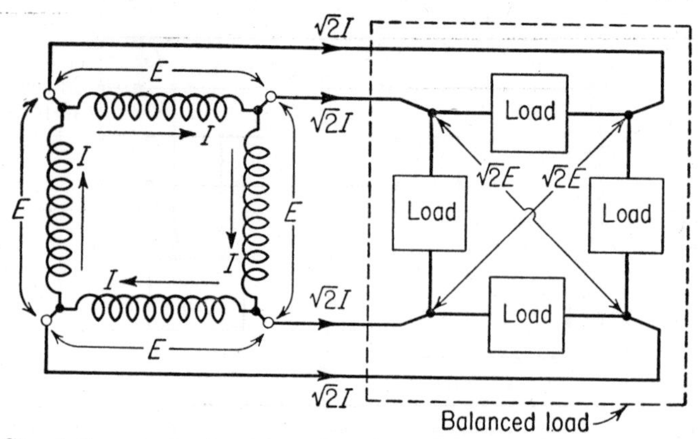

FIG. 226. Circuit diagram showing a four-phase four-wire source delivering a balanced load.

Two-wattmeter Power Measurements in Balanced Three-phase Systems. It is always possible to measure the total power in any system, however complex or unbalanced, by inserting as many wattmeters in the circuit as there are phases. For example, in the three-phase star-connected system, three wattmeters could be used with the current coils in the line wires and the potential coils across the respective *line-to-neutral* phases; in the three-phase delta-connected system the current coils would be *inside* the delta and the potential coils across the respective phases.

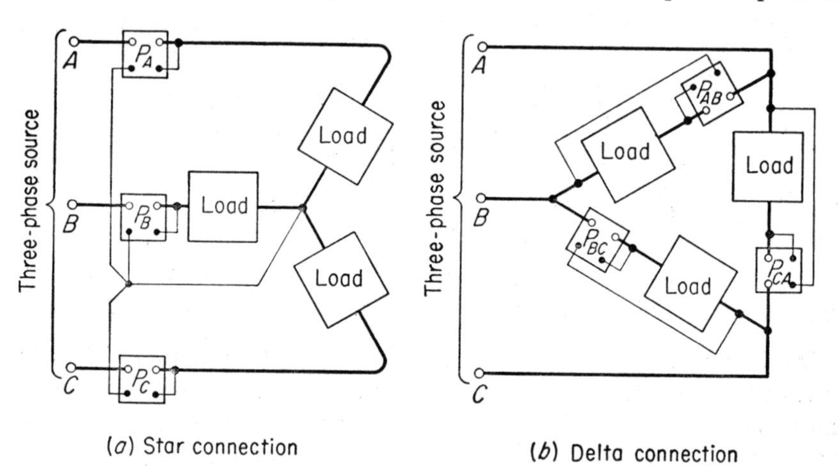

FIG. 227. Circuit diagrams illustrating how three wattmeters are connected to measure the total power.

These schemes, seldom used, are shown in the diagrams of Fig. 227; the connections are quite inconvenient, and often difficult to make, because the neutral point must be available in the star system, and it is necessary to break into the individual phases in the delta system.

A more convenient method, and one that is equally accurate whether the three-phase load is balanced or not, makes use of two wattmeters connected so that the current and potential elements register *line* quantities. Moreover, the same wattmeter connections are made for the star and delta systems; the latter condition may, in fact, be disregarded when the wattmeters are inserted in the three *line* wires. An analysis will now be made of the two-wattmeter methods of measuring power in star- and delta-connected loads.

The Balanced Star-connected Load. Assuming three similar *lagging-power-factor loads* and a phase sequence of voltages E_{AN}, E_{BN}, E_{CN}, Fig. 228 represents the circuit connections and a vector diagram for a star-connected system with two wattmeters inserted for the measurement

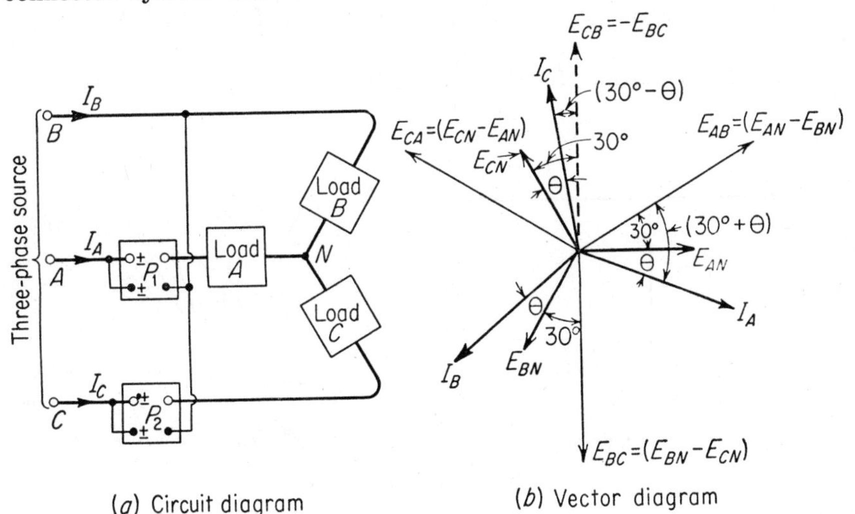

FIG. 228. Diagrams showing the wattmeter connections and the vector relations in a balanced star-connected lagging power-factor load.

of the total power. Before proceeding note particularly in Fig. 228*a* (1) that wattmeter 1 is connected with its current coil in line A and its potential coil across terminals AB to register line voltage E_{AB} and (2) that wattmeter 2 is connected with its current coil in line C and its potential coil across terminals CB to register line voltage E_{CB}. Also observe in the vector diagram of Fig. 228*b* (1) that line voltages E_{AB}, E_{BC}, and E_{CA} lead the respective phase voltages E_{AN}, E_{BN}, and E_{CN} by 30 elec deg; and (2) that voltage E_{CB} is the negative of voltage E_{BC}, an extremely important point in this discussion. For the lagging-power-factor load assumed, the two wattmeters will therefore indicate the following values:

$$P_1 = E_{AB}I_A \cos (30° + \Theta)$$
$$P_2 = E_{CB}I_C \cos (30° - \Theta)$$

But in a balanced system, $E_{AB} = E_{CB} = E_L$ and $I_A = I_C = I_L$ [see Eq. (138)]. Thus, substituting symbols for *line* voltage and current,

$$\left.\begin{aligned} P_1 &= E_L I_L \cos (30 + \Theta) \\ P_2 &= E_L I_L \cos (30 - \Theta) \end{aligned}\right\} \text{star connection} \qquad (139)$$

Now then, if $(P_1 + P_2)$ is to be the *total* power in the balanced system under consideration, that sum must equal $\sqrt{3}\, E_L I_L \cos \Theta$ in accordance with Eq. (138). This is readily shown to be the case by expanding the foregoing cosine terms and adding P_1 to P_2. When this is done,

$$P_1 = E_L I_L (\cos 30° \cos \Theta - \sin 30° \sin \Theta) = E_L I_L \left(\frac{\sqrt{3}}{2} \cos \Theta - \frac{1}{2} \sin \Theta \right)$$

$$P_2 = E_L I_L (\cos 30° \cos \Theta + \sin 30° \sin \Theta) = E_L I_L \left(\frac{\sqrt{3}}{2} \cos \Theta + \frac{1}{2} \sin \Theta \right)$$

Adding these equations for the two-wattmeter readings,

$$P_t = \sqrt{3}\, E_L I_L \cos \Theta$$

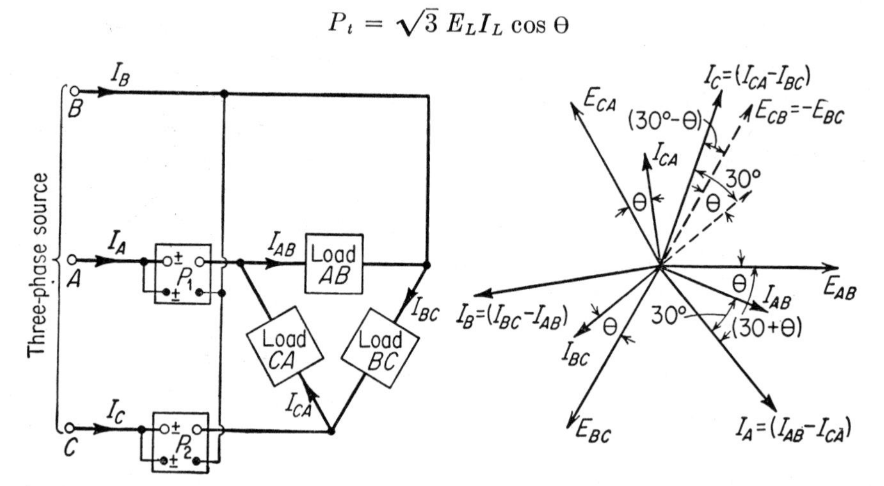

FIG. 229. Diagrams showing the wattmeter connections and the vector relations in a balanced delta-connected lagging-power-factor load.

The Balanced Delta-connected Load. Considering next a balanced *lagging-power-factor* delta-connected *load*, Fig. 229*a* represents the circuit diagram with two wattmeters inserted for the measurement of the total power, and Fig. 229*b* is a vector diagram for a phase sequence of voltages E_{AB}, E_{BC}, E_{CA}. It is important to note that the wattmeter connections are identical with those made in Fig. 228*a* for the star connection, i.e., wattmeter 1 is connected to register *line* current I_A and *line* voltage E_{AB}, and wattmeter 2 is connected to register *line* current I_C and *line* voltage E_{CB}. Referring to the vector diagram of Fig. 229*b*, observe also that the line currents I_A, I_B, and I_C lag behind the respective phase currents I_{AB}, I_{BC}, and I_{CA} by 30 elec deg. As a result of these conditions, both wattmeters will be subjected to exactly the same voltage, current, and phase-angle relationships as in the star-connected system; that is,

$$\left.\begin{aligned} P_1 &= E_L I_L \cos(30° + \Theta) \\ P_2 &= E_L I_L \cos(30° - \Theta) \end{aligned}\right\} \text{delta connection} \tag{140}$$

As previously shown, the total power is equal to P_1 plus P_2, because that sum is equal to $\sqrt{3}\, E_L I_L \cos \Theta$ for a balanced system.

Power-factor Effects in Balanced Three-phase Systems. It is important to understand that Eqs. (139) and (140) are based upon balanced loads that are *assumed* to be *lagging*. For a *leading* power factor the vector positions of the phase currents would be shifted ahead of the respective phase voltages, and this would result in a reversal of the angle Θ, i.e., $-\Theta$. Under this condition the two wattmeters would, as before, register the total power in the circuit, but the magnitudes of the deflections would be interchanged. For example, if the total load power is 6,000 watts, at a *lagging* power factor of 0.866, $P_1 = 2{,}000$ watts and $P_2 = 4{,}000$ watts; for a total power of 6,000 watts at a *leading* power factor of 0.866, however, $P_1 = 4{,}000$ watts and $P_2 = 2{,}000$ watts. To put it in general terms, for a leading power factor $P_1 = E_L I_L \cos(30° - \Theta)$ and $P_2 = E_L I_L \cos(30° + \Theta)$.

Table 12 was prepared to illustrate the relations between the wattmeter deflections P_1 and P_2 in terms of the total circuit power P_t, for a range of power factors that are both lagging and leading. Note particularly that (1) both wattmeters deflect equally, and each one registers one-half of the total power, at unity power factor only; (2) at a power factor of 0.866 one wattmeter reading is twice the other; (3) at a power factor of 0.5 one wattmeter reads zero while the other registers the total circuit power; (4) at power factors *below* 0.5 one wattmeter gives a negative reading, this value being measured by interchanging the current leads

TABLE 12

Power factor	θ	Lagging		Leading	
		P_1	P_2	P_1	P_2
1.0	0°	$0.500P_t$	$0.500P_t$	$0.500P_t$	$0.500P_t$
0.866	30°	$0.333P_t$	$0.667P_t$	$0.667P_t$	$0.333P_t$
0.707	45°	$0.211P_t$	$0.789P_t$	$0.789P_t$	$0.211P_t$
0.5	60°	0	P_t	P_t	0
0.259	75°	$-0.577P_t$	$1.577P_t$	$1.577P_t$	$-0.577P_t$
0.174	80°	$-1.135P_t$	$2.135P_t$	$2.135P_t$	$-1.135P_t$

on *that* wattmeter to give an upscale deflection; and (5) the values of P_1 and P_2 are interchanged in the lagging and leading power-factor columns.

EXAMPLE 8. Two wattmeters are connected as in Figs. 228*a* and 229*a* to register the total power in a three-phase balanced load. For a phase sequence of E_{AB}, E_{BC}, E_{CA} determine the deflections registered on the wattmeters in terms of the total power for the following power factors: (*a*) 0.866 lagging; (*b*) 0.259 lagging; (*c*) 0.309 leading.

Solution

(*a*) For $\cos\Theta = 0.866$ lagging, $\Theta = 30°$.

$$\frac{P_1}{P_2} = \frac{EI\cos(30° + 30°)}{EI\cos(30° - 30°)} = \frac{0.5}{1.0} = 0.5$$

and $$P_1 = 0.5P_2$$

But $$P_t = P_1 + P_2$$

so that $$P_t = 0.5P_2 + P_2 = 1.5P_2$$

Hence $$P_2 = \frac{P_t}{1.5} = 0.667P_t$$

and $$P_1 = 0.333P_t$$

(*b*) For $\cos\Theta = 0.259$ lagging, $\Theta = 75°$.

$$\frac{P_1}{P_2} = \frac{\cos(30° + 75°)}{\cos(30° - 75°)} = \frac{\cos 105°}{\cos(-45°)} = \frac{-0.259}{+0.707} = -0.366$$

Therefore

$$P_t = -0.366P_2 + P_2 = 0.634P_t$$

Hence

$$P_2 = \frac{P_t}{0.634} = 1.577P_t$$

and

$$P_1 = P_t - 1.577P_t = -0.577P_t$$

(*c*) For $\cos\Theta = 0.309$ leading, $\Theta = -72°$.

$$\frac{P_1}{P_2} = \frac{\cos(30° - 72°)}{\cos(30° + 72°)} = \frac{\cos(-42°)}{\cos 102°} = \frac{+0.743}{-0.208} = -3.57$$

Therefore

$$P_t = -3.57P_2 + P_2 = -2.57P_t$$

Hence

$$P_2 = \frac{P_t}{-2.57} = -0.389P_t$$

and

$$P_1 = 1.389P_t$$

Since the relative deflections of the two wattmeters in a balanced three-phase circuit depend upon the power factor, it seems logical that Eqs. (139) and (140) should, when manipulated mathematically, yield a formula from which the power factor may be determined when P_1 and P_2 are known. The derivation of such an equation follows:

Subtracting P_1 from P_2,

$$\begin{aligned}(P_2 - P_1) &= E_L I_L \cos(30 - \Theta) - E_L I_L \cos(30 + \Theta) \\ &= E_L I_L[(\cos 30^\circ \cos \Theta + \sin 30^\circ \sin \Theta) \\ &\qquad - (\cos 30^\circ \cos \Theta - \sin 30^\circ \sin \Theta)] \\ &= E_L I_L (2 \sin 30 \sin \Theta) = E_L I_L \sin \Theta\end{aligned}$$

Also

$$(P_1 + P_2) = P_t = \sqrt{3}\, E_L I_L \cos \Theta$$

Dividing $(P_2 - P_1)$ by $(P_2 + P_1)$,

$$\frac{(P_2 - P_1)}{(P_2 + P_1)} = \frac{E_L I_L \sin \Theta}{\sqrt{3}\, E_L I_L \cos \Theta} = \frac{\tan \Theta}{\sqrt{3}}$$

from which

$$\tan \Theta = \sqrt{3}\, \frac{(P_2 - P_1)}{(P_2 + P_1)} \qquad (141)$$

In using Eq. (141) to determine the tangent of the power-factor angle, from which the power factor may be evaluated, it is necessary to apply the *proper signs* to the values of P_1 and P_2. The following example will illustrate the application of the equation.

EXAMPLE 9. The two-wattmeter method is used to measure the total power in a three-phase balanced circuit. For a phase sequence E_{AB}, E_{BC}, E_{CA} calculate the power factor when (*a*) $P_1 = 3{,}200$ watts and $P_2 = 8{,}500$ watts; (*b*) $P_1 = 9{,}000$ watts and $P_2 = -3{,}000$ watts.

Solution

(*a*)

$$\begin{aligned}\tan \Theta &= \sqrt{3}\, \frac{8{,}500 - 3{,}200}{8{,}500 + 3{,}200} = 0.785 \\ \Theta &= \tan^{-1} 0.785 = 38.1^\circ \\ \text{PF} &= \cos 38.1^\circ = 0.787 \text{ lagging}\end{aligned}$$

(*b*)

$$\begin{aligned}\tan \Theta &= \sqrt{3}\, \frac{-3{,}000 - 9{,}000}{-3{,}000 + 9{,}000} = -3.464 \\ \Theta &= \tan^{-1}(-3.464) = -73.9^\circ \\ \text{PF} &= \cos(-73.9^\circ) = 0.277 \text{ leading}\end{aligned}$$

One-wattmeter Power Measurements in Balanced Three-phase Systems. It is sometimes necessary, when two wattmeters are not available, to measure the total power in a *balanced* three-phase system with a single wattmeter; this may be accomplished in one of several ways.

The Potential-lead Shift Method. In this scheme the current coil of the wattmeter is inserted in one line, line A, for example, and one of the potential-coil terminals is connected to the same line. The other potential-coil terminal is next touched to line B for one reading, and then shifted to line C for a second reading. The sum of the two deflections on the wattmeter, represented by P_1 and P_2, will be the total circuit power. Figure 230*a* illustrates the diagram of connections, and Fig. 230*b* is a vector diagram that shows the validity of the procedure. When the potential coil is across lines A and B it obviously indicates the power $P_1 = E_L I_L \cos(30° + \Theta)$ as in the previously described two-wattmeter method. Shifting the potential lead from line B to line C means that

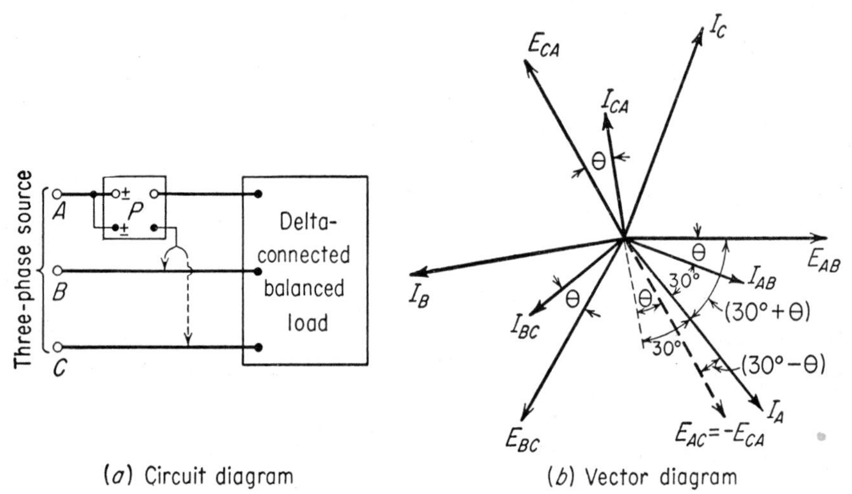

FIG. 230. Circuit and vector diagrams for the potential-lead shift method of measuring power in a three-phase balanced-load circuit.

the second deflection is represented by $E_{AC} I_A \cos(30° - \Theta)$, where E_{AC} is the negative of E_{CA}; this is clearly seen in Fig. 230*b*. Thus, $P_2 = E_L I_L \cos(30° - \Theta)$, and the total power, as before, is $P_1 + P_2 = \sqrt{3}\, E_L I_L \cos\Theta$. It should, however, be pointed out that the relative magnitudes of P_1 and P_2, and whether one or the other reading is plus or minus, will depend upon the phase sequence, and the value and kind (lagging or leading) of power factor.

The Artificial-neutral Method. In a balanced three-phase system one wattmeter, connected as shown in Fig. 231*a*, will measure the power P_A in phase A. Since the three loads are similar, the total power for the star-connected units will be $3P_A$, or, in general terms, three times the power per phase. If three *equal resistors* are then connected in star and across the *same* three-phase source its neutral point O will, at every instant of time, be at exactly the same electrical potential as the neutral point of the load. This means, therefore, that the wattmeter will give the same deflection P_A if the potential-coil lead is shifted from point N to point O. Figure 231b illustrates the suggested arrangement in which the star-connected resistors provide the wattmeter with a so-called artificial neutral. This one-wattmeter method of measuring the total power applies equally to the delta-connected load which may be regarded, for the purposes of this analysis, as the equivalent of a star (refer to Chap. 15,

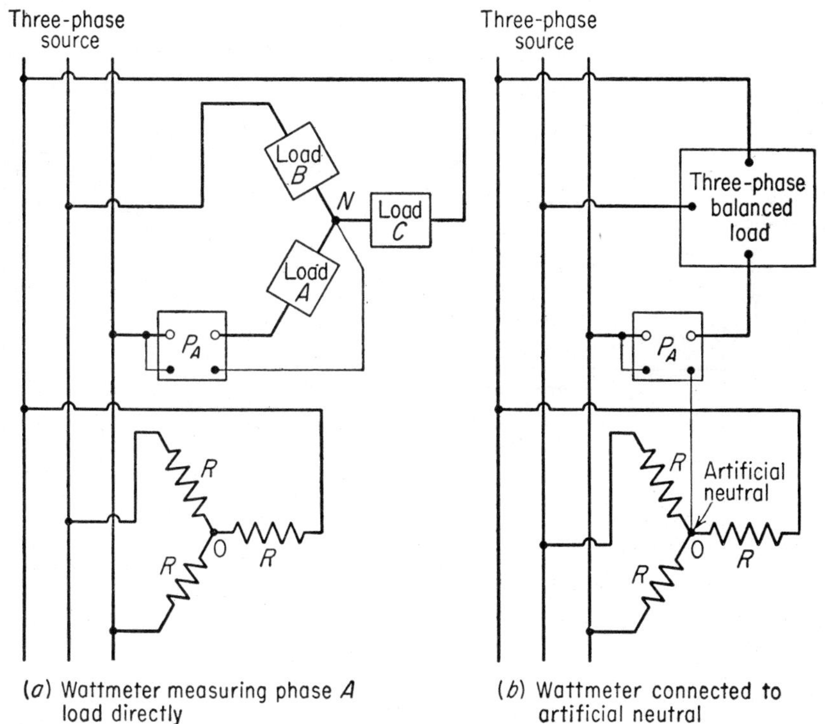

FIG. 231. Diagrams illustrating the evolution of the artificial-neutral method of measuring power in a balanced three-phase load.

pages 349–352); the kind of connection, star or delta, is therefore immaterial to the accuracy of the power measurement. This is fortunate because such information is not generally known, nor is the star point available when a star connection is used; it is only necessary to know that the load is balanced.

The T Method. Figure 232a illustrates another single-wattmeter method for measuring the total power in a three-phase balanced load. In this scheme the current coil of the wattmeter is inserted in one line, and one of the potential-coil terminals is connected to the same line. The other potential-coil terminal is then fastened to the junction of a pair of *equal* resistors, the free ends of which go to the other two lines. With this arrangement the wattmeter will register one-half of the total power, i.e., $(\sqrt{3}/2)P_t$, which means that the deflection must be multiplied by 2 to yield the correct value of power.

Assuming a balanced star-connected lagging-power-factor load for convenience, Fig. 232*b* represents the vector relations in such a system. First, note that the voltage E_{AB} leads the line current I_A by an angle of $(30° + \Theta)$. Next observe that the voltage E_{BO} is in phase with, and exactly one-half of, E_{BC} because it is represented by a voltage drop across one of the two equal resistors in series across lines B and C. Finally, adding vector E_{AB} to vector E_{BO} to determine the voltage E_{AO} across the

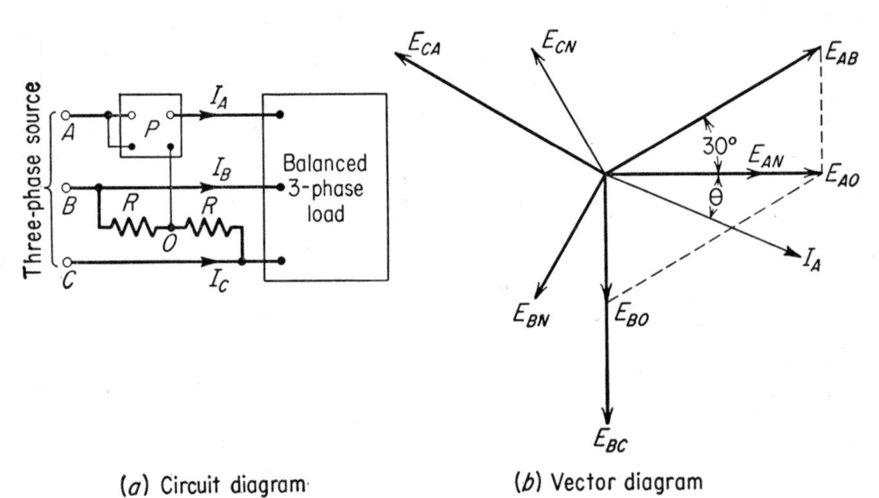

FIG. 232. Diagrams illustrating the T method of measuring power with a single wattmeter in a balanced three-phase circuit.

potential coil of the wattmeter, the latter is found (1) to fall directly in line with E_{AO}, $\Theta°$ ahead of I_A, and (2) to be equal to $(\sqrt{3}/2)E_{AB}$. Thus the power registered by the wattmeter as connected in Fig. 232*a* is $(\sqrt{3}/2)E_L \cos \Theta$; the wattmeter deflection must therefore be doubled to yield the total circuit power.

Validity of Two-wattmeter Power Measurements for Any Three-phase, Three-wire System. The two-wattmeter method of measuring power in three-phase three-wire systems (see Figs. 228 and 229) is the one most frequently employed. It is accurate not only for balanced loads as previously described, but in unbalanced systems as well. The following analysis proves the validity of the procedure for any degree of unbalance in star- and delta-connected loads.

Referring first to the star-connected load of Fig. 233, the total power *at any instant of time* is the sum of the products of the respective values

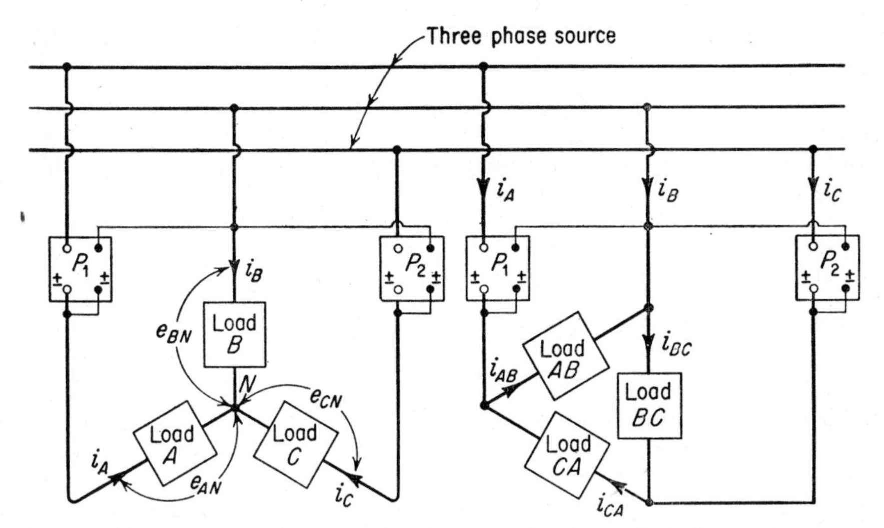

FIG. 233. Diagram illustrating connections for two-wattmeter method of measuring power in two types of three-phase load.

of *instantaneous* phase voltage e and current i. In equation form this is

$$p = (e_{AN}i_A) + (e_{BN}i_B) + (e_{CN}i_C)$$

But for *any* three-phase three-wire system, the vector sum of the line currents is equal to zero. Thus

$$i_A + i_B + i_C = 0$$

from which

$$i_B = -i_A - i_C$$

Substituting the latter equation in the one for power,

$$p = (e_{AN}i_A) - (e_{BN}i_A) - (e_{BN}i_C) + (e_{CN}i_C)$$

which, when simplified, becomes

$$p = (e_{AN} - e_{BN})i_A + (e_{CN} - e_{BN})i_C$$

But $(e_{AN} - e_{BN}) = e_{AB}$, and $(e_{CN} - e_{BN}) = e_{CB}$

Hence

$$p = (e_{AB}i_A) + (e_{CB}i_C)$$

Note that the final equation for the *instantaneous power* in *any* three-wire star-connected system is represented by the sum of two instantaneous products of e and i; one of them registers a voltage across lines A and B and a current in line A, while the other registers a voltage across lines C and B and a current in line C. Since this power is valid for *any* instant of time, the wattmeters are obviously connected properly, exactly as in Fig. 228, to measure total average power.

Referring next to the delta-connected load of Fig. 233, the total instantaneous power is

$$p = (e_{AB}i_{AB}) + (e_{BC}i_{BC}) + (e_{CA}i_{CA})$$

But for *any* three-phase three-wire system, the vector sum of the line voltages is equal to zero. Thus

$$e_{AB} + e_{BC} + e_{CA} = 0$$

from which $$e_{CA} = -e_{AB} - e_{BC}$$

Substituting the latter equation in the one for power,

$$p = (e_{AB}i_{AB}) + (e_{BC}i_{BC}) - (e_{AB}i_{CA}) - (e_{BC}i_{CA})$$

which, when simplified, becomes

$$p = e_{AB}(i_{AB} - i_{CA}) - e_{BC}(i_{CA} - i_{BC})$$

But $-e_{BC} = +e_{CB}$, also $(i_{AB} - i_{CA}) = i_A$ and $(i_{CA} - i_{BC}) = i_C$.

Hence $$p = (e_{AB}i_A) + (e_{CB}i_C)$$

Note that this final equation for the instantaneous power is exactly similar to the one derived for the star system. The two wattmeters, connected as in Fig. 229, obviously measure the total average power.

EXAMPLE 10. A 7.5-hp 230-volt three-phase motor takes a line current of 18.4 amp when operating at rated output at an efficiency of 88 per cent. Calculate the indications on wattmeters when these are inserted to measure power (*a*) by the two-wattmeter method, (*b*) by the artificial-neutral method, and (*c*) by the T method.

Solution

$$P_t = \frac{7.5 \times 746}{0.88} = 6{,}350 \text{ watts}$$

$$\text{PF} = \frac{6{,}350}{\sqrt{3} \times 230 \times 18.4} = 0.866$$

$$\theta = 30^\circ$$

(*a*) $$P_1 = 230 \times 18.4 \times \cos(30^\circ + 30^\circ) = 2{,}117 \text{ watts}$$
$$P_2 = 230 \times 18.4 \times \cos(30^\circ - 30^\circ) = 4{,}233 \text{ watts}$$

(*b*) $$P = \frac{6{,}350}{3} = 2{,}117 \text{ watts}$$

(*c*) $$P = \frac{6{,}350}{2} = 3{,}175 \text{ watts}$$

Unbalanced Delta-connected Loads. When balanced loads are connected to polyphase systems the magnitudes of the equal line currents are independent of the phase sequence of voltage. This is not true under conditions of load unbalance, i.e., when the load impedances are unequal and/or have dissimilar power-factor angles; it is for this reason that a correct solution of a polyphase circuit problem, involving any degree of unbalance, must be concerned with the order of the emfs.

There are two general phase sequences of voltage in three-phase systems; these are E_{AB}, E_{BC}, E_{CA} and E_{AB}, E_{CA}, E_{BC}. This means that a given set of *interconnected dissimilar impedances* will take currents whose magnitudes and/or phase angles are not related similarly to one another for the two combinations of phase sequence. Therefore, when the impedances are connected in delta, each sequence of emfs will yield a different set of line currents because each of the latter values is a vector difference of two phase currents. Two examples will now be given to illustrate and emphasize this aspect of polyphase circuits.

EXAMPLE 11. The following information is given for a delta-connected load of three numerically equal impedances that differ in power factor: line voltages = 120; $Z_{AB} = 15\underline{/30^\circ}$, $Z_{BC} = 15\underline{/0^\circ}$, $Z_{CA} = 15\underline{/-30^\circ}$; phase sequence of voltages is E_{AB}, E_{BC}, E_{CA}. Using the circuit and vector diagrams of Fig. 234 as a guide, calculate (*a*) the three phase currents I_{AB}, I_{BC}, and I_{CA}; (*b*) the three line currents I_A, I_B, and I_C; (*c*) the total power as determined from the phase voltages and currents; (*d*) the readings P_1 and P_2 indicated by the two wattmeters.

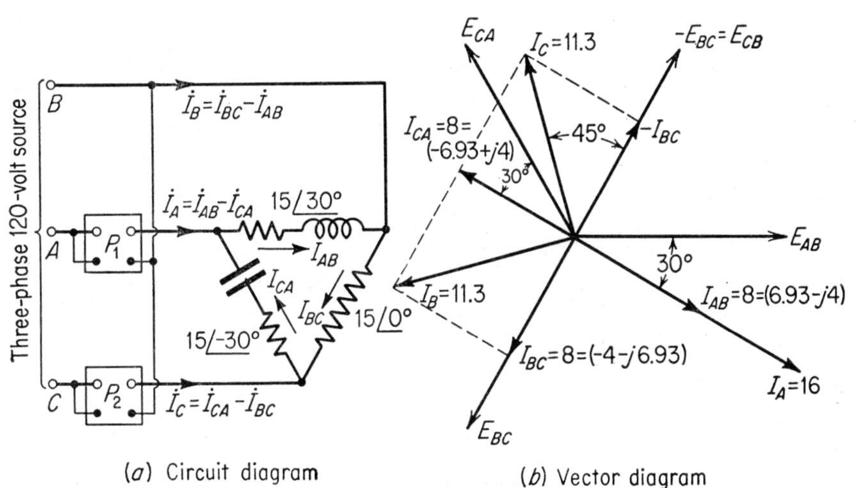

FIG. 234. Diagrams illustrating Example 11 for a phase sequence of voltages E_{AB}, E_{BC}, E_{CA}.

Solution

Before proceeding it will be well to note that the directions of the arrows in the delta of Fig. 234*a* correspond with the voltage arrows in Fig. 234*b* to indicate a phase sequence of E_{AB}, E_{BC}, E_{CA}.

(a)
$$I_{AB} = \frac{120}{15\underline{/30°}} = 8\underline{/-30°}$$
$$I_{BC} = \frac{120}{15\underline{/0°}} = 8\underline{/0°}$$
$$I_{CA} = \frac{120}{15\underline{/-30°}} = 8\underline{/30°}$$

On the vector diagram these currents are, in rectangular form,

$$I_{AB} = (6.93 - j4)$$
$$I_{BC} = (-4 - j6.93)$$
$$I_{CA} = (-6.93 + j4)$$

(b) $\dot{I}_A = \dot{I}_{AB} - \dot{I}_{CA} = (6.93 - j4) - (-6.93 + j4) = 13.86 - j8 = 16$ amp

$\dot{I}_B = \dot{I}_{BC} - \dot{I}_{AB} = (-4 - j6.93) - (6.93 - j4) = -10.93 - j2.93 = 11.3$ amp

$\dot{I}_C = \dot{I}_{CA} - \dot{I}_{BC} = (-6.93 + j4) - (-4 - j6.93) = -2.93 + j10.93 = 11.3$ amp

(c) $P_t = (120 \times 8 \times 0.866) + (120 \times 8 \times 1) + (120 \times 8 \times 0.866) = 120 \times 8\ (0.866 + 1 + 0.866) = 2{,}620$ watts

(d) $P_1 = E_{AB}I_A\,[\cos\Theta]^{A}_{AB} = 120 \times 16 \times \cos 30° = 1{,}660$ watts

$P_2 = E_{CB}I_C\,[\cos\Theta]^{C}_{CB} = 120 \times 11.3 \times \cos 45° = 960$ watts

$P_t = P_1 + P_2 = 1{,}660 + 960 = 2{,}620$ watts (*Check*)

EXAMPLE 12. Using the same given data, re-solve Example 11 for a phase sequence of voltages E_{AB}, E_{CA}, E_{BC}.

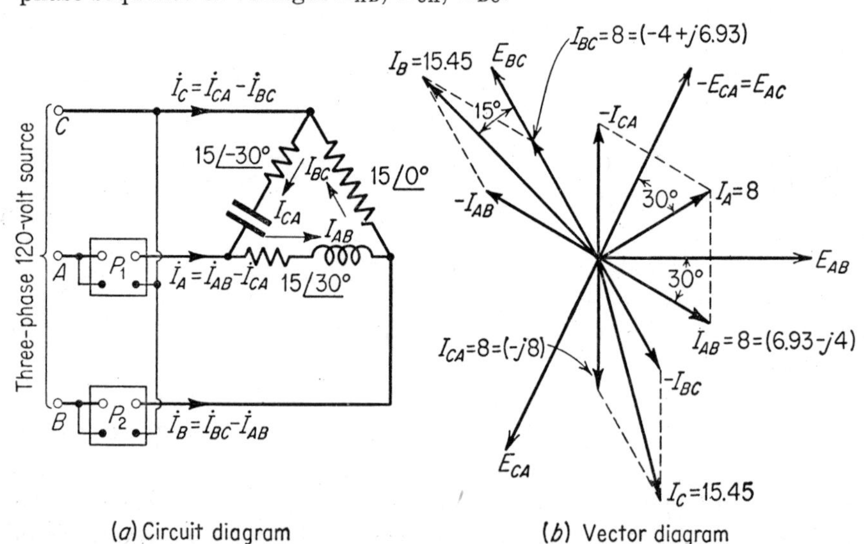

(a) Circuit diagram (b) Vector diagram

FIG. 235. Diagrams illustrating Example 12 for a phase sequence of voltages E_{AB}, E_{CA}, E_{BC}.

Solution

Refer to Fig. 235 and note that the arrow directions in the delta correspond with the voltage arrows in the vector diagram to indicate a phase sequence of E_{AB}, E_{CA}, E_{BC}.

(*a*)

$$I_{AB} = \frac{120}{15\underline{/30^\circ}} = 8\underline{/-30^\circ}$$

$$I_{BC} = \frac{120}{15\underline{/0^\circ}} = 8\underline{/0^\circ}$$

$$I_{CA} = \frac{120}{15\underline{/-30^\circ}} = 8\underline{/30^\circ}$$

On the vector diagram these currents are, in rectangular form,

$$I_{AB} = (6.93 - j4)$$
$$I_{BC} = (-4 + j6.93)$$
$$I_{CA} = (-j8)$$

(*b*) $\dot{I}_A = \dot{I}_{AB} - \dot{I}_{CA} = (6.93 - j4) - (-j8) = 6.93 + j4 = 8$ amp

$\dot{I}_B = \dot{I}_{BC} - \dot{I}_{AB} = (-4 + j6.93) - (6.93 - j4)$
$= -10.93 + j10.93 = 15.45$ amp

$\dot{I}_C = \dot{I}_{CA} - \dot{I}_{BC} = (-j8) - (-4 + j6.93) = -4 - 14.93$
$= 15.45$ amp

(*c*) $P_t = 120 \times 8\ (0.866 + 1.0 + 0.866) = 2{,}620$ watts

(*d*) $P_1 = E_{AC}I_A\,[\cos\theta]^{A}_{AC} = 120 \times 8 \times \cos 30^\circ = 830$ watts

$P_2 = E_{BC}I_B\,[\cos\theta]^{B}_{BC} = 120 \times 15.45 \times \cos 15^\circ = 1{,}790$ watts

$P_t = P_1 + P_2 = 830 + 1{,}790 = 2{,}620$ watts (*Check*)

Examples 11 and 12 clearly show that a phase-sequence change results in a completely different set of line currents. They also indicate that two wattmeters, properly connected, will measure the total power in an unbalanced three-phase circuit as well as one in which the loads are balanced.

Unbalanced Star-connected Loads. When three impedances are connected in star to a three-phase three-wire system the three line-to-neutral voltages will be numerically equal to $E_L/\sqrt{3}$ and 120° out of phase only under balanced load conditions; it is then that Eqs. (138), (139), and (141) also apply. For unbalanced loads, however, the voltages across the three impedances will no longer be equal, nor will they be displaced 120 elec deg with respect to one another. This means that the load currents, which are functions of a set of unknown line-to-neutral voltages, cannot be determined readily as in the delta connection. Several schemes have been devised to solve such problems, but these, involving the application of Kirchhoff's laws, make it necessary to handle complex simultaneous equations, or lengthy formulas in which the voltages to neutral may be evaluated. A simpler procedure, and one that seems to offer less difficulty, is to transform the known values of the star into an equivalent delta, after which the method explained in the previous article may be used. An example will now be given to illustrate the solution of this type of problem.

EXAMPLE 13. The following information is given for a star-connected load of three numerically equal impedances that differ in power factor: line voltages = 130; $Z_A = 10\underline{/36.9°}$, $Z_B = 10\underline{/-36.9°}$, $Z_C = 10\underline{/0}$; phase sequence of voltages is E_{AB}, E_{BC}, E_{CA}. Using the circuit and vector diagrams of Fig. 236 as a guide, calculate (*a*) the equivalent impedances Z_X, Z_Y, and Z_Z of an equivalent delta; (*b*) the phase currents I_X, I_Y, and I_Z in the equivalent delta; (*c*) the line currents I_A, I_B, and I_C in the actual star-connected system; (*d*) the total power taken by the load.

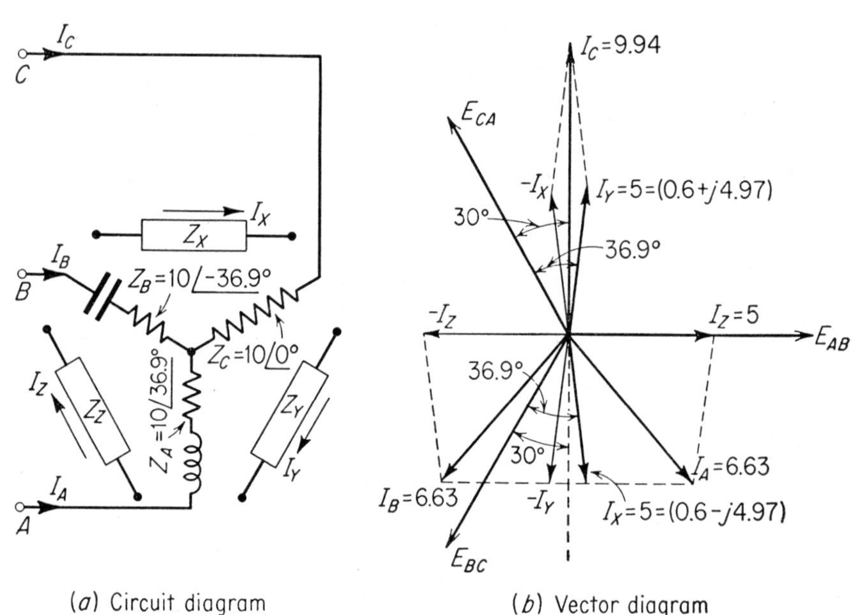

FIG. 236. Diagrams illustrating Example 13.

Solution

(*a*) To transform a star into an equivalent delta, Eq. (125), Chap. 15, will be used. Since the sum of the products Z_AZ_B, Z_BZ_C, and Z_CZ_A is common to the three equations for Z_X, Z_Y, and Z_Z, it will be evaluated first.

$$Z_AZ_B + Z_BZ_C + Z_CZ_A = (10\underline{/36.9°})(10\underline{/-36.9°}) + (10\underline{/-36.9°})(10\underline{/0°}) + (10\underline{/0°})(10\underline{/36.9°}) = (100) + (100\underline{/-36.9°}) + (100\underline{/36.9}) = 260$$

$$Z_X = \frac{260}{10\underline{/36.9°}} = 26\underline{/-36.9}$$

$$Z_Y = \frac{260}{10\underline{/-36.9°}} = 26\underline{/36.9°}$$

$$Z_Z = \frac{260}{10\underline{/0°}} = 26\underline{/0°}$$

(b)

$$I_X = \frac{130}{26\underline{/-36.9°}} = 5\underline{/36.9°}$$

$$I_Y = \frac{130}{26\underline{/36.9°}} = 5\underline{/-36.9°}$$

$$I_Z = \frac{130}{26\underline{/0°}} = 5\underline{/0°}$$

On the vector diagram these currents are, in rectangular form,

$$I_X = (0.6 - j4.97)$$
$$I_Y = (0.6 + j4.97)$$
$$I_Z = 5$$

(c) $\dot{I}_A = \dot{I}_Z - \dot{I}_Y = 5 - (0.6 + j4.97) = 4.4 - j4.97 = 6.63$ amp

$\dot{I}_B = \dot{I}_X - \dot{I}_Z = (0.6 - j4.97) - 5 = -4.4 - j4.97 = 6.63$ amp

$\dot{I}_C = \dot{I}_Y - \dot{I}_X = (0.6 + j4.97) - (0.6 - j4.97) = j9.94 = 9.94$ amp

(d) $P_t = [(6.63)^2 \times 8] + [(6.63)^2 \times 8] + [(9.94)^2 \times 10]$
$= 352 + 352 + 986 = 1{,}690$ watts

Also $P_t = P_X + P_Y + P_Z$
$= (EI_X \cos \Theta_X) + (EI_Y \cos \Theta_Y) + (EI_Z \cos \Theta_Z)$
$= (130 \times 5 \times 0.8) + (130 \times 5 \times 0.8) + (130 \times 5 \times 1.0)$
$= 520 + 520 + 650 = 1{,}690$ watts (*Check*)

Unbalanced Four-wire Star-connected Loads. An extremely popular type of distribution system for moderate power and lighting loads is the three-phase four-wire circuit. This consists of a source, usually a bank of transformers, whose windings are connected in star, with the three phase ends and the neutral brought out to service the loads. In practice the three line-to-neutral voltages are 120, so the three line-to-line voltages become $\sqrt{3} \times 120$, or 208. This arrangement makes it possible to supply three single-phase lighting and small-appliance loads as well as three-phase power loads such as motors.

Single-phase loads are served by any of three line wires and the common neutral wire; the latter conductor, returning to the neutral point of the source, therefore, carries the *vector sum* of the currents in the single-phase loads. Since the single-phase loads in the three phases, i.e., between lines A and N, B and N, and C and N, are completely independent of one another, the line-to-neutral voltages E_{AN}, E_{BN}, and E_{CN} are maintained in balance no matter how unbalanced these loads may be. Moreover, the line-to-line voltages are kept equal by the source, which means that the three-phase loads, generally balanced, are not affected by any degree of unbalance in the single-phase loads. The system therefore makes it possible to provide both single-phase and three-phase service at two values of voltage with one network of transmission wires.

Figure 237 illustrates a 120/208-volt three-phase four-wire system in which two single-phase loads and one three-phase load are shown connected to the distribution lines. Note particularly that (1) the neutral

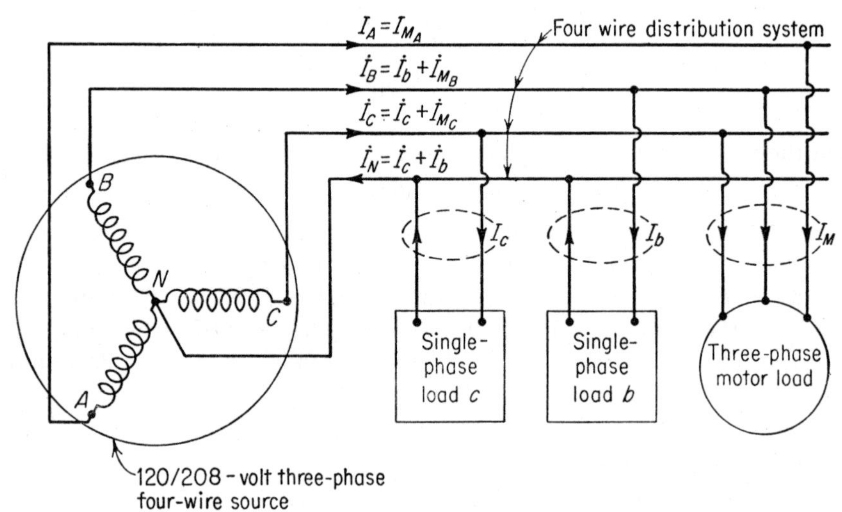

FIG. 237. Diagram illustrating a three-phase four-wire distribution system.

wire carries the vector sum of the two single-phase loads; (2) wire A carries one of the three-phase line currents supplied to the motor; (3) wire B carries a current represented by single-phase load b and the motor load; (4) wire C carries a current represented by single-phase load c and the motor load.

EXAMPLE 14. A three-phase four-wire 120/208-volt system (Fig. 237) delivers the following loads: single-phase load c is 5.4 kw at unity power factor; single-phase load b is 7.2 kw at unity power factor; three-phase motor load is a 25-hp motor that operates at a lagging power factor of 0.866 and an efficiency of 85.5 per cent. Calculate (a) the neutral current I_N; (b) the three line currents I_A, I_B, and I_C; (c) the total power delivered by the source. The phase sequence of voltages is E_{AN}, E_{BN}, E_{CN}.

Solution

The three load currents are

$$I_c = \frac{5{,}400}{120 \times 1.0} = 45 \text{ amp}$$

$$I_b = \frac{7{,}200}{120 \times 1.0} = 60 \text{ amp}$$

$$I_M = \frac{25 \times 746}{\sqrt{3} \times 208 \times 0.866 \times 0.855} = 70 \text{ amp}$$

Referring to Fig. 238, these currents are, in rectangular form,

$$I_c = -22.5 + j39$$
$$I_b = -30 - j52$$
$$I_{M_A} = 60.6 - j35$$
$$I_{M_B} = -60.6 - j35$$
$$I_{M_C} = j70$$

(a) $\dot{I}_N = \dot{I}_c + \dot{I}_b = (-22.5 + j39) + (-30 - j52) = (-52.5 - j13)$
$= 54.1$ amp

(b) $I_A = 70$ amp
$\dot{I}_B = \dot{I}_b + \dot{I}_{M_B} = (-30 - j52) + (-60.6 - j35) = (-90.6 - j87)$
$= 125.3$ amp
$\dot{I}_C = \dot{I}_c + \dot{I}_{M_C} = (-22.5 + j39) + (j70) = (-22.5 + j109)$
$= 111$ amp

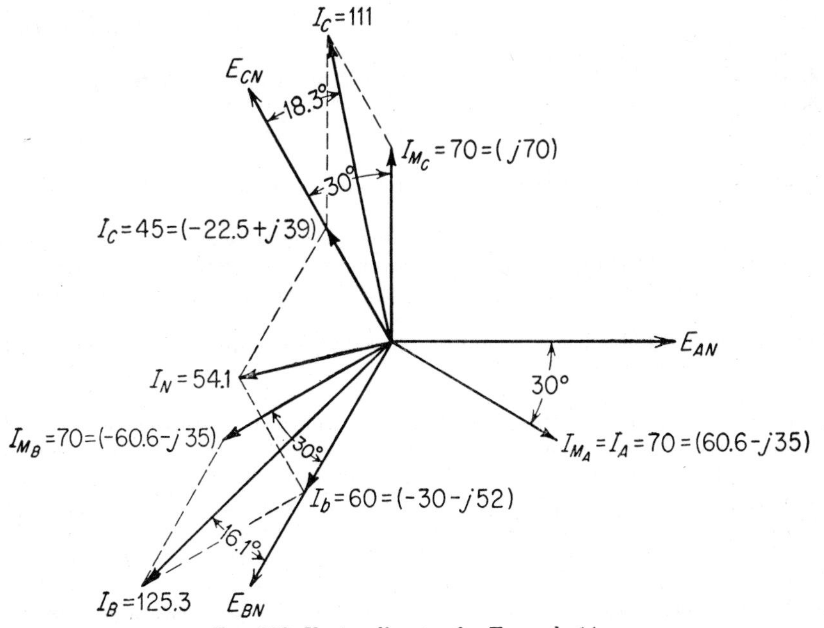

FIG. 238. Vector diagram for Example 14.

(c) $P_t = 5{,}400 + 7{,}200 + \dfrac{25 \times 746}{0.855} = 34{,}400$ watts, or 34.4 kw

The total power can also be determined by summing the values of power delivered by the three phases. Thus

$$P_t = E_{AN}I_A\,[\cos\Theta]_{AN}^{A} + E_{BN}I_B\,[\cos\Theta]_{BN}^{B} + E_{CN}I_C\,[\cos\Theta]_{CN}^{C}$$

From the vector diagram of Fig. 238,

$$[\Theta]_{AN}^{A} = 30^\circ$$
$$[\Theta]_{BN}^{B} = 16.1^\circ$$
$$[\Theta]_{CN}^{C} = 18.3^\circ$$

Therefore

$$P_t = (120 \times 70 \times \cos 30^\circ) + (120 \times 125.3 \times \cos 16.1^\circ) + (120 \times 111 \cos 18.3^\circ)$$
$$= (120 \times 70 \times 0.866) + (120 \times 125.3 \times 0.961) + (120 \times 111 \times 0.950)$$
$$= 7{,}270 + 14{,}480 + 12{,}650 = 34{,}400 \text{ watts, or } 34.4 \text{ kw} \qquad (Check)$$

Questions

1. What is a *polyphase system?* How does a two-phase system differ from a three-phase system?
2. What advantages do polyphase generators, motors, or other a-c equipment have over those used in single-phase service?
3. Discuss pulsating power as it applies to the operation of a single-phase motor. Explain why polyphase motors do not develop torque that is pulsating.
4. How can a single-phase source be obtained from a polyphase system?
5. For how many phases are alternators generally constructed?
6. What method is generally employed to obtain six or more phases from a three-phase source?
7. How are the windings arranged in the stator of an alternator for three-phase service? for two-phase service?
8. Write the expressions for the three voltage waves developed by a three-phase alternator; for the two voltage waves developed by a two-phase alternator.
9. Draw the vector diagrams of voltage for a three-phase system; for a two-phase system.
10. What is meant by *phase sequence?* Show by vector diagrams how one phase sequence differs from another when the system is three-phase; two-phase.
11. What is the effect upon the direction of rotation of an a-c motor when the phase sequence is changed? How is the latter accomplished in a three-phase system?
12. When the impedances in a three-phase load differ, i.e., when the load is unbalanced, how are the line currents affected by a change in phase sequence?
13. What is a *star connection?* Draw three windings that are connected in star.
14. In a balanced star system, what are the magnitudes of the line-to-line voltages with respect to the line-to-neutral voltages? What are the relative angular phase positions of the two sets of voltages?
15. What is meant by a *four-wire three-phase system?* What advantages does it possess?

16. When a three-phase load is balanced what is the magnitude of the neutral-wire current in a three-phase four-wire system? Explain.

17. With what voltages, E_N or E_L, are the currents in phase when the power factor is unity in a balanced star-connected three-phase system?

18. Make a diagram showing a delta-connected three-phase system. What precaution must be taken before the delta connection is completed?

19. What is the value of each of the line currents with respect to the phase currents in a delta-connected system? Write three line-current equations in terms of the phase currents for a delta-connected system.

20. What is the magnitude of the vector sum of the three line currents in a delta-connected system? in a three-wire star-connected system? Why?

21. In a balanced delta-connected system, what are the magnitudes of the line currents with respect to the equal phase currents? Prove this by drawing a vector diagram.

22. What are the relative angular phase positions of the two sets of currents, I_{PH} and I_L, in a balanced delta-connected system?

23. Write the general equation for the total power in a balanced three-phase star- or delta-connected system. Show that this expression can be derived from the phase currents and voltages in the two systems.

24. Make circuit diagrams showing a four-wire and a three-wire two-phase system. In the three-wire system what is the voltage between the outer two lines with respect to the phase voltage?

25. Make circuit diagrams showing a five-wire and a mesh-connected four-phase system. Indicate on the diagrams all possible voltages in terms of the phase voltage.

26. Write an expression for the total power in a four-wire two-phase system; in a three-wire two-phase system.

27. What advantages and disadvantages exist between the various types of two- and four-phase systems? Discuss in some detail.

28. Make diagrams showing how *three* wattmeters should be connected to measure the total power in star and delta systems.

29. Make a wiring diagram showing how *two* wattmeters should be connected into a three-phase system to measure the total power.

30. In a balanced three-phase system with two wattmeters connected to measure the total power, write the expressions for the values of P_1 and P_2 in terms of E_L, I_L, and Θ.

31. Outline the procedure to determine the load power factor from two wattmeter readings in a three-phase balanced load.

32. How are the readings on two wattmeters affected when a given balanced load changes from lagging to leading?

33. At what power factor will one of the two wattmeters in a balanced three-phase system be zero? be negative?

34. Write a general expression for tan Θ, in terms of two wattmeter readings, from which the power factor of a balanced three-phase load may be determined.

35. Describe the potential-lead shift method of measuring power, in a three-phase balanced circuit, with a single wattmeter. Explain why this method is similar to the two-wattmeter method.

36. Describe the artificial-neutral method of measuring power, in a three-phase balanced circuit, with a single wattmeter. Explain the validity of the method.

37. Describe the T method of measuring power, in a three-phase balanced circuit, with a single wattmeter. What should the wattmeter reading be multiplied by to yield the total power? Prove the latter relationship.

38. Is the two-wattmeter method for measuring power valid when the load is unbalanced? Prove this for star- and delta-connected loads.

39. When a three-phase load is unbalanced how are the line currents affected when the phase sequence is reversed? Does this condition exist when the load is balanced?

40. What difficulties exist in the solution of a three-phase three-wire star-connected circuit that is unbalanced? Explain why a solution is facilitated when the star is transformed into an equivalent delta.

41. Describe a four-wire three-phase system. What important advantages does it possess? What voltages are generally used for such a system?

42. Make a sketch showing how to insert three wattmeters in a four-wire three-phase system to measure the total power.

Problems

1. The voltage across each phase of Fig. 214*a* is 120. (*a*) If points *a* and *b* are connected what will be the voltage between *A* and *B*? (*b*) If *a* is joined to *C*, and *c* is joined to *b*, what will be the voltage between *A* and *B*? (*c*) If *a* is joined to *B*, and *b* is joined to *C*, what will be the voltage between *A* and *c*?

2. The voltage across each phase of Fig. 214*b* is 120. If points *A* and *b* are connected together, what will be the voltage between *a* and *B*?

3. The voltage across each phase of a star-connected source is 265. What will be the current in each of the three line wires if a balanced load of 200 kw at a power factor of 0.82 is delivered?

4. What is the voltage of a delta-connected source that delivers an 0.85 power-factor load of 500 kw at 148 amp?

5. A 10-hp 230-volt three-phase motor draws a line current of 25 amp when operating at rated output. If the motor efficiency is 91 per cent, calculate the power factor.

6. Two balanced loads are connected in parallel to a three-phase 460-volt source. Load *A* is 900 kva at a power factor of 0.6 lagging, and load *B* is 400 kw at a power factor of 0.8 leading. Calculate (*a*) total kilowatts and kilovolt-amperes, (*b*) over-all power factor, (*c*) line currents.

7. A 234-volt three-phase source serves a balanced load consisting of three equal impedances, each of which has a resistance of 3.6 ohms and an inductive reactance of 4.8 ohms. Calculate the line currents and the total power if the impedances are connected in star.

8. Solve Prob. 7 for a delta-connected load, assuming all other conditions to remain the same.

9. What should be the resistance and reactance of each of the impedances of Prob. 7 if, when connected in delta, the line currents and the total power are to be the same as for the star connection?

10. The voltage across each phase of a four-wire two-phase system (Fig. 223) is 115. Load *A* consists of lighting circuits (power factor = 1) totaling 4,140 watts, and load *B* represents lighting and motor circuits totaling 3,105 watts at a power factor of 0.6 lagging. Calculate the current in each phase and the total power.

11. The following information is given in connection with the two-phase three-wire circuit of Fig. 224: $E_{BA} = 170$; load *NA* is an impedance of $(6 + j8)$; load *BN* is an impedance of $(9.6 - j7.2)$; load *BA* takes a current of 15 amp at a lagging power factor of 0.99 ($\theta = 8.1°$). Calculate (*a*) currents I_{NA} and I_{BN}, (*b*) neutral current I_N, (*c*) line currents I_A and I_B, (*d*) the total power.

12. A two-phase three-wire circuit similar to that of Fig. 224 is connected so that phase *BN* is reversed, i.e., with the arrow directed from *B* to *N*, and has voltages

$E_{NA} = E_{NB} = 115$. The following unity-power-factor currents are then delivered by the source: $I_{NA} = 20$ amp, $I_{NB} = 30$ amp, $I_{AB} = 40$ amp. Calculate (*a*) I_N, I_A, and I_B; (*b*) the total power taken by the three loads.

13. Referring to the four-phase five-wire system of Fig. 225, the voltage between the neutral point N and any of the four terminal wires is 115. What three combinations of two-phase voltages are possible?

14. A three-phase balanced load takes a total of 6,360 watts. If two wattmeters are connected in the circuit to measure this power and one of them registers 2,120 watts, what is the load power factor?

15. A 460-volt three-phase source supplies a balanced load of 200 kw at a lagging power factor of 0.707, and two wattmeters are properly connected to measure the total power. Calculate (*a*) the line currents, (*b*) the deflections registered by the instruments.

16. In a balanced 230-volt three-phase circuit two wattmeters are connected to indicate the total power. If the readings are 8,140 watts and −2,980 watts, calculate the power factor and the line currents.

17. If a single wattmeter is used to measure the total power in Prob. 16, what will it register by (*a*) the artificial-neutral method? (*b*) the T method?

18. An unbalanced delta-connected load is delivered by a three-phase system whose phase sequence is E_{AB}, E_{BC}, E_{CA}. Load AB is $12\underline{/0}$ amp, load BC is $12\underline{/30°}$ amp, and load CA is $16\underline{/-30°}$ amp. Calculate the line currents I_A, I_B, and I_C.

19. A three-phase source has a phase sequence of E_{AB}, E_{BC}, E_{CA}, and delivers the following loads: $I_{AB} = 12\underline{/0°}$, $I_{BC} = 12\underline{/-60°}$, $I_{CA} = 16\underline{/60°}$. Calculate the line currents I_A, I_B, and I_C.

20. The three line voltages in Prob. 19 are 230. If one wattmeter is connected with its current coil in line A and its potential coil across lines A and B, and a second wattmeter is connected with its current coil in line C and its potential coil across lines C and B, what will each wattmeter register, and what is the total power?

21. A three-phase 120-volt circuit has a phase sequence E_{AB}, E_{BC}, E_{CA} and delivers power to a group of delta-connected impedances whose values are $Z_{AB} = (10 + j0)$, $Z_{BC} = (5 + j8.66)$, and $Z_{CA} = (8.66 + j5)$. Calculate (*a*) the three line currents I_A, I_B, and I_C; (*b*) the total power.

22. Solve Prob. 19 for a phase sequence E_{AB}, E_{CA}, E_{BC}.

23. Solve Prob. 21 for a phase sequence E_{AB}, E_{CA}, E_{BC}.

24. Three equal impedances, each one equal to $(6.12 + j5.13)$ ohms, are connected in star and to a three-phase 208-volt source. Calculate (*a*) the line currents, (*b*) the total power, (*c*) the reading on each of two wattmeters properly connected to register the total power.

25. The following information is given in connection with a circuit similar to that of the unbalanced star of Fig. 236: line voltages = 246; $Z_A = 15\underline{/0°}$, $Z_B = 15\underline{/30°}$, $Z_C = 15\underline{/-30°}$; phase sequence of voltages is E_{AB}, E_{BC}, E_{CA}. Calculate (*a*) the equivalent impedances Z_X, Z_Y, and Z_Z of an equivalent delta; (*b*) the phase currents I_X, I_Y, and I_Z in the equivalent delta; (*c*) the line currents I_A, I_B, and I_C in the actual star-connected system; (*d*) the total power taken by the load.

26. Referring to the 120/208-volt three-phase four-wire system of Fig. 237, the following information is given in connection with loads delivered by the source: 208-volt three-phase motor loads aggregating 75 hp, at a power factor of 0.8 lagging and an efficiency of 81 per cent; a 10.8-kw unity-power-factor load connected to lines AN; a 12.5-kw 0.866 leading power-factor load connected to lines BN; a 7.68-kw 0.866 lagging power-factor load connected to lines CN. Calculate (*a*) the neutral current I_N; (*b*) the line currents I_A, I_B, and I_C; (*c*) the total power delivered by the source. The phase sequence is E_{AN}, E_{BN}, E_{CN}.

CHAPTER 19

NONSINUSOIDAL WAVES

General Aspects of Complex Alternating-current Waves. Although the a-c circuit discussions of the foregoing chapters were concerned with *sinusoidal* variations of voltage, current, and power, such ideal wave shapes are seldom present in commercial systems. Alternators rarely generate voltages that are pure sine waves, and this is especially true under load conditions, when flux-density distributions are greatly distorted by the effects of magnetic saturation and armature reaction. Moreover, since circuit parameters that are inductive or capacitive tend to modify existing wave shapes, variations that may be good approximations of sinusoids originally often suffer considerable change when applied to practical loads. A good example of the latter is a nonsinusoidal wave of exciting current in a transformer that is energized by a reasonably good sine wave of voltage.

An extremely interesting and useful aspect of a nonsinusoidal wave, however complex, is that it may be expressed mathematically by a summation of sine-wave components of different frequencies. The predominant sinusoidal component, i.e., the one that represents the basic circuit frequency and has the greatest amplitude, is generally referred to as the *fundamental* while the others of higher frequency and considerably reduced amplitude are said to be *harmonics* that are superimposed on the fundamental. The complex wave may therefore be regarded as a combination of sine waves, where the harmonics act to distort the basic sine wave by amounts that are determined by their relative magnitudes with respect to the fundamental. In this connection, it will presently be shown that *odd harmonics* distort the sinusoidal variation without disturbing the symmetry between positive and negative lobes of the cycle, whereas *even harmonics* tend to cause dissymmetry between alternations as well as distortion.

In some types of communication systems and certain rectified circuits a-c waves may act in conjunction with an unvarying current or voltage. Under such conditions it is generally desirable to regard the complex wave as an alternating current or emf that is superimposed on a direct current or voltage; the resultant wave is then thought to represent an alternating current or emf that is raised or lowered, respectively, above or below the x axis by the constant magnitude of the plus or minus direct current or voltage.

In the discussions to follow an analysis will be made of nonsinusoidal waves in terms of the fundamental and harmonic components; also, equations and procedures will be developed to indicate how circuits react to voltages and/or currents that are not sinusoidal.

The Nonsinusoidal Wave Expressed by a Fourier Series. Alternating currents and voltages that are not sinusoidal can, for the most part, be expressed in terms of a fundamental sine wave *and* one or more harmonic sine-wave components. The laws governing sinusoidal variations, previously discussed, can then be applied to each frequency independently and, by methods that will be developed, may be combined properly to yield composite values of required electrical quantities.

On the assumption that a wave is periodic, i.e., one in which the variations in magnitude and/or direction repeat themselves at regular time intervals, and that it is single-valued and continuous, except as it is limited to a finite number of discontinuities, it may be represented by a Fourier series of sine and cosine terms as follows:

$$y = A_0 + (A_1 \sin \alpha + B_1 \cos \alpha) + (A_2 \sin 2\alpha + B_2 \cos 2\alpha) + (A_3 \sin 3\alpha + B_3 \cos 3\alpha) + \cdots + (A_n \sin n\alpha + B_n \cos n\alpha) \quad (142)$$

where A_0 is a constant term, represented by a d-c component

$A_1, A_2, A_3, \ldots, A_n$ and $B_1, B_2, B_3, \ldots, B_n$ are the amplitudes, i.e., the maximum values, of the harmonic components

α is an angle that represents an independent variable, measured from some arbitrary point on the x axis of the wave

n is an integer that is 1 for the fundamental, 2 for the second harmonic, 3 for the third harmonic, etc.

If there is no d-c component in the wave, as is generally the case, A_0 is zero. Moreover, when the positive and negative lobes of each nonsinusoidal cycle are completely symmetrical, the *even harmonics*, indicated by all values of n that are 2, 4, 6, etc., will be nonexistent; the equation of the wave will then be represented by a fundamental set of sine and cosine terms and one or more sets of odd-harmonic terms such as $(A_3 \sin 3\alpha + B_3 \cos 3\alpha)$, $(A_5 \sin 5\alpha + B_5 \cos 5\alpha)$, etc.

The general expression for a nonsinusoidal wave [Eq. (142)] first proposed by the French mathematician Joseph Fourier is obviously an infinite series, since it completely expresses a wave only when it contains an infinite number of terms; however, a good approximation of a wave's equation can usually be represented by a comparatively few terms.

Since the Fourier series contains pairs of sine and cosine terms for each of the harmonic components, it lends itself to some simplification in which sine terms alone may be employed. Such a mathematical transformation may be accomplished by taking advantage of the fact that the amplitudes A_n and B_n of any harmonic component n are respectively related to sine and cosine functions, which, in turn, are 90° out of phase; they may

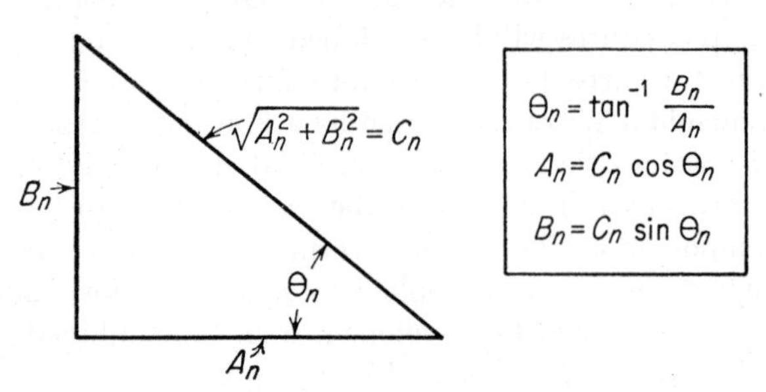

FIG. 239. Triangular relationship between amplitudes of the sine and cosine terms of a harmonic component in a nonsinusoidal wave.

therefore be represented by the sides of a right triangle such as Fig. 239. Thus

$$A_n = (\sqrt{A_n^2 + B_n^2}) \cos \Theta_n \qquad \text{and} \qquad B_n = (\sqrt{A_n^2 + B_n^2}) \sin \Theta_n$$

where Θ_n is $\tan^{-1} (B_n/A_n)$. Substituting the values of A_n and B_n for the nth harmonic terms in Eq. (142), and rearranging,

$$A_n \sin n\alpha + B_n \cos n\alpha = \sqrt{A_n^2 + B_n^2} (\sin n\alpha \cos \Theta_n + \cos n\alpha \sin \Theta_n)$$

But $\qquad (\sin n\alpha \cos \Theta_n + \cos n\alpha \sin \Theta_n) = \sin (n\alpha + \Theta_n)$

Therefore

$$(A_n \sin n\alpha + B_n \cos n\alpha) = (\sqrt{A_n^2 + B_n^2}) \sin (n\alpha + \Theta_n)$$

Replacing the radical term $\sqrt{A_n^2 + B_n^2}$ by C_n, Eq. (142) may be written as follows:

$$y = A_0 + C_1 \sin (\alpha + \Theta_1) + C_2 \sin (2\alpha + \Theta_2) + C_3 \sin (3\alpha + \Theta_3) + \cdots + C_n \sin (n\alpha + \Theta_n) \qquad (143)$$

EXAMPLE 1. Express the nonsinusoidal voltage wave $e = (96 \sin \alpha - 72 \cos \alpha) + (-15.4 \sin 3\alpha - 12.8 \cos 3\alpha) + (-4.5 \sin 5\alpha - 6 \cos 5\alpha)$ in terms of sine components only.

Solution

$$C_1 = \sqrt{(96)^2 + (-72)^2} = 120$$
$$C_3 = \sqrt{(-15.4)^2 + (12.8)^2} = 20$$
$$C_5 = \sqrt{(-4.5)^2 + (-6)^2} = 7.5$$

$$\theta_1 = \tan^{-1}\frac{-72}{96} = \tan^{-1}(-0.75) = -36.9° \qquad \text{(fourth quadrant)}$$

$$\theta_3 = \tan^{-1}\frac{12.8}{-15.4} = \tan^{-1}(-0.83) = 140.3° \qquad \text{(second quadrant)}$$

$$\theta_5 = \tan^{-1}\frac{-6}{-4.5} = \tan^{-1}(1.33) = 233.1° \qquad \text{(third quadrant)}$$

Therefore

$$e = 120 \sin(\alpha - 36.9°) + 20 \sin(3\alpha + 140.3°) + 7.5 \sin(5\alpha - 233.1°)$$

Symmetrical Nonsinusoidal Waves. A nonsinusoidal wave is said to be *symmetrical* when positive and negative lobes of each cycle are exactly alike; this implies that, beginning at the zero point on the x axis, the wave passes through a succession of ordinates in a positive direction that are identical with a succession of negative ordinates that begin 180 elec deg later. A composite wave has symmetry when it is made up of odd-harmonic components only. The generated emf wave developed in the windings of an alternator, for example, is always symmetrical because its similar positive and negative voltage variations are produced under *north* and *south* poles where the flux-density distributions are identical. In fact, most power circuits that are not disturbed by the presence of rectification equipment, d-c components, or transients will be characterized by current and voltage waves that are symmetrical.

Figure 240 illustrates two symmetrical nonsinusoidal voltage waves, each of which consists of a fundamental and a *third harmonic.* The latter is said to be *in phase* with the former when both start in a *positive* direction from the zero point on the x axis; this is shown in Fig. 240*a*, where the composite wave dips down in the middle of the positive and negative lobes to give the appearance of a sort of flat-top wave. When the third harmonic starts in a forward direction 60° *later* than does the fundamental on the *fundamental* scale, it is a *lagging* component that is equivalent to $3 \times 60° = 180°$ on the *third-harmonic scale;* this is shown in Fig. 240*b*, where the positive and negative lobes are likewise symmetrical, but with a peaked-wave appearance. Note particularly that the angle θ_3 for the third harmonic is specified in third-harmonic degrees which, referred to the fundamental scale of degrees represented by the x axis, is *three* times the latter. Thus, in Fig. 240*b*, the equation of the composite wave is

$$e = E_1 \sin \alpha + E_3 \sin(3\alpha - 180°)$$

where $-180°$ indicates that the third harmonic component *lags* behind the fundamental by 180° on the third-harmonic scale or $180/3 = 60°$ on the fundamental scale. Reference to Fig. 240 also indicates that each

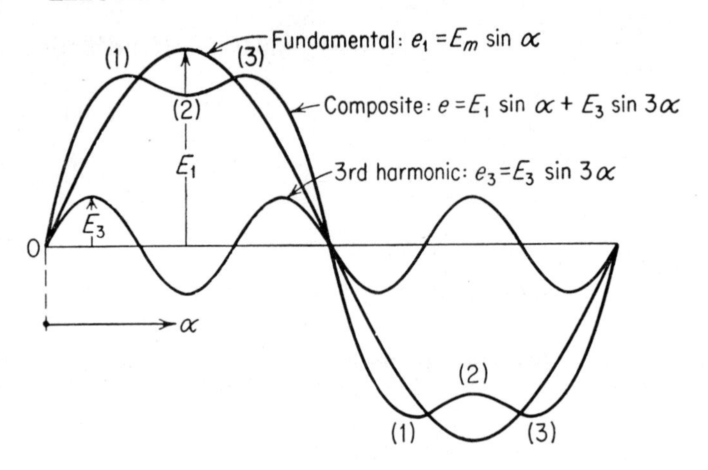

(*a*) Third harmonic in phase with the fundamental

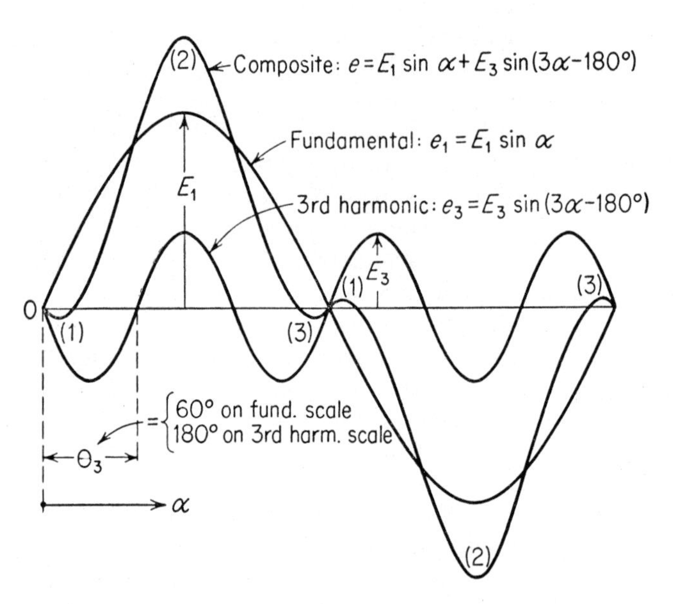

(*b*) Third harmonic lagging behind the fundamental

FIG. 240. Symmetrical nonsinusoidal waves.

of the nonsinusoidal waves, containing only a third harmonic component in addition to the fundamental, has *three* points of inflection labeled 1, 2, and 3; i.e., there are three points on the positive *or* negative lobes of the curve where the direction of the slope changes.

Two symmetrical nonsinusoidal voltage waves, each one consisting of a fundamental and a *fifth harmonic*, are shown in Fig. 241. When the

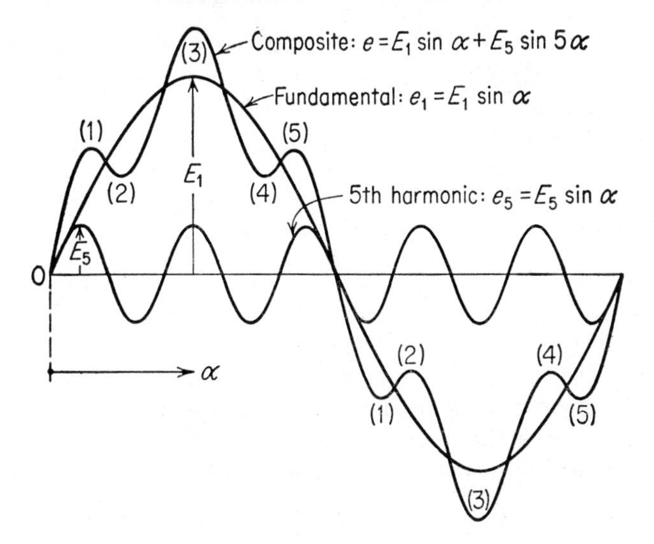

(a) Fifth harmonic in phase with the fundamental

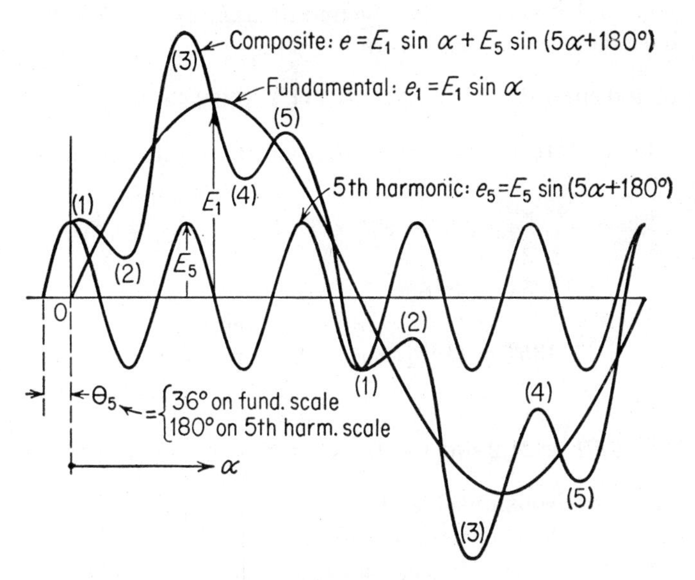

(b) Fifth harmonic leading the fundamental

FIG. 241. Symmetrical nonsinusoidal waves.

two components are in phase, as in Fig. 241*a*, they start together in a positive direction at the origin O on the x axis; the composite wave has major peaks at the centers of the positive and negative lobes, and minor peaks and dips on both sides of each major peak. With the fifth harmonic moved ahead in time (to the left) by 36° on the fundamental scale

(Fig. 241*b*) or $5 \times 36° = 180°$ on the fifth-harmonic scale, the composite wave takes on a distorted appearance; the positive and negative lobes are, however, symmetrical with respect to one another. Note particularly that both waves have five points of inflection labeled 1, 2, 3, 4, and 5, and the equations are

For Fig. 241*a*: $e = E_1 \sin \alpha + E_5 \sin 5\alpha$

For Fig. 241*b*: $e = E_1 \sin \alpha + E_5 \sin (5\alpha + 180°)$

EXAMPLE 2. A symmetrical nonsinusoidal voltage wave is composed of a 60-cycle fundamental, a 180-cycle third harmonic that leads the fundamental by 48° on the fundamental scale, and a 300-cycle fifth harmonic that lags behind the fundamental by 27° on the fundamental scale. If the amplitudes of the fundamental, and third and fifth harmonics are 160, 21.2, and 9.2 volts, respectively, determine the equation of the wave.

Solution

Third harmonic *leads* fundamental by $3 \times 48° = 144°$ on third harmonic scale. Fifth harmonic *lags* behind fundamental by $5 \times 27° = 135°$ on fifth harmonic scale. Therefore

$$e = 160 \sin \alpha + 21.2 \sin (3\alpha + 144°) + 9.2 \sin (5\alpha - 135°)$$

The sines in the foregoing equation may be written in terms of radians, as follows:

$$\begin{aligned} \alpha &= 2\pi \times 60t = 377t \\ 3\alpha &= 1{,}131t \\ 5\alpha &= 1{,}885t \\ 144° &= (144/180)\pi = 0.8\pi \text{ radians} \\ 135° &= (135/180)\pi = 0.75\pi \text{ radians} \end{aligned}$$

Therefore

$$e = 160 \sin 377t + 21.2 \sin (1{,}131t + 0.8\pi) + 9.2 \sin (1{,}885t - 0.75\pi)$$

Unsymmetrical Nonsinusoidal Waves. A nonsinusoidal wave is said to be *unsymmetrical* when one lobe of each cycle, starting at the zero point on the x axis, passes through a succession of ordinates in a positive direction that are *not* identical with a succession of negative ordinates that begin 180 elec deg later. As was previously pointed out, such dissymmetry results only because the composite wave contains one or more even harmonics and/or a d-c component. In connection with the latter point it should be clear that a symmetrical wave becomes an unsymmetrical wave to the extent that it is raised or lowered by the superposition of a d-c component.

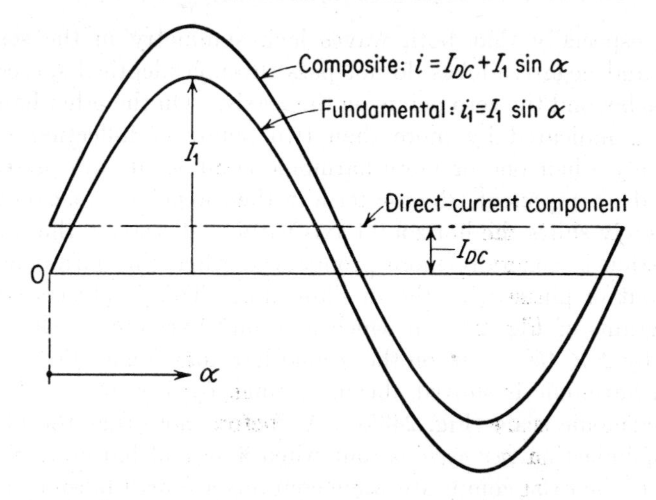

(*a*) Undistorted wave with a direct-current component

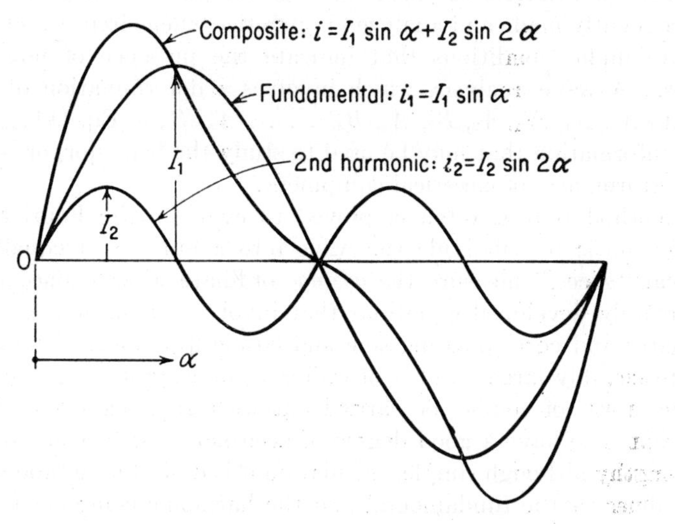

(*b*) Distorted wave with second-harmonic component

FIG. 242. Unsymmetrical nonsinusoidal waves.

Figure 242 illustrates two simple unsymmmetrical nonsinusoidal current waves. Note that the symmetry of the fundamental of Fig. 242*a* is altered by the presence of a d-c component, while the unsymmetrical shape of the composite wave of Fig. 242*b* results from a combination of a fundamental on a second harmonic; they may be represented by the equations

For Fig. 242*a*: $i = I_{DC} + I_1 \sin \alpha$

For Fig. 242*b*. $i = I_1 \sin \alpha + I_2 \sin 2\alpha$

Observe especially that both waves lack symmetry in the sense that positive and negative lobes do not pass through identical successions of ordinates beyond the zero points on the x axis. On the other hand, wave distortion, indicated by more than two points of inflection *per cycle*, results only when one or more harmonic components are present (Fig. 242*b*); a d-c component (the d-c term in the foregoing equation and Fig. 242*a*) merely shifts the horizontal axis without distorting the wave.

Distortion is generally more pronounced when the harmonic component is out of phase with the fundamental. This is illustrated by the two diagrams of Fig. 243, in which a second harmonic is shifted back, in time, by $2 \times 45° = 90°$ on the second-harmonic scale (Fig. 243*a*), and a fourth harmonic is shifted ahead, in time, by $4 \times 45° = 180°$ on the fourth-harmonic scale (Fig. 243*b*). As before, note that the number of points of inflection *per cycle* is four when a second harmonic is present and eight when the composite wave contains a fourth harmonic in addition to the fundamental.

Graphical Analysis of Nonsinusoidal Waves. Oscillographic records are frequently made and analyzed in practice when circuits and machines operate under conditions that indicate the presence of nonsinusoidal waves. A wave analysis, which involves a determination of the coefficients A_0, A_1, B_1, A_2, B_2, A_3, B_3, . . . , A_n, B_n in Eq. (142), will then yield information that may be used to study the behavior, or to improve the performance, of electrical equipment.

A method that is often employed to evaluate the Fourier-equation coefficients is to subdivide the wave into a number of equally spaced vertical "slices," measure the *average* ordinate of each one, and apply two readily developed equations that involve summations of measured ordinates and corresponding sine and cosine functions. The "scaling" of a reasonably large number of ordinates in a graphical procedure such as this must, of course, be carried out with great care if the resulting equation is to have a good degree of accuracy. Moreover, to facilitate the lengthy, although simple, calculation it is desirable to tabulate neatly the values for the fundamental and the harmonic components, as illustrated subsequently by an example. Also, if the nonsinusoidal wave appears to be symmetrical, having similar positive and negative lobes (see Figs. 240 and 241), it will only be necessary to analyze one alternation and make calculations for the fundamental and the *odd* harmonics.

Figure 244 represents the positive lobe of a symmetrical nonsinusoidal wave that is divided into m vertical "slices," i.e., at intervals of $180/m$ electrical degrees along the x axis. Note that the average ordinates of successive sections have values of y_1, y_2, y_3, . . . , y_m at angles from the origin that are, respectively, α_1, α_2, α_3, . . . , α_m. For the fundamental,

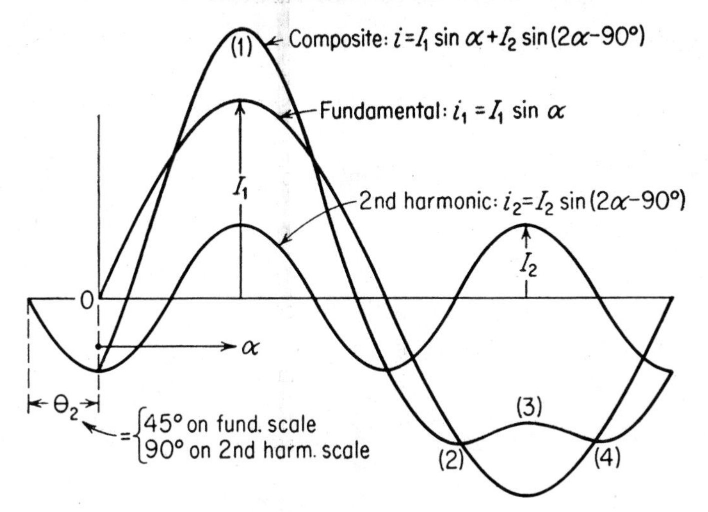

(a) Second harmonic lagging behind the fundamental

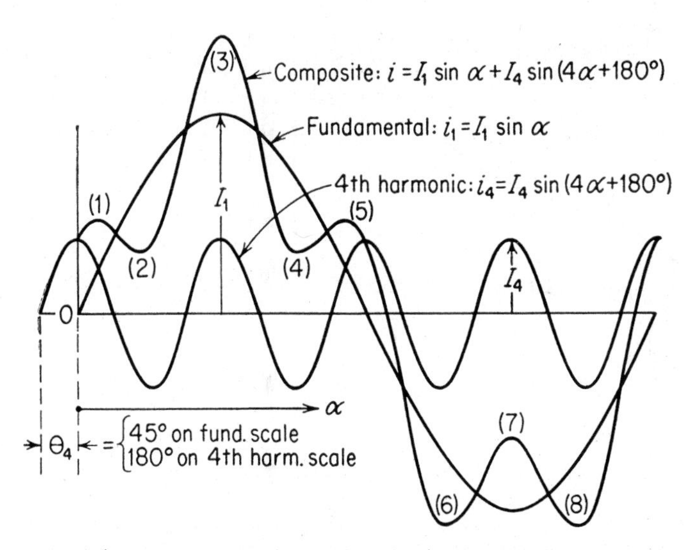

(b) Fourth harmonic leading the fundamental

FIG. 243. Unsymmetrical nonsinusoidal waves.

the Fourier-equation coefficients of Eq. (142) may be determined by using the following relations:

$$A_1 = \frac{2}{m}(y_1 \sin \alpha_1 + y_2 \sin \alpha_2 + y_3 \sin \alpha_3 + \cdots + y_m \sin \alpha_m)$$

$$B_1 = \frac{2}{m}(y_1 \cos \alpha_1 + y_2 \cos \alpha_2 + y_3 \cos \alpha_3 + \cdots + y_m \cos \alpha_m)$$

These may be simplified to the forms

$$A_1 = \frac{2}{m}\sum (y \sin \alpha) \qquad \text{and} \qquad B_1 = \frac{2}{m}\sum (y \cos \alpha)$$

For the third harmonic the coefficients are

$$A_3 = \frac{2}{m}\sum (y \sin 3\alpha) \qquad \text{and} \qquad B_3 = \frac{2}{m}\sum (y \cos 3\alpha)$$

In general, for the nth harmonic, they become

$$\begin{aligned} A_n &= \frac{2}{m}\sum (y \sin n\alpha) \\ B_n &= \frac{2}{m}\sum (y \cos n\alpha) \end{aligned} \tag{144}$$

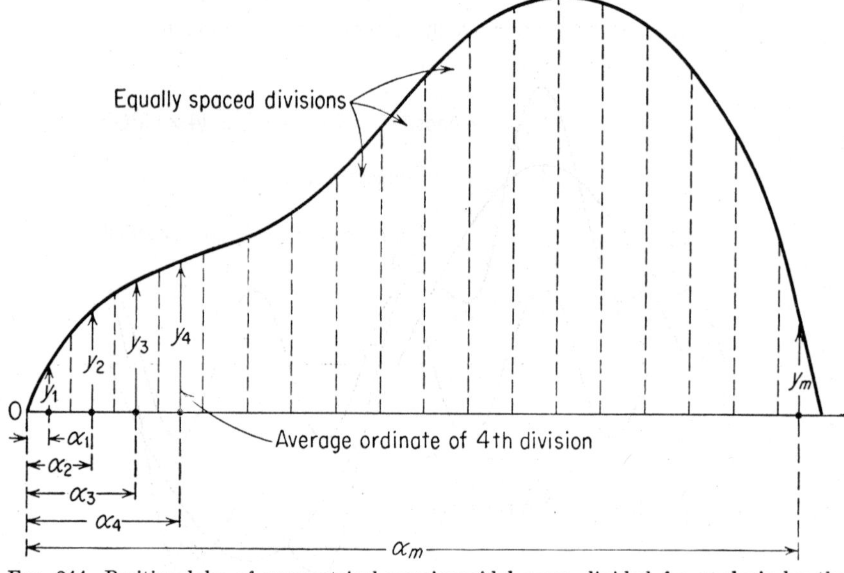

FIG. 244. Positive lobe of symmetrical nonsinusoidal wave divided for analysis by the graphical method.

After the wave is properly divided, the number of divisions depending upon the desired accuracy, the following procedure is indicated for the determination of the coefficients of the sine and cosine terms of any harmonic: (1) in the first column list the angles from the origin to the centers of the vertically divided sections; (2) using a table of sines and cosines list the values of sin $n\alpha$ and cos $n\alpha$ after each entry, being especially careful to apply the correct sign (+ or −); (3) scale off vertical distances y at the centers of divided sections, listing them beside corresponding angles; (4) for the coefficient of the sine term A_n make a column of calculated values of $y \sin n\alpha$ products; (5) for the coefficient of the cosine term B_n make a column of calculated values of $y \cos n\alpha$ products; (6) add *algebraically* the columns of $y \sin n\alpha$ and $y \cos n\alpha$; (7) apply Eq. (144).

An example will now be given to illustrate the graphical method as applied to a symmetrical nonsinusoidal wave.

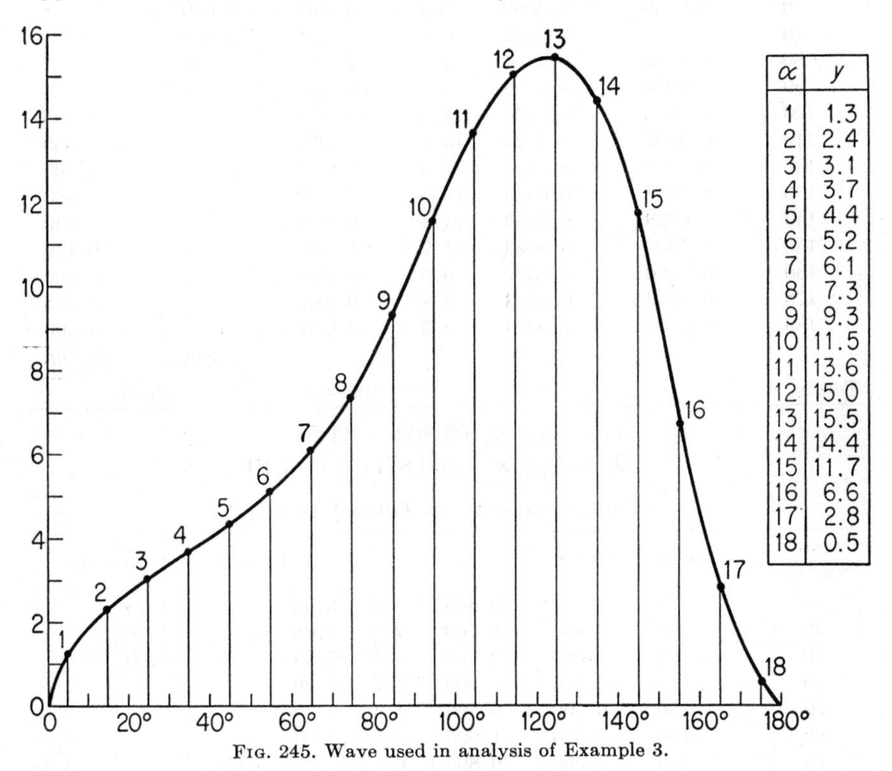

α	y
1	1.3
2	2.4
3	3.1
4	3.7
5	4.4
6	5.2
7	6.1
8	7.3
9	9.3
10	11.5
11	13.6
12	15.0
13	15.5
14	14.4
15	11.7
16	6.6
17	2.8
18	0.5

FIG. 245. Wave used in analysis of Example 3.

EXAMPLE 3. Figure 245 represents the positive lobe of a typical *symmetrical nonsinusoidal wave* of exciting current in a transformer. Analyze the wave graphically, determining the Fourier equation.

Solution

A wave such as this is known to have a rather prominent third harmonic and a weak fifth harmonic superimposed upon a strong fundamental; harmonics beyond the fifth are insignificant and will not be considered in this analysis.

Following the foregoing procedure, tabulations and calculations are given for the Fourier-equation coefficients. An equation of the curve is then expressed as a function of sine and cosine terms, and, in accordance with the discussion on page 441 and Example 1, in terms of sine terms only.

Tabulation for the Fundamental

α, degrees	$\sin \alpha$	$\cos \alpha$	y	$y(\sin \alpha)$	$y(\cos \alpha)$	
10	0.1736	0.9848	1.3	0.226	1.280	
20	0.3420	0.9397	2.4	0.821	2.255	
30	0.5000	0.8660	3.1	1.550	2.680	
40	0.6428	0.7660	3.7	2.380	2.840	
50	0.7660	0.6428	4.4	3.370	2.830	
60	0.8660	0.5000	5.2	4.510	2.600	
70	0.9397	0.3420	6.1	5.720	2.090	
80	0.9848	0.1736	7.3	7.190	1.268	
90	1.0000	0.0000	9.3	9.300	0.000	
100	0.9848	−0.1736	11.5	11.310	......	− 1.995
110	0.9397	−0.3420	13.6	12.760	......	− 4.650
120	0.8660	−0.5000	15.0	15.000	......	− 7.500
130	0.7660	−0.6428	15.5	11.880	......	− 9.960
140	0.6428	−0.7660	14.4	9.250	......	−11.030
150	0.5000	−0.8660	11.7	5.850	......	−10.130
160	0.3420	−0.9397	6.6	2.260	......	− 6.200
170	0.1736	−0.9848	2.8	0.485	......	− 2.755
180	0.0000	−1.0000	0.5	0.000	......	− 0.500
					17.843	−54.720
Totals........				103.862	−36.877	

$$A_1 = \tfrac{2}{18} \times 103.862 = 11.54$$
$$B_1 = \tfrac{2}{18} \times (-36.877) = -4.10$$

Tabulation for the Third Harmonic

α, degrees	3α, degrees	$\sin 3\alpha$	$\cos 3\alpha$	y	$y(\sin 3\alpha)$		$y(\cos 3\alpha)$	
10	30	0.500	0.866	1.3	0.65	......	1.13	
20	60	0.866	0.500	2.4	2.08	......	1.20	
30	90	1.000	0.000	3.1	3.10	......	0.00	
40	120	0.866	−0.500	3.7	3.20	......	....	− 1.85
50	150	0.500	−0.866	4.4	2.20	......	....	− 3.81
60	180	0.000	−1.000	5.2	0.00	......	....	− 5.20
70	210	−0.500	−0.866	6.1	....	− 3.05	....	− 5.28
80	240	−0.866	−0.500	7.3	....	− 6.32	....	− 3.65
90	270	−1.000	0.000	9.3	....	− 9.30	0.00	
100	300	−0.866	0.500	11.5	....	−10.00	6.75	
110	330	−0.500	0.866	13.6	....	− 6.80	11.78	
120	360 = 0	0.000	1.000	15.0	0.00	......	15.00	
130	390 = 30	0.500	0.866	15.5	7.75	......	13.40	
140	420 = 60	0.866	0.500	14.4	12.50	......	7.20	
150	450 = 90	1.000	0.000	11.7	11.70	......	0.00	
160	480 = 120	0.866	−0.500	6.6	5.72	......	....	− 3.30
170	510 = 150	0.500	−0.866	2.8	1.40	......	....	− 2.43
180	540 = 180	0.000	−1.000	0.5	0.00	......	....	− 0.50
					50.30	−35.47	56.46	−26.02
Totals........					14.83		30.44	

$$A_3 = \tfrac{2}{18} \times 14.83 = 1.65$$
$$B_3 = \tfrac{2}{18} \times 30.44 = 3.38$$

TABULATION FOR THE FIFTH HARMONIC

α, degrees	5α, degrees	$\sin 5\alpha$	$\cos 5\alpha$	y	$y(\sin 5\alpha)$		$y(\cos 5\alpha)$	
10	50	0.766	0.643	1.3	1.00	......	0.84	
20	100	0.985	−0.174	2.4	2.36	......	....	− 0.42
30	150	0.500	−0.866	3.1	1.55	......	....	− 2.68
40	200	−0.342	−0.940	3.7	....	− 1.26	....	− 3.47
50	250	−0.940	−0.342	4.4	....	− 4.13	....	− 1.50
60	300	−0.866	0.500	5.2	....	− 4.50	2.60	
70	350	−0.174	0.985	6.1	....	− 1.06	6.00	
80	400 = 40	0.643	0.766	7.3	4.70	......	5.59	
90	450 = 90	1.000	0.000	9.3	9.30	......	0.00	
100	500 = 140	0.643	−0.766	11.5	7.40	......	....	− 8.82
110	550 = 190	−0.174	−0.985	13.6	....	− 2.36	....	−13.40
120	600 = 240	−0.866	−0.500	15.0	....	−13.00	....	− 7.50
130	650 = 290	−0.940	−0.342	15.5	....	−14.55	5.30	
140	700 = 340	−0.342	0.940	14.4	....	− 4.92	13.50	
150	750 = 30	0.500	0.866	11.7	5.85	......	10.14	
160	800 = 80	0.985	0.174	6.6	6.50	......	1.15	
170	850 = 130	0.766	−0.643	2.8	2.15	......	....	− 1.58
180	900 = 180	0.000	−1.000	0.5	0.00	......	....	− 0.50
					40.81	−45.78	45.12	−39.87
Totals.					−4.97		5.25	

$$A_5 = \tfrac{2}{18} \times (-4.97) = -0.55$$
$$B_5 = \tfrac{2}{18} \times 5.25 = 0.58$$

Since, for this example, the ordinate y is in current units, the Fourier equation is

$$i = 11.54 \sin \alpha - 4.10 \cos \alpha + 1.65 \sin 3\alpha + 3.38 \cos 3\alpha - 0.55 \sin 5\alpha + 0.58 \cos 5\alpha$$

To express the equation in the more desirable form of Eq. (143), using sine terms only, the current amplitudes I_1, I_3, and I_5 and the angles Θ_1, Θ_3, and Θ_5 must be determined. These are

$$I_1 = \sqrt{(11.54)^2 + (-4.1)^2} = 12.25$$
$$I_3 = \sqrt{(1.65)^2 + (3.38)^2} = 3.76$$
$$I_5 = \sqrt{(-0.55)^2 + (0.58)^2} = 0.80$$
$$\Theta_1 = \tan^{-1}\left(\frac{-4.1}{11.54}\right) = \tan^{-1}(-0.355) = -19.5^\circ \text{ (fourth quadrant)}$$
$$\Theta_3 = \tan^{-1}\left(\frac{3.38}{1.65}\right) = \tan^{-1}(2.05) = 64^\circ \text{ (first quadrant)}$$
$$\Theta_5 = \tan^{-1}\left(\frac{0.58}{-0.55}\right) = \tan^{-1}(-1.055) = 133.5^\circ \text{ (second quadrant)}$$

The current equation is therefore

$$i = 12.25 \sin(\alpha - 19.5°) + 3.76 \sin(3\alpha + 64°) + 0.80 \sin(5\alpha + 133.5°)$$

Effective Value of a Nonsinusoidal Current or Voltage Wave. Since a nonsinusoidal wave of current or voltage is essentially a combination of one or more harmonics and/or a d-c component superimposed upon a fundamental, it is logical to expect the effective value of the composite wave to be *larger* than the value of the fundamental alone. Analytical and experimental analyses verify such a prediction and do, in fact, indicate that *the effective value of any nonsinusoidal wave is equal to the geometrical mean of the effective values of the individual components.*

It has been shown (page 230 and Appendix 1N) that a sinusoidal wave of current or voltage yields an effective value that is a measure of the *root-mean-square* of the simple sine function; i.e., it is the *square root* of the *average* or *mean value* of the *squared* current or voltage wave. The same relationship applies equally to nonsinusoidal waves, so that, using the general expression of Eq. (143), the effective current is

$$\begin{aligned} I &= \sqrt{\frac{1}{2\pi}\int_0^{2\pi} i^2\,d\alpha} \\ &= \left\{\frac{1}{2\pi}\int_0^{2\pi} [I_{DC} + I_1 \sin(\alpha + \Theta_1) + I_2 \sin(2\alpha + \Theta_2) \right. \\ &\qquad \left. + I_3 \sin(3\alpha + \Theta_3) + \cdots + I_n \sin(n\alpha + \Theta_n)]^2\,d\alpha\right\}^{1/2} \end{aligned}$$

and the effective voltage is

$$\begin{aligned} E &= \sqrt{\frac{1}{2\pi}\int_0^{2\pi} e^2\,d\alpha} \\ &= \left\{\frac{1}{2\pi}\int_0^{2\pi} [E_{DC} + E_1 \sin(\alpha + \Theta_1) + E_2 \sin(2\alpha + \Theta_2) \right. \\ &\qquad \left. + E_3 \sin(3\alpha + \Theta_3) + \cdots + E_n \sin(n\alpha + \Theta_n)]^2\,d\alpha\right\}^{1/2} \end{aligned}$$

where the symbols α and Θ are given in radians.

The foregoing equations represent, in mathematical form, the rms values of the current and voltage of *any* wave shape; the integral signs indicate that summations are to be made of continually varying squared quantities and, when divided by 2π, become the *average* of such squared quantities. The following general expressions for effective values of current and voltage can then be derived if these equations are properly integrated by the calculus:

$$I = \sqrt{I_{DC}^2 + \frac{I_1^2}{2} + \frac{I_2^2}{2} + \frac{I_3^2}{2} + \cdots + \frac{I_n^2}{2}}$$
$$E = \sqrt{E_{DC}^2 + \frac{E_1^2}{2} + \frac{E_2^2}{2} + \frac{E_3^2}{2} + \cdots + \frac{E_n^2}{2}} \quad (145)[1]$$

EXAMPLE 4. A nonsinusoidal emf having the equation $e = 141.4 \sin (\alpha - 60°) - 56.6 \sin (3\alpha - 30°) + 35.4 \sin (5\alpha - 90°)$ is impressed upon a circuit. If the current has the equation $i = 28.3 \sin (\alpha - 30°) + 17 \sin (3\alpha - 90°)$, calculate the effective values of the voltage and current.

Solution

$$\frac{E_1^2}{2} = 10{,}000$$
$$\frac{E_3^2}{2} = 1{,}600$$
$$\frac{E_5^2}{2} = 625$$
$$E = \sqrt{10{,}000 + 1{,}600 + 625} = 111 \text{ volts}$$
$$\frac{I_1^2}{2} = 400$$
$$\frac{I_3^2}{2} = 144$$
$$I = \sqrt{400 + 144} = 23.3 \text{ amp}$$

EXAMPLE 5. The voltage across one phase of a star-connected bank of transformers is known to contain a third-harmonic component in addition to a fundamental whose effective value is 133 volts. If the measured (effective) voltage is 140, determine the magnitude of the third harmonic.

Solution

$$140 = \sqrt{\frac{(133\sqrt{2})^2}{2} + \frac{E_3^2}{2}}$$
$$E_3 = \sqrt{2[(140)^2 - (133)^2]} = 61.6$$
$$E_{3\text{ effective}} = \frac{61.6}{\sqrt{2}} = 43.6$$

Power Resulting from Nonsinusoidal Waves of Voltage and Current. When a nonsinusoidal wave of voltage is impressed upon a circuit to produce a current that is nonsinusoidal, the resulting average power will be determined only by the reactions that are set up by combinations of voltage and current of the *same* frequency. No power can result from a

[1] See Appendix 1V for derivation.

component of voltage of one frequency that reacts with a component of current of a different frequency.

Since the instantaneous power in any circuit is the product of the instantaneous values of voltage e and current i, the average power per cycle may be expressed by the general equation

$$P = \frac{1}{2\pi} \int_0^{2\pi} ei\,dt$$

where the integral sign merely indicates that a summation is made of continually varying energy products $ei\,dt$. Assuming nonsinusoidal variations of e and i (neglecting the usually absent d-c components), the foregoing expression may be rewritten to include the varying functions of voltage and current; thus

$$P = \frac{1}{2\pi} \int_0^{2\pi} [E_1 \sin(\alpha + \Theta_1) + E_2 \sin(2\alpha + \Theta_2) + \cdots + E_n \sin(n\alpha + \Theta_n)][I_1 \sin(\alpha + \Theta_1') + I_2 \sin(2\alpha + \Theta_2') + \cdots + I_n \sin(n\alpha + \Theta_n')]\,d\alpha$$

This general equation may then be expanded and, when properly integrated by the calculus, becomes

$$P = \frac{E_1 I_1}{2} \cos(\Theta_1 - \Theta_1') + \frac{E_2 I_2}{2} \cos(\Theta_2 - \Theta_2') + \cdots + \frac{E_n I_n}{2} \cos(\Theta_n - \Theta_n') \qquad (146)^1$$

It is interesting to note that the average power given by Eq. (146) is represented by an *algebraic summation* of terms, each of which involves the power that results when a voltage of one frequency reacts with a current of the *same* frequency; moreover, the power-factor angle for each component of power is given by the displacement between a voltage wave and a corresponding *similar-frequency* current wave, i.e., $(\Theta_1 - \Theta_1')$, $(\Theta_2 - \Theta_2')$, . . . , $(\Theta_n - \Theta_n')$.

EXAMPLE 6. Calculate the power in a circuit in which the voltage and current equations are

$$e = 141.4 \sin(\alpha - 60°) - 56.6 \sin(3\alpha - 30°) + 35.4 \cos 5\alpha$$
$$i = 28.3 \sin(\alpha - 30°) + 17 \sin(3\alpha - 90°)$$

Solution

$$P = \frac{141.4 \times 28.3}{2} \cos(-60° + 30°) + \frac{(-56.6) \times 17}{2} \cos(-30° + 90°)$$
$$= 2{,}000 \cos(-30°) - 480 \cos 60°$$
$$= 1{,}732 - 240 = 1{,}492 \text{ watts}$$

[1] See Appendix 1W for derivation.

Power Factor in Nonsinusoidal-wave Circuits. Although the original definition of power factor was given for sinusoidal circuits on page 255 and in Eq. (97), it applies equally well to circuits in which the voltage and current waves are nonsinusoidal. Being merely a ratio of power to effective volt-amperes, i.e., P/EI, it may be written in equation form by substituting the equivalent of P in Eq. (146), and the equivalents of E and I in Eq. (145). Omitting the constant term $E_{DC}I_{DC}$, which occurs infrequently in a-c circuits, the general expression for power factor becomes

$$\mathrm{PF} = \frac{[E_1I_1\cos(\theta_1 - \theta_1') + E_2I_2\cos(\theta_2 - \theta_2') + \cdots + E_nI_n\cos(\theta_n - \theta_n')]/2}{(\sqrt{E_1^2+E_2^2+E_3^2+\cdots+E_n^2}/\sqrt{2})(\sqrt{I_1^2+I_2^2+I_3^2\cdots+I_n^2}/\sqrt{2})}$$

which reduces to

$$\mathrm{PF} = \frac{E_1I_1\cos(\theta_1 - \theta_1') + E_2I_2\cos(\theta_2 - \theta_2') + \cdots + E_nI_n\cos(\theta_n - \theta_n')}{\sqrt{E_1^2 + E_2^2 + E_3^2 + \cdots + E_n^2}\sqrt{I_1^2 + I_2^2 + I_3^2 + \cdots + I_n^2}} \tag{147}$$

EXAMPLE 7. Using the results of Examples 4 and 6, calculate the power factor for the circuit in which the voltage and current equations are

$$e = 141.4 \sin(\alpha - 60°) - 56.6 \sin(3\alpha - 30°) + 35.4 \cos 5\alpha$$
$$i = 28.3 \sin(\alpha - 30°) + 17 \sin(3\alpha - 90°)$$

Solution

From Example 4:

$$E = 111 \text{ volts}$$
$$I = 23.3 \text{ amp}$$

From Example 6:

$$P = 1{,}492 \text{ watts}$$

Therefore

$$\mathrm{PF} = \frac{1{,}492}{111 \times 23.3} = 0.577$$

An analysis of Eq. (147) indicates that the power factor cannot be unity in a circuit in which the voltage and/or the current waves are nonsinusoidal *unless* both have similar harmonic components. This is because a given harmonic in the voltage wave must be accompanied by a *like* harmonic in the current wave if both are to contribute to the total circuit power; the numerator of Eq. (147), the power term, will obviously be lessened to the extent that similar harmonic components do *not* exist in both waves, whereas the denominator, the volt-ampere term, involves ***all*** components of the voltage and current waves. Both waves must, moreover, be *in phase* as well as identical in shape to fulfill the unity power-factor condition. This implies, of course, that

$$\cos(\Theta_1 - \Theta_1') = \cos(\Theta_2 - \Theta_2') = \cos(\Theta_3 - \Theta_3') = \cdots = \cos(\Theta_n - \Theta_n{}^8) = 1$$

and that
$$\frac{E_1}{I_1} = \frac{E_2}{I_2} = \frac{E_3}{I_3} = \cdots = \frac{E_n}{I_n}$$

The Nonsinusoidal Series Circuit. The foregoing analyses should make it clear that a linear circuit that is energized by a nonsinusoidal wave of voltage appears to respond independently to each frequency component; moreover, the latter contributes its proper share of current and power in accordance with laws developed for simple single-frequency circuits. Because of this apparent behavior it therefore seems logical to apply a modified form of the superposition theorem to the solution of nonsinusoidal circuits.

The method will be illustrated by its application to a series *R-L-C* circuit that is energized by a nonsinusoidal voltage wave.

EXAMPLE 8. A series circuit consisting of an 8-ohm resistor, a 0.0053-henry inductor, and a 332-μf capacitor is connected to a source of emf whose equation is $e = 160 \sin 377t + 40 \sin (1{,}131t + \pi/3)$. (*a*) Determine the equation of the current in the circuit. Calculate (*b*) the effective voltage and current, (*c*) the circuit power and power factor.

Solution

Since the voltage equation indicates that the impressed emf wave contains a fundamental and an accompanying third harmonic, the superposition theorem will be applied to (1) the 60-cycle fundamental, (2) the 180-cycle third harmonic, and (3) a composite of the two frequencies.

(*a*) Fundamental:

$$E_1 = 160$$
$$R_1 = 8$$
$$X_{L_1} = 377 \times 0.0053 = 2$$
$$X_{C_1} = \frac{10^6}{377 \times 332} = 8$$
$$Z_1 = \sqrt{(8)^2 + (2-8)^2} = 10$$
$$\Theta_1 = \tan^{-1}\frac{(-6)}{8} = -36.9^\circ \text{ or } -0.205\pi \text{ radian}$$
$$I_1 = \frac{160}{10\underline{/-36.9^\circ}} = 16\underline{/36.9^\circ}$$
$$i_1 = 16 \sin (377t + 0.205\pi)$$

Third harmonic:

$$E_3 = 40$$
$$R_3 = 8$$
$$X_{L_3} = 3 \times 2 = 6$$
$$X_{C_3} = \frac{8}{3} = 2.67$$
$$Z_3 = \sqrt{(8)^2 + (6 - 2.67)^2} = 8.65$$
$$\Theta_3 = \tan^{-1} \frac{3.33}{8} = 22.6° \text{ or } 0.126\pi \text{ radian}$$
$$I_3 = \frac{40}{8.65/22.6°} = 4.63/\underline{-22.6°}$$
$$i_3 = 4.63 \sin \left(1{,}131t + \frac{\pi}{3} - 0.126\pi\right) = 4.63 \sin (1{,}131t + 0.207\pi)$$

Therefore

$$i = 16 \sin (377t + 0.205\pi) + 4.63 \sin (1{,}131t + 0.207\pi)$$

(*b*)
$$E = \frac{\sqrt{(160)^2 + (40)^2}}{2} = 116.6 \text{ volts}$$
$$I = \frac{\sqrt{(16)^2 + (4.63)^2}}{2} = 11.8 \text{ amp}$$

(*c*)
$$P = \frac{160 \times 16}{2} \cos (0° - 36.9°) + \frac{40 \times 4.63}{2} \cos (60° - 37.2°)$$
$$= (1{,}280 \times 0.8) + (92.6 \times 0.922) = 1{,}109 \text{ watts}$$
$$\text{PF} = \frac{1{,}109}{116.6 \times 11.8} = 0.806 \text{ lagging}$$

The Nonsinusoidal Parallel Circuit. The computations for a parallel circuit, although somewhat involved, follow essentially the same procedure as that given for the series circuit. Assuming, as before, that the equation of the impressed nonsinusoidal voltage wave is known, and that the parameters of the parallel branches are given, the following sequence of calculations is suggested:

1. Determine the currents (in the complex notation) in the individual branches for each of the frequency components.
2. Combine the individual branch currents for each frequency component; this will give the line current for each frequency component.
3. Applying Eq. (145), determine the effective values of line current and voltage.
4. Compute the circuit power and power factor.

The method will be illustrated by its application to a two-branch parallel circuit in which an *R-L* branch is in parallel with an *R-C* branch.

EXAMPLE 9. Referring to Fig. 246, the following information is given in connection with a two-branch parallel circuit: $e = 130 \sin (377t - \pi/4) + 49.2 \sin (1{,}131t + \pi/6)$; $R_A = 4$ and $X_A = j3$ at 60 cycles; $R_B = 5$ and $X_B = -j12$ at 60 cycles. Determine (*a*) the currents in the two branches and the line current for the 60-cycle fundamental; (*b*) the currents in the two branches and the line current for the 180-cycle third harmonic; (*c*) the *effective* line current and voltage; (*d*) the circuit power and power factor.

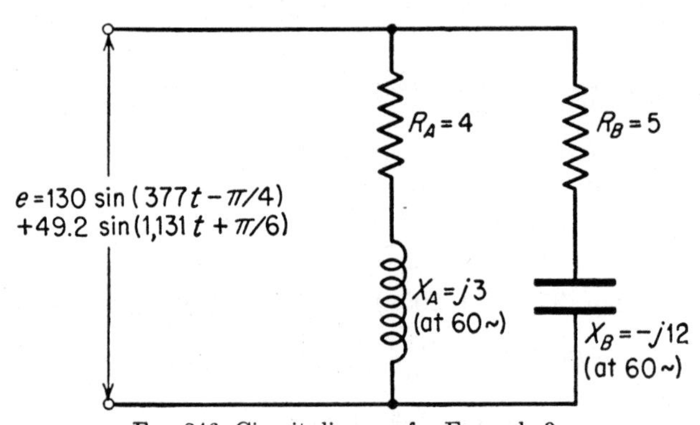

FIG. 246. Circuit diagram for Example 9.

Solution

(*a*) Fundamental:

$$E_1 = 130$$
$$R_{A_1} = 4$$
$$X_{A_1} = j3$$
$$R_{B_1} = 5$$
$$X_{B_1} = -j12$$
$$Z_{A_1} = \sqrt{(4)^2 + (3)^2} = 5$$
$$\theta_{A_1} = \tan^{-1} \frac{3}{4} = 36.9° \text{ or } 0.205\pi \text{ radian}$$
$$I_{A_1} = \frac{130}{5\underline{/36.9°}} = 26\underline{/-36.9°} = 20.8 - j15.6$$
$$Z_{B_1} = \sqrt{(5)^2 + (-12)^2} = 13$$
$$\theta_{B_1} = \tan^{-1} \frac{(-12)}{5} = -67.4° \text{ or } -0.374\pi \text{ radians}$$
$$I_{B_1} = \frac{130}{13\underline{/-67.4°}} = 10\underline{/67.4°} = 3.84 + j9.23$$
$$I_{L_1} = (20.8 - j15.6) + (3.84 + j9.23) = 24.64 - j6.37 = 25.4$$

(*b*) Third harmonic:

$$E_3 = 49.2$$
$$R_{A_3} = 4$$
$$X_{A_3} = j9$$
$$R_{B_3} = 5$$
$$X_{B_3} = -j4$$
$$Z_{A_3} = \sqrt{(4)^2 + (9)^2} = 9.84$$
$$\Theta_{A_3} = \tan^{-1}\frac{9}{4} = 66° \text{ or } 0.366\pi \text{ radians}$$
$$I_{A_3} = \frac{49.2}{9.84\underline{/66°}} = 5\underline{/-66°} = 2.03 - j4.57$$
$$Z_{B_3} = \sqrt{(5)^2 + (-4)^2} = 6.4$$
$$\Theta_{B_3} = \tan^{-1}\frac{(-4)}{5} = -38.7° \text{ or } -0.215\pi \text{ radian}$$
$$I_{B_3} = \frac{49.2}{6.4\underline{/-38.7°}} = 7.7\underline{/38.7°} = 6 + j4.8$$
$$I_{L_3} = (2.03 - j4.57) + (6 + j4.8) = 8.03 + j0.23 = 8.04$$

(*c*)

$$I_L = \frac{\sqrt{(25.4)^2 + (8.04)^2}}{\sqrt{2}} = 18.8 \text{ amp}$$
$$E = \frac{\sqrt{(130)^2 + (4.92)^2}}{\sqrt{2}} = 98 \text{ volts}$$

(*d*)

$$i_A = 26 \sin\left(377t - \frac{\pi}{4} - 0.205\pi\right) + 5 \sin\left(1{,}131t + \frac{\pi}{6} - 0.366\pi\right)$$
$$= 26 \sin(377t - 0.455\pi) + 5 \sin(1{,}131t - 0.2\pi)$$
$$i_B = 10 \sin\left(377t - \frac{\pi}{4} + 0.374\pi\right) + 7.7 \sin\left(1{,}131t + \frac{\pi}{6} + 0.215\pi\right)$$
$$= 10 \sin(377t + 0.124\pi) + 7.7 \sin(1{,}131t + 0.382\pi)$$
$$P_A = \frac{130 \times 26}{2}\cos(-45° + 81.8°) + \frac{49.2 \times 5}{2}\cos(30° + 36°)$$
$$= 1{,}352 + 50 = 1{,}402 \text{ watts}$$
$$P_B = \frac{130 \times 10}{2}\cos(-45° - 22.3°) + \frac{49.2 \times 7.7}{2}\cos(30° - 68.7°)$$
$$= 143 + 148 = 291 \text{ watts}$$
$$P_t = 1{,}402 + 291 = 1{,}693 \text{ watts}$$
$$\text{PF} = \frac{1{,}693}{98 \times 18.8} = 0.92$$

Questions

1. Give several reasons for the nonsinusoidal wave shapes of voltage that are developed in modern alternators.

2. What is meant by the *fundamental* and its *harmonics* when referring to a nonsinusoidal voltage or current wave?
3. How is it desirable to regard a rectified a-c wave?
4. Illustrate by sketches the effects of superimposing (*a*) a positive direct current upon a sinusoidal current; (*b*) a negative direct current upon a sinusoidal current.
5. Distinguish between *odd* and *even* harmonics, and indicate how they affect the symmetry and distortion of nonsinusoidal waves.
6. What is meant by a *periodic wave?* by a *single-valued continuous wave?*
7. Write a general Fourier equation for a nonsinusoidal current wave, using sine and cosine terms.
8. Write a general Fourier equation for a nonsinusoidal voltage wave, using sine terms only. Indicate how the constant terms and displacement angles are determined from the original sine-cosine equation.
9. Carefully distinguish between symmetrical and unsymmetrical nonsinusoidal waves. Make sketches to illustrate each type.
10. Why is the wave shape of voltage developed in an alternator symmetrical?
11. Make a sketch showing a symmetrical wave containing a fundamental and a third harmonic (*a*) in which the two components are in phase, (*b*) in which the third harmonic leads the fundamental by 60° on the fundamental scale. Write equations for both composite waves, assuming them to be waves of current.
12. Under what conditions will a nonsinusoidal wave be unsymmetrical? Make sketches to illustrate your answer.
13. Under what conditions will a nonsinusoidal wave exhibit a high degree of distortion? Make sketches to illustrate your answer.
14. When a nonsinusoidal wave contains a fundamental and one pronounced harmonic, explain how the order of the harmonic can be determined from the number of inflection points on the wave (*a*) when the wave is symmetrical, (*b*) when the wave is unsymmetrical.
15. Explain, in a general way, how the graphical method is employed to determine the Fourier-equation coefficients.
16. How is the effective value of a nonsinusoidal voltage or current wave determined if the effective values of the several frequency components are known?
17. Is the effective value of a nonsinusoidal voltage or current wave altered when the phase displacement between the various frequency components is changed? Explain.
18. Assuming a nonsinusoidal wave containing a fundamental and a third harmonic, under what conditions will the *maximum value* of the composite wave (*a*) be a maximum, (*b*) be a minimum? Will the same conditions prevail if the composite wave contains a fundamental and a fifth harmonic?
19. When a nonsinusoidal wave of voltage produces a current that is nonsinusoidal, do the reactions between voltage and current components of different frequencies contribute to the total circuit power? Explain.
20. Under what condition will components of voltage and current of the *same frequency* contribute no circuit power? Explain.
21. To what summation is the average power equal when a nonsinusoidal current in a circuit results from the application of a nonsinusoidal voltage?
22. Under what conditions will the average circuit power be a maximum when the voltage and current waves are both nonsinusoidal? Explain.
23. Define *power factor* when referring to a circuit in which the voltage and current waves are nonsinusoidal.
24. Why is it particularly helpful to employ the superposition theorem when solving series and parallel circuits in which voltages and currents are nonsinusoidal?

25. Outline the steps to be followed in solving a parallel circuit in which the voltage and currents are nonsinusoidal.

Problems

1. A nonsinusoidal current wave has the equation $i = (15 \sin \alpha + 10 \cos \alpha) + (6 \sin 3\alpha - 8 \cos 3\alpha) - (3 \sin 5\alpha - 4.5 \cos 5\alpha)$. Determine the equation in terms of sine components only.

2. A symmetrical nonsinusoidal voltage wave consists of a 50-cycle fundamental, a third harmonic that lags behind the fundamental by 45° on the fundamental scale, and a fifth harmonic that leads the fundamental by 54° on the fundamental scale. If the amplitudes of the fundamental and the third and fifth harmonics are 311, 82, and 63 volts, respectively, determine the equation of the wave.

3. Make a sketch, to scale, showing the fundamental, the third harmonic, and the composite waves for the equation $e = 100 \sin \alpha + 25 \sin (3\alpha + 180°)$.

4. Make a sketch, to scale, showing the fundamental, the fifth harmonic, and the composite waves, for the equation $i = 12 \sin \alpha + 3 \sin (5\alpha - 180°)$.

5. Make a sketch, to scale, showing the wave for the equation $i = 2.25 + 9 \sin \alpha$.

6. Make a sketch, to scale, showing all wave components and the composite wave for the equation $i = 2.25 + 9 \sin \alpha + 3 \sin (2\alpha + 90°)$.

7. A symmetrical current wave is *square-topped*, i.e., it has a constant positive value of 8.25 amp between 0 and 180° and a constant negative value of 8.25 amp between 180 and 360°. Determine the equation of the wave, making calculations for the fundamental, and the third, fifth, and seventh harmonics.

8. The following data were obtained from an oscillogram representing the positive alternation of a symmetrical nonsinusoidal current wave:

Angle	i	Angle	i	Angle	i
5°	1.0	65°	6.9	125°	9.8
15°	2.9	75°	7.4	135°	10.0
25°	4.2	85°	8.0	145°	9.8
35°	5.0	95°	8.5	155°	8.5
45°	5.6	105°	9.0	165°	5.2
55°	6.3	115°	9.4	175°	2.0

Determine the equation of the wave out to the seventh harmonic.

9. Calculate the effective value of the current in Example 1.

10. Calculate the effective value of the voltage in Example 2.

11. Referring to Fig. 240*b*, the equation of the composite voltage wave is, as indicated, $e = E_1 \sin \alpha + E_3 \sin (3\alpha - 180°)$. If the effective value is 123.8 volts and the maximum or peak value is 212 volts, determine E_1 and E_3.

12. Referring to Fig. 240*a*, the equation of the composite voltage wave is, as indicated, $e = E_1 \sin \alpha + E_3 \sin 3\alpha$. If the effective value is 111.8 volts and the value at 90° is 100 volts, determine E_1 and E_3.

13. A nonsinusoidal voltage wave consists of a fundamental and a third harmonic. If the effective values of the composite wave and the fundamental are 240 volts and 230 volts, respectively, calculate the effective value of the third harmonic.

14. The current in a circuit has the equation $i = 12 + 18 \sin \alpha - 12 \sin 2\alpha + 8 \cos 3\alpha$. Calculate the effective value of the current.

15. The current equation of a symmetrical *triangular wave* is $i = 8I/\pi^2[\sin \alpha - \frac{1}{9}(\sin 3\alpha) - \frac{1}{25}(\sin 5\alpha) - \frac{1}{49}(\sin 7\alpha) + \cdots]$ where I is the peak value of the triangle. Considering the first two terms only, calculate the effective value of the current in terms of I.

16. Calculate the total power in a circuit in which the nonsinusoidal equations of voltage and current are

$$e = 170 \sin(\alpha + 30°) - 40 \sin(3\alpha - 80°) - 15 \sin(5\alpha + 120°)$$
$$i = 16 \sin(\alpha - 30°) + 6 \sin(3\alpha - 35°) - 4 \sin(5\alpha + 90°)$$

17. Determine the circuit power factor for Prob. 16.

18. Calculate the power and power factor for a circuit in which the voltage and current have the following equations:

$$e = 240 \sin(\alpha + 60°) - 90 \cos(3\alpha + 30°) + 25 \sin(5\alpha - 75°)$$
$$i = 4.8 \sin(\alpha + 60°) - 1.8 \sin(3\alpha - 120°) + 0.5 \sin(5\alpha - 75°)$$

19. A voltage wave having the equation $e = 170 \sin(377t + \pi/4) + 50 \sin(1{,}131t - \pi/4)$ is impressed across a series circuit in which $R = 6$, $L = 0.0106$ henry, and $C = 221$ μf. (*a*) Determine the equation of the current wave. Calculate (*b*) the effective values of the voltage and current, (*c*) the circuit power and power factor.

20. The current in a series *R-L-C* circuit has the equation $i = 20 \sin(314t - \pi/6) + 8 \sin(628t - \pi/3)$ for values of $R = 5$ ohms, X_L (at 100 cycles) $= 8$ ohms, and X_C (at 100 cycles) $= 4.5$ ohms. (*a*) Determine the equation of the impressed voltage wave. Calculate (*b*) the effective values of the voltage and current, (*c*) the circuit power and power factor.

21. The following information is given in connection with a two-branch parallel circuit (similar to Fig. 246): $e = 195 \sin(377t - \pi/3) + 60 \sin(1{,}131t + \pi/2)$, $R_A = 9$, X_A (at 60 cycles) $= j4$, $R_B = 8$, X_B (at 60 cycles) $= -j15$. Determine (*a*) the currents in the two branches and the line current for the 60-cycle fundamental; (*b*) the currents in the two branches and the line current for the 180-cycle third harmonic; (*c*) the *effective* line current and voltage; (*d*) the circuit power and power factor.

APPENDIX 1

DERIVATIONS OF FUNDAMENTAL EQUATIONS

I—Direct-current Circuits

A. Average Value of Half-wave Rectified Current, Eq. (4). Assuming a sinusoidal current variation, such as that delivered by a half-wave gaseous-tube type of rectifier, the instantaneous current is given by the equation

$$i = I_m \sin \alpha$$

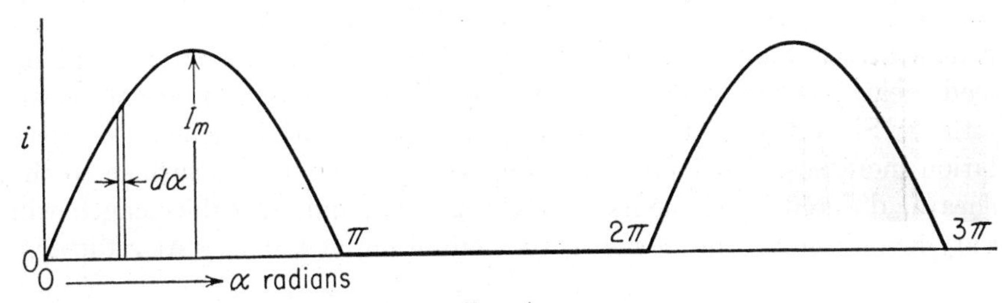

FIG. *A*.

where I_m is the maximum value of the sinusoidal function of current, and α is the angle, in radians, from the instant when $i = 0$ as the current proceeds to increase in a positive direction (see Fig. *A*). Note that the current varies sinusoidally between 0 and π radians and is zero between π and 2π radians. Since the average current I_{av} is the average ordinate taken over an angular range of 2π radians, its value may be determined by dividing the area under one loop of current by 2π. But a differential element of area is

$$dA = i\,d\alpha = I_m \sin \alpha\,d\alpha$$

Integrating the above expression between the limits of 0 and π, and dividing by 2π, the average value of the current becomes

$$I_{av} = \frac{1}{2\pi}\int_0^\pi dA = \frac{1}{2\pi}\int_0^\pi I_m \sin \alpha\,d\alpha = \frac{I_m}{2\pi}[-\cos \alpha]_0^\pi = \frac{I_m}{2\pi}[-(-1-1)]$$

Therefore

$$I_{av} = \frac{I_m}{\pi} \tag{4}$$

B. Average Value of Full-wave Rectified Current, Eq. (5). Referring to Fig. *B*, a differential area, as before, is $dA = i\,d\alpha$. For the full-wave

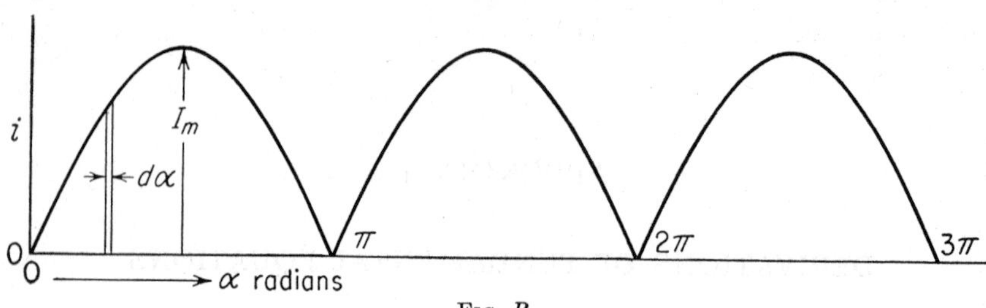

FIG. B.

rectified current, however, the average values for successive positive loops of current, each extending over a distance of π radians, are equal. Thus

$$I_{av} = \frac{1}{\pi}\int_0^\pi I_m \sin\alpha\, d\alpha = \frac{I_m}{\pi}[-\cos\alpha]_0^\pi = \frac{I_m}{\pi}[-(-1-1)] = \frac{2I_m}{\pi} \quad (5)$$

C. Cable-insulation Resistance, Eq. (9). The cross section of a lead-sheath cable is represented by Fig. *C*. With the central conductor at a comparatively high electrical potential with respect to the outer grounded lead sheath, *leakage* current would tend to pass radially *through* the insulation. Since the area of cross section of differential elements of insulation increases with increasing radii from the conductor surface to the sheath, differential elements of resistance per unit of cable length will vary from a maximum at $r = r_c$ to a minimum at $r = r_s$. At radius r,

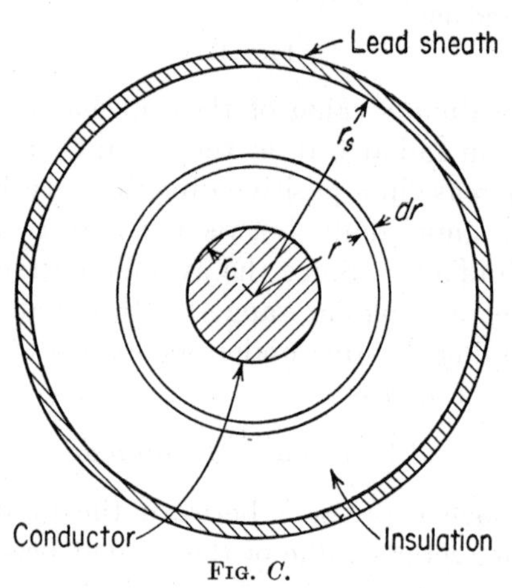

FIG. C.

$$dR = \rho\frac{dr}{2\pi r} \qquad \text{per centimeter of cable length}$$

where ρ = resistivity of the insulation, ohm-cm. The total insulation resistance of the cable per centimeter is therefore

$$R = \frac{\rho}{2\pi}\int_{r_c}^{r_s}\frac{dr}{r} = \frac{\rho}{2\pi}\log_\epsilon\frac{r_s}{r_c}$$

Written in more practical units,

$$R = \frac{\rho}{2\pi} \times 2.3 \times \frac{1}{2.54 \times 12 \times 5{,}280} \log_{10} \frac{r_s}{r_c}$$

whence
$$R = \frac{2.3}{10^6} \log_{10} \frac{r_s}{r_c} \qquad \text{ohms per mile} \tag{9}$$

where r_s and r_c are in *similar* units.

D. Flux-density Distribution Surrounding a Current-carrying Wire, Eqs. (31) and (32). By *Ampère's law*, the flux density at any point P in space, due to a differential element of a current-carrying conductor dl, is given by the expression

$$dB_p = \frac{I\,dl \cos \Theta}{10p^2} \qquad \text{gauss}$$

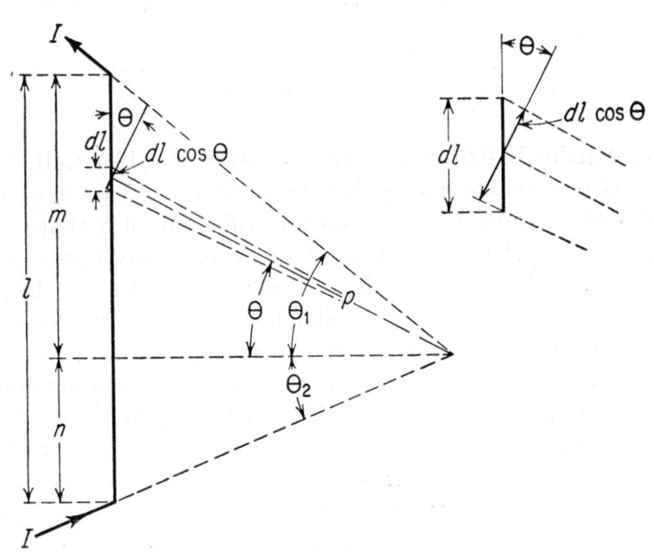

FIG. *D*.

where I is in amp, p is the point's distance in centimeters from the element of wire, and Θ is the angle by which the conductor *direction* departs from a perpendicular line drawn from the point to the wire (see Fig. *D*). For the portion m of the finite conductor length l, the flux density at point P will be

$$B_{Pm} = \int_0^{\Theta_1} \frac{I\,dl \cos \Theta}{10p^2}$$

But $l = r \tan \Theta$, whence $dl = r \sec^2 \Theta \, d\Theta$. Also $p = r \sec \Theta$, whence $p^2 = r^2 \sec^2 \Theta$. Substituting the values of dl and p^2 in the above equation,

$$B_{Pm} = \frac{I}{10} \int_0^{\Theta_1} \frac{r \sec^2 \Theta \, d\Theta \cos \Theta}{r^2 \sec^2 \Theta} = \frac{I}{10r} \int_0^{\Theta_1} \cos \Theta \, d\Theta = \frac{I}{10r} \sin \Theta_1$$

Similarly, for portion n of the finite conductor length l,

$$B_{Pn} = \frac{I}{10r}\sin(-\Theta_2) = -\frac{I}{10r}\sin\Theta_2$$

The entire conductor of length ($l = m + n$) therefore establishes a flux density at point P that is

$$B_P = \frac{I}{10r}(\sin\Theta_1 - \sin\Theta_2) \tag{31}$$

where Θ is a positive angle above the x axis and a negative angle below the x axis.

When the current-carrying conductor is extremely long so that Θ_1 and Θ_2 approach angles of 90°, one plus (+) and the other minus (−), Eq. (31) reduces to

$$B_P = \frac{I}{10r}[\sin 90° - \sin(-90°)] = \frac{2I}{10r} \tag{32}$$

E. Flux-density Distribution along the Axis of a Flat Coil, Eqs. (33) and (34). A flat coil containing N turns of wire, such as that illustrated by Fig. E, and carrying I amp as shown, will create flux that is directed to the right. Considering any point P *on the axis*, any *upper* element of wire dl will establish a flux density dB_U at right angles to a line joining element dl and point P; also, a similar lower element of wire dl that is *diametrically opposite* the upper element will establish a like flux density dB_L. Now then, if dB_U and dB_L are each resolved into horizontal and vertical components it is observed that $+dB_y$ for the upper element is nullified by an equal and opposite $-dB_y$ for the lower element. This means, therefore, that each element of wire dl will create only a horizontally directed flux density at point P which, by Ampère's rule, is

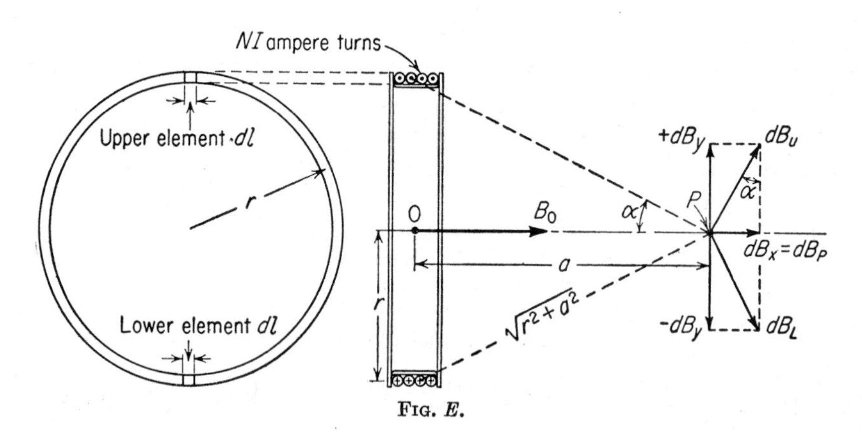

Fig. E.

$$dB_P = \frac{I\,dl}{10(r^2 + a^2)} \sin \alpha$$

But
$$\sin \alpha = \frac{r}{\sqrt{r^2 + a^2}}$$

so that
$$dB_P = \frac{Ir}{10(r^2 + a^2)^{3/2}} dl$$

For N turns of wire, the flux density at point P, on the axis of the coil, is

$$B_P = \frac{NIr}{10(r^2 + a^2)^{3/2}} \int_0^{2\pi r} dl = \frac{0.2\pi r^2 NI}{(r^2 + a^2)^{3/2}} \tag{34}$$

An important point on the coil axis is point O at the exact center. Since $a = 0$ at this point, Eq. (34) reduces to

$$B_O = \frac{2\pi NI}{10r} \tag{33}$$

F. Flux-density Distribution along the Axis of a Long Solenoid, Eqs. (35) and (36). Figure F represents a cross section of a long solenoid of N turns carrying current as indicated. If the individual turns are placed very close together, and it is assumed that the current is uniform per unit length of solenoid, the number of ampere-turns in differential element dx is $(NI/l)\,dx$. This differential value of magnetomotive force will establish a differential flux density at point P on the *axis*, x cm from dx, that, by Eq. (34), is

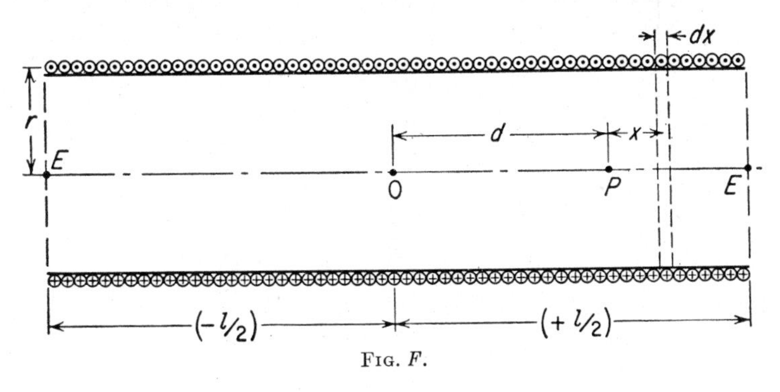

Fig. F.

$$dB_P = \frac{0.2\pi r^2 (NI/l)\,dx}{(r^2 + x^2)^{3/2}}$$

and is directed to the right.

Since the absolute magnitude of the flux density at point P is established by a succession of differential values of magnetomotive force, each of which acts at a different distance from point P, it follows that

$$B_P = \int_{-(l/2)-d}^{(+l/2)-d} \frac{0.2\pi r^2(NI/l)\,dx}{(r^2+x^2)^{3/2}} = \frac{0.2\pi r^2 NI}{l} \int_{-(l/2)-d}^{(+l/2)-d} \frac{dx}{(r^2+x^2)^{3/2}}$$

$$= \frac{0.2\pi r^2 NI}{l} \left[\frac{x}{r^2(r^2+x^2)^{1/2}} \right]_{-(l/2)-d}^{(+l/2)-d}$$

$$= \frac{0.2\pi NI}{l} \left\{ \frac{(l/2)-d}{\sqrt{r^2+[(l/2)-d]^2}} + \frac{(l/2)+d}{\sqrt{r^2+[(l/2)+d]^2}} \right\}$$

An important point on the axis of the solenoid is point O, at the exact center. Since $d = 0$ at this point, the above equation reduces to

$$B_O = \frac{2\pi NI}{10\sqrt{r^2+(l/2)^2}} \tag{35}$$

Other important points on the axis of the solenoid are represented by points E, along both edges of the solenoid. Since $d = l/2$ at either end of the coil, the fundamental equation reduces to

$$B_E = \frac{2\pi NI}{10\sqrt{r^2+l^2}} \tag{36}$$

G. Flux Enclosed between a Conductor and a Concentric Cylinder. Eq. (39). The flux density at any point in space x cm from a straight current-carrying conductor was shown to be $B = 0.2I/x$ [see Eq. (32)]. Since *flux* = (flux density) × (area), the differential flux enclosed in a differential cylinder thickness dx and length l cm will be

$$d\Phi = B_x l\,dx = \frac{0.2I}{x} l\,dx$$

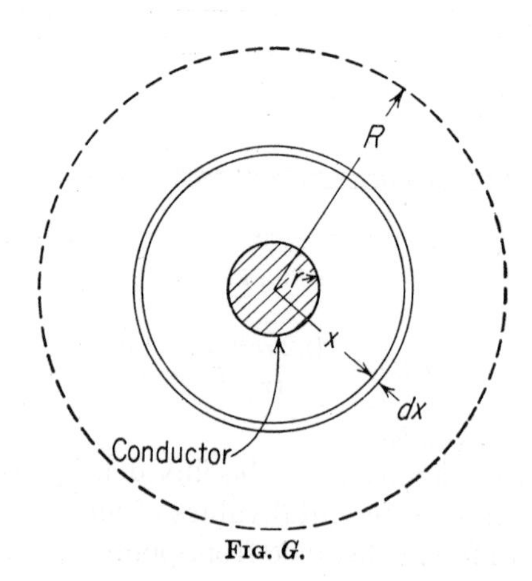

FIG. G.

The total flux enclosed by the conductor and a concentric cylinder of radius R cm in a length l cm (see Fig. G) will therefore be

$$\Phi = \int_r^R 0.2Il\left(\frac{dx}{x}\right) = 0.2Il \log_\epsilon \frac{R}{r}$$

Written in more practical units,

$$\Phi = 0.2I(l \times 12 \times 2.54)\left(2.3 \log_{10} \frac{R}{r}\right) = 14Il \log_{10} \frac{R}{r} \qquad (39)$$

where l is expressed in feet, and R and r are in any *similar* units.

H. Current Growth in Inductive Circuits, Eq. (62). In a resistance-inductance circuit with lumped constants (see Fig. H), often called an R-L circuit, the current i will rise from zero to E/R after the switch is closed; however, because of the inductive property of the circuit, the current change will not take place instantly. Moreover, since the opposition to current change results from a *counter emf* whose value is $L\,di/dt$, the current at any instant of time t may be expressed by the equation

$$i = \frac{E - L(di/dt)}{R}$$

This equation indicates that (1) at $t = 0$, when $L\,di/dt = E$, the current will be zero, and (2) at $t = \infty$, when $L\,di/dt = 0$, the current will be E/R.

Rearranging the terms in the formula for solution purposes,

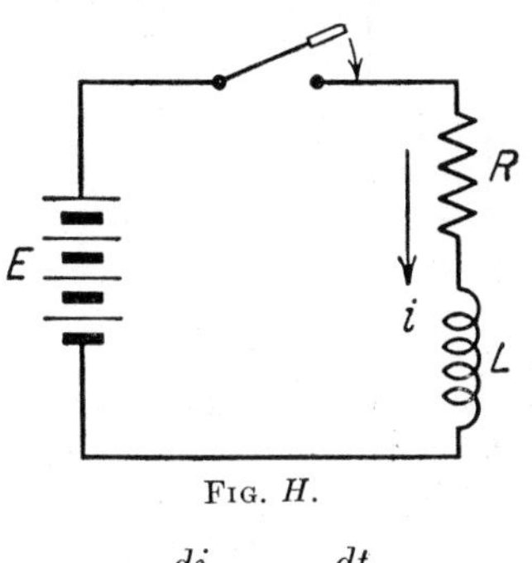

FIG. H.

$$\frac{di}{E - iR} = \frac{dt}{L}$$

When both sides of the latter are multiplied by $-R$,

$$\frac{-R\,di}{E - iR} = \frac{R}{L}\,dt$$

which, when integrated, becomes

$$\log_\epsilon (E - iR) = -\frac{R}{L}t + k$$

the symbol k being a constant that results from the process of integration.

The last equation may be written in the exponential form to yield

$$E - iR = \epsilon^{-(R/L)t+k} = \epsilon^{-(R/L)t}\epsilon^{k} = k_1\epsilon^{-(R/L)t}$$

where k_1 is a new constant of integration that conveniently represents ϵ^k. Rewriting the equation in terms of current,

$$i = \frac{E}{R} - \frac{k_1}{R}\epsilon^{-(R/L)t} = \frac{E}{R} - k_2\epsilon^{-(R/L)t}$$

where k_2 is a new constant made equal to k_1/R.

The value of k_2 may be readily evaluated by setting t equal to zero. Then $\epsilon^0 = 1$; moreover, under this condition, $i = 0$ at $t = 0$. Thus $k_2 = E/R$, and the final form of the equation is

$$i = \frac{E}{R}[1 - \epsilon^{-(R/L)t}] \tag{62}$$

I. Current Decay in Inductive Circuits, Eq. (64). After an inductive circuit, i.e., an R-L circuit, is established and is in a steady-state condition, energy is stored in the magnetic field [see Eq. (65)]. This energy may be dissipated, albeit not in zero time, by short-circuiting the R-L

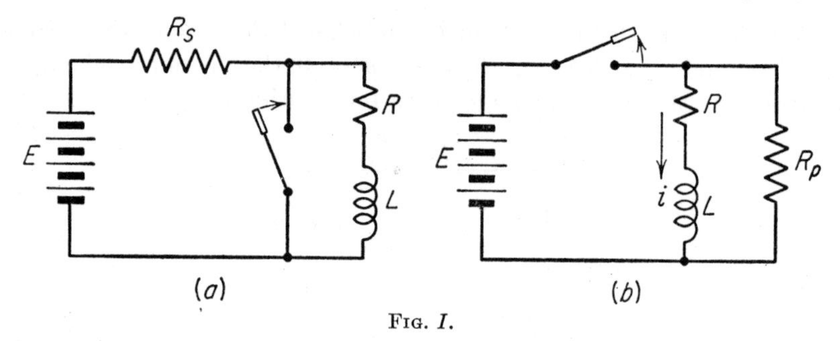

Fig. *I*.

circuit as illustrated by Fig. *Ia*, or by opening the line switch and simultaneously permitting the R-L circuit to be connected in series with another resistor as in Fig. *Ib*. In the first of these the initial current is $E/(R + R_s)$ and discharge takes place through resistor R, while in the second arrangement the initial current is E/R and discharge takes place through $(R + R_p)$.

Considering Fig. *Ia* first, assume that the circuit is in a steady-state condition, after which the short-circuiting switch is *closed*. Since *zero* voltage exists across the R-L circuit the current will decay from its original $E/(R + R_s)$ value to zero. Writing the equation for the current at any instant of time, it should be clear from foregoing discussions that

$$i = \frac{0 - L(di/dt)}{R}$$

Rearranging terms for solution purposes,

$$\frac{di}{i} = -\frac{R}{L}\,dt$$

which, when integrated, becomes

$$\log_\epsilon i = -\frac{R}{L}t - k$$

the symbol k being a constant that results from the process of integration.

The last equation may be written in exponential form to yield

$$i = \epsilon^{-(R/L)t+k} = \epsilon^{-(R/L)t}\epsilon^{k} = k_1\epsilon^{-(R/L)t}$$

where k_1 is a new constant of integration that conveniently represents ϵ^k.

The value of k_1 may be readily evaluated by setting t equal to zero: $\epsilon^0 = 1$; moreover, under this condition, $i = E/(R + R_s)$ at $t = 0$. Thus $k_1 = E/(R + R_s)$, and the final form of the equation for circuit Ia is

$$i = \frac{E}{(R + R_s)}\,\epsilon^{-(R/L)t} \tag{64b}$$

Referring next to Fig. *Ib*, assume that the circuit is in a steady-state condition, after which the line switch is *opened*. Since zero voltage exists across the R-L and R_p circuits the current will decay from its original E/R value to zero. Writing the equation for the current at any instant of time, it should be clear from the foregoing discussions that

$$i = \frac{0 - L(di/dt)}{(R + R_p)}$$

Rearranging terms for solution purposes,

$$\frac{di}{i} = -\frac{(R + R_p)}{L}\,t$$

which, when integrated, becomes

$$\log_\epsilon i = \frac{(R + R_p)}{L}\,t + k$$

the symbol k being a constant that results from the process of integration.

The last equation may be written in exponential form to yield

$$i = \epsilon^{-[(R+R_p)/L]t}\epsilon^{k} = k_1\epsilon^{-[(R+R_p)/L]t}$$

where k_1 is a new constant of integration that conveniently represents ϵ^k.

The value of k_1 may be evaluated by setting t equal to zero: $\epsilon^0 = 1$; moreover, under this condition, $i = E/R$ at $t = 0$. Thus $k_1 = E/R$, and the final form of the equation for circuit *Ib* is

$$i = \frac{E}{R} \epsilon^{-[(R+R_p)/L]t}$$

J. Magnetic-field Energy, Eq. (65). When an *R-L* circuit is energized, the current, at any instant of time, is given by Eq. (62); this is

$$i = \frac{E}{R} [1 - \epsilon^{-(R/L)t}]$$

Since the voltage drop across the resistance is equal to $e_R = iR$, the counter emf developed by the inductor becomes $e_L = E - iR$. Thus

$$e_L = E - \left\{\frac{E}{R} [1 - \epsilon^{-(R/L)t}] R\right\} = E\epsilon^{-(R/L)t}$$

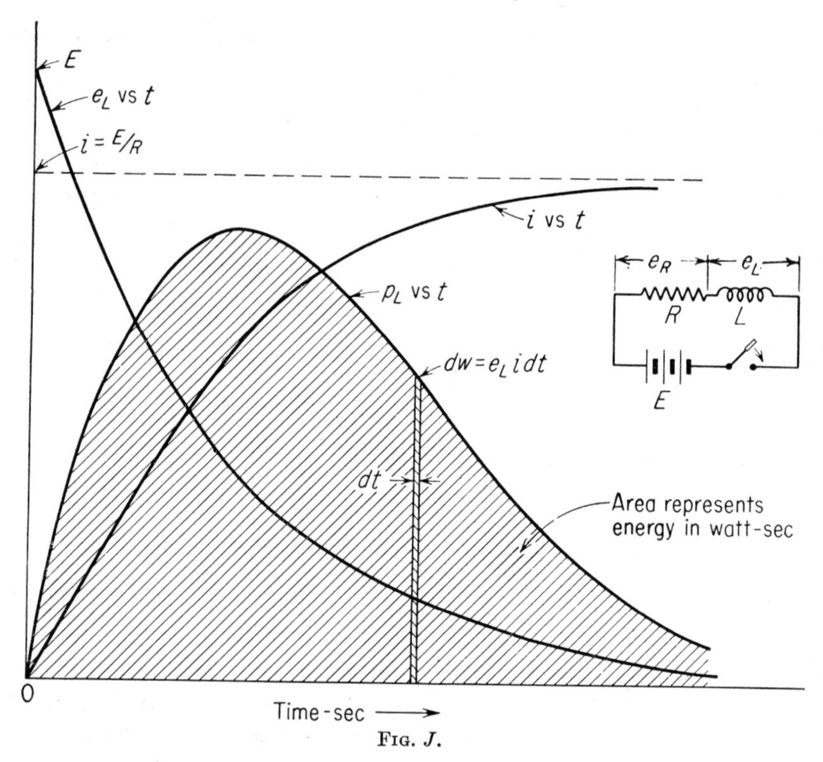

FIG. *J*.

This exponential form of equation is plotted in Fig. *J*; also shown is a *current* vs. *time* curve for the same circuit. Since the power delivered to the inductor is, at any instant,

$$p_L = e_L i$$

a curve of *power* vs. *time* will start at zero when $t = 0$, rise to a maximum when $e_R = e_L$, and then decrease to zero as the circuit current tends toward its ultimate value I; such a curve is also indicated on Fig. *J*.

A differential amount of energy, dw joules, being equal to $p\,dt$, it follows that

$$dw = p\,dt = e_L i\,dt$$

But, as previously shown, $e_L = L(di/dt)$. Thus

$$dw = \left(L\frac{di}{dt}\right) i\,dt = Li\,di$$

The total amount of energy delivered to the inductor is obviously the summation of an infinite succession of values delivered during differential periods of time; it follows, therefore, that the area under the p vs. t curve, between $t = 0$ and $t = \infty$, is the total energy in watt-seconds (joules). Hence

$$W = \int_0^t Li\,di = \int_0^I Li\,di = \tfrac{1}{2}LI^2 \tag{65}$$

If the current varies between two values such as I_1 and I_2,

$$W = \tfrac{1}{2}L\,(I_2^2 - I_1^2) \tag{65a}$$

K. Capacitance of a Cable, Eq. (79). An underground cable, consisting of a conductor that is surrounded by insulating material and an outer lead-sheath covering, is a capacitor. For each unit of length of cable, the outer surface of the conductor, represented by $2\pi r_1$, is one "plate" of the capacitor, while the larger inner surface of the lead sheath,

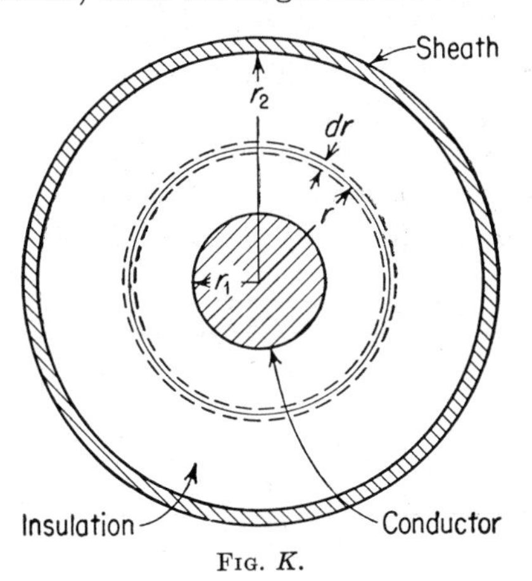

FIG. *K*.

represented by $2\pi r_2$, is the other "plate" (see Fig. *K*). Since any concentric cylinder such as $2\pi r$ is an equipotential surface, a differential radial element of thickness dr may be regarded as a differential capacitor whose capacitance per unit length is, by Eq. (75),

$$dC = \frac{2.25k \times 2\pi r}{10^7\, dr}$$

At the conductor surface a differential capacitor has the smallest capacitance, i.e., $(2.25k \times 2\pi r_1/10^7\, dr)$, while a differential capacitor at the lead-sheath surface has the largest value, i.e., $(2.25k \times 2\pi r_2/10^7\, dr)$. Regarding the cable as comprising an infinite succession of capacitors in *series*, from its smallest element at the conductor surface to its largest element at the lead sheath, it should be clear that the total capacitance may be determined by applying Eq. (77) to an infinite succession of differential capacitors; this obviously involves an integration in which

$$C = \frac{1}{1\Big/\int_{r_1}^{r_2} \frac{2.25k \times 2\pi r}{10^7\, dr}} = \frac{1}{\int_{r_1}^{r_2} \frac{10^7\, dr}{2.25k \times 2\pi r}}$$

When this equation is integrated between the limits indicated,

$$C = \frac{1}{\left(\frac{10^7}{2.25k \times 2\pi r}\right) \log_\epsilon \frac{r_2}{r_1}} = \frac{14.1k}{10^7 \log_\epsilon \frac{r_2}{r_1}} \qquad \mu\text{f per in.}$$

Converted to more convenient units, i.e., $\log_{10}$ and microfarads per mile of cable length,

$$C = \frac{14.1k}{10^7 \times 2.3 \log_{10} (r_2/r_1)} \times 12 \times 5{,}280 = \frac{0.0388k}{\log_{10} (r_2/r_1)} \qquad \mu\text{f per mile} \tag{79}$$

L. Charging Current in a Resistance-Capacitance (R-C) Circuit, Eq. (80). The current that charges a capacitor in an R-C circuit must, of course, pass through the resistor, and in doing so incurs a voltage drop equal to iR. Assuming a constant potential source, of voltage E (see Fig. L), the resistance voltage e_R will be equal to E at $t = 0$ and will be

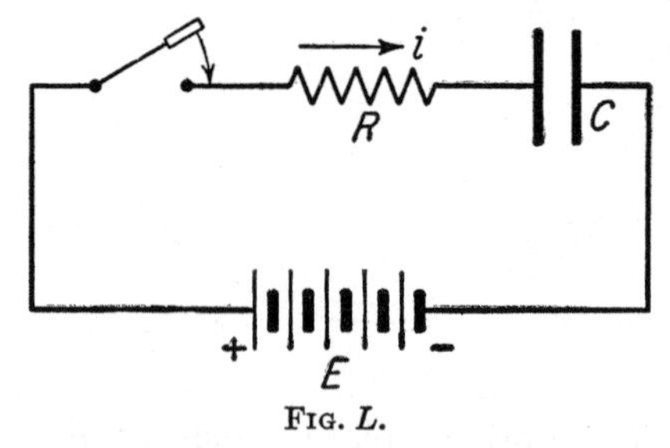

FIG. L.

zero at $t = \infty$; this follows from the fact that the capacitor is initially uncharged, i.e., $e_C = 0$ at $t = 0$, and is completely charged after a comparatively long period of time, i.e., $e_C = E$ at $t = \infty$. Writing the general equation that relates the three voltages,

$$e_R = iR = E - e_C$$

But the capacitance voltage e_C is, at any instant of time, equal to q/C, where q is the value of the charge on the capacitor in coulombs and C is in farads. Moreover, since q is the *accumulated* charge between the closing of the switch and the instant in question, i.e., at the instant when the capacitor voltage is e_C, it follows that $q = \int_0^t i\, td$. Making the proper substitutions and rearranging terms,

$$E = iR + \int_0^t \frac{i\,dt}{C}$$

Putting this relationship into the form of a simple differential equation,

$$0 = R\frac{di}{dt} + \frac{i}{C}$$

Rearranging the terms for the next step in the derivation,

$$\frac{di}{i} = -\frac{1}{RC}\,dt$$

Integrating both sides,

$$\log_\epsilon i = -\frac{t}{RC} + k$$

the symbol k being a constant that results from the process of integration. The last equation may be written in exponential form to yield

$$i = \epsilon^{-t/RC}\epsilon^{k} = k_1\epsilon^{-t/RC}$$

where k_1 is a new constant of integration that conveniently represents ϵ^k.

The value of k_1 may be evaluated by setting t equal to zero: $\epsilon^0 = 1$; moreover, under this condition, $i = E/R$ at $t = 0$. Thus, $k_1 = E/R$, and the final form of the equation is

$$i = \frac{E}{R}\epsilon^{-t/RC} \tag{80}$$

M. Discharge Current in a Resistance-Capacitance (R-C) Circuit, Eq. (82). Assuming a capacitor to be perfect, in the sense that there will be no leakage after it is charged, it will retain its charge indefinitely unless the stored energy is dissipated in some way. Thus, if the capacitor is originally charged to voltage E (see Fig. M, with switch closed to the

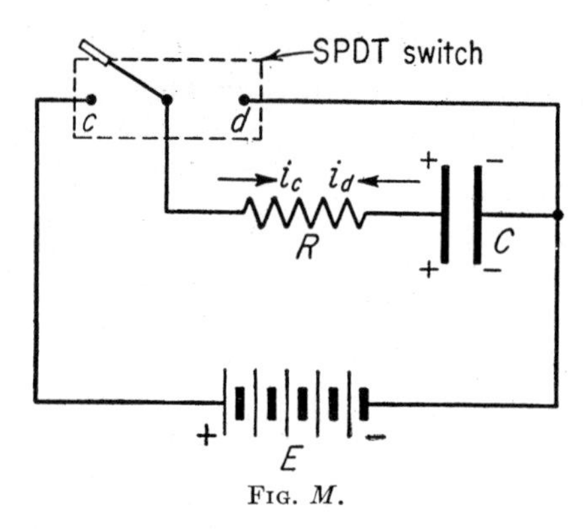

FIG. *M*.

c side) the energy will be dissipated when a resistor is connected to its terminals (with the switch closed to the d side); moreover, since the capacitor acts as a source of emf whose voltage is diminishing progressively from its initial value of E to zero, the discharge current will drop from $i = E/R$ at $t = 0$ to $i = 0$ at $t = \infty$. Remembering that the *impressed* emf is zero during the period of discharge, a general equation, similar to that given in Appendix 1L, may be written to indicate the voltage relations in the discharge circuit:

$$e_R = iR = 0 - e_C$$

As before, the capacitance voltage e_C is, at any instant, equal to q/C, and this in turn is $\int_0^t idt/C$. Making substitutions and rearranging gives

$$0 = iR + \int_0^t \frac{i\,dt}{C}$$

and when differentiated it yields a simple differential equation:

$$0 = R\frac{di}{dt} + \frac{i}{C}$$

Rearranging terms by separating variables for the next step,

$$\frac{di}{i} = -\frac{1}{RC}\,dt$$

Integrating both sides,

$$\log_\epsilon i = -\frac{t}{RC} + k$$

the symbol k being a constant that results from the process of integration.

Writing the last equation in the desirable exponential form, it becomes

$$i = \epsilon^{-t/RC}\epsilon^k = k_1\epsilon^{-t/RC}$$

where k_1 is a new constant of integration that conveniently represents ϵ^k.

The value of k_1 may be evaluated by setting t equal to zero: $\epsilon^0 = 1$; moreover, under this condition, $i = E/R$ at $t = 0$, whence $k_1 = E/R$. The final form of the equation is therefore

$$i = -\frac{E}{R}\epsilon^{-t/RC} \tag{82}$$

the negative sign being used to indicate a discharge current.

II—Alternating-current Circuits

N. Effective Value of a Sinusoidal Current, Eq. (88). The effective current in an a-c circuit is equivalent to a direct current when both produce heat in a given resistance at exactly the same rate. However, the heating effect of a current that varies sinusoidally changes from instant to instant, being zero during a differential time period as the current wave passes through zero, and a maximum during a differential time period as the current wave is passing through its maximum value. Since the heat produced electrically is proportional to the *square* of the current, the differential amount of heat developed by a current i during time dt is

$$dh = ki^2\,dt$$

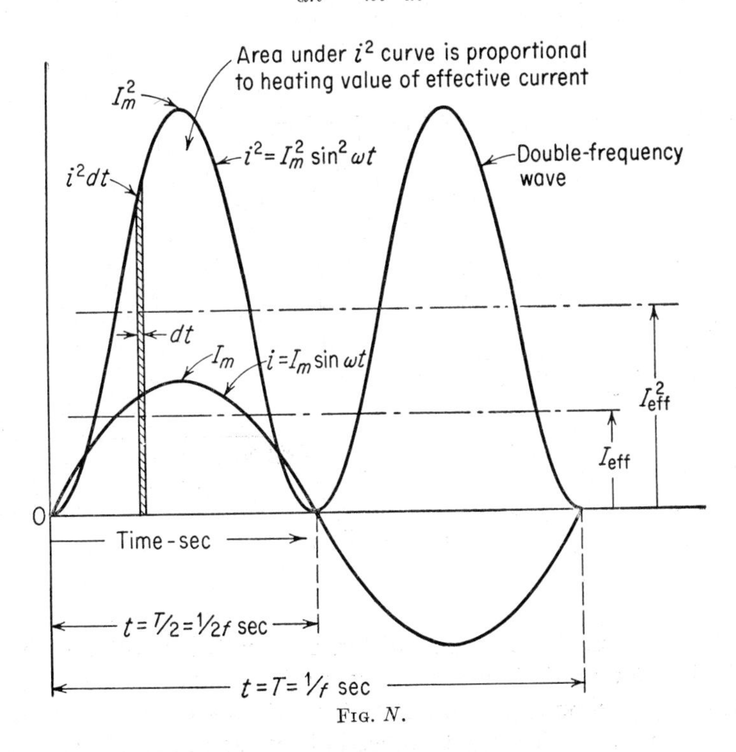

FIG. *N*.

Figure N shows a sinusoidal wave of current, $i = I_m \sin \omega t$, and a wave representing the *square* of this current, i.e., $i^2 = I_m{}^2 \sin^2 \omega t$. In addition to the fact that the latter is a double-frequency wave, it should be clear that, since it is entirely *above* the x axis, *positive heating* is produced on both halves of the current cycle.

The diagram also shows a differential area $i^2\,dt$ which, in accordance with the given differential equation, is obviously a *measure* of the heating produced by i in time dt. Moreover, the total area under the i^2 curve for one alternation of current is a *measure* of the heating effect during a one-half-cycle period; equal heating effects are produced during all half-cycle periods. Rewriting the foregoing relationships in terms of the sinusoidal variation,

$$dh = kI_m{}^2 \sin^2 \omega t\,dt$$

Integrating this equation over a one-half-cycle period of $T/2$ sec, where $T = 1/f$ sec, will yield the heating developed during one alternation:

$$H_{T/2} = \int_0^{T/2} kI_m{}^2 \sin^2 \omega t\,dt$$

As indicated previously, this heating may also be represented in terms of an *effective current*, I_{eff}, as follows:

$$H_{T/2} = kI_{\text{eff}}{}^2 \frac{T}{2}$$

Setting both values of H equal to each other,

$$I_{\text{eff}}{}^2 = \frac{I_m{}^2}{T/2} \int_0^{T/2} \sin^2 \omega t\,dt$$

from which $$I_{\text{eff}} = I_m \sqrt{\frac{2}{T} \int_0^{T/2} \left(\frac{1}{2} - \frac{1}{2} \cos 2\omega t\right) dt}$$

Solving,

$$I_{\text{eff}} = I_m \sqrt{\left[\frac{t}{T} - \frac{\sin 2\omega t}{2\omega T}\right]_0^{T/2}}$$

$$= I_m \sqrt{\frac{1}{2} - \frac{\sin 2\omega T/2}{2\omega T}} = I_m \sqrt{\frac{1}{2} - \left[\frac{\sin 2 \times 2\pi \times (1/T) \times (T/2)}{2 \times 2\pi \times (1/T) \times T}\right]}$$

$$= I_m \sqrt{\frac{1}{2} - \underset{(0)}{\frac{\sin 2\pi}{4\pi}}} = \frac{I_m}{\sqrt{2}} = 0.707 I_m \qquad (88)$$

O. Current Equation in an Inductance Circuit, Eq. (91). When a sinusoidal emf wave is impressed across a pure inductance (negligible resistance) a voltage will be induced in the latter that will at any instant be proportional to both the inductance in henrys and the rate of current change; i.e., $e_L = L\,di/dt$. Moreover, the circuit will be in dynamic equilibrium when the induced emf is equal to the instantaneous applied voltage; thus,

$$e_L = L\frac{di}{dt} = E_m \sin \omega t$$

Rewriting this equation in terms of current change,

$$di = \frac{E_m}{L} \sin \omega t \, dt$$

When both sides are integrated,

$$i = \frac{E_m}{\omega L} \cos \omega t + k$$

If the transient component, generally of extremely short duration, is neglected and the current is assumed to be periodic, the constant term k is zero. Also, $\cos \omega t = \sin (\omega t - \pi/2)$. Hence

$$i = \frac{E}{\omega L} \sin \left(\omega t - \frac{\pi}{2}\right) \tag{91}$$

P. Power in a Resistance-Inductance (R-L) Circuit, Eq. (97a). When a sinusoidal emf wave is impressed across a series circuit consisting of resistance and inductance, the current will not be in phase with the voltage but will lag behind it by an angle that is less than $\pi/2$ radians. Representing the angle of lag by Θ radians, its value depending on the relative magnitudes of R and X_L, the equations for voltage and current are

$$e = E_m \sin \alpha$$
$$i = I_m \sin (\alpha - \Theta)$$

Since the instantaneous value of power is the product of e and i,

$$\begin{aligned} p &= E_m I_m \sin \alpha \sin (\alpha - \Theta) = E_m I_m \sin \alpha(\sin \alpha \cos \Theta - \cos \alpha \sin \Theta) \\ &= E_m I_m(\sin^2 \alpha \cos \Theta - \sin \alpha \cos \alpha \sin \Theta) \\ &= E_m I_m \left[\left(\frac{1}{2} - \frac{1}{2}\cos 2\alpha\right) \cos \Theta - \frac{\sin 2\alpha}{2} \sin \Theta\right] \\ &= \frac{E_m I_m}{2} (1 - \cos 2\alpha) \cos \Theta - (\sin 2\alpha \sin \Theta) \\ &= EI(\cos \Theta - \cos 2\alpha \cos \Theta - \sin 2\alpha \sin \Theta) \end{aligned}$$

The average power per cycle is the total area under the power curve (see Fig. 131) divided by the base, or 2π; that is,

$$P_{av} = \int_0^{2\pi} \frac{p\, d\alpha}{2\pi}$$

Therefore

$$P_{av} = \frac{EI}{2\pi}\int_0^{2\pi} [\cos \Theta - \cos 2\alpha \cos \Theta - \sin 2\alpha \sin \Theta] \, d\alpha$$

$$= \frac{EI}{2\pi}\left[\cos \Theta \times \alpha - \frac{\sin 2\alpha}{2} \cos \Theta + \frac{\cos 2\alpha}{2} \sin \Theta\right]_0^{2\pi}$$

$$= \frac{EI}{2\pi}\left[\cos \Theta \times 2\pi - \underset{(0)}{\frac{\sin 4\pi - \sin 0}{2}} \cos \Theta - \underset{(0)}{\frac{\cos 4\pi - \cos 0}{2}} \sin \Theta\right]$$

$$P_{av} = EI \cos \Theta \qquad (97a)$$

Q. Inductance for Maximum E_L in a Variable-inductance R-L-C Series Circuit, Eq. (113). The current in any series R-L-C circuit is

$$I = \frac{E}{\sqrt{R^2 + (X_L - X_C)^2}}$$

Since the voltage drop across the inductor is IX_L,

$$E_L = \frac{EX_L}{\sqrt{R^2 + (X_L - X_C)^2}}$$

Considering a circuit in which the inductance may be varied over wide limits, it should be clear that E_L will be zero when L is zero ($X_L = 2\pi fL$) (see Fig. 151) and zero when L is infinite ($I = 0$). At some intermediate value of inductance, not at the inductance of resonance, the voltage drop across the inductor will be a maximum; moreover, at this point of maximum E_L the slope of the E_L vs. L curve will be zero. Therefore, the derivative of the foregoing equation with respect to X_L will be zero when E_L is a maximum; it will also be zero for the derivative of the *squared* value of E_L. Thus

$$\frac{dE_L^2}{dX_L} = 0 = \frac{d}{dX_L}\left[\frac{E^2X_L^2}{R^2 + (X_L - X_C)^2}\right]$$

$$0 = \frac{(R^2 + X_L^2 - 2X_LX_C + X_C^2)2E^2X_L - E^2X_L^2(2X_L - 2X_C)}{(\text{denominator})^2}$$

$$2E^2X_L(R^2 + X_L^2 - 2X_LX_C + X_C^2) = 2E^2X_L^2(X_L - X_C)$$

from which

$$X_L = \frac{R^2 + X_C^2}{X_C}$$

Since $X_L = 2\pi fL$ and $X_C = 10^6/(2\pi fC)$, it follows that

$$2\pi fL = \frac{R^2 + X_C^2}{10^6/(2\pi fC)} = 2\pi f \times 10^{-6}C(R^2 + X_C)^2$$

Hence

$$L = C(R^2 + X_C^2)10^{-6} \qquad (113)$$

R. Capacitance for Maximum E_C in a Variable-capacitance R-L-C Series Circuit, Eq. (114). The current in any series R-L-C circuit is

$$I = \frac{E}{\sqrt{R^2 + (X_C - X_L)^2}}$$

Since the voltage drop across the capacitor is IX_C,

$$E_C = \frac{EX_C}{\sqrt{R^2 + (X_C - X_L)^2}}$$

Considering a circuit in which the capacitance may be varied over wide limits, it should be clear that E_C will be zero when C is zero ($I = 0$) (see Fig. 152) and zero when C is infinite ($X_C = 10^6/2\pi fC$). At some intermediate value of capacitance, not at the capacitance of resonance, the voltage drop across the capacitor will be a maximum; moreover, at this point of maximum E_C the slope of the E_C vs. C curve will be zero. Therefore the derivative of the foregoing equation with respect to X_C will be zero when E_C is a maximum; it will also be zero for the derivative of the *squared* value of E_C. Thus

$$\frac{dE_C^2}{dX_C} = 0 = \frac{d}{dX_C}\left[\frac{E^2X_C^2}{R^2 + (X_C - X_L)^2}\right]$$

$$0 = \frac{(R^2 + X_C^2 - 2X_CX_L + X_L^2)2E^2X_C - E^2X_C^2(2X_C - 2X_L)}{(\text{denominator})^2}$$

$$2E^2X_C(R^2 + X_C^2 - 2X_CX_L + X_L^2) = 2E^2X_C^2(X_C - X_L)$$

from which

$$X_C = \frac{R^2 + X_L^2}{X_L}$$

Since $X_C = 10^6/(2\pi fC)$ and $X_L = 2\pi fL$, it follows that

$$\frac{10^6}{2\pi fC} = \frac{R^2 + X_L^2}{2\pi fL}$$

Hence

$$C = \frac{L \times 10^6}{(R^2 + X_L^2)} \tag{114}$$

S. Frequency Separation between Half-power Points in a Series R-L-C Circuit, Eq. (115). Because of the symmetry of the *current* vs. *frequency* curve (see Fig. 153) there will be two frequencies, equally spaced to either side of the resonant frequency f_r, at which the equivalent reactance of the circuit is equal to the resistance; these are called half-power points because the circuit power is exactly one-half the value at resonance. Also, the equivalent reactance at the lower of the two half-power frequencies, i.e., f_1, is $X = (X_{C_1} - X_{L_1})$, and is $X = (X_{L_2} - X_{C_2})$ at the higher frequency f_2. The frequency separation $(f_2 - f_1)$ is generally referred to as the *band pass*.

Writing a general expression for the current at f_1 and f_2,

$$I_1 = I_2 = \frac{E}{\sqrt{2}\,R} = \frac{E}{R^2 + (X_L - X_C)^2}$$

from which $$2R^2 = R^2 + (X_L - X_C)^2$$
and $$R = \pm(X_L - X_C)$$

Since $X_L = \omega_x L$ and $X_C = 10^6/\omega_x C$, where $\omega_x = 2\pi f_1$ or $\omega_x = 2\pi f_2$,

$$R = \pm\left(\omega_x L - \frac{10^6}{\omega_x C}\right)$$

This equation may be rearranged to yield two quadratics for the solution of ω_x. Thus

$$\omega_x{}^2 LC - \omega_x RC - 10^6 = 0 \qquad \text{and} \qquad \omega_x{}^2 LC + \omega_x RC - 10^6 = 0$$

from which

$$\omega_x = \frac{RC \pm \sqrt{R^2C^2 + (4LC)10^6}}{2LC} \qquad \omega_x = \frac{-RC \pm \sqrt{R^2C^2 + (4LC)10^6}}{2LC}$$

$$= \frac{R}{2L} \pm \sqrt{\frac{R^2}{4L} + \frac{10^6}{LC}} \qquad = -\frac{R}{2L} \pm \sqrt{\frac{R^2}{4L} + \frac{10^6}{LC}}$$

Since $R^2/4L$ is very much smaller than $10^6/LC$ it may be neglected, and

$$\omega_x = \frac{R}{2L} \pm \sqrt{\frac{10^6}{LC}} \qquad \text{and} \qquad \omega_x = -\frac{R}{2L} \pm \sqrt{\frac{10^6}{LC}}$$

But $$f_r = \frac{10^3}{2\pi\sqrt{LC}}$$

so that $$2\pi f_r = \omega_x = \frac{10^3}{\sqrt{LC}} = \sqrt{\frac{10^6}{LC}}$$

Thus $$\omega_x = \frac{R}{2L} \pm \omega_r \qquad \text{and} \qquad \omega_x = -\frac{R}{2L} \pm \omega_r$$

Using the positive value of ω_r, and substituting $2\pi f$ for ω,

$$2\pi f_2 = \frac{R}{2L} + 2\pi f_r \qquad \text{and} \qquad 2\pi f_1 = -\frac{R}{2L} + 2\pi f_r$$

from which $$f_2 = f_r + \frac{R}{4\pi L} \qquad \text{and} \qquad f_1 = f_r - \frac{R}{4\pi L}$$

Hence $$(f_2 - f_1) = \left(f_r + \frac{R}{4\pi L}\right) - \left(f_r - \frac{R}{4\pi L}\right) = \frac{R}{2\pi L} \qquad (115)$$

T. Maximum Power Transfer in Resistance Circuit, Eq. (122). When a constant-voltage generator delivers load to a variable resistor R_l

through a line resistor R the circuit current will be

$$I = \frac{E}{R + R_l}$$

and the load power, being equal to I^2R_l, becomes

$$P_l = \frac{E^2R_l}{(R + R_l)^2} = \frac{E^2R_l}{R^2 + 2RR_l + R_l^2}$$

An examination of this equation indicates that zero power will be taken by the load when R_l is zero or infinite ohms; when $R_l = 0$, the load voltage is zero, and when $R_l = \infty$, the load current is zero. At some point

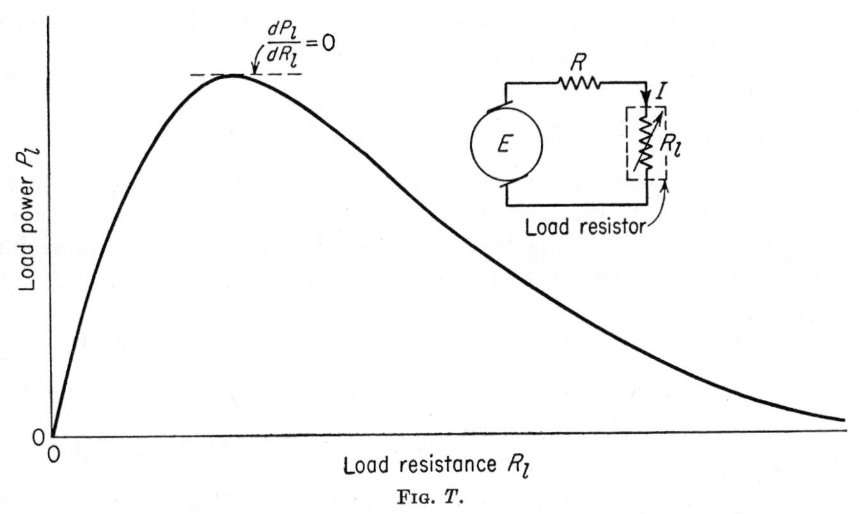

FIG. *T*.

on the P_l vs. R_l curve, shown in Fig. *T*, the load power will pass through a maximum, and this will occur when the slope is zero, i.e., when dP_l/dR_l is zero. Differentiating the foregoing equation with respect to the variable R_l and setting the result equal to zero will then yield the condition for maximum power. Thus

$$\frac{dP_l}{dR_l} = 0 = \frac{(R^2 + 2RR_l + R_l^2)(E^2) - (E^2R_l)(2R + 2R_l)}{(\text{denominator})^2}$$

Equating the two terms of the numerator,

$$(R^2 + 2RR_l + R_l^2)E^2 = (2RR_l + 2R_l^2)E^2$$

from which

$$R = R_l$$

Substituting the value of R for R_l in the original power equation,

$$P_l = \frac{E^2R_l}{(R + R)^2} = \frac{E^2}{4R} \tag{122}$$

U. Condition for Maximum Power in a Variable-impedance Constant-power-factor Load, Eq. (123). When a constant-voltage generator delivers load to a circuit consisting of a constant line impedance and a variable load impedance, the current will be

$$I = \frac{E}{\sqrt{(R + Z_l \cos \Theta_l)^2 + (X + Z_l \sin \Theta_l)^2}}$$

where R and X = line resistance and reactance, respectively
Z_l = load impedance
Θ_l = power-factor angle of the load
$Z_l \cos \Theta$ and $Z_l \sin \Theta$ = load resistance and reactance, respectively

Assuming constant load power factor, i.e., under the condition of a constant R_l to Z_l ratio, the load power will be

$$P_l = \frac{E^2 Z_l \cos \Theta_l}{(R + Z_l \cos \Theta_l)^2 + (X + Z_l \sin \Theta_l)^2}$$

As in the previous article, maximum load power will be delivered when the slope of the P_l vs. Z_l curve, a graphical plot of the relation between load power and load impedance, is zero. Differentiating the foregoing equation and setting the result equal to zero,

$$\begin{aligned}\frac{dP_l}{dZ_l} = 0 = [(R^2 + 2RZ_l \cos \Theta_l + Z_l^2 \cos^2 \Theta_l + X^2 + 2XZ_l \sin \Theta_l \\ + Z_l^2 \sin^2 \Theta)(E^2 \cos \Theta_l) - (E^2 Z_l \cos \Theta_l)(2R \cos \Theta_l + 2Z_l \cos^2 \Theta_l) \\ + 2X \sin \Theta_l + 2Z_l \sin^2 \Theta_l] \times \frac{1}{(\text{denominator})^2}\end{aligned}$$

Equating the two terms of the numerator, canceling $E^2 \cos \Theta_l$, and rearranging,

$$\begin{aligned}(R^2 + X^2) + Z_l(2R \cos \Theta_l + 2X \sin \Theta_l) + Z_l^2(\cos^2 \Theta_l + \sin^2 \Theta_l) \\ = Z_l(2R \cos \Theta_l + 2X \sin \Theta_l) + 2Z_l^2(\cos^2 \Theta_l + \sin^2 \Theta_l)\end{aligned}$$

After the proper cancellations are made, setting $(\cos^2 \Theta_l + \sin^2 \Theta_l) = 1$,

$$(R^2 + X^2) = Z_l^2 = Z^2$$

from which

$$Z = Z_l \tag{123}$$

This derivation indicates that for a variable-impedance constant-power-factor load, maximum load power occurs when the load impedance, in ohms, is equal to the line impedance, in ohms.

V. Effective Value of a Nonsinusoidal Current or Voltage, Eq. (145). It was stated in Appendix 1N that the effective current in an a-c circuit is equivalent to a direct current when both produce heat in a given resistance at exactly the same rate; this relationship between the two kinds of current is *independent* of the wave shape of the alternating current. It follows, therefore, that the effective current is the root-mean-square value, i.e., the rms value, and may be expressed by the general equation

$$I = \sqrt{\frac{1}{2\pi}\int_0^{2\pi} i^2\,d\alpha}$$

where α is given in radians and

$$i = I_{DC} + I_1 \sin(\alpha + \Theta_1) + I_2 \sin(2\alpha + \Theta_2) + I_3 \sin(3\alpha + \Theta_3) + \cdots + I_n \sin(n\alpha + \Theta_n)$$

Thus

$$i = \left\{\frac{1}{2\pi}\int_0^{2\pi} [I_{DC} + I_1 \sin(\alpha + \Theta_1) + I_2 \sin(2\alpha + \Theta_2) + I_3 \sin(3\alpha + \Theta_3) + \cdots + I_n \sin(n\alpha + \Theta_n)]^2\,d\alpha\right\}^{1/2}$$

The integration of the rather long *squared* expression under the radical may be performed by considering the four general kinds of terms that result when the current i is squared; these are

1. The square of the d-c component, i.e., I_{DC}^2.
2. The square of each of the individual a-c components, one of which is the general nth harmonic $I_n^2 \sin^2(n\alpha + \Theta_n)$.
3. Quantities containing the product of the d-c component and, in turn, each of a-c components; one of these is $I_{DC}I_n \sin(n\alpha + \Theta_n)$.
4. Quantities containing the products of two a-c harmonic components, one of which is the general product of the mth and the nth harmonics, i.e., $I_m \sin(m\alpha + \Theta_m)I_n \sin(n\alpha + \Theta_n)$.

Integrating by parts,

$$(1) \qquad \frac{1}{2\pi}\int_0^{2\pi} I_{DC}^2\,d\alpha = \frac{1}{2\pi} \times I_{DC}^2[\alpha]_0^{2\pi} = I_{DC}^2$$

$$(2) \qquad \frac{1}{2\pi}\int_0^{2\pi} I_n^2 \sin^2(n\alpha + \Theta_n)\,d\alpha = \frac{I_n^2}{2\pi}\int_0^{2\pi}\left[\frac{1}{2} - \frac{1}{2}\cos(2n\alpha + 2n\Theta_n)\right]d\alpha$$

$$= \frac{I_n^2}{2\pi}\int_0^{2\pi}\left[\frac{1}{2} - \frac{1}{2}(\cos 2n\alpha \cos 2n\Theta_n - \sin 2n\alpha \sin 2n\Theta_n)\right]d\alpha$$

The integrals of the *variables* $\cos 2n\alpha$ and $\sin n\alpha$ between the limits of 0 and 2π are zero. Therefore the above expression reduces to

$$\frac{I_n^2}{2\pi}\int_0^{2\pi}\frac{d\alpha}{2} = \frac{I_n^2}{2\pi}\left(\frac{2\pi}{2}\right) = \frac{I_n^2}{2}$$

$$(3) \qquad \frac{1}{2\pi}\int_0^{2\pi} I_{DC}I_n \sin(n\alpha + \Theta_n)\,d\alpha = 0$$

because, as in (2), the integral of any sine term between the limits of 0 and 2π is zero.

$$(4)\quad \frac{1}{2\pi}\int_0^{2\pi} [I_m \sin (m\alpha + \Theta_m) I_n \sin (n\alpha + \Theta_n)]\, d\alpha$$

$$= \frac{I_m I_n}{2\pi}\int_0^{2\pi} [(\sin m\alpha \cos \Theta_m + \cos m\alpha \sin \Theta_m) \times (\sin n\alpha \cos \Theta_n + \cos n\alpha \sin \Theta_n)]\, d\alpha$$

$$= k\int_0^{2\pi} [k_a(\sin m\alpha \sin n\alpha) + k_b(\cos m\alpha \cos n\alpha) + k_c(\cos m\alpha \sin n\alpha) + k_d(\sin m\alpha \cos n\alpha)]\, d\alpha$$

where $k = I_m I_n/2$

$k_a = \cos \Theta_m \cos \Theta_n$

$k_b = \sin \Theta_m \sin \Theta_n$

$k_c = \sin \Theta_m \cos \Theta_n$

$k_d = \cos \Theta_m \sin \Theta_n$

But

$$\sin m\alpha \sin n\alpha = \frac{\cos (m\alpha - n\alpha) - \cos (m\alpha + n\alpha)}{2}$$

$$\cos m\alpha \cos n\alpha = \frac{\cos (m\alpha + n\alpha) + \cos (m\alpha - n\alpha)}{2}$$

$$\cos m\alpha \sin n\alpha = \frac{\sin (m\alpha + n\alpha) - \sin (m\alpha - n\alpha)}{2}$$

$$\sin m\alpha \cos n\alpha = \frac{\sin (m\alpha + n\alpha) + \sin (m\alpha - n\alpha)}{2}$$

The last integral, therefore, reduces to

$$\frac{k}{2}\int_0^{2\pi} [k_a(\cos p\alpha - \cos q\alpha) + k_b(\cos q\alpha + \cos p\alpha) + k_c(\sin q\alpha - \sin p\alpha) + k_d(\sin q\alpha + \sin p\alpha)]\, d\alpha$$

Finally, when each of the sine and cosine terms is integrated between the limits of 0 and 2π it becomes zero.

It follows, therefore, that the effective value of the current depends *only* upon the d-c component and those terms that are represented by *sine-squared* quantities in the original expression. Thus

$$I = \sqrt{I_{DC}^2 + \frac{I_1^2}{2} + \frac{I_2^2}{2} + \frac{I_3^2}{2} + \cdots + \frac{I_n^2}{2}}$$

and an equivalent voltage equation is (145)

$$E = \sqrt{E_{DC}^2 + \frac{E_1^2}{2} + \frac{E_2^2}{2} + \frac{E_3^2}{2} + \cdots + \frac{E_n^2}{2}}$$

W. Power Resulting from Nonsinusoidal Waves of Voltage and Current, Eq. (146). The general expression for the average power in *any* a-c circuit, regardless of the degree of complexity of the wave shapes of voltage and current, is

$$P = \frac{1}{2\pi}\int_0^{2\pi} ei\,dt$$

where e and i are instantaneous values of voltage and current which, omitting possible d-c components, are given by the equations

$$e = E_1 \sin(\alpha + \Theta_1) + E_2 \sin(2\alpha + \Theta_2) + \cdots + E_n \sin(n\alpha + \Theta_n)$$
$$i = I_1 \sin(\alpha + \Theta_1') + I_2 \sin(2\alpha + \Theta_2') + \cdots + I_n \sin(n\alpha + \Theta_n')$$

When the latter are substituted in the original expression, it expands to

$$P = \frac{1}{2\pi}\int_0^{2\pi} [E_1 \sin(\alpha+\Theta_1) + E_2 \sin(2\alpha+\Theta_2) + \cdots + E_n \sin(n\alpha+\Theta_n)]$$
$$\times [I_1 \sin(\alpha + \Theta_1') + I_2 \sin(2\alpha + \Theta_2') + \cdots + I_n \sin(n\alpha + \Theta_n')]$$

The product of the long trigonometric equations of voltage and current results in two kinds of terms; these are (1) terms in which a voltage at one frequency is multiplied by a current at *another* frequency, and (2) terms in which a voltage at a given frequency is multiplied by a current of the *same* frequency. Since an integration performed upon a product of two sine terms of different frequencies, between the limits of 0 and 2π, is zero, it is only necessary to consider those terms that are represented by the products of sine terms of the same frequency. To simplify the derivation it will be desirable to perform an integration upon the general term

$$\sin(n\alpha + \Theta_n)\sin(n\alpha + \Theta_n')$$

which may be written in the following form:

$$(\sin n\alpha \cos \Theta_n + \cos n\alpha \sin \Theta_n)(\sin n\alpha \cos \Theta_n' + \cos n\alpha \sin \Theta_n')$$

The latter expression expands to

$$(\sin^2 n\alpha \cos \Theta_n \cos \Theta_n') + (\cos^2 n\alpha \sin \Theta_n \sin \Theta_n')$$
$$+ (\sin n\alpha \cos n\alpha \cos \Theta_n \sin \Theta_n') + (\sin n\alpha \cos n\alpha \sin \Theta_n \cos \Theta_n')$$

Integrating by parts,

$$\int_0^{2\pi} (\sin^2 n\alpha \cos \Theta_n \cos \Theta_n')\,d\alpha$$
$$= \cos \Theta_n \cos \Theta_n' \int_0^{2\pi} \left(\frac{1}{2} - \frac{1}{2}\cos 2n\alpha\right) d\alpha = \pi(\cos \Theta_n \cos \Theta_n')$$

$$\int_0^{2\pi} (\cos^2 n\alpha \sin \Theta_n \sin \Theta_n')\,d\alpha$$
$$= \sin \Theta_n \sin \Theta_n' \int_0^{2\pi} \left(\frac{1}{2} + \frac{1}{2}\cos 2n\alpha\right) d\alpha = \pi(\sin \Theta_n \sin \Theta_n')$$

$$\int_0^{2\pi} (\sin n\alpha \cos n\alpha \cos \Theta_n \sin \Theta_n')\, d\alpha = \cos \Theta_n \sin \Theta_n' \int_0^{2\pi} \frac{\sin 2n\alpha}{2}\, d\alpha = 0$$

$$\int_0^{2\pi} (\sin n\alpha \cos n\alpha \sin \Theta_n \cos \Theta_n')\, d\alpha = \sin \Theta_n \cos \Theta_n' \int_0^{2\pi} \frac{\sin 2n\alpha}{2}\, d\alpha = 0$$

Thus

$$\frac{1}{2\pi} \int_0^{2\pi} E_n \sin (n\alpha + \Theta_n) I_n \sin (n\alpha + \Theta_n')$$
$$= \frac{E_n I_n}{2\pi} \times \pi(\cos \Theta_n \cos \Theta_n' + \sin \Theta_n \sin \Theta_n') = \frac{E_n I_n}{2} \cos (\Theta_n - \Theta_n')$$

It follows, therefore, that each frequency component, the order of which is indicated by the subscript n, will contribute its share to the total power, so that

$$P = \frac{E_1 I_1}{2} \cos (\Theta_1 - \Theta_1') + \frac{E_2 I_2}{2} \cos (\Theta_2 - \Theta_2') + \frac{E_3 I_3}{2} \cos (\Theta_3 - \Theta_3') + \cdots + \frac{E_n I_n}{2} \cos (\Theta_n - \Theta_n') \quad (146)$$

APPENDIX 2

PRIMARY AND SECONDARY BATTERIES

General Aspects of Cells and Batteries. As applied to a device that is capable of converting chemical energy into electrical energy, a *cell* is a combination of solid materials, usually metals, called *electrodes*, immersed in a chemical solution, called an *electrolyte*, that is held in a *single* container. Several practical electrode-electrolyte combinations are: carbon and zinc in a mixture of manganese dioxide and acetylene black as in the so-called *dry cell;* lead peroxide and lead in a solution of sulphuric acid and water as in the *lead-acid* cell; nickelous hydroxide–nickel and iron–ferrous oxide–mercuric oxide in a solution of potassium hydroxide in water as in the *Edison* cell.

Although many kinds of cell are in common use, it is customary to classify them under two general headings, namely, *primary* and *secondary* cells; these are distinguished by whether or not the chemical reactions are reversible. Primary cells are most active in converting chemical energy into electrical energy when they are first assembled, lose activity in service and with age, and are discarded when completely exhausted. After they are depleted, they cannot be rejuvenated, because, subject to chemical reactions that are irreversible, they cannot be recharged when a current of electricity, opposite in direction to that of discharge, is passed through them. Secondary cells, on the other hand, are characterized by chemical reactions that are reversible and may, therefore, be recharged after they become discharged in service. It is for this reason that secondary cells are frequently referred to as "accumulators" or "storage cells."

When two or more cells are interconnected to serve as a source of higher voltage, higher current, or both, than that provided by a single unit, the combination is called a *battery.* Although only two elementary kinds of cell connection are possible, i.e., the *series* and *parallel* connections, a number of identical cells may be joined together in several ways to form a battery. Just how this should be done will, in general, be determined by the requirements of voltage and current capacity, and these will, in turn, be governed by the following two rules:

1. The resultant voltage of a battery depends upon the number of cells that are connected in series aiding, i.e., when there is a succession of plus-to-minus connections of adjacent cells arranged in a row.

2. The resultant current capacity of a battery depends upon the number of cells connected in parallel, i.e., when all positive electrodes are joined together to form one of the source terminals, and all of the negative electrodes are joined together to form the other terminal of the source.

Battery Connections. Figure *A* illustrates how eight cells may be connected in four different ways, with *a* and *b* showing, respectively, the fundamental series and parallel arrangements, and *c* and *d* each showing *combinations* of both the series and parallel arrangements. If it is assumed that all cells are identical, with each one having an open-circuit

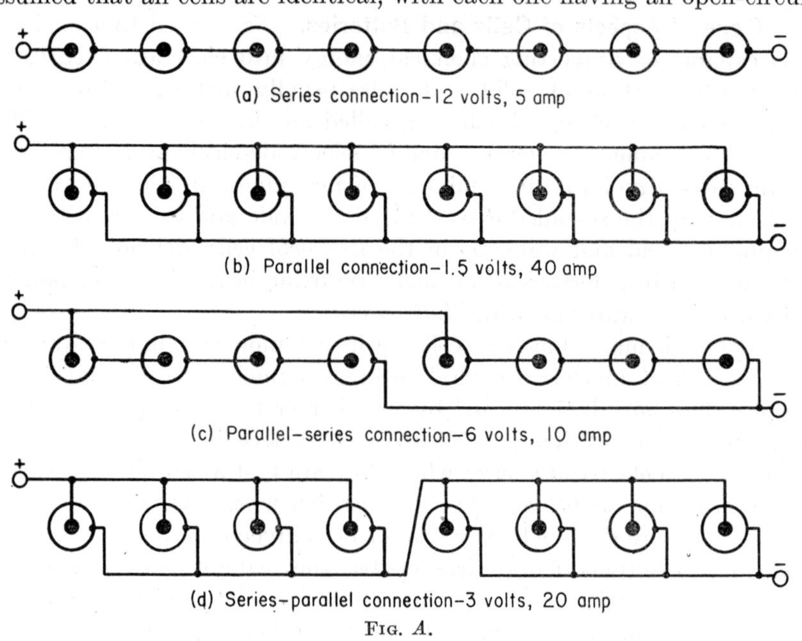

FIG. *A*.

emf of 1.5 volts and a current capacity of 5 amp, the following ratings apply:

For part *a*, $8 \times 1.5 = 12$ volts and 5 amp
For part *b*, 1.5 volts and $8 \times 5 = 40$ amp
For part *c*, $4 \times 1.5 = 6$ volts and $2 \times 5 = 10$ amp
For part *d*, $2 \times 1.5 = 3$ volts and $4 \times 5 = 20$ amp

When cells are to be connected in any of the three parallel combinations of parts *b*, *c*, and *d*, it is imperative that all cells within any parallel grouping be identical as to size, age, and time of service. This ensures equal discharge currents for all cells and uniform depletion of the individual units in a battery. If, for example, a group of *dissimilar* cells are connected in parallel, it should be inferred that their internal resistances are not the same. This difference generally means that, with the load terminals open-circuited, the better cells (those chemically more active) will discharge into the poorer ones, or, under load conditions, the poorer cells will deliver a smaller than proper share of the total load.

Particular attention should be called to the fact that in part *c*, the parallel-series connection, each of the two parallel sections has exactly the same number of cells in series. It is, in fact, extremely important that the individual sections of any parallel connection be exactly alike with respect to voltage and internal resistance; this uniformity is possible only when all cells are identical.

The eight cells of the illustration can also be connected as follows:

1. In parallel-series with four parallel groups of two cells in series, under which condition the rating would be $2 \times 1.5 = 3$ volts and $4 \times 5 = 20$ amp.

2. In series-parallel with four series groups of two cells in parallel, in which case the rating would be $4 \times 1.5 = 6$ volts and $2 \times 5 = 10$ amp.

Dry Cells. The first primary battery, invented by Alessandro Volta in 1800, was a crude "pile" of cells consisting of silver and zinc electrodes separated by animal hide soaked in liquids such as salt water or lye. Called the "crown of cups," it was modified by a succession of improvements in construction and by the use of different combinations of electrode-electrolyte materials and finally led to the development of the Leclanché cell, the forerunner of the present-day widely used dry cell. The latter, employed for many years on railroads and telegraph lines, consisted of a carbon electrode placed in a porous earthenware jar containing ground carbon and manganese dioxide which, in turn, was immersed in a large glass jar, half filled with ammonium chloride and holding a zinc electrode.

The present-day dry cell, although consisting essentially of the same materials as the Leclanché cell, is simpler in construction, more rugged, more portable, and more efficient in operation and in its use of active chemicals. A sketch showing a cross section of a typical dry cell is shown in Fig. *B*. The container is the zinc (negative) electrode and holds the central, carbon-rod (positive) electrode surrounded by a black mixture composed of manganese dioxide, a definite amount of acetylene black, and an aqueous solution of ammonium chloride (sal ammoniac) and zinc chloride. After the active materials are assembled in the zinc container, a cardboard washer is slipped over the central carbon rod and positioned above the gelatinous paste to provide an air space for possible expansion of the black mix. A sealing compound of hot wax or pitch is then poured over the top washer to keep the electrolyte moist during its period of service.

Dry cells are made in many sizes and for a great variety of applications. The largest standard cell, the No. 6, is cylindrical in shape, has a height of 6 in. and a diameter of 2½ in., and is used for telephone service and general purposes. For flashlights, the type C is generally employed, being $1\frac{13}{16}$ in. in height and $1\frac{5}{16}$ in. in diameter. Other sizes include: the type F ($h = 3\frac{7}{16}$ in. $\times$ $d = 1\frac{1}{4}$ in.) for railroad lanterns and radio batteries; the type D ($h = 2\frac{1}{4}$ in. $\times$ $d = 1\frac{1}{4}$ in.) for flashlights and radios; the type CL ($h = 2\frac{5}{8}$ in. $\times$ $d = 1\frac{5}{16}$ in.) for hearing aids; the miniature type U ($h = \frac{1}{2}$ in. $\times$ $d = \frac{5}{16}$ in.) for radios.

The terminal voltage of a dry cell depends upon such factors as (1) its size, (2) its temperature, (3) the current drain at which it operates, and (4) its age and chemical depletion in service. A new No. 6 cell, for

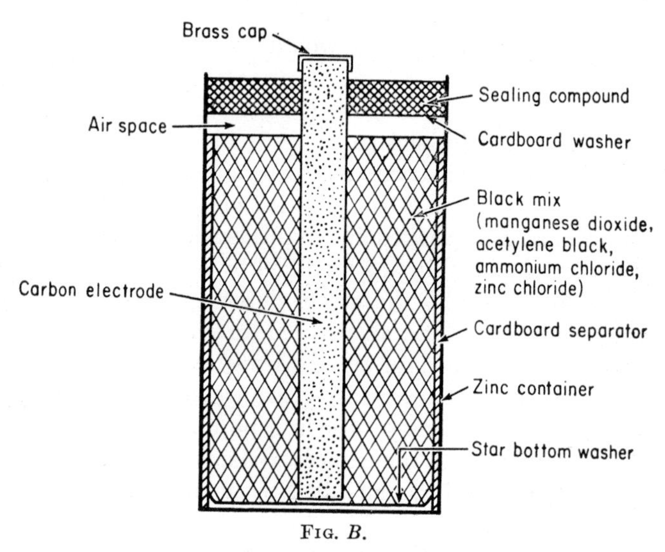

FIG. *B*.

example, has open-circuit voltages at 70°F and −4°F, respectively, of 1.59 and 1.56. When discharging at 5 amp, its 70°F and −4°F terminal voltages are, respectively, 1.33 and 0.81; also, for a current drain of 10 amp the respective voltages drop to the low values of 1.12 and 0.15. Similar comparative voltage ranges may be expected for other types of dry cell.

The internal resistance of a cell is, in general, an excellent indication of its condition. When the cell is new, under which condition the chemical gelatinous mix between carbon rod and zinc container is most active, its resistance is comparatively low; however, as the cell continues to exhaust itself, the black mixture undergoes chemical reactions and tends to dry out, with the result that the internal resistance continues to rise. Because of such cell depletion, the internal voltage drop increases, so that, with nominal or even low discharge currents, the terminal voltage, i.e., the load voltage, diminishes. This is why a flashlight fails to function properly after a cell has been used for some time. Average internal resistances of previously mentioned new No. 6, F and D cells are, respectively, 0.038, 0.227, and 0.173 ohm.

Another good measure of a cell's condition is its *flash* or *short-circuit* current. This is defined as the maximum current, observed on a dead-beat ammeter, which the cell can deliver through a circuit of 0.01-ohm resistance, including the ammeter. A measurement such as this will indicate indirectly the internal resistance of the cell, since the foregoing definition may be written in equation form as

$$R_i = \frac{E_{oc}}{I_{sc}} - 0.01$$

where R_i = internal resistance of cell
E_{oc} = open-circuit voltage
I_{sc} = flash current

Average short-circuit currents for new No. 6, F and D cells are, respectively, 32, 8.8, and 6.6 amp. Another point that should be mentioned is that the internal resistance of a cell increases as its temperature is lowered; in a No. 6 cell, for example, the internal resistance rises by about 28 per cent when the temperature is lowered from 70°F to −4°F.

Although a dry cell undergoes rather complex chemical changes as it discharges, the principal chemical reaction is

$$Zn + 2MnO_2 \rightarrow ZnO \cdot Mn_2O_3$$

Note particularly that the central carbon electrode is inactive in the cell's chemical change and is, in fact, not the positive electrode, as it is frequently called; the function of the carbon rod is to act as a collector and conductor of electric current. As the equation shows, the true electrode surface is at the depolarizer, i.e., the MnO_2 where chemical ions through the electrolyte are changed to electron conduction through the black mixture and the carbon.

Lead-acid Batteries. Two important limitations of the primary cell are (1) its inability to deliver comparatively high values of current and (2) its rather short life (it must be discarded after it is depleted by chemical reaction). These disadvantages, recognized early in its development, were responsible for investigations that led to a cell possessing *reversible* chemical reactions, that is, one which can be "recharged" after each period of discharge. Called a *secondary cell*, it was first given practical form by Planté in 1859 when he devised a simple arrangement of lead plates in a dilute solution of sulphuric acid which could be charged and discharged repeatedly; in this original cell the charging process converted the positive plate to lead peroxide and the negative plate to a spongy lead, while the discharge process tended to transform the coating of peroxide on the positive plate to lead sulphate.

Since the conversion of natural lead by charging was found to be a costly and lengthy procedure, methods were later developed by which a properly prepared compound of lead, the active material, was *pasted* on the surface of a lead-alloy grid. Such a process was first patented by Faure in 1881 and is presently, in modified form, the standard method of manufacture of lead-acid batteries.

The essential parts of a lead-acid battery are:

1. The *positive plate*, which consists of a thin rectangular skeleton grid framework, cast of an alloy of lead and antimony, the mesh of which is filled with the active material *lead peroxide*. The latter is a dark brown crystalline material made up of small grains or particles to permit the electrolyte to penetrate to the plate freely.

2. The *negative plate*, consisting of a grid framework similar to that of the positive plate, the mesh of which is filled with a spongy form of lead which, as a porous mass, permits the electrolyte to pass to the grid freely.

3. The *separators*, which are thin sheets of nonconducting porous material (made of chemically treated wood, porous rubber, sheets of perforated rubber, or mats of glass fibers) used to insulate the positive plates from the negative plates; they are grooved on the side facing the positive plates to provide greater acid volume next to the surface for improved efficiency, to facilitate acid circulation within the cell, and to minimize the area of contact with the positive plate which has a highly oxidizing effect on wood separators.

4. The *electrolyte*, which is a solution of sulphuric acid (specific gravity of about 1.28 to 1.19) whose purpose it is to supply the sulphate that combines with the active materials on the plates to release the electrical energy.

A completely charged battery (often consisting of three, six, or more cells in series) will have an open-circuit voltage of about 2.1 volts per cell and will contain sulphuric acid electrolyte with a specific gravity of 1.28. During discharge, when the battery is delivering current to a load, the sulphuric acid acts on *both* the positive and negative plate materials to form a new chemical compound called *lead sulphate* ($PbSO_4$); this action tends to weaken the concentration of the sulphuric acid in direct proportion to the discharge current, with the result that the specific gravity of the electrolyte is reduced. As discharge proceeds, the specific gravity drops to 1.25 at 75 per cent charge, to 1.22 at 50 per cent charge, to 1.19 at 25 per cent charge, and to about 1.16 when the battery has little useful energy. This double-sulphate theory, involving the formation of sulphate on both plates, is conveniently expressed *for discharge* by the chemical equation

$$PbO_2 + Pb + 2H_2SO_4 \rightarrow 2PbSO_4 + 2H_2O$$

When an electric current is passed through the battery in a direction opposite to that of discharge, the lead sulphate on the plates is decomposed; this causes the sulphate to be expelled and to return to the solution, with the result that the concentration, i.e., specific gravity, of the electrolyte is restored to its original strength. The active material on the plates is thus freed of sulphate and is again ready to resume its function of converting chemical energy into electrical energy. Rewriting the foregoing chemical equation in reverse gives the reaction that takes place *on charge* as

$$2PbSO_4 + 2H_2O \rightarrow PbO_2 + Pb + 2H_2SO_4$$

The construction of the grids that hold the active materials is extremely important to the operation of the battery. Since its conductivity is about 10,000 times that of lead peroxide, it is mainly responsible for maintaining a uniform current distribution throughout the mass of active material. Under abnormal conditions, when the charging or discharging current is extremely high, the current distribution will be uneven, with the result that the active material on the plates will tend to buckle or crumble. To avoid nonuniform plate heating, it is customary to use light grids in batteries that are subject to heavy discharges of short duration, while heavy grids are used in batteries that are designed for long life and where the discharge is intermittent or extended over considerable periods of time.

Although the *size* of a battery is generally rated in terms of *ampere-hours*, its *discharge rate* will indicate the type of service for which it is designed. For the purposes of standardization, the Association of American Battery Manufacturers (AABM) and the Society of Automotive Engineers (SAE) have classified batteries on the basis of the following kinds of service:

The 20-hr Rating. This indicates the *lighting* ability of the battery. The fully charged battery is brought to a temperature of 80°F and is discharged at a rate equal to $\frac{1}{20}$ of the published 20-hr capacity in ampere-hours; under this condition the voltage should not drop below 1.75 volts per cell after a 20-hr period.

The 300-amp 0°F Rating. This indicates the *cranking* ability of the battery at low temperatures and is expressed as the number of minutes required for a fully charged three-cell battery to reach a terminal voltage of not less than 1.0 volt per cell when discharged at 300 amp for 4.5 min at a starting temperature of 0°F. (For a six-cell battery, it would reach a terminal voltage of not less than 1.0 volt per cell when discharged at 150 amp for 4.5 min.)

The 5-sec Voltage Rating. This is also the *cranking* ability of a battery at low temperatures. It is the voltage of a three-cell battery taken 5 sec after the start of the discharge at 300 amp at a starting temperature of 0°F; under this condition the voltage should not drop below 1.4 volts per cell.

The 4-hr Motor-coach Rating. This is the *lighting* ability of a battery used in *motor-coach service* and is expressed in ampere-hours. The fully charged battery is brought to a temperature of 80°F and is discharged at a rate equal to ¼ of the published ampere-hour rating; under this condition the terminal voltage should not drop below 1.75 volts per cell.

If a lead-acid battery is to deliver long, trouble-free service, several important precautions must be taken. These are:

1. It should not be overcharged, because overcharging decomposes the water in the electrolyte into hydrogen and oxygen gas, which, in turn, tend to wash the active material from the plates. Also, the decomposed water leaves the acid highly concentrated, with the result that wood separators, when used, and the negative plate material are harmed.

2. It should not be left with an insufficient charge for a long period of time, because a dense, hard, crystalline form of sulphate tends to form, which cannot be converted electrochemically into active material again. Also, an uncharged battery is liable to freeze during severe winter weather.

3. It should not be permitted to operate with the electrolyte below the top of the plates, because exposed wood separators, when used, char, and, with highly concentrated electrolyte the plates may become permanently sulphated and impaired; when the liquid drops sufficiently, distilled water should be added, since this is the only part of the electrolyte that is lost.

The Edison (Alkaline Type) Battery. A storage (secondary) battery that is completely different from the lead-acid type in its use of electrode-electrolyte materials and its construction and principle of operation is the familiar *Edison* battery. It consists of sets of finely perforated steel tubes and pockets that hold the active materials, which cannot be dislodged by the charge and discharge reactions to form an accumulation of sediment which might cause a short-circuit at the bottom of the cell. Being light in weight and extremely rugged and durable, the Edison battery is used extensively for the operation of battery-propelled trucks, locomotives and tractors, for lighting and other equipment in railway trains, and for marine applications.

The positive plates are made up of nickel-plated steel tubes, perforated with 560 holes per square inch and filled with nickelous hydroxide, the nonconducting active material, and flake nickel, the substance that provides the necessary conductivity. The negative plates consist of nickel-plated steel pockets with perforated sides that hold a finely divided mixture of metallic iron, ferrous oxide, and mercuric oxide. For the electrolyte, a 21 per cent solution of potassium hydroxide is used;

to this solution is added a small amount of lithium hydroxide because it has a beneficial effect upon the cell's capacity.

In a fully charged condition, the active material in the tubes of the positive electrode is nickel dioxide (NiO_2), while that in the pockets of the negative electrode is iron (Fe). During the discharge process, oxygen is transferred from the positive plates to the negative plates; this reaction reduces the NiO_2 to NiO and oxidizes the iron so that it changes to FeO. The chemical equation *for discharge* of the Edison battery is, therefore,

$$NiO_2 + Fe \rightarrow NiO + FeO$$

When the battery is charged, the positive and negative plates revert to their original condition and become, respectively, NiO_2 and Fe. Rewriting the foregoing equation in reverse gives the reaction that takes place *on charge* as

$$NiO + FeO \rightarrow NiO_2 + Fe$$

Note particularly that the electrolyte, potassium hydroxide in water ($2KOH + 2H_2O$) does not take part in the chemical reactions, but does, in fact, maintain its original concentration both on discharge and charge; there is, however, evidence that important changes do occur in the electrolyte within the pores of the plates. It is for this reason that the specific gravity of the electrolyte in an Edison battery, unlike that in the lead-acid type, does not indicate its condition of charge.

After an Edison battery is completely charged, its open-circuit voltage rises to about 1.47 volts; this voltage is reduced to about 1.42 volts after the battery stands idle for 6 hr. As the battery continues to discharge at its recommended *normal* rate, its terminal voltage drops gradually until, at 75 per cent charge it is 1.26 volts, at 50 per cent charge it is 1.22 volts, at 25 per cent charge it is 1.20 volts, and when completely discharged, it is 1.13 volts.

Although the chemical reactions during charge and discharge do not change the concentration of the electrolyte, the level of the solution does drop with continued service; this is because, on charge, electrolysis tends to decompose the water into hydrogen and oxygen, with the result that small particles of liquid escape through a valve in the filler cap near the top of the cell. Of special design, the hemispherical valve is equipped with a spring so that the cell may be opened for filling with electrolyte or water. The specific gravity of the original solution is usually about 1.2, but this tends to drop in service as distilled water is added to make up for liquid lost during the charging process; when the concentration of the electrolyte drops to about 1.16, it is customary to replace it with a new solution of the proper specific gravity.

The Edison battery possesses several important advantages over the lead-acid type that make it particularly suitable for severe and rugged service. Because the active materials are held in steel tubes and the plates are solidly assembled in a steel container, the battery is not subject to warping and buckling and can withstand shock, vibration, and abuse without harmful effects. Moreover, unlike the lead-acid battery, it has no fragile separators to break down; sulphation, sedimentation, or terminal corrosion cannot take place, and freezing, overcharging, or undercharging are not harmful. Also, its useful service life is normally indicated by a *gradual* decline in its capacity rather than by any sudden or complete loss of function. In fact, an Edison battery no longer capable of delivering full values of current can still be made to serve dependably in any other application for which its limited output is still ample.

APPENDIX 3

NATURAL SINES, COSINES, TANGENTS, AND COTANGENTS

0° to 2°

	sin	cos	tan	cot	
0	.000000	1.00000	.00000	∞	**90°**
5′	1454	1.00000	145	687.55	55′
10′	2909	1.00000	291	343.77	50′
15′	4363	0.99999	436	229.18	45′
20′	5818	998	582	171.89	40′
25′	7272	997	727	137.51	35′
30′	.008727	996	.00873	114.59	30′
35′	.010181	995	.01018	98.218	25′
40′	1635	993	164	85.940	20′
45′	3090	991	309	76.390	15′
50′	4544	989	455	68.750	10′
55′	5998	987	600	62.499	5′
1°	.017452	.99985	.01746	57.290	**89°**
5′	.01891	982	.01891	52.882	55′
10′	.02036	979	.02036	49.104	50′
15′	181	976	182	45.829	45′
20′	327	973	328	42.964	40′
25′	472	969	473	40.436	35′
30′	618	966	619	38.188	30′
35′	763	962	764	36.178	25′
40′	.02908	958	.02910	34.368	20′
45′	.03054	953	.03055	32.730	15′
50′	199	949	201	31.242	10′
55′	345	944	346	29.882	5′
2°	.03490	.99939	.03492	28.636	**88°**
5′	635	934	638	27.490	55′
10′	781	929	783	26.432	50′
15′	.03926	923	.03929	25.452	45′
20′	.04071	917	.04075	24.542	40′
25′	217	911	220	23.695	35′
30′	362	905	366	22.904	30′
35′	507	898	512	22.164	25′
40′	653	892	658	21.470	20′
45′	798	885	803	20.819	15′
50′	.04943	878	949	20.206	10′
55′	.05088	870	.05095	19.627	5′
	cos	sin	cot	tan	

87° to 90°

3° to 8°

	sin	cos	tan	cot	
3°	.05234	.99863	.05241	19.081	**87°**
10′	524	847	533	18.075	50′
20′	.05814	831	.05824	17.169	40′
30′	.06105	813	.06116	16.350	30′
40′	395	795	408	15.605	20′
50′	685	776	700	14.924	10′
4°	.06976	.99756	.06993	14.301	**86°**
10′	.07266	736	.07285	13.727	50′
20′	556	714	578	13.197	40′
30′	.07846	692	.07870	12.706	30
40′	.08136	668	.08163	12.251	20′
50′	426	644	456	11.826	10′
5°	.08716	.99619	.08749	11.430	**85°**
10′	.09005	.99594	.09042	11.059	50′
20′	295	567	335	10.712	40′
30′	.0585	540	629	.385	30′
40′	.9874	511	.09923	10.078	20′
50′	.10164	482	.10216	9.7882	10′
6°	.10453	.99452	.10510	9.5144	**84°**
10′	.10742	421	.10805	.2553	50′
20′	.11031	390	.11099	9.0098	40′
30′	320	357	394	8.7769	30′
40′	609	324	688	.5555	20′
50′	.11898	290	.11983	.3450	10′
7°	.12187	.99255	.12278	8.1443	**83°**
10′	476	219	574	7.9530	50′
20′	.12764	182	.12869	.7704	40′
30′	.13053	144	.13165	.5958	30′
40′	341	106	461	.4287	20′
50′	629	067	.13758	.2687	10′
8°	.13917	.99027	.14054	7.1154	**82°**
10′	.14205	.98986	351	6.9682	50′
20′	493	944	648	.8269	40′
30′	.14781	902	.14945	.6912	30′
40′	.15069	858	.15243	.5606	20′
50′	356	814	540	.4348	10′
	cos	sin	cot	tan	

81° to 87°

NATURAL SINES, COSINES, TANGENTS, AND COTANGENTS (*Continued*)

9° to 14°

	sin	cos	tan	cot	
9°	.15643	.98769	.15838	6.3138	**81°**
10′	.15931	723	.16137	.1970	50′
20′	.16218	676	435	6.0844	40′
30′	505	629	.16734	5.9758	30′
40′	.16792	580	.17033	.8708	20′
50′	.17078	531	333	.7694	10′
10°	.17365	.98481	.17633	5.6713	**80°**
10′	651	430	.17933	.5764	50′
20′	.17937	378	.18233	.4845	40′
30′	.18224	325	534	.3955	30′
40′	509	272	.18835	.3093	20′
50′	.18795	218	.19136	.2257	10′
11°	.19081	.98163	.19438	5.1446	**79°**
10′	366	107	.19740	5.0658	50′
20′	652	.98050	.20042	4.9894	40′
30′	.19937	.97992	345	.9152	30′
40′	.20222	934	648	.8430	20′
50′	507	875	.20952	.7729	10′
12°	.20791	.97815	.21256	4.7046	**78°**
10′	.21076	754	560	.6382	50′
20′	360	692	.21864	.5736	40′
30′	644	630	.22169	.5107	30′
40′	.21928	566	475	.4494	20′
50′	.22212	502	.22781	.3897	10′
13°	.22495	.97437	.23087	4.3315	**77°**
10′	.22778	371	393	.2747	50′
20′	.23062	304	.23700	.2193	40′
30′	345	237	.24008	.1653	30′
40′	627	169	316	.1126	20′
50′	.23910	100	624	.0611	10′
14°	.24192	.97030	.24933	4.0108	**76°**
10′	474	.96959	.25242	3.9617	50′
20′	.24756	887	552	.9136	40′
30′	.25038	815	.25862	.8667	30′
20′	320	742	.26172	.8208	20′
50′	601	667	483	.7760	10′
	cos	sin	cot	tan	

75° to 81°

15° to 20°

	sin	cos	tan	cot	
15°	.25882	.96593	.26795	3.7321	**75°**
10′	.26163	517	.27107	.6891	50′
20′	443	440	419	.6470	40′
30′	.26724	363	.27732	.6059	30′
40′	.27004	285	.28046	.5656	20′
50′	284	206	360	.5261	10′
16°	.27564	.96126	.28675	3.4874	**74°**
10′	.27843	.96046	.28990	.4475	50′
20′	.28123	.95964	.29305	.4124	40′
30′	402	882	621	.3759	30′
40′	680	799	.29938	.3402	20′
50′	.28959	715	.30255	.3052	10′
17°	.29237	.95630	.30573	3.2709	**73°**
10′	515	545	.30891	.2371	50′
20′	.29793	459	.31210	.2041	40′
30′	.30071	372	530	.1716	30′
40′	348	284	.31850	.1397	20′
50′	625	195	.32171	.1084	10′
18°	.30902	.95106	.32492	3.0777	**72°**
10′	.31178	.95015	.32814	.0475	50′
20′	454	.94924	.33136	3.0178	40′
30′	.31730	832	460	2.9887	30′
40′	.32006	740	.33783	.9600	20′
50′	282	646	.34108	.9319	10′
19°	.32557	.94552	.34433	2.9042	**71°**
10′	.32832	457	.34758	.8770	50′
20′	.33106	361	.35085	.8502	40′
30′	381	264	412	.8239	30′
40′	655	167	.35740	.7980	20′
50′	.33929	.94068	.36068	.7725	10′
20°	.34202	.93969	.36397	2.7475	**70°**
10′	475	869	.36727	.7228	50′
20′	.34748	769	.37057	.6985	40′
30′	.35021	667	388	.6746	30′
40′	293	565	.37720	.6511	20′
50′	565	462	.38053	.6279	10′
	cos	sin	cot	tan	

69° to 75°

Natural Sines, Cosines, Tangents, and Cotangents (*Continued*)

21° to 26° / **63° to 69°**

	sin	cos	tan	cot	
21°	.35837	.93358	.38386	2.6051	**69°**
10′	.36108	253	.38721	.5826	50′
20′	379	148	.39055	.5605	40′
30′	650	.93042	391	.5386	30′
40′	.36921	.92935	.39727	.5172	20′
50′	.37191	827	.40065	.4960	10′
22°	.37461	.92718	.40403	2.4751	**68°**
10′	730	609	.50741	.4545	50′
20′	.37999	499	.41081	.4342	40′
30′	.38268	388	421	.4142	30′
40′	537	276	.41763	.3945	20′
50′	.38805	164	.42105	.3750	10′
23°	.39073	.92050	.42447	2.3559	**67°**
10′	341	.91936	.42791	.3369	50′
20′	608	822	.43136	.3183	40′
30′	.39875	706	481	.2998	30′
40′	.40141	590	.43828	.2817	20′
50′	408	472	.44175	.2637	10′
24°	.40674	.91355	.44523	2.2460	**66°**
10′	.40939	236	.44872	.2286	50′
20′	.41204	.91116	.45222	.2113	40′
30′	469	.90996	573	.1943	30′
40′	734	875	.45924	.1775	20′
50′	.41998	753	.46277	.1609	10′
25°	.42262	.90631	.46631	2.1445	**65°**
10′	525	507	.46985	.1283	50′
20′	.42788	383	.47341	.1123	40′
30′	.43051	259	.47698	2.0965	30′
40′	313	133	.48055	809	20′
50′	575	.90007	414	655	10′
26°	.43837	.89879	.48773	2.0503	**64°**
10′	.44098	752	.49134	353	50′
20′	359	623	495	204	40′
30′	620	493	.49858	2.0057	30′
40′	.44880	363	.50222	1.9912	20′
50′	.45140	232	587	768	10′
	cos	sin	cot	tan	

27° to 32° / **57° to 63°**

	sin	cos	tan	cot	
27°	.45399	.89101	.50953	1.9626	**63°**
10′	658	.88968	.51319	486	50′
20′	.45917	835	.51688	347	40′
30′	.46175	701	.52057	210	30′
40′	433	566	427	.9074	20′
50′	690	431	.52798	1.8940	10′
28°	.46947	.88295	.53171	1.8807	**62°**
10′	.47204	158	545	676	50′
20′	460	.88020	.53920	546	40′
30′	716	.87882	.54296	418	30′
40′	.47971	743	.54673	291	20′
50′	.48226	603	.55051	165	10′
29°	.48481	.87462	.55431	1.8040	**61°**
10′	735	321	.55812	1.7917	50′
20′	.48989	178	.56194	796	40′
30′	.49242	.87036	577	675	30′
40′	495	.86892	.56962	556	20′
50′	.49748	748	.57348	437	10′
30°	.50000	.86603	.57735	1.7321	**60°**
10′	252	457	.58124	205	50′
20′	503	310	513	.7090	40′
30′	.50754	163	.58905	1.6977	30′
40′	.51004	.86015	.59297	864	20′
50′	254	.85866	.59691	753	10′
31°	.51504	.85717	.60086	1.6643	**59°**
10′	.51763	567	483	534	50′
20′	.52002	416	.60881	426	40′
30′	250	264	.61280	319	30′
40′	498	.85112	.61681	212	20′
50′	745	.84959	.62083	107	10′
32°	.52992	.84805	.62487	1.6003	**58°**
10′	.53238	650	.62892	1.5900	50′
20′	484	495	.63299	798	40′
30′	730	339	.63707	697	30′
40′	.53975	182	.64117	597	20′
50′	.54220	.84025	528	497	10′
	cos	sin	cot	tan	

Natural Sines, Cosines, Tangents, and Cotangents (*Continued*)

33° to 38°

	sin	cos	tan	cot	
33°	.54464	.83867	.64941	1.5399	**57°**
10′	708	708	.65355	301	50′
20′	.54951	549	.65771	204	40′
30′	.55194	389	.66189	108	30′
40′	436	228	.66608	.5013	20′
50′	678	.83066	.67028	1.4919	10′
34°	.55919	.82904	.67451	1.4826	**56°**
10′	.56160	741	.67875	733	50′
20′	401	577	.68301	641	40′
30′	641	413	.68728	550	30′
40′	.56880	248	.69157	460	20′
50′	.57119	.82082	.69588	370	10′
35°	.57358	.81915	.70021	1.4281	**55°**
10′	596	748	455	193	50′
20′	.57833	580	.70891	106	40′
30′	.58070	412	.71329	.4019	30′
40′	307	242	.71769	1.3934	20′
50′	543	.81072	.72211	848	10′
36°	.58779	.80902	.72654	1.3764	**54°**
10′	.59014	730	.73100	680	50′
20′	248	558	547	597	40′
30′	482	386	.73996	514	30′
40′	716	212	.74447	432	20′
50′	.59949	.80038	.74900	351	10′
37°	.60182	.79864	.75355	1.3270	**53°**
10′	414	688	.75812	190	50′
20′	645	512	.76272	111	40′
30′	.60876	335	.76733	.3032	30′
40′	.61107	.79158	.77196	1.2954	20′
50′	337	.78980	.77661	876	10′
38°	.61566	.78801	.78129	1.2799	**52°**
10′	.61795	622	.78598	723	50′
20′	.62024	442	.79070	647	40′
30′	251	261	.79544	572	30′
40′	479	.78079	.80020	497	20′
50′	706	.77897	498	423	10′
	cos	sin	cot	tan	

51° to 57°

39° to 45°

	sin	cos	tan	cot	
39°	.62932	.77715	.80978	1.2349	**51°**
10′	.63158	531	.81461	276	50′
20′	383	347	.81946	203	40′
30′	608	.77162	.82434	131	30′
40′	.63832	.76977	.82923	.2059	20′
50′	.64056	791	.83415	1.1988	10′
40°	.64279	.76604	.83910	1.1918	**50°**
10′	501	417	.84407	847	50′
20′	723	229	.84906	778	40′
30′	.64945	.76041	.85408	708	30′
40′	.65166	.75851	.85912	640	20′
50′	386	661	.86419	571	10′
41°	.65606	.75471	.86929	1.1504	**49°**
10′	.65825	280	.87441	436	50′
20′	.66044	.75088	.87955	369	40′
30′	262	.74896	.88473	303	30′
40′	480	703	.88992	237	20′
50′	697	509	.89515	171	10′
42°	.66913	.74314	.90040	1.1106	**48°**
10′	.67129	.74120	.90569	1.1041	50′
20′	344	.73924	.91099	1.0977	40′
30′	559	728	.91633	913	30′
40′	773	531	.92170	850	20′
50′	.67987	333	.92709	786	10′
43°	.68200	.73135	.93252	1.0724	**47°**
10′	412	.72937	.93707	661	50′
20′	624	737	.94345	599	40′
30′	.68835	537	.94896	538	30′
40′	.69046	337	.95451	477	20′
50′	256	.72136	.96008	416	10′
44°	.69466	.71934	.96569	1.0355	**46°**
10′	675	732	.97133	295	50′
20′	.69883	529	.97700	235	40′
30′	.70091	325	.98270	176	30′
40′	298	.71121	.98843	117	20′
50′	505	.70916	.99420	058	10′
45°	.70711	.70711	1.00000	1.0000	**45°**
	cos	sin	cot	tan	

45° to 51°

APPENDIX 4

COMMON LOGARITHMS OF NUMBERS

Number	0	1	2	3	4	5	6	7	8	9
10	0000	0043	0086	0128	0170	0212	0253	0294	0334	0374
11	0414	0453	0492	0531	0569	0607	0645	0682	0719	0755
12	0792	0828	0864	0899	0934	0969	1004	1038	1072	1106
13	1139	1173	1206	1239	1271	1303	1335	1367	1399	1430
14	1461	1492	1523	1553	1584	1614	1644	1673	1703	1732
15	1761	1790	1818	1847	1875	1903	1931	1959	1987	2014
16	2041	2068	2095	2122	2148	2175	2201	2227	2253	2279
17	2304	2330	2355	2380	2405	2430	2455	2480	2504	2529
18	2553	2577	2601	2625	2648	2672	2695	2718	2742	2765
19	2788	2810	2833	2856	2878	2900	2923	2945	2967	2989
20	3010	3032	3054	3075	3096	3118	3139	3160	3181	3201
21	3222	3243	3263	3284	3304	3324	3345	3365	3385	3404
22	3424	3444	3464	3483	3502	3522	3541	3560	3579	3598
23	3617	3636	3655	3674	3692	3711	3729	3747	3766	3784
24	3802	3820	3838	3856	3874	3892	3909	3927	3945	3962
25	3979	3997	4014	4031	4048	4065	4082	4099	4116	4133
26	4150	4166	4183	4200	4216	4232	4249	4265	4281	4298
27	4314	4330	4346	4362	4378	4393	4409	4425	4440	4456
28	4472	4487	4502	4518	4533	4548	4564	4579	4594	4609
29	4624	4639	4654	4669	4683	4698	4713	4728	4742	4757
30	4771	4786	4800	4814	4829	4843	4857	4871	4886	4900
31	4914	4928	4942	4955	4969	4983	4997	5011	5024	5038
32	5051	5065	5079	5092	5105	5119	5132	5145	5159	5172
33	5185	5198	5211	5224	5237	5250	5263	5276	5289	5302
34	5315	5328	5340	5353	5366	5378	5391	5403	5416	5428
35	5441	5453	5465	5478	5490	5502	5514	5527	5539	5551
36	5563	5575	5587	5599	5611	5623	5635	5647	5658	5670
37	5682	5694	5705	5717	5729	5740	5752	5763	5775	5786
38	5798	5809	5821	5832	5843	5855	5866	5877	5888	5899
39	5911	5922	5933	5944	5955	5966	5977	5988	5999	6010
40	6021	6031	6042	6053	6064	6075	6085	6096	6107	6117
41	6128	6138	6149	6160	6170	6180	6191	6201	6212	6222
42	6232	6243	6253	6263	6274	6284	6294	6304	6314	6325
43	6335	6345	6355	6365	6375	6385	6395	6405	6415	6425
44	6435	6444	6454	6464	6474	6484	6493	6503	6513	6522
45	6532	6542	6551	6561	6571	6580	6590	6599	6609	6618
46	6628	6637	6646	6656	6665	6675	6684	6693	6702	6712
47	6721	6730	6739	6749	6758	6767	6776	6785	6794	6803
48	6812	6821	6830	6839	6848	6857	6866	6875	6884	6893
49	6902	6911	6920	6928	6937	6946	6955	6964	6972	6981

COMMON LOGARITHMS OF NUMBERS (*Continued*)

Number	0	1	2	3	4	5	6	7	8	9
50	6990	6998	7007	7016	7024	7033	7042	7050	7059	7067
51	7076	7084	7093	7101	7110	7118	7126	7135	7143	7152
52	7160	7168	7177	7185	7193	7202	7210	7218	7226	7235
53	7243	7251	7259	7267	7275	7284	7292	7300	7308	7316
54	7324	7332	7340	7348	7356	7364	7372	7380	7388	7396
55	7404	7412	7419	7427	7435	7443	7451	7459	7466	7474
56	7482	7490	7497	7505	7513	7520	7528	7536	7543	7551
57	7559	7566	7574	7582	7589	7597	7604	7612	7619	7627
58	7634	7642	7649	7657	7664	7672	7679	7686	7694	7701
59	7709	7716	7723	7731	7738	7745	7752	7760	7767	7774
60	7782	7789	7796	7803	7810	7818	7825	7832	7839	7846
61	7853	7860	7868	7875	7882	7889	7896	7903	7910	7917
62	7924	7931	7938	7945	7952	7959	7966	7973	7980	7987
63	7993	8000	8007	8014	8021	8028	8035	8041	8048	8055
64	8062	8069	8075	8082	8089	8096	8102	8109	8116	8122
65	8129	8136	8142	8149	8156	8162	8169	8176	8182	8189
66	8195	8202	8209	8215	8222	8228	8235	8241	8248	8254
67	8261	8267	8274	8280	8287	8293	8299	8306	8312	8319
68	8325	8331	8338	8344	8351	8357	8363	8370	8376	8382
69	8388	8395	8401	8407	8414	8420	8426	8432	8439	8445
70	8451	8457	8463	8470	8476	8482	8488	8494	8500	8506
71	8513	8519	8525	8531	8537	8543	8549	8555	8561	8567
72	8573	8579	8585	8591	8597	8603	8609	8615	8621	8627
73	8633	8639	8645	8651	8657	8663	8669	8675	8681	8686
74	8692	8698	8704	8710	8716	8722	8727	8733	8739	8745
75	8751	8756	8762	8768	8774	8779	8785	8791	8797	8802
76	8808	8814	8820	8825	8831	8837	8842	8848	8854	8859
77	8865	8871	8876	8882	8887	8893	8899	8904	8910	8915
78	8921	8927	8932	8938	8943	8949	8954	8960	8965	8971
79	8976	8982	8987	8993	8998	9004	9009	9015	9020	9025
80	9031	9036	9042	9047	9053	9058	9063	9069	9074	9079
81	9085	9090	9096	9101	9106	9112	9117	9122	9128	9133
82	9138	9143	9149	9154	9159	9165	9170	9175	9180	9186
83	9191	9196	9201	9206	9212	9217	9222	9227	9232	9238
84	9243	9248	9253	9258	9263	9269	9274	9279	9284	9289
85	9294	9299	9304	9309	9315	9320	9325	9330	9335	9340
86	9345	9350	9355	9360	9365	9370	9375	9380	9385	9390
87	9395	9400	9405	9410	9415	9420	9425	9430	9435	9440
88	9445	9450	9455	9460	9465	9469	9474	9479	9484	9489
89	9494	9499	9504	9509	9513	9518	9523	9528	9533	9538

Common Logarithms of Numbers (*Continued*)

Number	0	1	2	3	4	5	6	7	8	9
90	9542	9547	9552	9557	9562	9566	9571	9576	9581	9586
91	9590	9595	9600	9605	9609	9614	9619	9624	9628	9633
92	9638	9643	9647	9652	9657	9661	9666	9671	9675	9680
93	9685	9689	9694	9699	9703	9708	9713	9717	9722	9727
94	9731	9736	9741	9745	9750	9754	9759	9763	9768	9773
95	9777	9782	9786	9791	9795	9800	9805	9809	9814	9818
96	9823	9827	9832	9836	9841	9845	9850	9854	9859	9863
97	9868	9872	9877	9881	9886	9890	9894	9899	9903	9908
98	9912	9917	9921	9926	9930	9934	9939	9943	9948	9952
99	9956	9961	9965	9969	9974	9978	9983	9987	9991	9996

VISUAL AIDS

The films listed below and on the following pages can be used as visual aids to the study of this book. Since many of the films can be used in the study of different chapters, it is recommended that they be reviewed before using in order to determine their suitability for particular groups or units of work.

Motion pictures and filmstrips are included in this bibliography, the character of each being indicated by the abbreviations MP and FS. Immediately following this identification is the name of the producer and, if different from the producer, the name of the distributor. Abbreviations are used for names of producers and distributors, and these abbreviations are identified in the list of sources at the end of the bibliography. In most instances, the films can be borrowed or rented from local or state 16mm film libraries. (A nation-wide list of these local sources is given in *A Directory of 2660 16mm Film Libraries*, available for 50 cents from the Superintendent of Documents, Washington 25, D.C.) Unless otherwise indicated, the motion pictures are 16mm black-and-white sound films and the filmstrips are 35mm black-and-white and silent. The length of motion pictures is given in minutes (min) and that of filmstrips in frames (fr).

This bibliography is a selective one, and film users should examine the latest edition and supplements of *Educational Film Guide* and *Filmstrip Guide*, published by the H. W. Wilson Co., New York. The *Guides*, standard reference books, are available in most school, college, and public libraries. Readers should also write to the National Electrical Manufacturers Association for a copy of *Nema Movie Guide* and to individual companies such as General Electric and Westinghouse for charts, posters, models, and other visual aids dealing with electrical circuits.

Alternating Current (FS, USAF/UWF, 50 fr) An elementary introduction to the principles of alternating current. Demonstrates and explains Lenz' law, simple wave alternator, frequency, effective value, voltage-current-time relationship, and power.

Amperes, Volts, and Ohms (MP, USN/UWF, 8 min) Explains the meaning, relationship, and measurement of amperes, volts, and ohms. Correlated filmstrip, same title, 23 fr, also available.

Basic Electricity (MP, USAF/UWF, 20 min color) An animated cartoon explaining the fundamentals of electricity, including voltage, current, resistance, magnetic fields, induction, primary and secondary coils, series and parallel circuits.

Basic Electronics (MP, USAF/UWF, 18 min color) An animated cartoon explaining the meaning of atoms and electrons, vacuum tube, cathode, rectifier tube, amplifier tube, grid, and bridge circuits.

Capacitance (MP, USN/UWF, 31 min) Demonstrates electron flow through a circuit, the charging and discharging of capacitors, variations of a charge on a capacitor in relation to time, and the behavior of capacitance with alternating current. Correlated filmstrip, same title, 22 fr, also available.

Circuit Testing with Meters and Multimeters. Part 1: Theory (MP, USA/UWF, 30 min) Explains the theory and construction of meters and shows various types of meters used for circuit testing and associated external equipment.

Circuit Testing with Meters and Multimeters. Part 2: Practical Application (MP, USA/UWF, 37 min) Demonstrates how to use meters in testing transformers, capacitors, resistors, telephone loop circuits, etc.

Coils and Electric Currents (MP, Ed Pic, 9 min) Nature of the fields of force about a current-carrying wire, and the theory of solenoids and electromagnets, induction coils, and electric motors.

Current and Electromotive Force (MP, USN/UWF, 11 min) Explains electron theory, the arrangement of molecules, building up of current, conductors, electromotive force, resistance, and chemical and mechanical sources of electromotive force. Correlated filmstrip, same title, 38 fr, also available.

D-C Motor. Part 1: Mechanical Overhaul (MP, USOE/UWF, 20 min) How to test for electrical and mechanical faults; dismantle d-c motor; turn the commutator; repair and replace field coils; assemble the motor; and adjust and make final tests. Correlated filmstrip, same title, 37 fr, also available.

D-C Motor. Part 2: Rewinding (MP, USOE/UWF, 37 min) How to dismantle and clean an armature core; determine commutator pitch; reinsulate the core; insert coils; band an armature; shape coil ends; lay in and solder leads; balance and impregnate the armature; and turn a commutator. Correlated filmstrip, same title, 43 fr, also available.

Direct-Current Controllers (MP, USOE/UWF, 15 min) Shows shunt motors and direct-current controllers in operation and, by animation, a direct-current faceplate controller connected to a shunt motor. Correlated filmstrip, same title, 27 fr, also available.

Electrical Circuit Faults (MP, USOE/UWF, 19 min) How to test for and locate common circuit faults, grounds, resistance deterioration, and interference in circuits. Correlated filmstrip, same title, 39 fr, also available.

Electrodynamics (MP, EBF, 11 min) Presents the fundamental principles of current electricity and electromagnetism, including induction by a magnet d-c generator.

Elements of Electrical Circuits (MP, EBF, 11 min) Explains with animated drawings and photographic demonstrations the nature of electric circuits and currents, including conductors, insulators, and factors affecting resistance. Filmstrip with same title covering same subject matter, 89 fr, also available.

Inductance (MP, USN/UWF, 35 min) Shows how a magnetic force reacts around a coil, the nature of self-inductance, and how to increase the inductance of a coil. Correlated filmstrip, same title, 38 fr, also available.

Maintaining Good Voltage on Rural Distribution Lines (MP, USDA, 37 min) An electrical engineer explains, through blackboard illustrations, methods that may be used to evaluate voltage conditions on rural distributive systems of electricity and suggests means for voltage improvement.

Ohm's Law (MP, USA/UWF, 19 min) Explains the elements of electricity; electrical energy, its source, transmission, and use; composition of matter; use of force and energy; how Ohm's law functions; resistance; and the purpose and use of meters.

Principles of Electricity (MP, GE, 20 min color) Explains the principles involved in the flow of electricity; defines volt, ampere, and ohm; and covers magnetism and magnetic fields as applied to motors.

RCL: Resistance-Capacitance (MP, USN/UWF, 34 min) Explains current and voltage in relation to time; voltage and current curves; the relationship of current and voltage; the measurement of voltage at source; the addition of phase components; and the effect of impedance on resonance.

Repulsion Motor Principles (MP, USOE/UWF, 18 min) Explains construction of repulsion motor; rotor circuits and effect of brush position; short-circuiting and brush-lifting mechanism; and applications of repulsion motors. Correlated filmstrip, same title, 40 fr, also available.

Rotating Magnetic Fields (MP, USOE/UWF, 13 min) Explains a rotating magnetic field pattern; three-phase winding in a demonstration stator; factors that cause rotation of the magnetic field; and the construction of polyphase motors. Correlated filmstrip, same title, 44 fr, also available.

Series and Parallel Circuits (MP, EBF, 11 min) Explains the relationship between resistance, current, and voltage in series and parallel circuits and discusses the advantages and disadvantages of each type of circuit.

Series and Parallel Circuits (MP, USN/UWF, 8 min) Illustrates series and parallel circuits, explaining current and voltage drop across each lamp. Correlated filmstrip, same title, 26 fr, also available.

Single-phase and Polyphase Circuits (MP, USOE/UWF, 17 min) Explains a single-phase synchronous generator; the use of sine curves to illustrate flow changes; a two-phase system and three-phase system; and ways to simplify wiring. Correlated filmstrip, same title, 51 fr, also available.

Traveling Electrical Waves (MP, MIT, 50 min silent) Series of studies, in animation, of the behavior of direct-current waves on a power transmission line. For students in electrical engineering.

Using Electricity Safely (FS, McGraw, 33 fr) Cautions in using and repairing electrical equipment—making splices, soldering, repairing cords, connecting plugs and sockets, etc.

Volt-ohmmeter Operation (MP, USN/UWF, 15 min) Shows how to operate a volt-ohmmeter, Weston and other types, including the selection of the proper scale range, adjustment for zero on the scale, and the setup for either direct or alternating current.

What Is Electricity? (MP, EBF, 14 min) Presents classical electrostatic experiments, including those of Oersted and Faraday, and illustrates industrial achievements made possible by man's electrical knowledge.

SOURCES OF FILMS

EBF—Encyclopaedia Britannica Films, Inc., Wilmette, Ill.
Ed Pic—Edited Pictures System, 165 W. 46th St., New York 19, N. Y.
GE—General Electric Company, Schenectady, N. Y.
McGraw—McGraw-Hill Book Company, Inc., Text-Film Dept., 330 W. 42d St., New York 36, N. Y.
MIT—Massachusetts Institute of Technology, Cambridge, Mass.
*USA—U.S. Dept. of the Army, Washington 25, D. C.
*USAF—U.S. Dept. of the Air Force, Washington 25, D. C.
USDA—U.S. Dept. of Agriculture, Washington 25, D. C.
*USN—U.S. Dept. of the Navy, Washington 25, D. C.
*USOE—U.S. Office of Education, Washington 25, D. C.
UWF—United World Films, Inc., 1445 Park Ave., New York 29, N. Y.

* Films distributed by United World Films.

INDEX

K

L

M

N

ANSWERS

Chapter 1

1. 0.8 amp. **2.** (*a*) 146 coulombs; (*b*) 3.4 amp. **3.** 0.0107 in. per sec. **4.** 3.27×10^{26}. **5.** 3.62 amp. **6.** 0.0164 sq. in. **7.** 2.42. **8.** 366 ft. **9.** 3.77 ohms. **10.** (*a*) zero; (*b*) 17.95 amp. **11.** (*a*) 5 amp; (*b*) 2.5 amp. **12.** (*a*) 9.0 amp; (*b*) 3.4 amp. **13.** (*a*) 7.6 amp; (*b*) 4.8 amp. **14.** 7.85 amp. **15.** 15.7 amp.

Chapter 2

1. 6.07 ohms. **2.** 260 turns. **3.** 74 turns. **4.** (*a*) 660 ohm–cir mils per ft; (*b*) Nichrome II. **5.** 175 ohms. **6.** 0.065 ohm. **7.** (*a*) 10.85; (*b*) 1.808. **8.** 60 per cent. **9.** 55.5 ohms. **10.** 7 ohms. **11.** 0.0042, 9.39 ohms. **12.** 250°C. **13.** 61°C rise. **14.** 0.00715 ohm. **15.** 104 mils. **16.** 0.827 ohm. **17.** 169. **18.** 86.3 ohms–cir mils per ft. **19.** 34.2 per cent. **20.** 317 megohms per mile. **21.** 1,670 megohms per 1,000 ft.

Chapter 3

1. $R_B = 80$ ohms, $R_C = 90$ ohms. **2.** (*a*) 18.4 amp, 110.4 volts; (*b*) 9.2 volts. **3.** (*a*) $I_B = 3.6$ amp, $I_C = 1.8$ amp; (*b*) 120 volts; (*c*) $R_B = 33.3$ ohms, $R_C = 66.6$ ohms. **4.** (*a*) 144 ohms; (*b*) 17.7 ohms; (*c*) 9.3 ohms. **5.** 144 volts, 18 amp. **6.** (*a*) 0.072 to 1.6 amp; (*b*) 31 ohms. **7.** 45.8 watts. **8.** 21.6 volts. **9.** $R_A = 9$ ohms, $R_B = 12$ ohms, $R_C = 15$ ohms. **10.** $I_A = 1.25$ amp, $I_B = 48.75$ amp. **11.** (*a*) 124.8 volts; (*b*) 192 watts. **12.** (*a*) 28 ohms; (*b*) 26 ohms; (*c*) 365.4 watts. **13.** (*a*) $E_A = 30$ volts, $E_B = 90$ volts; (*b*) $E_A = 48$ volts, $E_B = 72$ volts. **14.** (*a*) 124 volts; (*b*) $I_t = 15.5$ amp; (*c*) $R_5 = 35$ ohms. **15.** (*a*) 180 amp; (*b*) 10 volts; (*c*) 240 volts. **16.** 15 minutes, 30 ohms. **17.** 235 ft. **18.** 24 ohms. **19.** $7.76. **20.** 40, 80, 180, and 360 ohms. **21.** 36 and 72 ohms. **22.** 27, 13.5, 9, 4.5, and 1.5 volts. **23.** (*a*) 28 ohms; (*b*) 8 amp; (*c*) 64 watts.

Chapter 4

1. (*a*) $I_F - I_E - I_B = 0$; (*b*) $E_B + I_CR_C + I_DR_D - I_FR_F - I_BR_B = 0$. **2.** (*a*) $I_L = 40$ amp, $I_A = 20$ amp, $I_B = 20$ amp; (*b*) $V_L = 20$ volts; (*c*) $P_L = 800$ watts, $P_A = 480$ watts, $P_B = 520$ watts. **3.** (*a*) 12 amp; (*b*) 13 amp. **4.** 2.5 amp. **5.** 782 watts. **6.** (*a*) $I_A = 16.8$ amp, $I_B = 25.2$ amp; (*b*) $I_A = 15.2$ amp, $I_B = 22.8$ amp. **7.** (*a*) 240 watts; (*b*) 60 watts; (*c*) 15 watts. **8.** $R_L = 90$ ohms, $P_L = 25.6$ watts. **9.** $V_A = 226.8$ volts, $V_B = 231.6$ volts. **10.** (*a*) $I_A = 140$ amp, $I_B = 125$ amp; (*b*) $V_L = 216$ volts. **11.** (*a*) $I_1 = 30$ amp, $I_2 = 50$ amp; (*b*) $I_B = 80$ amp; (*c*) $P_B = 8{,}960$ watts. **12.** (*a*) $I_1 = 80$ amp, $I_2 = 120$ amp; (*b*) $E_A = 235$ volts, $E_B = 239$ volts. **13.** (*a*) $E_A = 106.5$ volts, $E_B = 115.5$ volts, $E_C = 222$ volts; (*b*) $P_A = 5{,}325$ watts, $P_B = 3{,}465$ watts, $P_C = 4{,}640$ watts. **14.** 20 amp. **15.** $I_A = I_B = 40$ amp. **16.** (*a*) 48 ohms;

(*b*) 2.5 amp. **17.** (*a*) 10 ohms; (*b*) 36 volts; (*c*) 2 amp. **18.** (*a*) 0.8 ohm; (*b*) 180 watts, 50 per cent. **19.** (*a*) $I_L = 43.3$ amp; (*b*) $E_L = 52$ volts; (*c*) $P_L = 2{,}170$ watts. **20.** (*a*) $I_A = 11.05$ amp, $I_B = 8.83$ amp, $I_C = 7.36$ amp; (*b*) $I_L = 27.24$ amp, $P_L = 594$ watts. **21.** (*a*) 25 amp; (*b*) 0.417 ohm.

Chapter 5

1. 15.75 gauss. **2.** 9.3 gauss, away from observer. **3.** (*a*) 5.87 gauss; (*b*) 1.59 gauss. **4.** 55.2 gauss. **5.** 3.75 in. **6.** zero. **7.** 10.5 gauss. **8.** 0.23 in. **9.** (*a*) 60 gauss; (*b*) 21.2 gauss. **10.** (*a*) 24.6 gauss; (*b*) 12.85 gauss. **11.** (*a*) 22.9 gauss; (*b*) 2.95 gauss. **12.** (*a*) 200 gauss; (*b*) 100 gauss. **13.** No. **14.** (*a*) 39.4 gauss, vertically up; (*b*) 39.4 gauss, vertically up. **15.** (*a*) 316.2 gauss; (*b*) 218.3 gauss. **16.** (*a*) 300.4 gauss; (*b*) 194.6 gauss. **17.** 12 inches to right of wire *B*. **18.** 5.82 gauss, 29° with horizontal, northwest. **19.** 9.45 lb. **20.** 2.57 lb. **21.** 0.455 lb repulsion. **22.** 1.685 lb to the right. **23.** 1.73 lb. **24.** 1.58 lb vertically up. **25.** 1.98×10^6 maxwells. **26.** 3.95×10^6 maxwells.

Chapter 6

1. 131,000 maxwells. **2.** 235. **3.** 0.009375 in. **4.** 1,385. **5.** 59,600 maxwells per sq in. **6.** 0.008. **7.** 3,320 amp-turns. **8.** 260,000 maxwells. **9.** 1,590 amp-turns. **10.** 620 lb. **11.** (*a*) 36,800 maxwells per sq in.; (*b*) 63,600 maxwells per sq in. **12.** (*a*) 100 lb; (*b*) 53.2 ohms. **13.** 1,455 amp-turns. **14.** 370 lb. **15.** $B_{\text{in}_A} = 74{,}500$ maxwells per sq in., $B_{\text{in}_B} = 50{,}800$ maxwells per sq in. **16.** 477,000 maxwells. **17.** (*a*) 1,295 amp-turns; (*b*) 30,000 maxwells per sq in. **18.** 26,800 maxwells per sq in. **19.** 3,150 amp-turns. **20.** No. 14 AWG wire, 4,107 cm. **21.** (*a*) 9,200 amp-turns; (*b*) 4,600 amp-turns. **22.** (*a*) 93,300 maxwells per sq in.; (*b*) 87,200 maxwells per sq in.

Chapter 7

1. 8.47 dyne-cm per deg. **2.** 6 per cent low. **3.** (*a*) 0.05102 ohm; (*b*) 0.05 ohm. **4.** 7,497.5 ohms. **5.** 7,500 ohms. **6.** (*a*) 0.02 amp; (*b*) 24.98 amp. **7.** 75 volts. **8.** (*a*) 2; (*b*) 4; (*c*) 3.4. **9.** 27,700 ohms, tapped at 1,200 ohms and 14,700 ohms. **10.** 154 volts. **11.** 119 volts, 221 volts. **12.** 278.5 volts. **13.** (*a*) 42.5 ohms; (*b*) 51.8 per cent deflection. **14.** 35 per cent deflection. **15.** 1,682 ohms. **16.** 3,150 ft. **17.** 200, 60, 0.9. **18.** 3.75 megohms.

Chapter 8

1. 0.8 henry. **2.** 0.2 henry. **3.** Zero. **4.** 92 turns. **5.** 0.465 to 1.21 henrys. **6.** (*a*) $i = 6(1 - \epsilon^{-80t})$; (*b*) 0.0125 sec, 3.792 amp. **7.** 240 amp per sec. **8.** 2.36 amp. **9.** (*a*) 75 amp per sec, 48 volts; (*b*) 20 volts, 31.2 amp per sec. **10.** (*a*) 0.192 amp; (*b*) 0.272 amp. **11.** $i = 0.312 - 0.12\epsilon^{-625t}$. **12.** 375 amp per sec. **13.** (*a*) $i = 1.6\epsilon^{-700t}$; (*b*) 0.00143 sec, 0.589 amp; (*c*) 1,120 amp per sec; (*d*) 1.146 amp. **14.** (*a*) $i = 2\epsilon^{-1000t}$; (*b*) 0.001 sec, 0.736 amp; (*c*) −200 amp per sec. **15.** 480 volts, 400 amp per sec. **16.** 360 volts, 39.6 amp per sec. **17.** 100 ohms. **18.** 322 joules. **19.** 110 joules, 212 joules. **20.** 3.91 amp. **21.** 0.712. **22.** 0.393. **23.** $M = 0.013$, $L_A = 0.069$, $L_B = 0.042$. **24.** $E_A = 120$ volts, $E_B = 68.6$ volts. **25.** 51.5 volts. **26.** $M = 0.09$, $L_A = L_B = 0.36$, $K = 0.25$.

Chapter 9

1. (*a*) 0.015 coulomb; (*b*) 0.8 sec. **2.** 320 volts. **3.** 5.88×10^{16} elec. **4.** 75 μf. **5.** 3.6. **6.** 0.117 μf. **7.** 342 glass and 343 aluminum sheets. **8.** 2.53 μf. **9.** 184 ft. **10.** (*a*) 27 μf; (*b*) 1.8 μf. **11.** (*a*) 9, 21, and 24 μf; (*b*) 2.57 and 4.5 μf. **12.** 2.67, 4.67, and 6 μf. **13.** 7.5, 8.57, and 20 μf. **14.** 0.00072 coulomb, 30 and 90 volts. **15.** 0.00018 and 0.00054 coulomb, 22.5 volts. **16.** (*a*) 12.5 μf; (*b*) 0.0075 coulomb; (*c*) 250, 200, and 150 volts. **17.** (*a*) 0.00192, 0.00239, 0.00319 coulomb; (*b*) 117.5 μf; (*c*) 63.75 volts. **18.** 6 μf. **19.** 35 μf. **20.** (*a*) 30 μf; (*b*) $E_{10} = 240$ volts, $E_{30} = 160$ volts, $E_{20} = E_{40} = 80$ volts. **21.** (*a*) 4.8 μf; (*b*) $E_{10} = 115.2$ volts, $E_{20} = 57.6$ volts, $E_{30} = 38.4$ volts, $E_{40} = 28.8$ volts. **22.** (*a*) 100 μf; (*b*) $Q_{10} = 0.0024$ coulomb, $Q_{20} = 0.0048$ coulomb, $Q_{30} = 0.0072$ coulomb, $Q_{40} = 0.0096$ coulomb. **23.** (*a*) 12 μf; (*b*) $E_a = 100$ volts, $E_d = 150$ volts, $E_b = 120$ volts, $E_c = 30$ volts. **24.** C_a in parallel with C_b, C_c in parallel with C_d, then C_{ab} in series with C_{cd}. **25.** $G_a = 82$ volts per mil, $G_b = 77$ volts per mil. **26.** 32,500 volts; 106.5 volts per mil. **27.** (*a*) 53.8 volts per mil; (*b*) 130 volts per mil, Yes. **28.** G(porcelain) = 94 volts per mil, G(paper) = 223 volts per mil, G(rubber) = 186 volts per mil. **29.** 1.49 μf. **30.** 8,850 ft. **31.** (*a*) $i = 0.00125\epsilon^{-0.08t}$; (*b*) 1.25 ma; (*c*) 12.5 sec, 0.46 ma. **32.** 0.1 ma per sec. **33.** (*a*) 12.5 ma; (*b*) 1.25 sec; (*c*) 10 ma per sec. **34.** (*a*) 1.25 ma; (*b*) 25 sec; (*c*) 0.05 ma per sec. **35.** $R = 25{,}000$ ohms, $C = 80$ μf. **36.** 30,000 ohms, 120 μf. **37.** 44.2 volts. **38.** 86 volts, 72.8 volts. **39.** (*a*) 0.5 amp, 22.2 amp per sec, 2 amp; (*b*) 0.417 amp, 13.9 amp per sec, zero. **40.** 2.25 watt-sec. **41.** $W_{15} = 1.2$ watt-sec, $W_{30} = 0.6$ watt-sec. **42.** 0.72 amp, 0.24 amp. **43.** 1.56 watts, 0.125 amp.

Chapter 10

1. 4.6 volts. **2.** 1,190 turns. **3.** 2.15 volts. **4.** 85, 147, 164, 164, 120, 0, −170, −85 volts. **5.** 20°, 45°, 70°, 140°, 220°, 290°, 335°. **6.** (*a*) 900, 375, 750 rpm; (*b*) 55, 90, 120, 30 cps. **7.** (*a*) 60 cps; (*b*) 25 cps; (*c*) 50 cps. **8.** (*a*) 214 volts; (*b*) −340 volts. **9.** 5.95 amp, 16.1 amp, 46 ma. **10.** $e = 162.6 \sin 377t$. **11.** (*a*) $i = 39.6 \sin 377t$; (*b*) 12 amp, 16 amp, 28 amp. **12.** 1.3 amp, 26 volts, 39 volts, 52 volts. **13.** (*a*) 2.83 amp; (*b*) $i_r = 4 \sin 377t$. **14.** 228.8 volts. **15.** 48.7 amp. **16.** 220 volts. **17.** 30 amp. **18.** 1,270 volts and 2,200 volts. **19.** (*a*) 62.6 amp; (*b*) 28.5° lag. **20.** 51.1 amp, 24.8° leading.

Chapter 11

1. 51.7 amp. **2.** 30.2 ohms. **3.** 3,400 watts. **4.** (*a*) 78 ohms; (*b*) 1.5 amp; (*c*) 175.5 watts; (*d*) zero; (*e*) $i = 2.22 \sin (314t - \pi/2)$; (*f*) $p = -175.5 \sin 628t$. **5.** 796 cps. **6.** 2.5 μf. **7.** (*a*) 59 ohms; (*b*) 2 amp; (*c*) 236 watts; (*d*) zero; (*e*) $i = 2.83 \sin (377t + \pi/2)$; (*f*) $p = 236 \sin 754t$. **8.** 38.5 μf. **9.** 400 cps. **10.** 4 amp leading. **11.** 0.314 henry. **12.** 30 cps. **13.** 10 cps. **14.** (*a*) 2.5 μf; (*b*) 0.712 μf. **15.** 0.6 lagging. **16.** 2.65 amp. **17.** (*a*) 120 volts, 20 amp; (*b*) 50 cps; (*c*) 0.5 lagging; (*d*) 1,200 watts. **18.** 10 ohms. **19.** $R = 23.2$ ohms, $L = 0.0462$ henry. **20.** $L = 0.0605$ henry, 2.5 amp, 1,450 watts. **21.** $E_A = 50$ volts, $E_B = 65$ volts. **22.** 0.819, 1,324 watts, 33 ohms, 27 ohms, 18.9 ohms. **23.** (*a*) 6 amp; (*b*) 25.6 ohms; (*c*) 192 volts; (*d*) 0.8 leading. **24.** (*a*) 400 ohms, 283 ohms, 283 ohms; (*b*) 4.69 μf; (*c*) 0.707 leading, 102 watts. **25.** 6.12 μf, 360 watts, 0.5 leading. **26.** 30 ohms, 53.3 ohms. **27.** 125 volts.

28. 41.6 cps, unity. **29.** E_{coil} = 15.8 ohms, L = 0.175 henry. **30.** 0.85, 0.525, 5.44 kvar. **31.** 348 amp, 120 kw, 105.8 kvar, 0.661. **32.** 255 volts.

Chapter 12

1. (*a*) 15.6 amp, 24 amp; (*b*) 35.7 amp; (*c*) 3,450 watts; (*d*) 0.842 lagging; (*e*) 2,108 vars. **2.** (*a*) 0.707 leading; (*b*) 30 amp, 5,558 watts. **3.** (*a*) 56.2 amp; (*b*) 11 kw; (*c*) 5.7 kvar; (*d*) 0.888 lagging. **4.** 3.91 ohms, 3.47 ohms, 1.8 ohms. **5.** (*a*) $24 + j18 = 30$ amp; (*b*) $8 - j26 = 27.2$ amp; (*c*) $-8 + j26 = 27.2$ amp. **6.** $1{,}648 - j1{,}432$. **7.** $-j11$. **8.** $0.176 - j0.294$. **9.** $118.8\underline{/19.7°}$, $18.35\underline{/-60.6°}$, $2{,}180\underline{/-40.9°}$, $1{,}648 - j1{,}432$. **10.** $220\underline{/-36.9°}$, $20\underline{/53.1°}$, $11\underline{/-90°}$, $-j11$. **11.** $225\underline{/50°}$, $64\underline{/-68°}$, -256. **12.** $78\underline{/77°}$. **13.** $8.33\underline{/0°}$. **14.** X_C = 8 ohms, R = 20 ohms. **15.** $11.45\underline{/-13°}$. **16.** P = 1,822 watts, R-va = 764 vars inductive. **17.** P = 1,578 watts, R-va = 1,204 vars lagging. **18.** 0.922 lagging, 0.794 lagging. **19.** P = 15,600 watts, R-va = 9,600 vars. **20.** $3.33\underline{/-40.9°}$ ohms. **21.** 4.4 ohms, 0.832 lagging. **22.** 0.1 mho, 0.133 mho, $0.1 - j0.133$ mho. **23.** X_C = 7.5 ohms. **24.** (*a*) G_L = 0.0495, B_L = 0.043, G_C = 0.01725, B_C = 0.043; (*b*) G = 0.06675, B = 0, Y = 0.06675; (*c*) I_1 = 7.85 amp, I_2 = 5.55 amp, I = 8 amp, PF = 1.0. **25.** (*a*) $Z_{eq} = 23 + j13.3 = 26.6\underline{/30°}$ ohms; (*b*) I = 9 amp; (*c*) PF = 0.866 lagging, P = 1,860 watts. **26.** R = 8.3 ohms, I = 7.1 amp, P = 418 watts.

Chapter 13

1. (*a*) 60 cps; (*b*) 2 amp, 220 watts; (*c*) 239, 212, 110 volts. **2.** 4 μf, 34.5 ohms. **3.** (*a*) 4.88 amp; (*b*) 4.96 amp. **4.** (*a*) 0.1275 henry, 7.25 amp, 290 volts; (*b*) 0.1475 henry, 6.75 amp, 312 volts. **5.** 55.3 μf, 24 ohms. **6.** (*a*) 890 kilocycles, 5 ohms; (*b*) 890 kilocycles, 7.2 ohms. **7.** (*a*) 79.5 μf, 7.25 amp, 290 volts; (*b*) 68.7 μf, 6.73 amp, 311 volts. **8.** 796 cps, 40. **9.** 786 cps, 806 cps. **10.** 12,000 cps, 11,920 cps, 12,080 cps. **11.** $10^6/(R^2 + 4\pi f_r{}^2L^2)$. **12.** $(R^2 + X_C{}^2)/X_C$. **13.** (*a*) 48 μf and 365 μf; (*b*) 2.23 amp and 7.05 amp. **14.** 70.5 cps. **15.** 25.6 cps. **16.** (*a*) 3,820 cps; (*b*) 3,980 cps. **17.** 29 ohms, 3.78 amp, 4,536 watts. **18.** 21.2 ohms. **19.** C = 0.9 μf, L_p = 2.21 mh. **20.** L = 0.00188 henry, C_s = 0.01875 μf. **21.** R = 60 ohms, C = 40 μf. **22.** 15 ohms.

Chapter 14

1. (*a*) 13 amp; (*b*) 12 amp and 4.21 amp; (*c*) 67.3° and 18.9° lagging. **2.** (*a*) 30 amp; (*b*) 24 amp and 8.57 amp; (*c*) 36.9° and 73.4° lagging. **3.** (*a*) 36 volts; (*b*) 45 volts and 126 volts; (*c*) 36.9° and 73.4° leading the current. **4.** (*a*) 5 amp; (*b*) 4.9 amp and 2.46 amp; (*c*) 78.7° and 24° leading. **5.** (*a*) 6 amp, 45.6 cps; (*b*) 1.9 amp, 71.6° leading; (*c*) 1.85 amp, 72° lagging. **6.** (*a*) 4.94 amp, 0.447 leading; (*b*) 8 amp, 0.8 leading. **7.** (*a*) 8 amp; (*b*) 3.3 amp, 0.707 lagging; (*c*) 17.88 amp, 0.895 lagging. **8.** (*a*) 12 amp; (*b*) 19.6 amp, 0.896 lagging; (*c*) 17 amp, 0.707 lagging. **9.** (*a*) 8 amp; (*b*) 0.707 leading, 11.3 amp; (*c*) 14.24 amp, 0.971 leading; (*d*) 8.94 amp, 0.895 lagging. **10.** (*a*) 4.8 amp; (*b*) 0.8 lagging, 6 amp; (*c*) 0.6 leading, 8 amp. **11.** 5 amp, zero lagging power factor at 5 amp, zero leading power factor at 5 amp. **12.** (*a*) 0.7 amp; 0.896 leading; (*b*) 12.35 amp, 0.972 leading; (*c*) 0.81 amp, 11.19 amp; (*d*) 0.6 lagging, 3 amp. **13.** 40 ohms, 1.5 amp. **14.** (*a*) 6.03 amp, 0.707 leading; (*b*) 0.895 leading, 5.59 amp. **15.** (*a*) 155 amp; (*b*) 12 amp, 78° lagging; (*c*) 141 amp, 65.7° lagging.

Chapter 15

1. $E_1\underline{/\alpha} - I_1Z_1 + I_2Z_2 - E_2\underline{/\beta} = 0$. **2.** $4\underline{/90^\circ}$, $1\underline{/0^\circ}$, $4.12\underline{/104.1^\circ}$. **3.** $4.47\underline{/63.4^\circ}$, $2.235\underline{/63.4^\circ}$, $2.235\underline{/63.4^\circ}$. **4.** $I_L = 4.42\underline{/45^\circ}$, $E_L = 44.2\underline{/-8.1^\circ}$. **5.** $I_L = 1.44\underline{/0^\circ}$, $E_L = 57.6\underline{/-90^\circ}$. **6.** $I_L = 9.6\underline{/-73.8^\circ}$, $E_L = 90.2\underline{/-141^\circ}$. **7.** $I_{sc} = 6.25\underline{/-110.7^\circ}$. **8.** $I_L = 5\underline{/0^\circ}$, $E_L = 42.5\underline{/45^\circ}$. **9.** $13.75\underline{/0^\circ}$. **10.** $132\underline{/60^\circ}$. **11.** (*a*) $4.55 + j3.53$; (*b*) $11.31 + j4.6$. **12.** 1.5 ohms, 16 amp, 384 watts, 384 watts.
13. (*a*) $7.5\underline{/-36.9^\circ}$ ohms; (*b*) 19 amp; (*c*) 2,166 watts, 0.6 leading. **14.** 7.5 ohms, 1,930 watts. **15.** (*a*) 10 ohms, 10.6 ohms; (*b*) 12.75 amp, 1,628 watts.
16. (*a*) 11.7 ohms, 12.6 ohms; (*b*) 11.7 amp, 657 watts. **17.** 12 amp. **18.** 12 amp.
19. $Z_x = 6\underline{/-90^\circ}$, $Z_y = 6\underline{/0^\circ}$, $Z_z = 6\underline{/90^\circ}$. **20.** $Z_c = 8\underline{/0^\circ}$, $Z_b = 6\underline{/-90^\circ}$, $Z_a = 6\underline{/90^\circ}$.

Chapter 16

1. 0.106 henry. **2.** 61.2 volts. **3.** (*a*) 0.015 henry; (*b*) 0.056 henry.
4. 0.162 henry. **5.** 61 ohms. **6.** 9 volts, 12.5 volts. **7.** 27.5 volts. **8.** 40.9 volts.
9. (*a*) $10\underline{/36.9^\circ}$; (*b*) $12\underline{/-36.9^\circ}$; (*c*) $4.8\underline{/83.1^\circ}$. **10.** $Z_a = 6.615 + j9.2$, $Z_b = 8.66 - j1$, $Z_c = -j4$. **11.** 12 volts. **12.** $I_P = 2\underline{/-90^\circ}$, $I_S = 1\underline{/90^\circ}$.
13. 10 to 1, $I_P = 2.08$ amp, $I_S = 20.8$ amp. **14.** 11.55 ohms, 1,155 ohms.
15. $3.25\underline{/-45^\circ}$ amp. **16.** 37.5 ohms, 417 watts. **17.** 1.2 to 1 step down.
18. $R = 24.5$ ohms, $C = 27.1\ \mu f$, $P = 1{,}985$ watts. **19.** $R = 24.5$ ohms, $L = 0.26$ henry, $P = 116.5$ watts. **20.** (*a*) $1.25\underline{/-30^\circ}$ amp, 135 watts; (*b*) $1.4\underline{/-14.3^\circ}$, 170 watts. **21.** (*a*) $Z_1 + Z_2 + 2X_L$; (*b*) $Z_1 + Z_2$. **22.** 4 amp.
23. $I_1 = 12\underline{/0^\circ}$ amp, $I_2 = 15\underline{/-36.9^\circ}$ amp, $I_t = 25.6\underline{/-20.6^\circ}$ amp.
24. $I_1 = 15\underline{/36.9^\circ}$ amp, $I_2 = 12\underline{/0^\circ}$ amp, $I_t = 25.6\underline{/20.6^\circ}$ amp. **25.** For circuit B: $0 = I_B(Z_B + X_B + X_D) - I_AX_{MAB} + I_C(X_{MBC} - X_{MDE})$; for circuit C: $0 = I_C(Z_C + X_C + X_E) - I_AX_{MAC} + I_B(X_{MBC} - X_{MDE})$.

Chapter 17

1. 960 watts, 8 amp. **2.** 4. **3.** 26,000. **4.** 2.5. **5.** 64.8 kwhr. **6.** $5.35.
7. $1,122.12. **8.** $1,044.12. **9.** 421 watts. **10.** 276 watts. **11.** 0.845.
12. 5 amp, 75 volts: SF = 1; 5 amp, 150 volts and 10 amp, 75 volts: SF = 2; 5 amp, 300 volts and 10 amp, 150 volts: SF = 4; 10 amp, 300 volts: SF = 8.
13. (*a*) 210 watts; (*b*) 820 watts; (*c*) 1,241 watts. **14.** 0.75.

Chapter 18

1. (*a*) 208 volts; (*b*) 240 volts; (*c*) zero. **2.** 170 volts. **3.** 306 amp. **4.** 2,300 volts.
5. 0.823. **6.** (*a*) 940 kw, 1,030 kva; (*b*) 0.912 lagging; (*c*) 1,292 amp. **7.** 22.5 amp, 5,460 watts. **8.** 67.5 amp, 16,380 watts. **9.** $R = 10.8$, $X_L = 14.4$.
10. $I_A = 36$ amp, $I_B = 45$ amp, $P_t = 7{,}245$ watts. **11.** (*a*) $I_{NA} = 12$ amp, $I_{BN} = 10$ amp; (*b*) $I_N = 2$ amp; (*c*) $I_A = 27$ amp, $I_B = 25$ amp; (*d*) $P_t = 4{,}344$ watts. **12.** (*a*) $I_N = 36$ amp, $I_A = 55.9$ amp, I_B 64.7 amp; (*b*) 12,250 watts. **13.** 115/115/163 volts, 163/163 volts, 230/230 volts. **14.** 0.866.
15. (*a*) 356 amp; (*b*) 42,250 watts, 157,750 watts. **16.** 0.259, 50 amp.
17. (*a*) 1,720 watts; (*b*) 2,580 watts. **18.** $I_A = 20$ amp, $I_B = 17$ amp, $I_C = 28$ amp.
19. $I_A = 28$ amp, $I_B = 24$ amp, $I_C = 4$ amp. **20.** $P_1 = 6{,}440$ watts, $P_2 = -460$ watts, $P_t = 5{,}980$ watts. **21.** (*a*) $I_A = 17$ amp, $I_B = 24$ amp, $I_C = 17$ amp; (*b*) 3,410 watts. **22.** $I_A = 14.4$ amp, $I_B = 12$ amp, $I_C = 24.3$ amp.

23. (*a*) $I_A = 23.2$ amp, $I_B = 12$ amp, $I_C = 23.3$ amp; (*b*) 3,410 watts. **24.** (*a*) 15 amp; (*b*) 4,130 watts; (*c*) 1,060 watts, 3,070 watts. **25.** (*a*) $Z_X = 41\underline{/0°}$, $Z_Y = 41\underline{/-30°}$, $Z_Z = 41\underline{/30°}$; (*b*) $I_X = 6\underline{/0°}$, $I_Y = 6\underline{/30°}$, $I_Z = 6\underline{/-30°}$; (*c*) $I_A = 12$ amp, $I_B = 8.5$ amp, $I_C = 8.5$ amp; (*d*) $P_t = 4{,}040$ watts. **26.** (*a*) $I_N = 101$ amp; (*b*) $I_A = 317$ amp, $I_B = 307$ amp, $I_C = 314$ amp, $P_t = 100$ kw.

Chapter 19

1. $i = 18 \sin (\alpha + 33.7°) + 10 \sin (3\alpha - 53.1°) + 5.4 \sin (\alpha + 123.7°)$. **2.** $e = 311 \sin 314t + 82 \sin (942t - 0.75\pi) + 63 \sin (1{,}570t + 1.5\pi)$. **7.** $i = 10.5 \sin \alpha + 3.5 \sin 3\alpha + 2.1 \sin 5\alpha + 1.5 \sin 7\alpha$. **8.** $i = 9.8 \sin (\alpha + 39°) + 2.1 \sin (3\alpha - 180°) + 0.64 \sin (5\alpha - 49°) + 27 \sin (7\alpha - 90°)$. **9.** 15 amp. **10.** 231.5 volts. **11.** $E_1 = 170$ volts, $E_3 = 42$ volts. **12.** $E_1 = 150$ volts, $E_3 = 50$ volts. **13.** 68.5 volts. **14.** 17.6 amp. **15.** $0.577I$. **16.** 621 watts. **17.** 0.405. **18.** $P = 663.25$ watts, PF = 1.0. **19.** (*a*) $i = 17 \sin (377t + 0.545\pi) + 5 \sin (1{,}131t - 0.545\pi)$; (*b*) $E = 125.1$ volts, $I = 12.51$ amp; (*c*) $P = 942$ watts, PF = 0.6. **20.** (*a*) $e = 141.4 \sin (314t - 0.417\pi) + 48.8 \sin (628t - 0.139\pi)$; (*b*) $E = 105.7$ volts, $I = 15.2$ amp; (*c*) $P = 1{,}160$ watts, PF = 0.723. **21.** (*a*) $I_{A1} = 19.8\underline{/-23.9°}$, $I_{B1} = 11.46\underline{/61.9°}$, $I_{L1} = 23.6\underline{/5.1°}$; (*b*) $I_{A3} = 4\underline{/-53.1°}$, $I_{B3} = 6.37\underline{/32°}$, $I_{L3} = 7.8\underline{/1.3°}$; (*c*) $I_L = 17.55$ amp, $E = 144$ volts; (*d*) $P = 2{,}522$ watts, PF = 1.0.